1968

ndamental Mathematical Structures | *Fundamental Mathematical Structures*

Fundamental Mathematical Structures

GEOMETRY

Paul J. Kelly

Norman E. Ladd

Scott, Foresman and Company

Chicago, Atlanta, Dallas, Palo Alto, Fair Lawn, N.J.

This is one of the books in the Fundamental Mathematical Structures series, which is a part of the Basic Mathematics Program, published by Scott, Foresman and Company.

The major authors of the Fundamental Mathematical Structures series, jointly responsible for the content of all the books and individually responsible for a particular book, are
Paul J. Kelly, Professor of Mathematics, University of California, Santa Barbara (Geometry);
Charles J. A. Halberg, Jr., Associate Professor of Mathematics, University of California, Riverside (Functions);
Ralph Crouch, Head, Department of Mathematics, New Mexico State University (Linear Algebra and Algebraic Structures).

The advisory authors of the series, critical readers of all the manuscripts, are
Henry Van Engen, Professor of Education and Mathematics, University of Wisconsin;
Maurice L. Hartung, Professor of Education, University of Chicago;
Harold C. Trimble, Professor of Education, Ohio State University;
Michael Millar, Assistant Professor of Mathematics, State College of Iowa.

The specialists in mathematics education, serving as consultants to the authors, are
Emil J. Berger, Coordinator of Mathematics, St. Paul Public Schools, St. Paul, Minnesota;
Ray W. Cleveland, Supervisor of Elementary and Secondary Mathematics, Rahway Public Schools, Rahway, New Jersey;
A. B. Evenson, Assistant Superintendent of Secondary Education, Edmonton Public Schools, Edmonton, Alberta, Canada;
Ray Walch, Director of Mathematics, K-12, Public Schools, Westport, Connecticut.

The responsibility for assuring that the content of this book is appropriate for its intended audience is that of
Norman E. Ladd, Chairman, Mathematics Department, Maine Township High School West, Des Plaines, Illinois.

The manuscript was read for the accuracy of its mathematical content by
E. G. Straus, Professor of Mathematics, University of California, Los Angeles.

This book was designed by William Nicoll and illustrated by Paul Hazelrigg.

Contents

Contents, continued

Some geometric ideas **1/1**

A simple answer to the question "What is geometry?" is necessarily incomplete, is usually misleading, and is seldom truly helpful. Geometry includes an enormous range of ideas and can be viewed in many different ways. Throughout its development during the past twenty-five centuries, geometry has been interlocked with many other subjects and different kinds of human activity. We will not attempt, therefore, to give any single, simple answer to the question "What is geometry?" Instead, in this introductory chapter, we will try to convey some ideas about the nature of geometry by talking about it in different ways. With this background, we then will explain the kind of geometry that is to be developed in this book and how we propose to develop it. In this introductory section, we simply want to look at geometry in the most common-sense way, to see something of the naturalness of geometric ideas, their interest, their variety, sometimes their unexpectedness, and their importance.

Broadly speaking, geometry is the study of the properties of shapes. Since the shape of an object is something visible, we begin to acquire geometric knowledge and understanding in early childhood. We learn to distinguish such geometric figures as lines, planes, and circles long before we know their names. We also early recognize many simple properties associated with these figures. For example, we recognize that a circular object, such as a wheel or a hoop, will roll; that an object shaped like a cone, such as a top, will spin on its point, or vertex; that the oval shape of a football and the spherical shape of a basketball make them quite different to throw. Thus, the most obvious property of geometry is that it is graphic. You literally can "see" what geometry is about.

We use sight perhaps more than any other sense and enjoy seeing things "in the mind's eye." That is, we enjoy seeing things in our imagination as we do when planning to build something. As a matter of fact, one appeal of geometry is its challenge to our ability to picture things accurately. This type of challenge is evident in connection with puzzles that can be solved simply by seeing things in the correct way. Consider, for example, Diagram 1 (D1).* Three holes have been cut in a board. One hole is shaped like a circle, one like a square, and one like a triangle. Can you imagine a solid object that will pass through each of the three holes and, at some point in passing through, will be a snug fit that completely fills the hole?

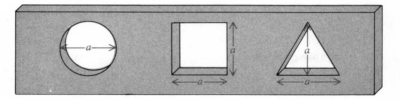

Diagram 1

Here is a different example of this type of problem, and one that is sometimes used in intelligence tests. Suppose that a cube of wood that is three inches on each edge is painted. If the cube is sawed through the lines indicated in D2, then twenty-seven cubes, each one inch on an edge, are produced. How many of these cubes will have no paint on them? How many will have paint on just one face? On two faces? On three faces? Can you answer these same questions for the sixty-four one-inch cubes that you would get by starting with a cube four inches on each edge? If you were to do the problem for the general case, beginning with a cube n inches on each edge, then adding the number of one-inch cubes in the different classes would produce a total of n^3. This equality is an algebraic identity.

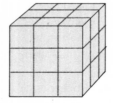

Diagram 2

* The symbol D1 means Diagram 1.

6

We see geometric shapes everywhere in the world around us, and even a slight curiosity about them leads to interesting questions. For example, the cube shown in D3 has six faces, twelve edges, and eight corner points, or vertices. If we let F represent the number of faces, let E represent the number of edges, and let V represent the number of vertices, then, corresponding to each solid with plane faces, there will be a set of numbers, F, E, and V. A natural question to ask is whether or not there is some relationship or law that these numbers satisfy in all the different possible cases of solids. One experimental way to attack the problem is simply to take several different solids, make a table for the values of F, E, and V in each case, and then, from these numbers, try to guess some formula that fits the special cases in the table. In D3,

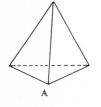

A

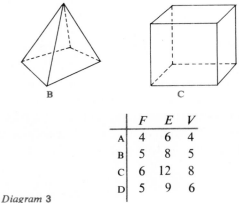

B   C

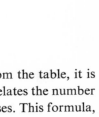

D

	F	E	V
A	4	6	4
B	5	8	5
C	6	12	8
D	5	9	6

Diagram 3

we have done this for four particular solids. From the table, it is not hard to find a famous formula that, in fact, relates the number of faces, edges, and vertices in infinitely many cases. This formula, which was stated by the mathematician Euler, applies to all solids that have plane faces and have no holes through them. Such solids are called polyhedra.

It is typical of mathematicians—in fact, of scientists in general—to try to extend methods or results that have been successful in one situation to different, but similar, situations. Consider, for example, the figures in a plane that we can form by putting line segments end to end like sticks in such a way that no two of them cross each other and every endpoint of one touches some other endpoint. These figures are not solids. However, if we let E represent the number of segments, let V represent the number of junctions of endpoints, and let R represent the number of regions that are enclosed by segments and do not contain any smaller such regions, then the situation is similar to the one that concerned solids. In D4, we have given the values of R, E, and V for four of these plane figures. As before, the table suggests a relationship among the values of R, E, and V, and this relationship is, in fact, a general truth.

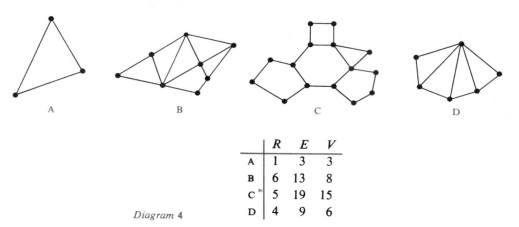

	R	E	V
A	1	3	3
B	6	13	8
C	5	19	15
D	4	9	6

Diagram 4

Unexpected geometric properties can exist in the simplest and most familiar things. Nearly everyone, at some time, has seen the "seven-penny property." This property concerns the grouping of six pennies around a seventh so that each of the six touches the middle penny and two neighbors (D5).

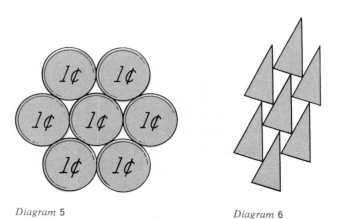

Diagram 5

Diagram 6

You may wonder if the "seven-penny property" is a special property of circles, or if it is a more general property. For example, consider seven identical triangles (D6). Can six of these triangles be grouped around the seventh so that each touches the middle one and two neighbors? Can this be done so that the triangles are all positioned the same way? That is, can it be done so that any one of them can be moved to the position of any other by sliding it without turning it? You could explore these questions by actually cutting triangles out of cardboard and by working with different arrangements of them. The surprising fact, for which a mathematical proof only recently was given, is that the arrangement is possible for any shape that you can cut from cardboard (D7).*

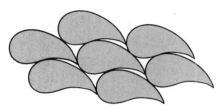

Diagram 7

In many cases, it is clear that the properties of an object that come from its shape are related to other physical properties of the object. Because of this relationship, problems in geometry and problems in physics are often closely connected, and, historically, each subject has enriched the other. In particular, problems posed in one of these subjects often have had surprising consequences in the other. As just one example, consider the following seemingly useless problem. If a tire has a spot of tar on its outside edge, then as the wheel rolls along a flat road, the spot traces out a certain curve that it repeats with each turn of the wheel (D8).

Diagram 8

One can ask: What kind of curve is this? The curve is called a cycloid and it was known to the ancient Greeks. Around 200 A.D., this curve was used by Ptolemy in one of the first attempts to describe the motions of planets. Later, it was found to have advantages as an arch of support in bridges. Still later, the cycloid was found to apply to the motion of pendulums.

* C. J. A. Halberg, S. Levin, and E. Straus, "On Contiguous Congruent Sets in Euclidean Space," *Proceedings of the American Mathematical Society 10* (1959), 335-344.

A very different property of the cycloid is related to the problem of finding the best hill for snow sledding. If you ask what shape a path on a hill should have for a sled to reach the bottom in the least amount of time, the answer is the cycloid. Think of a point A above and offset from a point B, and think of the two points joined by a wire (D9). Then, neglecting friction, a bead will slide down the wire from A to B in the least time when the wire is bent in the shape of a cycloid. The curve turns out to have another interesting property. If the bead is released on the wire at any point between A and B, it will take the same length of time to reach B as when the bead is released from A. Thus, if two beads are released at the same time, one from A and the other from a point as close to B as one wishes, then the two beads will reach B at the same moment.

Diagram 9

To solve the previous problem, it is necessary, of course, to know the force of gravity acting on the bead. In the discovery of the law for this force, a different curve played a vital role. The Greek geometer Apollonius had defined the ellipse as a curve of intersection between a plane and a cone (D10*).

The ellipse also can be defined as the path of a point P moving in a plane so that the sum of its distances from two fixed points A and B in the plane remains constant (D11). That is, the length of segment $\overline{PA}$ changes as does that of segment $\overline{PB}$, but the sum of these two lengths stays the same for all the positions of P. The fixed points are called foci, and each of these fixed points is a focus.

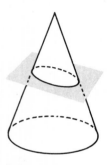

Diagram 10 ⌒

The astronomer Kepler (1571-1630), using records that had been compiled for many centuries concerning the actual observed positions of planets, was able to show that the path of a planet about the sun, the planet's orbit, is approximately an ellipse with the sun at a focus. Using estimates for the masses of the sun and planets, Newton (1642-1727) was able to discover, by methods of the calculus, what force of attraction would have to exist between the sun and a planet for the latter to be kept in an elliptical orbit. This discovery was the famous law of gravitation: The force is directly proportional to the product of the masses and inversely proportional to the square of the distance between them.

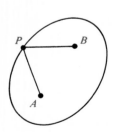

Diagram 11

* Notice that one difficulty in representing a three-dimensional figure is the problem of trying to represent the three-dimensional figure on a two-dimensional piece of paper. To help you visualize the three-dimensional pictures in this book, we have included a special set of pictures and a viewer in the booklet *Anaglyphs for geometry* that you will find in the back of the book. The symbol ⌒ informs you that you can get a better visual image of the three-dimensional figure by viewing it in the "Anaglyph Booklet."

Exercises

1 To obtain a solid for the puzzle in D1, think of the circle, the square, and the triangle, each made of wire. Place the square in such a way that one of its sides is a diameter of the circle and the plane of the square is perpendicular to that of the circle. Now it is easy to see how the triangle can be placed so that its base is also a diameter of the circle and so the wire figure will satisfy the puzzle. Try to sketch the figure. Then use your sketch to help you describe how you could cut such a solid from a broom handle.

You will find the answers for some of the exercises in the answer section in the back of the book. The word *Answer* appears at the end of every exercise for which the answer is given. Exercise 2 is the first such exercise.

2 What is the algebraic identity for n^3 referred to in the "painted cube" problem in D2? *Answer*

3 Use the table in D3 to compare E with $F + V$. Check your conclusion with a different solid.

4 The solid pictured in D12 has a hole through its center and has slanting faces on the top and bottom. Show that the relation of E with $F + V$ is not the same as the relation you obtained for exercise 3.

5 Use the table in D4 to compare E with $R + V$. Check your conclusion with a different example.

6 Consider a circle with diameter b and a circle with diameter $4b$. Sketch the path traced by a point of the smaller circle if the smaller circle rolls inside the larger circle. Sketch the path of a point of the smaller circle if the smaller circle rolls outside the larger circle. How do these two paths change if the diameter of the larger circle is $2b$?

7 Draftsmen often make six "plane perspective" pictures of a solid. These pictures show how the solid looks from front and back, from top and bottom, and from each side. Dotted lines are used for edges that cannot be seen from a particular view and that do not lie behind the edges that can be seen. Four plane perspectives of a solid are shown in D13. Imagine a solid that will fit these perspectives, and sketch its other two perspectives.

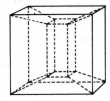

Diagram 12

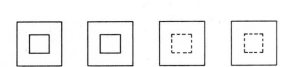

Diagram 13

11

Although we gave answers to several of the questions presented
in the previous section, we did not justify the answers. In fact, we
will not be able to justify all of them in this book because some
of their proofs are found only in more advanced systems of mathematics. Proofs of Euler's formula and of the general "seven-penny
property" require mathematics called topology; the fact that the
cycloid is the "least time of descent" curve involves the calculus of
variations; Newton's law of gravitation is obtained from certain principles of physics and the use of the mathematics of
differential equations. The fact that these advanced systems of
mathematics are related to, and in some degree based on, a
system of Euclidean geometry that we will develop indicates the
importance of geometry.

But what is a mathematical system? This question, like "What
is geometry?" is not easy to answer. We will be dealing with the
question throughout this book, and our best answer will be given
by constructing such a system, Euclidean geometry, in step-by-
step detail. At this point, however, we can establish some general
ideas about systems in the following way.

In attempting to convince someone of something, we have
two problems. The first is to explain *what* we are talking about,
and the second is to explain *why* something is so. In both cases,
there is a difficulty that is familiar to all parents of small children.
A child asks, "What is rain?" Mother says, "It is water that falls
from the clouds." "Why does it fall?" "Because it gets too heavy
for the cloud to hold." "Why does it get too heavy?" "Because
the temperature of the cloud changes." "What is temperature?"
And so it goes, with each explanation simply leading to another
question.

As we develop our mathematical system, we will explain *what*
things we will be talking about, and *why* these things have certain
properties. But since there is no way to avoid the difficulty of
explaining what something is except in terms of what something
else is, there will be no attempt to explain the simplest ideas of the
system. For example, we will not define what is meant by a point.
Since this idea is as simple as any of the terms we could use to
define it, no purpose is served by trying to explain a point. Instead,
it will be an *undefined element* of the system. In the same way,
some simple relationships between elements of the system will
be stated without explanation as *undefined relationships* of
the system.

We will deal with the "why" of the system's most basic facts
in a similar way. The simplest properties in the system will be

stated without any attempt to justify them. We will accept, for example, the statement "Two points belong to exactly one line" without giving any reason why this is so. Such unproved statements are called the *axioms*, or the *postulates*, of the system. It may be noted here that, at one time, the term "postulate" was used for an assumption in geometry, while the word "axiom" was reserved for an assumption in logic and algebra. Now these terms are used interchangeably.

Thus, one of the first things that you might notice about a mathematical system is that it is something like a game. For example, in a game such as chess, the names of certain objects to be used, such as pawn, bishop, knight, rook, queen, and king, are given. The nature of the chessboard is explained next. Then the rules of the game are stated. These rules tell how the various pieces are to be placed on the board and how each may move. Finally, the purpose of the game is defined by particular positions of the pieces. That is, the particular positions define how one player or the other is a winner or there is a tie. In a mathematical system, you also are given the elements of the system. In our geometry, these elements will be such things as points, lines, and planes. Space is somewhat like the "board" on which, or in which, all the "moves" will take place. Certain beginning properties for the system, like "Two points belong to exactly one line" and "If two points belong to a plane, then the line of the points also belongs to the plane," are stated next. Just as no attempt is made to define a pawn or a rook in chess, so no attempt is made to define a point or a line in the mathematical system. The system's initial properties are accepted just as the rules of chess are accepted. The rules of a game tell you certain properties that relate the pieces to each other, but they do not tell you what the pieces are or why the properties are true. The axioms of a mathematical system give certain relationships between the elements of the system, but the system does not explain what these elements are or why the axioms are so. Moreover, when you are told how a pawn can move in chess, you are not told what "move" means. In the same way, an axiom of a mathematical system may assert some relationship between elements of the system without defining the relationship. We will not explain, for example, what "belong to" means in the axiom "Two points belong to exactly one line." This will be an undefined relationship in our system.

In a mathematical system, while there is no competition of one player against another or any winning in the sense of a game, there is a sense in which mathematicians "do" mathematics. They have an objective, and there are rules, so to speak, by which they must "play." The objective is to obtain, from the axioms, as many interesting and useful relationships as possible between the undefined elements of the system or between the new elements that can be defined in terms of these undefined elements. The rules require that the relationships obtained must be shown to be logical consequences of the initial axioms. That is, the new relationships must be obtained by logical reasoning. These new relationships are the *theorems* of the system, and the logical explanation of a theorem is its proof. When a student "does" mathematics, he ordinarily is studying theorems and proofs that are well known but that are new to him. When a creative mathematician does mathematics, he is deriving new theorems to add to a system.

The comparison of a mathematical system to a game helps to explain another important idea. You might argue that, if a system fails to define the basic elements of the system and does not justify the simplest properties between elements in the system, why do you have to accept the system? The answer to this argument, of course, is that you don't. Mathematics simply says that, *if* you accept the undefined elements, the undefined relationships, and the axioms of a system, and *if* you accept the rules of logic, *then* you must accept the conclusions or theorems of the system. Thus, mathematics does not claim that anything is true but only that certain things must be true if certain other things are true. Again, the situation is like that of a game. In baseball, you might decide to run from first base to home plate because it is shorter than going by second and third. But if you do this, you really are not playing baseball. If you accept the rules of the game, then you must touch second and third.

What we have been saying about mathematical systems, particularly a system of geometry, seems to contradict the point of view in section 1/1. That is, in section 1/1, we worked with examples that showed how naturally geometry is related to physical objects and to the experiences of sight and touch. We now seem to be saying that geometry is a system of ideas, that geometric facts are obtained by reason rather than by observation, and that geometry is a matter of logic. How can these two very different points of view be reconciled?

The answer is that there are two worlds of geometry, one physical, the other mathematical. In physical geometry, we make actual measurements, directly or indirectly, of those properties of physical objects that relate to such ideas as distance, angle, size, and shape. This measurement process is an important part of many sciences, such as astronomy, and of many crafts, such as carpentry. By contrast, mathematical or intellectual geometry is a system of ideas and is not necessarily involved with physical measurements, objects, equipment, or diagrams. Mathematical geometry may owe its origin to the physical world, which suggests the simple ideas and relationships upon which the geometric system is formulated. But the way in which mathematical geometry is formulated brings the system into existence as an independent structure with which one can work solely by the rules of logic.

The use of intellectual systems that have been obtained from the world of sense experience is basic in science. While this use may have its purest form in mathematics, certain systems of physics are almost as completely deductive as systems of mathematics. Other subjects in both the natural and the social sciences also are finding mathematical models increasingly useful. By abstracting certain ideas or concepts from reality, a "game of optics," a "game of geometry," or a "game of economics" can be devised. Then, by logical reasoning, new relationships can be derived in the abstract model. These relationships then can be interpreted in the physical world and checked for usefulness by measurements and experiments. Thus, there is a constant interplay between the two worlds, the intellectual and the physical, though they exist independently.

Some historical background 3/1

The basic idea of a mathematical system originated in geometry some twenty-two or twenty-three hundred years ago. However, the modern way of viewing such systems had a long and slow development. A brief account of this development may help to explain why mathematical systems have become so important.

It is not surprising that some knowledge about physical, or practical, geometry existed even in very ancient civilizations. The moment one begins to make something, to plan a dress, to build a box, or to lay out plans for a town, he becomes involved with questions of shape and how to make things fit. Early man experimented with shapes for utensils, weapons, and shelters just as he tested, in different ways, the hardness of materials, their colors, their durability, and other useful physical properties.

We do not know the full extent to which geometric and numerical relationships were understood and used in very ancient times. But the evidence that we have seems to indicate that, until about 600 B.C., all mathematical knowledge consisted of various "rule of thumb" formulas or procedures that were obtained from experience and that gave useful approximations, at least in special cases. One ancient Egyptian document, for example, gives the following rule for the area of a triangle: If two sides of the triangle have the same length, then the area is one half that length times the length of the third side, or the base. If the length of the base were short in comparison with the length of the sides, then this rule would give a good approximation of the correct answer obtained from one half the length of the altitude times the length of the base. An example of a correct rule that seems to have been known and used in very ancient times is that, if the lengths of the sides of a triangle are respectively three, four, and five, then the angle opposite the longest side is a right angle.

It is not certain who first had the idea of trying to prove a mathematical rule by reasoning rather than by testing it in different cases. Although both Thales (640-546 B.C.) and Pythagoras (born 582 B.C.) have been given credit for the idea, all that seems reasonably certain is that mathematics, in the sense of a science, originated in Greece around the sixth century B.C. Like so many great ideas, the notion of a mathematical proof was basically very simple. It was the idea of first assuming, or taking for granted, a number of the simplest relationships between points, lines, and planes and then seeing what other relationships or rules would have to follow as a logical consequence of what had been assumed.

Once the idea of this mathematical method had been discovered or invented, the mathematics of geometry grew with astonishing speed. By 300 B.C., a large body of geometric knowledge was in existence. At this time, the mathematician Euclid brought together and unified this knowledge by constructing the first definite, formal system of mathematics. In time, his work, called the *Elements*, became so famous that it has been reproduced in more languages and read by more people than perhaps any other book with the exception of the Bible.

Following Euclid, such great mathematicians as Archimedes and Apollonius, who lived in the third century B.C., invented a great deal of new mathematics; however, by 100 B.C., the truly brilliant period of Greek mathematics was over. With a few exceptions, such as the work of Pappus around 350 A.D., the work of most mathematical writers for the next five hundred years consisted largely of reproducing earlier results. Interest in mathematics and in science in general seemed to die. In particular, through the first few centuries after Christ, the Roman Empire placed a great emphasis on practical rather than on theoretical learning. The decline of this empire was followed by centuries in which European education was devoted almost entirely to the humanities and to theology.

One of the oddest facts of history is that, for centuries, the brilliant mathematical achievements of the Greeks were almost completely unknown to Western Europeans and information concerning these achievements first came to them from the Arabs. By the ninth century A.D., the Mohammedan conquest of North

Africa and parts of Spain was completed. While the Arabs added little to geometry, they translated many of the Greek manuscripts that came into their possession at Alexandria, Constantinople, and other centers of culture. In the twelfth century, a few adventurous Christian scholars visited the Moorish universities in Spain and made Latin translations of these Arabic versions of Greek mathematical works. Although these Latin translations included Euclid's *Elements*, Euclid's geometry did not become a part of general knowledge in Western Europe until the latter part of the fifteenth century.

By the end of the sixteenth century, the formal structure of Euclidean geometry was widely understood. In the seventeenth century, genuinely new geometric ideas and methods were introduced. In particular, algebra, which had had a rich development of its own, was combined with geometry in the invention of analytic geometry by Descartes in 1619. This event is sometimes called "the birth of modern mathematics."

Throughout this time, the Greek method of doing mathematics within a clearly stated system, with all reasoning referred to definite axioms, was restricted primarily to elementary geometry. The notion that all mathematics had the same systematic character, and could and should be developed in the same way, did not crystallize as an idea until the end of the nineteenth century. In fact, it has become a common practice only within the last thirty years. Actually, what caused this point of view to emerge and to become the dominant one of our times was a surprising discovery made in 1829. It, therefore, is worth while to give a brief sketch of this event.

In section 2/1, we indicated that mathematical geometry is a kind of abstract model of certain parts of reality. That is, by abstracting from experience certain simple relationships about geometric shapes, one can formulate an intellectual space consisting of the ideas of points, lines, and planes. These ideas differ from physical points, lines, and planes just as an idea of an object differs from the object. This distinction was understood quite clearly by the early Greek mathematicians. However, it was felt by them, and by succeeding mathematicians up to the nineteenth century, that the initial rules of this abstract geometry were dictated by the simple facts of physical experience. They believed that these rules were not to be doubted, even though they had been taken on faith as axioms. Thus, axioms were thought of as self-evident truths.

One basic fact of experience that Euclid formulated as an axiom (in a slightly different form) was the following: If a point P is not in a line t, then, in the plane of P and t, there is exactly one line that passes through *P* and does not intersect *t*. This so-called parallel postulate is illustrated in D14. Because Euclid developed many theorems before he made any use of this postulate, many mathematicians thought that it could be proved from the other axioms and, therefore, did not need to be assumed. There were many attempts to prove it, but none succeeded. Then, in 1829, Nikolai Lobachevsky made a revolutionary discovery.

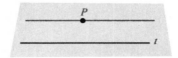

Diagram 14

Lobachevsky constructed a system of geometry by beginning in the same way as Euclid had and by developing the same theorems until the parallel postulate was needed. Then, instead of Euclid's parallel postulate, Lobachevsky made the following assumption: If point *P* is not in line *t*, then in the plane of *P* and *t*, there are always at least two different lines that pass through *P* and do not intersect *t* (D15). Using this postulate, Lobachevsky then went on to develop a geometry that was quite different from that of Euclid, but one that was built in the same step-by-step way by means of logical reasoning.

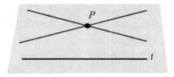

Diagram 15

At first, this non-Euclidean geometry seemed ridiculous, but after careful examination it was found to be just as logically consistent as the geometry of Euclid. Though one could claim that Lobachevsky's geometry did not fit our physical world, one could not show that his reasoning led to any logical contradiction.

As one might guess, if one geometry that was fundamentally different from Euclid's could be constructed, then still others could be constructed that differed from both Euclid's and Lobachevsky's. As mathematicians became more familiar with several new geometries that had been obtained from different sets of axioms, new ideas about mathematics began to emerge. One of these ideas was the realization that mathematical systems, even those of geometry, are simply structures of logic. Such structures have no self-evident truths as a starting point, and they can be logical even when they seem to contradict common sense. But if mathematics is actually a type of applied logic, then all of mathematics, and not just geometry, should exhibit the logical assumptions upon which it is built. As a result, the notion of treating such subjects as algebra and trigonometry as mathematical systems became more and more accepted. There is some irony in the fact that this notion, born with Euclid in 300 B.C. and reborn with Lobachevsky in 1829, is an important part of the "new mathematics" talked about today.

The discovery of non-Euclidean geometry had another important consequence. This was the realization that, even in physical geometry, geometric relationships can be verified in only a limited way. That is, although we imagine physical space to extend indefinitely, we can verify relationships between only those figures that are in a limited portion of space near to us. So in physical geometry, as well as in mathematical geometry, it is an arbitrary assumption that the same geometric relationships are true regardless of the sizes of the figures involved in the relationships.

The following example makes the possibilities about physical space easier to understand. Imagine a perfect sphere the size of our earth, but without any mountains or valleys. To a person on this sphere, it would seem that he lived on an absolutely flat plane. Moreover, if he applied the rules of Euclidean plane geometry to many practical problems, such as laying out a rectangular pattern for the streets of a town, he would find that the rules "worked." Of course, there would be no straight lines in the surface, but the radii of the circular arcs would be so great that the arcs would appear to be straight lines, and, for figures that were not too large, they would "act" like straight lines. In short, two different sets of rules, those of plane geometry and those of spherical geometry, would give the same practical answers to ordinary problems. Although the rules of plane geometry actually would be wrong, they would seem to be the right rules according to common sense.

We now can explain more precisely the term "Euclidean geometry" with which this book is concerned. By "Euclidean geometry" we do not mean the same system of axioms and theorems that Euclid used in the *Elements*. Instead, we mean a system of mathematical geometry that serves as the same model of reality as Euclid's did, that is, a geometry that corresponds to the way that we are most accustomed to thinking about physical space.

It is reasonable to ask, "Which of the possible mathematical geometries is the best representation of physical space, and what is the use of the others?" The answer to the first part of this question is not known. Any kind of complete answer to the second part of the question would be too long and too technical to be given here. Quite independent of the question concerning which geometry is the best description of physical space, non-Euclidean geometries have been found useful in many branches of modern mathematics and physics. It is still true, however, that, for a great range of human purposes, the relationships of Euclidean geometry are basic. They play a vital role in much of science and mathematics.

Exercises

1 Use any standard reference to find the following information:
   a The definition of geometry
   b Some significant facts about Thales, Euclid, Pythagoras, Archimedes, and Apollonius

2 This exercise illustrates the fact that, even in Euclidean geometry, where sight and intuition are valuable aids, we must not jump to conclusions from the way things *appear*. Two of the following statements are false as *general statements*, and two of the statements are true in every case. By experimenting with different cases, try to decide which two statements are false.
   a The greatest number of regions into which n lines can separate a plane is $1 + \dfrac{n(n+1)}{2}$. (D16 shows the case $n = 3$.)

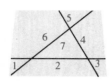

Diagram 16

   b Point P is inside a triangle $\triangle ABC$ (D17). Points Q and R are two points between A and B in side $\overline{AB}$. If the lengths of sides $\overline{AC}$, $\overline{BC}$, $\overline{PQ}$, and $\overline{PR}$ are a, b, c, and d, respectively, then $a + b > c + d$.

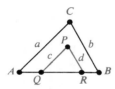

Diagram 17

   c If n points of a circle are selected, then the maximum number of regions into which the circle is separated by the lines determined by pairs of these points is 2^{n-1}. (D18 shows the case $n = 3$.)

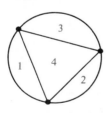

Diagram 18

   d Let $ABCD$ be any four-sided figure in a plane such that the figure has an outside and just one region as an inside (D19). Use the sides $\overline{AB}$, $\overline{BC}$, $\overline{CD}$, and $\overline{DA}$ to construct squares toward the outside of and in the same plane as $ABCD$. Let P, Q, R,

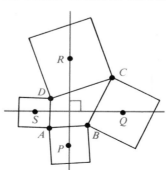

Diagram 19

20

and S be the centers of these squares. Then the length of $\overline{PR}$ is the same as that of $\overline{QS}$, and the line through P and R is perpendicular to the line through Q and S.

3 Why can you not determine by experiment which two statements in exercise 2 are true?

4 What is wrong with the following reasoning?

D20 shows an automobile tire (large circle) and its hubcap (small circle). The tire, with radius $\overline{OA}$, makes one complete

Diagram 20

revolution when it rolls from A to B. The hubcap, with radius $\overline{OC}$, also makes one complete revolution. The distance from A to B is the circumference of the tire, while the distance from C to D is the circumference of the hubcap. Since these distances are equal, the circumference of the tire equals the circumference of the hubcap.

The general 4/1

plan of the You will understand this book more easily if you know some

book of the things we planned to accomplish and if you understand how these purposes forced us to give up some things in favor of others. First, we wanted to present Euclidean geometry as a formal system of mathematics. By a formal system, we mean one in which the theorems are proved by logical reasoning from axioms and definitions and do not depend in any way on drawings or results in the physical world. Next, we wanted you to understand not only *where* the system came from, but also *how* and *why* this system was put together. We also wanted you to see *what* the system means in terms of human purposes. These different goals led us to adopt the following plan.

We will construct a formal system of Euclidean geometry, but we also will talk informally about how and why we are putting the system together. To keep these two kinds of material (formal and informal) distinct from each other, we will use the device of indenting all of our informal discussion. The formal system, including the axioms, definitions, theorems, and proofs, will be numbered, and the material will *not* be indented. In this formal system, we will be bound by the rules of logic, and the system will show what geometry *is*. In the informal (indented) discussion, our concern will be not with logic, but rather with our natural ideas and feelings about the world around us and with how we can express these ideas in a mathematical way.

To involve you in "doing" mathematics, as well as in understanding it, we will give exercises, or problems. These, too, will reflect different purposes. Some exercises will be just practice in calculation, while others will be an invitation to guess the geometric relationships that may exist. Some will be exercises in trying to picture mentally three-dimensional relationships and to make sketches of these relationships. In the great majority of the exercises, you will obtain the answers by reasoning logically from facts and relations that have been established in the formal system. Your results then will belong to the formal system and could be restated as theorems. Occasionally, when we want you to write your proof in as careful and as formal a way as possible, we will state the exercise as a theorem.

It should be clearly understood that by "informal" material, we do not, in any way, mean "unimportant." In both the text and the exercises, the informal material is intended to be an important part of the course.

Another goal that affected the planning of the book seemed, at first, to contradict the plans that we had already made. That is, we wanted the book to emphasize the wide range of ideas in geometry, as well as some of the relations of geometry to other parts of mathematics. But how could we find time for any such broad overview, and still show the logical step-by-step structure of the system? Our solution to this problem was to make a distinction between ideas with which we expect you to be familiar and ideas that we expect you to know with some real mastery. Throughout the book, and particularly at the beginning, we will state some theorems that we will mark with a star. No proof will be given for these starred theorems. However, in almost all of these cases, it will be made clear, from discussion and by the proofs of similar theorems, both that we could prove the starred theorems and how we could do so. A few theorems, marked with a double star, have long proofs involving ideas that are in the system but that we seldom need to use. Even for these theorems, we usually will give some explanation of the general nature of the proof.

The starring of theorems might be considered unfair if the proofs were omitted because they are too difficult. But all that a starred theorem represents is our judgment that the time required to prove it could be better spent on other ideas that give a broader view of our subject. The starred theorems are stated to show their place in the structure of the system; but, to move along, we take them, in effect, as axioms. They differ, however, from axioms in that axioms of a system cannot be proved in the system. We are not apologetic about the use of these starred theorems or the number of them. Their proofs are details that one could always go back and fill in after he has seen the general picture.

Our final major problem in planning the book concerned the selection of properties to be included. Over hundreds of years, mathematicians have found thousands of properties of Euclidean geometry. Obviously we could include only a few of these. But which ones should we select and for what reason?

We answered these questions in the following way. In this book, we will place the major emphasis on the methods and the ideas of geometry that relate it to other branches of mathematics and make it a preparation for them. We will prove many of the standard theorems given in Euclid's *Elements* and in other older books. Although some of the unexpected and challenging properties of figures will be stated in the exercises, we will not spend so much time on these special properties as formerly was done. We also will deal briefly with some topics that previously have not been included in high-school geometry. In doing this, we hope to show the many natural connections of elementary geometry with more advanced mathematics.

To conclude, what sets Euclidean geometry apart as a separate subject is the kind of properties with which it deals. What unites Euclidean geometry with other parts of mathematics is the methods by which it establishes these properties. Thus, right from the start, we will be using rules of logic, rules of algebra, properties of real numbers, and simple union and intersection properties of sets. We will consider these to be automatically a part of our formal mathematics and a part not requiring any justification in this book. At different places in the text, we will discuss and review some of these ideas in an informal way. Also, some of this material is given in Appendix 1.

The nature of **5/2**
foundation The study of how geometric systems can be constructed is a special
properties field of mathematics called the *foundations of geometry*. Experts
in this field study and compare different sets of axioms from which
the same theorems can be derived. They ask such questions as
"What is the least number of axioms that are needed for a
Euclidean geometry?" and "What is the least number of undefined elements and undefined relations that are needed?" They
also study the *consistency* of mathematical systems, a topic that
we will consider in this chapter.

The foundations of geometry, in the strictest sense, is too
specialized a subject for this book. Also, the job of building the
foundations would be a lengthy task, as can be judged from two
facts. First, we want the system we are considering to be a mathematical representation of the geometric nature of physical space.
That is, we want it to be a mathematical representation of the
entire universe about us. Second, we want the system to stand by
itself. This means that we cannot study any property of a geometric figure in our space until we have established the space,

have defined both the property and the figure, and have shown that the figure actually exists in the space. To do this in complete detail for every simple figure and property that we need would require a whole course and would become extremely monotonous. Instead, since we must have the foundations to build on, we will make use of the starring of theorems that we mentioned in section 4/1.

Before we begin the formal mathematics, it will be helpful to have a general picture of the job to be done and to understand the nature of foundation properties. We can describe a foundation property, in a general way, as a geometric relation that nearly everyone is aware of or would accept from his experience with physical space. Clearly, this description is not a precise definition, and there is no sharp distinction between a foundation property and an ordinary property. Foundation properties can be grouped under some general classifications, and we will discuss briefly some of the main ones.

Existence properties Under this heading comes the job of naming and defining everything that we want to talk about. Occasionally, this itself is difficult. (Try, for example, to define what you mean by "curve.") More specifically, an existence property usually states that there exists some figure with a given property. The property also states how many of these figures there are in the system (exact-number property). When the exact number is one, the property is called a *uniqueness theorem*. For example, later we will prove that, for a given triangle, there exists a circle that passes through all three vertices of the triangle (existence), and there is exactly one such circle (uniqueness).

Intersection properties We need to establish different conditions under which two sets, such as two lines or a line and a plane, do or do not intersect.* If they do intersect, we often want to know the precise nature of the intersection set. For example, if a line intersects a plane, then the intersection set either contains just one point or it contains† the line. If a line and a plane do not intersect, then the intersection set is the empty set. Two sets that have at least one point in common are called *incident* sets, and intersection properties are called *incidence relations*.

* For a review of the idea of intersection, see Appendix 1.
† We will use "contained" to mean either that one element belongs to a set or that one set is a subset of another. This causes no confusion of ideas, but some books make a logical distinction between the two kinds of relations.

25

Order properties deal with the position of points, or sets of points, in relation to each other. Suppose that *a*, *b*, *c*, and *d* are parallel lines in a plane (D21a). Suppose also that *t* intersects these lines at points *A*, *B*, *C*, and *D*, respectively.* We can think of the intersection points in many different orders. One example is the ordering (*B*, *D*, *A*, *C*), in which point *B* is first, *D* is second, *A* is third, and *C* is fourth. But if we require that two successive intersection points in our ordering never have another intersection point between them, then it is clear from the diagram that only the ordering (*A*, *B*, *C*, *D*) or the reverse ordering (*D*, *C*, *B*, *A*) will do.

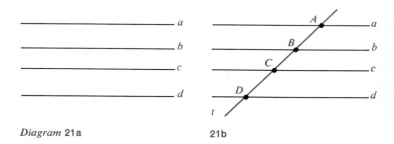

Diagram 21a   21b

In the example in the preceding paragraph, we used the idea of one point being *between* two others. For D21b, *B* is between *A* and *C*. *Betweenness* is an order relation and it occurs again and again in different situations. Closely related to betweenness is the idea of *separation*. A point *P* in a line separates all other points in the line into two opposite sides of *P* (D22). In the line, you cannot go from a point to the left of *P* to a point to the right of *P* without passing through *P*. Point *P* is between any point in one side and a point in the other.

Diagram 22

Viewed in a slightly different way, separation properties also are *connection* properties. A given link in a chain separates the links in either side from each other. However, the separating link also is the connecting link between those in either side. Thus, it is sometimes only the point of view that determines whether a property is stated as a separation property or as a connection property.

---

* This use of "respectively" is a common device to tell you that the intersection point *A* is in *a*, *B* is in *b*, *C* is in *c*, and *D* is in *d*.

Congruence Two sets that have the same shape and size are said to be *congruent*.
properties That is, if two sets are congruent, then one, in a sense, is a "copy" of the other. To establish properties of this type, we first will have to find ways of giving meaning to the terms "shape" and "size." Then we will have to find conditions that determine when two sets have the same shape and size. Consider, for example, pieces of lines called segments. It is clear that they need be only the same length to be congruent. But establishing congruence for more complicated sets will be one of our major tasks.

We now can summarize the job of building the foundations. We need existence properties, including definitions of both figures and relations; we need intersection properties; we need order properties, including those of separation and connection; and we need congruence properties. Moreover, these properties are needed for sets of one dimension, that is, for sets contained in a line; for sets of two dimensions that are contained in a plane but not in a line; and for sets of three dimensions that are contained in space but are not contained in either a plane or a line.* This suggests a natural order of procedure. After stating some general properties of space as a whole, we will work from the line to the plane to space.

To obtain all of these foundation properties in the formal system, we will simply state the majority of them as starred theorems. A sufficient number of them will be proved to make clear the nature of their proofs and to illustrate some different ways of writing proofs. However, we do not think it is important that you learn these proofs in detail, and we do not expect you to construct formal proofs of your own immediately.

In this chapter then, you simply will be learning or reviewing the basic definitions, properties, and symbols that are needed for the system. You will see how the construction of a geometric space is begun, and you will see how experiences with physical space serve as guides in forming definitions and in establishing properties. Although the facts of many of the theorems will be familiar, you may be surprised by the number of geometric relations that you use without even thinking about them. Also, you may be interested to see how many of these very simple relations in the system can be proved. Finally, we hope you will observe how patterns of relations recur in different geometric situations.

With this simplification of purpose and with an understanding of how the foundations are being constructed, it should be possible to complete the foundation material rather quickly. Even so,

---

* An accurate definition of "dimension" is complicated, and we will not use the term in the formal system.

27

the job would become tiresome if we first established all of the foundations that we need. So in this chapter, we will consider only the principal facts about sets in a line and about rays and angles in a plane. We then will define some plane figures, such as polygons and circles. Then in the next chapter, we will introduce material that will enable you to take a more active part and to develop proofs of your own. From then on, the remaining foundation material will be included along with the ordinary theorems. This procedure should make the work more interesting.

Defining the space

6/2

Since we will begin our system with a definition, one might ask "What is a definition?" This is a good example of a question whose answer we do not consider to be part of geometry. A scientific answer is difficult. Defining a definition is like explaining the meaning of "meaning." Therefore, we will simply say that a definition usually names something and states properties of the object named. Thus the definition gives us a way of recognizing the object named and a way of distinguishing it from other objects. For example, a definition of a circle names certain sets as circles and states properties of these sets. Any set that has these properties is a circle, and any set that does not have these properties is not a circle. However, it is extremely important to understand that, in all of our definitions, we are saying only what something is *in this system* and what *we* will call it.

We begin our system just as one might begin a game.

Definition 1/2 *Space*

The set of all points is space.

Axiom 1/2

A line is a nonempty set of points, and each two points belong to exactly one line.

Definition 2/2 *Linear set, collinear*

A set of points is a linear set and its points are collinear if the set is contained in a line. A set of points is nonlinear and its points are noncollinear if the set is not contained in a line.*

---

* It is common mathematical practice that, when a name or term is *defined* by certain properties, then the term is used *only* when the properties are present. Therefore, we do not have to use "if and only if" in our definitions. For example, from Definition 2/2, we know that a set contained in a line is a linear set. But we also know that a set is linear only if it is contained in a line.

The game, then, is to be played with certain things called *points*, and the set of all points is defined as *space*. Axiom 1/2 is like a first "rule of the game." It states that certain nonempty sets of points, called *lines*, are such that each two points belong to one and only one line. However, unlike a game, where the pieces are taken for granted, we will have to establish that there are points and that there are lines in our space. As yet, we know only that, *if* there are any points, then they belong to space. And *if* there is any line, then there is at least one point that belongs to the line. So at present, space could be empty. Axiom 4/2, however, will assure us that points and lines do exist.

Notice that, although a definition of a point or a line has not been given and will not be given, we cannot imagine a point or a line to be anything that we wish. Axiom 1/2 has already put conditions on a point and a line. Whatever we take a point and a line to be, each two of these points must belong, by the first rule of our game, to a line and to just one line. Of course, we made the first rule to correspond with our ideas of a physical point and a physical line. But in no direct way do we say that geometric points and lines are like physical points and lines. Instead, by means of axioms, we will simply add properties to points and lines that correspond to the notions we commonly associate with physical points and lines.

As an example of how this process works, notice that Axiom 1/2 already has established "straightness" for lines. If lines could curve, then two of them could intersect at more than one point (D23). That is, points A and B could belong to more than one line. This example points out how a careful selection of axioms can avoid trouble.* Although "straightness" is easy to picture, it is difficult to define. We will not have to define it. Our lines will correspond to straight lines simply from the axioms.

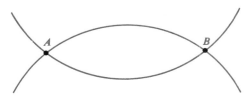

Diagram 23

As you have probably noticed, we have been using capital letters in the diagrams to denote points. There is nothing standard

---

* The set of axioms that we will use is a slight modification of a set first proposed by the American mathematician George Birkhoff (1884-1944). This set and an earlier one given by David Hilbert (1862-1943) are the two most commonly used today.

about this symbolism, and we indicate this fact by putting a *convention* in the system. The term "convention" is almost a synonym for "definition." We use the term "convention" when what is being defined is not a mathematical object or an idea, but is some special agreement about language or symbols. Thus, a convention reminds you that a practice being adopted is not standard and may be done differently in other books.

Convention

Points commonly will be denoted by capital letters, such as *A*, *B*, and *C*.

Notice that this convention does not say that a capital letter will always denote a point, but only that a point often will be denoted by a letter such as *A*. Since we will be talking about more kinds of things than we have kinds of letters, we will have to use some letters in more than one way.

There is one particular language problem that occurs throughout mathematics and that seems to have no completely satisfactory solution. If *A* and *B* denote points, then, because *A* and *B* are different letters, we clearly have two labels for points. Are these letters labels for one point, or are they labels for different points? Some books indicate that different points are referred to by saying that *A* and *B* denote two *distinct* points. We prefer, however, to make the following agreement: *When the number of objects to be considered is given specifically, we always will mean that number of different objects.*

With the agreement given above, two points *A* and *B* automatically will mean two distinct points *A* and *B*, and, hence, $A \neq B$. Three lines will mean three different lines. When "differentness" is not stated by words or by a number, then different labels may denote the same object. For example, the sentence "Let *A* and *B* denote points" will not exclude the possibility that $A = B$; whereas the sentence "Let *A* and *B* denote two points" does exclude the possibility that $A = B$.

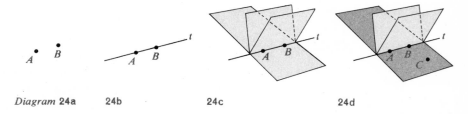

Diagram 24a   24b   24c   24d

From ordinary experience, we recognize that, if we have two points *A* and *B* (D24a), then there is just one line *t* through both of them. But since there is a whole family of planes passing through t, points A and B belong to all of these planes. However, if C is any point not in t, then only one plane of the family of planes passes through C. It is this property that Axiom 2/2 gives to our space.

Axiom 2/2

A plane is a nonempty set of points, and each three noncollinear points belong to exactly one plane.

Definition 3/2 *Planar set, coplanar*

A set of points is a planar set and its points are coplanar if the set is contained in a plane. A set of points is nonplanar and its points are noncoplanar if the set is not contained in a plane.

Axiom 3/2

If two points belong to a plane, then the line to which the points belong is contained in the plane.

Conventions

Lines commonly will be denoted by lower-case letters such as a, b, and c. The line through two points A and B also will be denoted by the symbols AB and BA.
Planes commonly will be denoted by lower-case Greek letters, such as α, β, and γ.* When A, B, and C are three noncollinear points, the symbol $\alpha(A, B, C)$ also will denote the particular plane to which A, B, and C belong.

In Axiom 3/2, we use the straightness that we already have for lines to give us the "flatness" that we want for planes. Consider a pipe extending indefinitely in opposite directions to form an infinite cylinder. The surface of the cylinder contains infinitely many straight lines, such as r, s, and t (D25a). However, there are

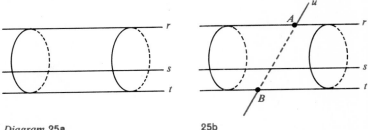

Diagram 25a   25b

lines, such as u through A and B, that intersect the surface of the cylinder in two points and that are not contained in the surface. By Axiom 3/2, this situation cannot occur with a plane.

---

* For reference, the Greek alphabet is given in Appendix 4.

As we mentioned earlier, our space could be empty. We now prevent this by an existence axiom that tells us that no line and no plane is all of space. Axiom 4/2 also implies the existence of different lines and planes. You may find it interesting to reason this out for yourself.

Axiom 4/2

There are four points that are noncoplanar and noncollinear.

We have now the existence of at least four points, *A, B, C,* and *D*, that are like the four corners, or vertices, of a triangular pyramid (D26). Since *A, B,* and *C* are noncollinear (Why?), by Axiom 2/2, they belong to a plane α(*A, B, C*). By Axiom 1/2, there are three lines, *AB, BC,* and *CA*. By Axiom 3/2, these lines are in α.

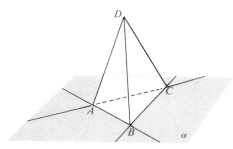

Diagram 26

If a line must have infinitely many points and extend endlessly in opposite directions (we still need to give it these properties), then we will get the plane α covered by lines (D27a). These will be lines such as *XY*, where *X* is in one of the lines *AB, BC,* and *CA* and point *Y* is in another.

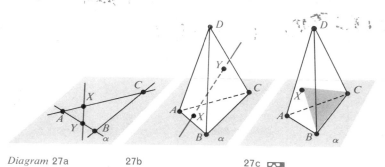

Diagram 27a   27b   27c

Next, since *D* is not in α (Why?) and is not collinear with any two of the points *A, B,* and *C* (Why?), then planes β(*A, B, D*),

32

$\gamma(B, C, D)$, and $\delta(C, A, D)$ exist. Hence, infinitely many lines such as XY exist, where X is in one of these planes and Y is in another (D27b).

Similarly, all the noncollinear triples of points in the union of these four planes will determine planes (D27c); so our space will contain infinitely many lines and planes. In other words, space will be filled with crisscrossing lines and planes.

Before we complete this plan of filling space with points and lines, we will take up, in the next section, a different kind of question concerning our work so far.

Exercises

1 If two points A and B belong to line t and also to line m, what can you conclude about t and m? *Answer*
2 If all points of a set belong to a line, then the set is a ~~~~~ set.
3 What does the notation $\alpha(P, Q, R)$ represent?
4 If P is a point of line AB, explain why P must be a point of the plane $\alpha(A, B, C)$. *Answer*
5 From the information given in D28, which of the following statements appear to be correct?

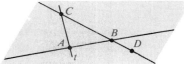

  a $t = AC$.
  b C belongs to both t and BD.
  c $BC = BD$.
  d $AB \neq CD$.
  e $\alpha(A, B, C) = \beta(B, C, A)$.

Diagram 28

We have labeled the more difficult exercises, such as exercise 6, with a "diamond."

◆ 6 Assume that the "points" of a "space" are the five segments in D29 labeled A, B, C, D, and E. A "line" of "space" is a set consisting of exactly two "points." A "plane" of "space" is a set consisting of exactly three "points," which, as segments in the diagram, form a triangle.

  a How many "lines" are in "space"?
  b How many "planes" are in "space"?
  c Are there any three collinear "points" in "space"?
  d Name three "points" that are coplanar and three "points" that are noncoplanar.
  e Name four "points" that are noncoplanar and noncollinear.
  f Does this "space" satisfy our four axioms?

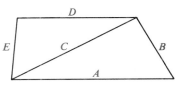

Diagram 29

g What ordinary property that we associate with two intersecting planes is not a property of the two intersecting "planes" of "space"? *Answer*

♦ **7 a** Does Axiom 1/2 imply that a line must contain at least two points?

b Do Axioms 1/2 through 4/2 imply that a point is never a line?

c Does Axiom 2/2 imply that a plane must contain at least three points? At least two points?

d Do the four axioms imply that a point is never a plane? That a line is never a plane?

e Do the four axioms imply that some line is not a point? That some plane is not a line and is not a point?

Consistency 7/2
and indirect Though we have not proved anything yet, our space, so far, seems
proof reasonable. This is because the properties we have given to it are drawn from our experiences with physical space. But already we could question whether or not the system is *consistent*.

Let us, for the moment, use letters such as A, B, and C for statements. Let us use the symbols $\sim A$, $\sim B$, and $\sim C$ for the denials of these statements. Thus, statement A could be Axiom 1/2, "Each two points belong to exactly one line." Then $\sim A$ would be "It is not the case that each two points belong to exactly one line." If we regard a system as a collection of statements, or assertions (the axioms, the definitions, and the theorems), one basic requirement is that it must be consistent. That is, the system must not contain both a statement and the denial of that statement. Consequently, if statement A belongs to the system, then $\sim A$ must not belong to the system. But a second basic rule is that, if A belongs to the system and if A implies B (that is, if B is a logical consequence of A), then B must belong to the system. Thus, any logical deduction from statements in the system must be added to the system. Finding these new statements is, in fact, a large part of the process of doing mathematics.

Now one could ask, "How do we know that the system is not already inconsistent?" Suppose, for example, that from Axioms 1/2 and 2/2, one can get some assertion C and, from Axioms 2/2 and 3/2, one can deduce $\sim C$. As logical deductions from these axioms, both C and $\sim C$ belong to the system. However, then the system has a contradiction, since it asserts C and also denies the assertion of C. How do we know that our system does not contain a contradiction such as this?

The simple fact of the matter is that we do not know if the system contains a contradiction. Experts in the foundations of geometry have not found any such contradiction, but that does not prove there is not one. They also have been able to show that the system of Euclidean geometry is as consistent as the system for the arithmetic of real numbers. That is, both systems are consistent, or both are inconsistent. This is the best result known at present. To those who like to think of mathematics as representing some form of absolute certainty, this state of affairs could come as a shock. But to logicians, the situation is simply a challenge. Since, in any case, it is a problem of logic rather than of geometry, we will just go cheerfully ahead.

From the idea that we will not accept both a statement and its denial as being valid, we easily can obtain a *principle of contradiction*, one form of which is the following.

If statements A and B together imply both the statement T and the statement $\sim T$, then A implies $\sim B$ and B implies $\sim A$.

All this principle of contradiction tells us is that A and B together lead to the contradiction T and $\sim T$. Therefore, if you accept A, you cannot accept B; and if you accept B, you cannot accept A. So A implies $\sim B$, and B implies $\sim A$. If we use the symbol $\Rightarrow$ for "imply" or "implies," the principle becomes the following.

If A and $B \Rightarrow T$ and $\sim T$, then $A \Rightarrow \sim B$ and $B \Rightarrow \sim A$.

Mathematical theorems typically are "if . . . then" statements. An example is the theorem "If the three sides of a triangle have the same length, then the three angles of the triangle have the same size." Let A stand for the statement "The three sides of the triangle have the same length." Let B stand for the statement "The three angles of the triangle have the same size." Then A is the given condition, or the *hypothesis*, of the theorem, and B is the *conclusion*. The theorem is the assertion "$A \Rightarrow B$." Strictly speaking, the assertion, or proposition, "$A \Rightarrow B$" is not a theorem unless it can be proved to be a correct assertion. (Thus, the phrase "incorrect theorem" is self-contradictory.) Later, we will prove that this assertion about triangles is a theorem.

From the principle of contradiction, we can obtain a very useful method of proving theorems in an *indirect* way. Suppose that H stands for certain given conditions or hypotheses, that C stands for a conclusion, and that we want to prove the theorem "H implies C." To prove this theorem, we can consider H and $\sim C$ together. If together they imply some statement T, and if T is the denial of a proven statement or axiom, then H and $\sim C$ together give us T and $\sim T$. By the principle of contradiction, it follows that $H \Rightarrow \sim(\sim C)$, that is, H implies not-not C. But not-not C is just C, so $H \Rightarrow C$ as we wished to prove.

Actually, talking about this method of indirect proof in terms of logical symbols makes it sound more complicated than it really is. Everyone uses the method of indirect proof all the time. Each of the statements "He was not at the party or I would have seen him" and "She must be older than I am because I am the same age as her younger sister" basically involves an indirect proof. In practice, all that indirect proof amounts to is the following. If an assertion contradicts some axiom or theorem in our system, we consider the assertion to be false and, therefore, consider the denial of the assertion to be true.*

To give an example of an indirect proof, let us state a theorem about a property of lines that we already have noticed.

Theorem 1/2

If two lines intersect at a point, then they do not intersect at any other point.

Proof

Assume that there are two lines that intersect at more than one point. Then each two of these intersection points belong to both lines. Hence, they belong to at least two lines. But this contradicts Axiom 1/2. (Each two points belong to exactly one line.) It, therefore, is false that there are two lines that intersect at more than one point. So if two lines intersect at a point, then they do not intersect at any other point.

Exercises

1 Give a denial of each of the following statements.
   a $3 + 8 = 11$.
   b Tuesday follows Monday.
   c A square is not a rectangle.
   d It is not the case that my dog has eight legs. *Answer*
   e Six is greater than five.
   f All cats are fat.
2 Determine which of the following statements are meaningless for our system, which are meaningful, and which are both meaningful and correct.
   a A line is longer than a plane. *Answer*
   b A plane contains at least one point.

---

* Mathematically speaking, a true, or valid, statement is simply an axiom or a logical consequence of the axioms. A false, or invalid, statement is one that contradicts an axiom or a logical consequence of the axioms. A statement like "Trees are pretty" is neither true nor false. We simply do not regard it as a mathematical statement.

c A line has length but no breadth.

d A line cannot contain two points.

e A plane is flat.

f The plane determined by three noncollinear points contains at least three lines.

3 Suppose that A and B denote meaningful statements for our system, and $A \Longrightarrow B$. Which of the following statements might be correct and which statements must be correct?

a A is true.

b B is false. *Answer*

c $B \Longrightarrow A$.

d If A is true, then B is true.

4 State a hypothesis (H) and a conclusion (C) for each of the following theorems.

a If $ab = 0$, then $a = 0$ or $b = 0$.

b If $a = b$ and $b = c$, then $a = c$.

c Two lines in the same plane that are both perpendicular to a third line are parallel to each other. *Answer*

d If $a > b$, then $a + c > b + c$.

5 Give an example of the *chain rule* that, if A implies B and if B implies C, then A implies C.

6 Give an example of statements A and B such that A implies B, but B does not imply A.

7 Suppose that statements E and F together imply both of the statements W and $\sim W$. Which of the following statements must be necessarily true (T), which must be necessarily false (F), and which could be possibly true or false (P)?

a E is true and F is false. *Answer*

b E and F are both true.

c F is true.

d If E is true, then F is true.

e If F is true, then E is false. *Answer*

8 From the rules of logic that we have discussed, it follows that, if A implies B, then $\sim B$ implies $\sim A$. (This rule is called the *contrapositive rule*.) Let s denote a point set. Let r denote a subset of s, that is, let r be contained in s. Also, let A denote the statement "s is a linear set," and let B denote the statement "r is a linear set."

a Prove the theorem "A implies B," that is, prove that every subset of a linear set is a linear set.

b From exercise 8a and the contrapositive rule, it follows that $\sim B$ implies $\sim A$. State in words the theorem "$\sim B \Longrightarrow \sim A$."

♦ **9** Suppose that A, B, C, and D denote four noncoplanar and noncollinear points. Explain why each three of the points, say A, B, and C, are noncollinear.

10 Suppose that three points A, B, and C belong to plane α and are coplanar with a point P. If P is not in α, explain why A, B, and C must be collinear.

Basic **8/2**
properties of
sets in a line

We will now concentrate on making a line in the system have the properties that we expect it to have. In particular, we want a line to have infinitely many points and to extend endlessly in opposite directions.

Axiom 5/2

To each two points A and B, there corresponds one positive real number that is the distance between A and B.

Convention

The distance between two points A and B will be denoted by the symbol $d(A, B)$.

Comment*

$d(A, B) = d(B, A)$. (Symmetric property for distance)

By taking just one number for the distance between a pair of points, we have chosen, in effect, an absolute unit. This is logically convenient. Since the unit has not been specified, we can always interpret our results in inches, in yards, or in any other unit that we choose.

Our next axiom is suggested by a familiar experience. Suppose that along the edge of a ruler you draw a piece of a line, that is, a line segment (D30). It is natural to think of a numeral on the

Diagram 30

ruler as indicating, or marking, a point in the segment. In a similar way, we can imagine a ruler of infinite length with a zero position on it, with names of positive numbers marking the units in one direction from zero, and with names of negative numbers

---

* We frequently will use a *comment* in our system to point out simple and immediate properties instead of stating these properties as theorems.

indicating units in the opposite direction (D31). If we also think of a line along the edge of the infinite ruler, then every integer named on the ruler has a point of the line corresponding to it.

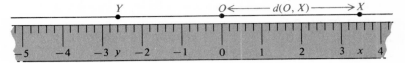

Diagram 31

We can imagine each real number that is not an integer as being associated with a mark between the integers named on the ruler. Hence, each of these numbers marks, or is a *coordinate* of, a point in the line.

　　If point O is the point with coordinate zero, then the positive number x is the distance between point O and the point X corresponding to x. A negative number, such as -3, corresponds to a point that is 3 units from point O in the negative direction. Thus, the distance between these two points is not -3, but $|-3|$. And, of course, $|-3| = 3$. It is now easy to see that the distance between any two points X and Y, with coordinates x and y respectively, is the positive number of the pair $x - y$ and $y - x$. This positive number, of course, is just $|x - y|$, which equals $|y - x|$. Therefore, in all cases, $|x - y|$ is the distance between each two points X and Y.

　　We put these ideas into the formal system by the following axiom.

Axiom 6/2 *Ruler axiom*

For each line, there exists a one-to-one correspondence between the points of the line and the set of all real numbers such that the distance between each two points of the line is the absolute value of the difference of the real numbers that correspond to the two points.

　　In other words, there is a correspondence such that the following is true:

1) To each point A of the line, there corresponds exactly one real number a.
2) To each real number b, there corresponds exactly one point B of the line.
3) If point A and the number a correspond and if another point B and the number b correspond, then $d(A, B) = |a - b|$.

Definition 4/2 *Coordinate system for a line*

A correspondence between the real numbers and the points of a line that has the properties of Axiom 6/2 is a *coordinate system* for the line. The number a corresponding to point A is the coordinate of point A.

Real numbers commonly will be denoted by lower-case letters such as a, b, and c.

Since, by Axiom 6/2, every line has a coordinate system and numbers x and y exist such that $|x - y|$ is as great as one wishes, there must exist points X and Y in every line for which $d(X, Y)$ is as great as one wishes. Thus, we now have the "stretching away" property of lines, as well as the existence of infinitely many points in every line.

We now add to the system another axiom that also is suggested by experience. Suppose that a ruler has been placed along a line and has assigned a coordinate x to each point X in the line. If we slide the ruler along the line to a new position, or turn the ruler around and again place it along the line, or combine these two movements, then the ruler, in its new position, assigns a new coordinate x' to each point X in the line. The distance between points X and Y can now be given by the new coordinates. In other words, now the distance between X and Y is $|x' - y'|$. Since the distance between points X and Y in the line is not changed by moving the ruler, we must have $|x' - y'| = |x - y|$.

We put these properties into our system with the following axiom.

Axiom 7/2 *Ruler placement axiom*

If A and B are two points of a line, then there exists a coordinate system for the line that has the properties of Axiom 6/2 and is such that the coordinate of A is zero and the coordinate of B is a positive number.

Axiom 7/2 just says that, no matter what coordinates have been given to A and B in a line, there must exist a coordinate system (that is, we could move the ruler) so that A has the coordinate zero and B has a positive coordinate.

In some cases, we may have a point A and a point B defined by conditions that do not make clear, in advance, whether A and B denote different points or are two labels for the same point. If they denote the same point, the symbol $d(A, B)$ has no meaning. Therefore, it is simply convenient to give a meaning to the symbol $d(A, B)$ in this case also. Definition 5/2 does not define zero to be a distance; it merely defines another way of denoting the fact that $A = B$.

Definition 5/2 *Equality of points*

The relation denoted by $d(A, B) = 0$ is $A = B$, that is, A and B are labels for the same point.

Comment

$d(A, B) = 0$ if and only if $d(B, A) = 0$.

Exercises

1 Simplify the following.
   a $|10|$
   b $|-11|$ *Answer*
   c $|0|$
   d $|8 - 2|$
   e $|13 - 14|$
   f $|(-4) - (-8)|$
   g $|-4 - 8|$
   h $|0 - 3|$
   i $|-3 - (-1)|$
   j $|3\frac{1}{4} - 6\frac{1}{2}|$ *Answer*

2 By definition, the number $|x|$ is always nonnegative and is either x or $-x$. For each of the following cases, determine whether $|x| = x$ or $|x| = -x$.
   a $|x|$ if $x > 0$
   b $|x|$ if $x < 0$ *Answer*
   c $|x|$ if $-x < 0$
   d $|x|$ if $-x \geq 0$
   e $|x|$ if $x = 0$
   f $|x|$ if $-x \leq 0$

3 Suppose that points P and Q have coordinates p and q respectively. Determine $d(P, Q)$ for each of the following values of p and q.
   a $p = 3; q = 12.$
   b $p = -2; q = 10.$
   c $p = -10; q = 3.$
   d $p = -3; q = 20.$
   e $p = 0; q = -14.$
   f $p = \sqrt{3}; q = \sqrt{5}.$ *Answer*

4 The coordinates of P and Q are p and q respectively. For each of the following values of p and q, decide if $d(P, Q) = p - q$, or if $d(P, Q) = q - p$.
   a $p = -8; q = 4.$
   b $p = 10; q = 3.$
   c $p = 0; q = -10.$ *Answer*
   d $p = -20; q = 20.$
   e $p = 3; q = \sqrt{11}.$
   f $p = \pi; q = \frac{22}{7}.$

5 Use the property $|x| = |-x|$ to show that each of the following is true.
   a $|a - b| = |b - a|.$
   b $|b - a + c| = |a - c - b|.$ *Answer*
   c $|a^3 - b| = |b - a^3|.$

6 Explain why Axiom 7/2 implies that there are infinitely many coordinate systems for a line.

7 In a line, point A has the coordinate $a = -3$, and point B has the coordinate b. For each of the following, determine all of the possible values of b.
   a $d(A, B) = 12.$ *Answer*
   b $d(A, B) = 0.$
   c $b < 0$ and $d(A, B) = 6.$

d $|b - a| = 8$.

e $b > 0$ and $d(A, B) = 2$.

◆ **8 a** In one coordinate system for a line m, the points A, B, and C have the coordinates -2, -5, and 4 respectively. In a second coordinate system for m, the coordinates of A and B are 8 and 5 respectively. What is the coordinate of C in the second coordinate system? *Answer*

b In a third coordinate system for m, the coordinates of A and B are 8 and 11 respectively. Use the information given in exercise 8a to determine the coordinate of C in this third coordinate system.

We now can establish the basic properties of separation, connection, and order for sets in a line by using order properties of the real-number system and our ruler axiom. We know that a number separates the set of real numbers into two sets, those numbers greater than the given number and those numbers less than the given number. Also, a number is between two other numbers if it is less than one of them and greater than the other. Clearly, the real numbers can be ordered by use of the "less than" relation.

Convention

That the number b is between the numbers a and c will be denoted by the symbol $<a, b, c>$.

Comment

$<a, b, c> \Leftrightarrow <c, b, a>$.*

Definition 6/2 *Betweenness for points*

For three points A, B, and C, point B is between A and C if the three points are collinear and if the sum of the distances from A to B and from B to C is equal to the distance from A to C. That is, B is between A and C if A, B, and C are three collinear points and $d(A, B) + d(B, C) = d(A, C)$.

Convention

That point B is between points A and C will be denoted by the symbol $<A, B, C>$.

Comment

From the definition of betweenness for points,
$<A, B, C> \Leftrightarrow <C, B, A>$.

The next three theorems give us the basic relationships that we want for points and numbers. Their proofs are good examples of how numbers enter our system at the very start.

---

* The double-headed arrow denotes the idea of "implies and is implied by."

It may seem odd that, in defining betweenness for points, we have used both a distance property and collinearity. Later, we will prove that, if $d(A, B) + d(B, C) = d(A, C)$, then points A, B, and C are collinear. But first, to make use of Axiom 3/2, which applies only to lines, we add the extra requirement of collinearity to betweenness for points.

Theorem 2/2

For three collinear points A, B, and C with coordinates a, b, and c respectively, if b is between a and c, then B is between A and C. That is, $\langle a, b, c\rangle \Rightarrow \langle A, B, C\rangle$.

Proof

Since b is between a and c, then either $a < b < c$ or $c < b < a$. In either case, a, b, and c denote three numbers, so A, B, and C denote three points.

If $a < b < c$, then

$$b - a > 0, \text{ so } b - a = |b - a| = d(A, B);$$
$$c - b > 0, \text{ so } c - b = |c - b| = d(B, C);$$
$$c - a > 0, \text{ so } c - a = |c - a| = d(A, C).$$

By direct calculation, then

$$d(A, B) + d(B, C) = (b - a) + (c - b) = c - a = d(A, C).$$

Therefore, if $a < b < c$, then B is between A and C.

If $c < b < a$, then

$$b - c > 0, \text{ so } b - c = |b - c| = d(B, C);$$
$$a - b > 0, \text{ so } a - b = |a - b| = d(A, B);$$
$$a - c > 0, \text{ so } a - c = |a - c| = d(A, C).$$

By direct calculation, then

$$d(A, B) + d(B, C) = (a - b) + (b - c) = a - c = d(A, C).$$

Therefore, if $c < b < a$, then B is between A and C.

Since either $a < b < c$ or $c < b < a$ is true, and since both imply $\langle A, B, C\rangle$, it follows that B is between A and C.

Theorem 3/2

Exactly one of three collinear points is between the other two.

Proof

Let A, B, and C denote three collinear points. Let a, b, and c denote their respective coordinates in a coordinate system. Since a, b, and c are three different numbers, one is between the other two. Thus, one of the relations $\langle a, b, c\rangle$, $\langle c, a, b\rangle$, and $\langle b, c, a\rangle$ is true. Then, by Theorem 2/2, it follows that at least one of the relations $\langle A, B, C\rangle$, $\langle C, A, B\rangle$, and $\langle B, C, A\rangle$ is true.

From the definition of betweenness for points, we know the following.

1 $<A, B, C> \Rightarrow d(A, B) + d(B, C) = d(A, C)$, or

$$d(A, B) = d(A, C) - d(B, C).$$

2 $<C, A, B> \Rightarrow d(C, A) + d(A, B) = d(C, B)$, or

$$d(A, B) = d(B, C) - d(A, C).$$

3 $<B, C, A> \Rightarrow d(B, C) + d(C, A) = d(B, A)$, or

$$d(A, B) = d(B, C) + d(A, C).$$

From statements 1 and 2, $d(A, B) = d(A, C) - d(B, C)$ and $d(A, B) = d(B, C) - d(A, C)$ imply $d(A, B) = 0$, or $A = B$, which is false. Similarly, $d(A, B) = d(A, C) - d(B, C)$ and $d(A, B) = d(B, C) + d(A, C)$ imply $d(B, C) = 0$, or $B = C$, which is false. Finally, $d(A, B) = d(B, C) - d(A, C)$ together with $d(A, B) = d(B, C) + d(A, C)$ implies $d(A, C) = 0$, or $A = C$, which is false. Since each two of the three relations $<A, B, C>$, $<C, A, B>$, and $<B, C, A>$ taken together imply a contradiction, no two of the three relations are true. Therefore, at most one of the relations is true.

Since at least one of the relations $<A, B, C>$, $<C, A, B>$, and $<B, C, A>$ is true, and since at most one is true, then exactly one is true.

Theorem 4/2

For three collinear points A, B, and C with coordinates a, b, and c respectively, if B is between A and C, then b is between a and c. That is, $<A, B, C> \Rightarrow <a, b, c>$.

Proof

Since B is between A and C, it follows from Theorem 3/2 that:

1 A is not between C and B;

2 C is not between B and A.

Because A, B, and C are three different points, a, b, and c are three different numbers. Therefore, exactly one of the relations $<a, b, c>$, $<c, a, b>$, and $<b, c, a>$ is true. But from Theorem 2/2, $<c, a, b>$ would imply $<C, A, B>$, which would contradict statement 1; and $<b, c, a>$ would imply $<B, C, A>$, which would contradict statement 2. Therefore, since neither $<c, a, b>$ nor $<b, c, a>$ is true, $<a, b, c>$ is true.

These theorems in our system simply establish that, if three points A, B, and C are in a line, then one of them is between the other two and just one is between the other two. Also, if a, b, and c are coordinates of the points, then betweenness for the points and betweenness for the coordinates correspond in such a way that $<a, b, c> \Rightarrow <A, B, C>$ and $<A, B, C> \Rightarrow <a, b, c>$.

We now use betweenness for points in a line to define some standard subsets of a line.

44

Definition 7/2 *Segment*

The set consisting of two points *A* and *B* and all points between *A* and *B* is a segment. The two points *A* and *B* are the endpoints of the segment.

Conventions

The segment whose endpoints are the two points *A* and *B* will be denoted by the symbol $\overline{AB}$ (D32). The length of $\overline{AB}$ will be denoted by the symbol $d(A, B)$. A segment will be longer than or shorter than another according as the length of the segment is greater than or less than that of the other segment. The segment determined by two points will be called the join of the two points.

Diagram 32

Definition 8/2 *Closed ray, open ray*

The set consisting of two points *A* and *B* and all points *P* such that *P* is between *A* and *B* or *B* is between *A* and *P* is the closed ray from *A* through *B*. The set that consists of all points in the closed ray from *A* through *B* except point *A* is the open ray from *A* through *B*. Point *A* is the origin of both the open ray and the closed ray.*

Conventions

The closed ray that has *A* as its origin and that contains *B* will be denoted by the symbol $\overset{\cdot\rightarrow}{AB}$, and the open ray will be denoted by the symbol $\overset{\rightarrow}{AB}$ (D33). Notice that $\overset{\cdot\rightarrow}{AB}$ and $\overset{\cdot\rightarrow}{BA}$ are different closed rays and $\overset{\rightarrow}{AB}$ and $\overset{\rightarrow}{BA}$ are different open rays.

Diagram 33a

33b

Definition 9/2 *Collinear rays*

Two or more rays are collinear rays if their union is a linear set.† That is, two or more rays are collinear if the rays are contained in the same line.

Definition 10/2 *Opposite rays*

Two rays are opposite rays if they have the same origin and are collinear but intersect only at their origin or not at all. (D34)

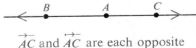

$\overset{\rightarrow}{AC}$ and $\overset{\cdot\rightarrow}{AC}$ are each opposite to both $\overset{\rightarrow}{AB}$ and $\overset{\cdot\rightarrow}{AB}$.

Diagram 34

Convention

General point sets commonly will be denoted by capital script letters, such as the letters $\mathcal{R}$, $\mathcal{S}$, and $\mathcal{T}$.

---

* What we have called open and closed rays often are called open and closed half-lines. The origin of the rays is called the boundary, or the endpoint, of each half-line.
† For a review of the idea of *union*, see Appendix 1.

We have been illustrating some of the definitions with diagrams. These diagrams help us understand more quickly the ideas in the definitions. We also will use diagrams as aids in following the reasoning of proofs. In every case, however, it should be understood that, because diagrams are physical objects, they are *never part of our formal system.* If all of the diagrams in this book were removed, the mathematics in the book would not be changed in any way.

From the fact that, in a coordinatized line, betweenness for points corresponds with betweenness for the coordinates of these points, we can obtain several properties of rays. The convention just given provides a way of denoting the general point sets that are involved in these properties.

---

* Theorem 5/2

If point A in a coordinatized line t has the coordinate a, then the set of all points in t whose coordinates are greater than a forms an open ray $\mathcal{R}$ with origin A. The set of all points in t whose coordinates are less than a forms an open ray $\mathcal{S}$ with origin A. The rays $\mathcal{R}$ and $\mathcal{S}$ are opposite rays and are the only two opposite open rays in t that have A as their origin.

* Corollary* 5a/2

Corresponding to a point A in a line t, there are exactly two opposite open rays $\mathcal{R}$ and $\mathcal{S}$ that are contained in t and have A as their common origin. The closed rays of $\mathcal{R}$ and $\mathcal{S}$ are the only two opposite closed rays that are contained in t and have A as their common origin. Line t is the union of these two closed rays.

* Corollary 5b/2

There is exactly one open ray and there is exactly one closed ray opposite a given ray.

* Corollary 5c/2

A ray is determined by its origin and any one of its other points. That is, if point D belongs to $\overset{\rightarrow}{AB}$, then $\overset{\rightarrow}{AB} = \overset{\rightarrow}{AD}$, and $\overset{\rightarrow}{AB} = \overset{\rightarrow}{AD}$.

* Corollary 5d/2

Open rays $\overset{\rightarrow}{BA}$ and $\overset{\rightarrow}{BC}$ are opposite rays if and only if B is between A and C.

The idea of "if and only if," as used in Corollary 5d/2, is a common mathematical way of putting together two statements. In Corollary 5d/2, one statement is "If B is between A and C, then

---

* When one theorem implies another in a very direct and obvious way, the second is called a *corollary* of the first. Proofs of corollaries often are omitted or are stated very briefly.

$\overrightarrow{BA}$ and $\overrightarrow{BC}$ are opposite rays." Another statement is "If $\overrightarrow{BA}$ and $\overrightarrow{BC}$ are opposite rays, then B is between A and C." Since this corollary consists of two statements, there must be two parts to its proof. We will see many examples of such proofs as we go along.

We think of a ray as having *direction*. In fact, this is why we use an arrow in the symbol for a ray. So far, we do not have enough properties in the system to define what we mean by direction, but we can easily define *same* direction and *opposite* direction for two rays in a line. Two collinear rays with the same, or like, direction, like $\overrightarrow{AB}$ and $\overrightarrow{CD}$, are such that one contains the other (D35). In this illustration, $\overrightarrow{AB}$ contains $\overrightarrow{CD}$.

$\overrightarrow{AB}$ and $\overrightarrow{CD}$ are like-directed collinear rays.

Diagram 35

Oppositely directed rays, such as $\overrightarrow{CA}$ and $\overrightarrow{BD}$, may overlap, but neither contains the other (D36).

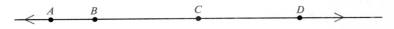

$\overrightarrow{CA}$ and $\overrightarrow{BD}$ are oppositely directed collinear rays.

Diagram 36

Definition 11/2 *Like-directed rays*

Ray $\mathcal{R}$ and ray $\mathcal{S}$ are like-directed rays, or have the same direction, if they are collinear and one contains the other.

Comment

Since a ray contains itself, a ray has the same direction as itself.

Definition 12/2 *Oppositely directed rays*

Ray $\mathcal{R}$ and ray $\mathcal{S}$ are oppositely directed rays, or have opposite directions, if they are collinear and neither contains the other.

* **Theorem 6/2**

If $\mathcal{R}$ and $\mathcal{S}$ are collinear rays, then they have either the same direction or opposite directions.

* **Theorem 7/2**

If $\mathcal{R}$, $\mathcal{S}$, and $\mathcal{T}$ are collinear rays and if $\mathcal{R}$ and $\mathcal{S}$ are like directed and $\mathcal{S}$ and $\mathcal{T}$ are like directed, then $\mathcal{R}$ and $\mathcal{T}$ are like directed.

* **Theorem 8/2**

Opposite rays are oppositely directed.

Convention

If a line t is coordinatized, then from Theorem 5/2, the points with positive coordinates form a ray $\mathcal{R}$. We will say that this ray $\mathcal{R}$ and all rays in t with the same direction as $\mathcal{R}$ are positively directed. All rays in t that are oppositely directed from $\mathcal{R}$ are negatively directed. Thus with reference to a coordinate system in a line t, we can speak of the positive and the negative direction in t.

Exercises

1 If the numbers a, b, and c are such that $\langle a, b, c \rangle$, why is each of the following statements not a valid conclusion?
   a c is between a and b. *Answer*
   b a is less than b.
   c c is greater than a.
   d b is the average of a and c.

2 If the number b is between the numbers a and c, use each of the following statements to give any valid conclusion you can concerning a, b, or c.
   a $a > 0$ and $c > 0$.
   b $a < 0$ and $c < 0$. *Answer*
   c $a = 0$.
   d $b = 0$.
   e $b < 0$ and $c < 0$. *Answer*

3 The coordinates of collinear points A, B, and C are a, b, and c respectively. In each of the following cases, if the given coordinates are in the order a, b, and c, decide which point is between the other two.
   a $-11, -3, 100$ d $\sqrt{11}, 3, \frac{5}{2}$ *Answer*
   b $4, 3, 5$ e $\frac{1}{2}, \frac{5}{11}, \frac{9}{17}$
   c $-5, -4, -10$ f $-\frac{1}{3}, -\frac{1}{4}, -\frac{1}{2}$

4 For each of the following cases, verify that B is between A and C by showing that $d(A, B) + d(B, C) = d(A, C)$. In each case, the numbers are given in the order a, b, and c and these numbers are the coordinates of collinear points A, B, and C respectively.
   a $3, 10, 11$ d $4, -3, -11$
   b $-4, 0, 6$ e $-23, -30, -49$
   c $-9, -4, -1$ f $14\frac{1}{2}, 16\frac{1}{4}, 19$

5 The collinear points P, Q, R, and S have the coordinates -5, -8, 3, and s respectively. For each value of s given below, indicate whether point S belongs to $\overline{PQ}$ or $\overline{PR}$.
   a -6 d -5
   b 1 e 4
   c 3 *Answer*   f -8

6 Collinear points P, Q, and R have the coordinates p, q, and r respectively. For each of the following, find the length of $\overline{PQ}$, $\overline{QR}$, and $\overline{RP}$ and indicate which is the longest segment.

   a $p = -3; q = 5; r = 7.$

   b $p = 0; q = -\sqrt{13}; r = \pi.$

7 If collinear points A, B, and C have coordinates -6, -4, and 8 respectively, which of the following statements are correct? *Answer*

   a C belongs to $\overset{\rightarrow-}{AB}$.   **e** A belongs to $\overset{\rightarrow-}{AB}$.

   b C belongs to $\overset{\rightarrow-}{BA}$.   **f** A belongs to $\overset{\rightarrow-}{AB}$.

   c B belongs to $\overset{\rightarrow-}{AC}$.   **g** B belongs to $\overset{\rightarrow-}{AB}$.

   d B belongs to $\overset{\rightarrow-}{CA}$.   **h** B belongs to $\overset{\cdot\cdot\rightarrow-}{AB}$.

8 Which of the following statements are correct if the coordinates of A, B, and C again are -6, -4, and 8 respectively?

   a $\overset{\rightarrow-}{AB} = \overset{\rightarrow-}{AC}$.

   b $\overset{\rightarrow-}{BA} = \overset{\rightarrow-}{BC}$.

   c $\overset{\rightarrow-}{CB} = \overset{\rightarrow-}{CA}$.

   d $\overset{\rightarrow-}{CB} = \overset{\cdot\cdot\rightarrow-}{CB}$.

   e $\overset{\rightarrow-}{AB}$ and $\overset{\rightarrow-}{BC}$ are like directed.

   f $\overset{\rightarrow-}{BC}$ and $\overset{\rightarrow-}{CB}$ are like directed.

   g $\overset{\rightarrow-}{AB}$ and $\overset{\cdot\cdot\rightarrow-}{AB}$ are like directed.

   h $\overset{\cdot\cdot\rightarrow-}{AB}$ and $\overset{\rightarrow-}{BC}$ are oppositely directed.

9 **a** Can the union of two open rays be a line? Give an example.

   b Can the union of two closed rays be a line? Give an example.

   c Can the intersection of two closed rays be a line segment? Give an example.

   d Can the intersection of two open rays be a line segment? Give an example.

10 **a** If B is between the two points A and C, what relation is true concerning $\overset{\rightarrow-}{BA}$ and $\overset{\rightarrow-}{BC}$?

   b If $\overset{\rightarrow-}{BA}$ and $\overset{\rightarrow-}{BC}$ are opposite rays, what is the relation of B to A and C?

11 Collinear points A, B, and C have the coordinates 0, 5, and 10 respectively.

   a Does $\overset{\rightarrow-}{AB}$ contain $\overset{\rightarrow-}{BC}$?

   b Does $\overset{\rightarrow-}{BC}$ contain $\overset{\rightarrow-}{AB}$?

   c Does $\overset{\rightarrow-}{AC}$ contain $\overset{\rightarrow-}{AC}$?

   d Does $\overset{\rightarrow-}{AB}$ contain $\overset{\cdot\cdot\rightarrow-}{AB}$?

   e Are $\overset{\rightarrow-}{AB}$ and $\overset{\rightarrow-}{AC}$ collinear? Like directed? Contained in each other? The same ray?

♦ 12 For each of the following, describe the set (open ray, line segment, and so on) consisting of those points X

49

in a line such that the coordinate x of each of these points
satisfies the given inequality.

a $x < -3$.

b $x \geq 6$.

c $-5 \leq x \leq 8$.

d $|x| > 100$. *Answer*

e $|x| \leq \pi$.

f $8 \leq x \leq 8$. *Answer*

g $|x| \geq \sqrt{3}$.

h $|x - 6| \leq 10$.

i $|3 - x| > -2$.

j $6\frac{1}{2} \geq x \geq -1\frac{1}{2}$.

We will now consider some simple distance properties that are
related to rays and segments.

Theorem 9/2

If point A is a point in a line t, then there
are exactly two points in t
at a given distance r from A, and A is
between these two points. (D37)*

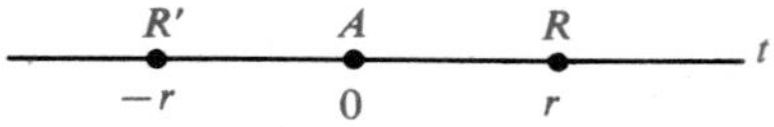

Diagram 37

Proof

There exists a coordinate system for line t in which point A
is the origin of the system and has zero as its coordinate.
Let R and R' be the points with coordinates r and $-r$
respectively, where $r > 0$. By direct calculation,

1 $d(A, R) = |r - 0| = |r| = r$;

2 $d(A, R') = |-r - 0| = |-r| = r$.

So R and R' are two points of t at a given distance r from A.

   To prove that there are exactly two such points, let X
with coordinate x be a point in t at distance r from A.
Then by assumption,

3 $d(A, X) = r$.

By calculation,

4 $d(A, X) = |x - 0| = |x|$.

From statements 3 and 4, $|x| = r$. So $x = r$, or $x = -r$.
Therefore, $X = R$, or $X = R'$. Thus R and R' are
the only two points in t at a given distance r from A.

   Because $-r < 0 < r$, point A is between R' and R.

Notice that there are two parts to the statement "There are
exactly two points in t at a given distance r from A." One statement is that there are two points, and the second is that there are
only two points. We could have said "two and only two points"
instead of "exactly two points."

---

* To check that a proof does not depend on any diagram, you can cover the diagram and
see that, without it, the statements of a proof follow each other logically. Notice also that the
statements of a proof never mention a diagram.

Corollary 9/2

There is exactly one point of a ray
at a given distance *r* from the origin
of the ray. (D38)

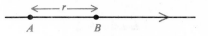

Diagram **38**

★ Theorem 10/2

Point *C* of line *AB* is
between *A* and *B* if and only if
$d(A, C) < d(A, B)$
and $d(B, C) < d(A, B)$. (D39)

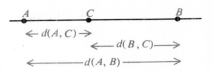

Diagram **39**

★ Corollary 10/2

Point *C* of *AB* is between *A* and *B* if and only if
$d(A, C) < d(A, B)$.

Convention

A point that is the same distance
from two or more points is said to be
equidistant from them. Thus, *A* is
equidistant from *B, C,* and *D*
if $d(A, B) = d(A, C) = d(A, D)$. (D40)

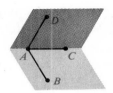

Diagram **40**

Definition 13/2 *Midpoint of a segment*

A point is a midpoint of a segment if it
belongs to the segment and is equidistant
from the endpoints of the segment.
A midpoint of a segment also bisects
the segment. (D41)

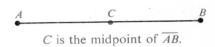

C is the midpoint of $\overline{AB}$.

Diagram **41**

★ Theorem 11/2

There is exactly one point of line *AB* that is
equidistant from *A* and *B*, and this point is between
A and *B*.

★ Corollary 11/2

A segment has one and only one midpoint.

★ Theorem 12/2

If each of points *C* and *D*
in line *AB* is between *A* and *B*,
then $d(C, D) < d(A, B)$. (D42)

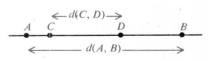

Diagram **42**

We often want to "extend" a segment such as $\overline{AB}$ by a definite
amount in the direction either of $\overrightarrow{AB}$ or of $\overrightarrow{BA}$. The next theorem
permits us to do this.

★ Theorem 13/2

If *r* is a positive number, then there is
exactly one point *P* of $\overrightarrow{AB}$ such that *B* is
between *A* and *P* and $d(B, P) = r$. (D43)

Diagram **43**

Basic 9/2

properties of rays and angles

Next we turn our attention to the plane. From the axiom that three noncollinear points determine a plane and from the axiom that a line is contained in a plane if two of its points are in the plane, we can get other conditions that determine a plane. Remember that we are using "contained" to indicate either that an element belongs to a set or that one set is a subset of another. Suppose that P is not in line AB. Then there is just one plane α through A, B, and P. Because A and B are in α, line AB is in α. So there is a plane through P that contains AB. On the other hand, any plane through P that contains AB is a plane through A, B, and P. Therefore, plane α must be the only plane that contains AB and P.

Theorem 14/2

If a point is not in a line, then there is exactly one plane that contains both the point and the line. (D44)

Proof

Statement	Reason
PART I	
1 Let P denote a point not in a line t.	1 Hypothesis, or given condition
2 There exist two points A and B in t.	2 By Axiom 6/2, there are infinitely many points in a line.
3 Points P, A, and B are noncollinear.	3 From statement 1, point P is not in t.
4 There is exactly one plane α to which P, A, and B belong.	4 Axiom 2/2
5 Line t is contained in α.	5 By Axiom 3/2, since A and B are in α
6 Plane α contains P and t.	6 Statements 4 and 5
PART II	
7 Let β denote a plane that contains P and t.	7 Assumption

Diagram 44a

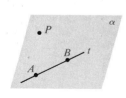

44b

52

8 Points A and B belong to β.	8 Statement 7 and the fact that A and B belong to t
9 β contains the three noncollinear points P, A, and B.	9 Statements 7 and 8
10 $\beta = \alpha$.	10 From statement 4, plane α is the only plane that contains P, A, and B.
11 There is exactly one plane that contains P and t.	11 From statement 4, plane α contains P and t. From statement 10, any plane that contains P and t is α.

The proof of Theorem 14/2 has been written in two columns with a reason opposite each statement. This method of writing a proof shows the step-by-step structure of the proof, as well as the argument for each step. It also makes it easier to "check" the proof. Because of these advantages, many teachers insist that proofs be written in column form. This is particularly true when students are first learning to develop proofs. It should be understood, however, that a *good* proof is simply a clear and logical explanation. The column method is just one form of writing such an explanation, and sometimes it has the disadvantage of being clumsy.

Notice the two parts necessary for a proof of Theorem 14/2. The first part proves the existence of α. The second part proves the uniqueness of α. Statement 7 of our proof is a good example of a case in which we do *not* want to exclude the possibility that the symbol β is just another label for plane α.

Corollary 14/2

If a point is not in the line of a ray, then there is exactly one plane that contains both the point and the ray. If a point is not in the line of a segment, there is exactly one plane that contains both the point and the segment.

* Theorem 15/2

If two lines intersect, then there is exactly one plane that contains both lines.

* Corollary 15/2

Each of the following pairs of sets determines exactly one plane that contains both sets: two noncollinear intersecting rays; two noncollinear intersecting segments; a ray and a segment that are noncollinear and that intersect.

1 The *average* (arithmetic mean) of two numbers p and q is $\dfrac{p+q}{2}$.

For each of the following cases, first use the given values of p and q to find their average m, and then verify $<p, m, q>$.

a $p = 10; q = 20.$

b $p = 4; q = -6.$ *Answer*

c $p = -8; q = 0.$

d $p = \sqrt{3}; q = \sqrt{5}.$

e $p = \frac{1}{2}; q = \frac{1}{3}.$

f $p = -18; q = -\frac{1}{2}.$

2 If three collinear points P, M, and Q have coordinates p, m, and q respectively, then M is the midpoint of $\overline{PQ}$ if and only if m is the average of p and q. Find m for each of the following cases, and verify that $d(M, P) = d(M, Q)$.

a $p = 6; q = 10.$

b $p = 0; q = 14.$

c $p = -8; q = 4.$ *Answer*

d $p = -6; q = -4.$

e $p = \sqrt{5}; q = \sqrt{7}.$

f $p = -6\frac{1}{2}; q = -3\frac{1}{2}.$

3 Point A in line t has the coordinate a, and points B and B' in t are at a given distance r from A. For each of the following cases, use the given values of a and r to find the coordinates b and b' of the two points B and B' respectively.

a $a = 0; r = 13.$

b $a = 5; r = 8.$ *Answer*

c $a = -23; r = 15.$

d $a = \sqrt{7}; r = \frac{1}{3}.$

e $a = 5 - \sqrt{3}; r = 2\sqrt{3} + 5.$

f $a = -2\frac{1}{4}; r = 8.$

4 Points A, P, and Q are in line t and have the coordinates 0, 8, and -1 respectively. For each of the rays named below, find the coordinate m of the one point M that belongs to the ray and is at the given distance r from the origin of that ray.

a $\overrightarrow{AP}; r = 17.$

b $\overrightarrow{AQ}; r = 23.$

c $\overrightarrow{QP}; r = 10.$

d $\overrightarrow{PQ}; r = 9.$ *Answer*

e $\overrightarrow{PQ}; r = \sqrt{11}.$

f $\overrightarrow{QA}; r = 16.$

5 For each of the following cases, use the given distances to determine which of the collinear points A, B, and C is between the other two.

a $d(A, B) = 11; d(C, B) = 3; d(A, C) = 8.$ *Answer*

b $d(A, B) = 2; d(C, B) = 3; d(A, C) = 5.$

c $d(C, A) = 10; d(C, B) = 30; d(B, A) = 20.$

6 If the points A, B, C, and D are collinear and if $d(A, B) = 5$ and $d(C, D) = 6$, which of the following statements must be false?

a Point B is between C and D.

b $B = C$ and $<C, A, D>$.

c The points C and D belong to $\overline{AB}$.

◆ 7 Let $\overrightarrow{AB}$ denote the closed ray and let r denote the positive number in Theorem 13/2. There is a coordinate system for AB in which A has the coordinate zero and the coordinate b of B is a positive number. There is a point P with the coordinate $p = b + r$. Show that each of the following statements is true.

1) B is between A and P.
2) $d(B, P) = r$.

Let X, with the coordinate x, denote any point of the line such that $\langle A, B, X \rangle$ and $d(B, X) = r$. Show that each of the following statements is true.

3) $0 < b < x$.
4) $x = b + r$.

Hence, $X = P$, which completes a proof of Theorem 13/2.

Next we will consider some order properties of separation. These properties form a pattern as we go from the line to the plane to space.

A one-dimensional space, such as line t (D45), is separated, by any point P in t, into two opposite open rays $\overrightarrow{PA}$ and $\overrightarrow{PB}$. If you restrict yourself to the line, you cannot go from A to B without passing through P. Thus, any point P, which we can think of as a zero-dimensional space, separates the one-dimensional line into two opposite open rays, or opposite open half-lines.

Diagram 45

A line t in a two-dimensional plane α separates α into two opposite regions α' and α'' (D46a). These opposite regions are the opposite sides of the line. If you restrict yourself to α, you cannot go from a point C in α' to a point D in α'' without crossing t. Thus, the one-dimensional line separates the two-dimensional plane into opposite regions α' and α''. These opposite regions are called *opposite open half-planes.*

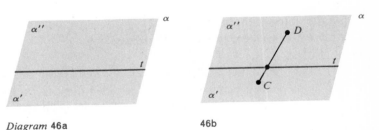

Diagram 46a   46b

Three-dimensional space is separated, by a plane α, into two opposite regions $\mathcal{R}'$ and $\mathcal{R}''$ (D47a). These opposite regions are

the opposite sides of α, and are called *opposite open half-spaces.*
You cannot go from a point P in $\mathcal{R}'$ to a point Q in $\mathcal{R}''$ without
crossing α.*

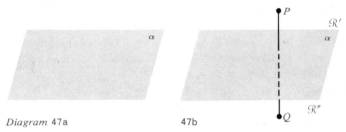

Diagram 47a   47b

Exercises

1 Two points A and B are in a line t, and point P is not in t.
Explain your answers to the following questions.
   a If A and B are in a plane α, must t be in α? *Answer*
   b Must P be contained in this same plane α?
   c If P is contained in a plane β, is AB necessarily in β?
   d If P and t are in β, are A and B in β?
   e If P and t also are in a plane δ, is $\beta = \delta$?
2 If the two points A and B are in line t, why is each
of the following statements false?
   a If P is any point not contained in $\overrightarrow{AB}$, then there is
   only one plane that contains both P and $\overrightarrow{AB}$.
   b If P is any point such that the intersection of $\overline{AB}$ and
   $\overline{PB}$ is $\overline{AB}$, then there is exactly one plane that contains
   both P and $\overline{AB}$.
   c If $\overline{AB}$ and $\overline{PB}$ intersect at exactly one point, then there
   is just one plane that contains both segments. *Answer*
   d If $\overline{CD}$ is any segment that does not intersect $\overline{AB}$, then
   there cannot be just one plane that contains both segments.
3 Give conditions so that a unique plane is determined
by each of the following pairs of sets.
   a Two nonintersecting segments *Answer*
   b Two nonintersecting rays
   c A ray and a segment that do not intersect

Just as the open rays $\overrightarrow{PA}$ and $\overrightarrow{PB}$ in t become closed rays if
their common origin P is added to them, so the open half-planes
α' and α'' become closed half-planes if their common *edge* t is

---

* This time we have not included the phrase "If you restrict yourself to three-space." We have
supposed that you *must* stay in three-space. But the pattern suggests that, if there were a
four-space, we could get from P to Q without crossing α if we did not have to stay in three-space.

added to them. Similarly, the open half-spaces $\mathcal{R}'$ and $\mathcal{R}''$ become *closed half-spaces* if their common *face* α is added to them.

Lines, planes, and space, as well as rays, half-planes, and half-spaces, have the following important property in common. If two points belong to one of these sets, then the segment joining these two points is contained in the set. This property is called *convexity*. That is, a set is convex if it contains every segment that joins two of its points.

Because one-, two-, and three-dimensional spaces are convex, the empty set and a set consisting of a single point also are called convex sets.

Definition 14/2 *Convex set*

A set of points is a convex set if it is the empty set, if it consists of only one point, or if it contains every segment whose endpoints are in the set.*

Axiom 8/2

Corresponding to each line t in a plane α, there are exactly two sets α' and α'' with the following properties. Sets α' and α'' are nonempty convex sets. No two of the three sets α', α'', and t have a point in common. Plane α is the union of α', α'', and t. Every segment that joins a point of α' to a point of α'' intersects t. (D48)

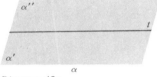

Diagram 48a

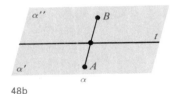

48b

Definition 15/2 *Open half-planes, closed half-planes*

Each of the sets α' and α'', in Axiom 8/2, that corresponds to a line t in a plane α is an open half-plane. Each open half-plane also is a side of t in α. The two sets are opposite open half-planes and also are opposite sides of t. Line t is the edge of each of the open half-planes α' and α''. The union of an open half-plane and its edge is a closed half-plane. Thus, $\alpha' \cup t$ and $\alpha'' \cup t$ are closed half-planes.

Conventions

We commonly will denote opposite open half-planes by prime and double prime Greek letters, such as α' and α'' or β' and β''. We also will speak of the A-side of a line. This will mean the side to which a point A belongs. (In D48b, the symbol α' denotes the A-side of t.)

---

* Strictly speaking, the last condition implies the first two, for if a set is a single point or the empty set, then the set of segments with endpoints in the set is empty, and an empty set is regarded as being contained in every set. The definition of a convex set does not depend on dimension. Bounded, three-dimensional, convex sets are called *convex bodies*, and the study of these is a special branch of mathematics. We will discuss this subject further in Chapter 6.

Theorem 16/2

If two points A and B are in the same plane
as a line t and if neither point is
in t, then the points belong to the
same side of t if and only if
$\overline{AB}$ does not intersect t. (D49)

Proof

By Axiom 8/2, the side of a line is
a convex set. Therefore, if A and B belong
to one side of t, then $\overline{AB}$ is in that side.
Since t does not intersect either
of its sides, it does not intersect $\overline{AB}$.

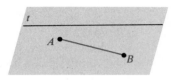

Diagram 49

To prove the second part of the theorem, if $\overline{AB}$ does not
intersect t, then A and B cannot be in opposite sides of t
because then, by Axiom 8/2, $\overline{AB}$ would intersect t.
By assumption, A and B are either in the same side of t or
in opposite sides. Hence, they must be in the same side.

Notice again that, because Theorem 16/2 includes the idea of
"if and only if," there must be two parts to its proof. To say "P
is true if and only if Q is true" is just to say "$P \Leftrightarrow Q$." Because
of this, there must be a proof of "$P \Rightarrow Q$" and a proof of "$Q \Rightarrow P$."

The following theorem relates the two opposite directions in
a line to the two opposite sides of a line in a plane.

Theorem 17/2

If point B is not in line t, and point A is
in t, then, in the plane of B and t,
the open ray $\overrightarrow{AB}$ belongs to the B-side of t
and the open ray opposite $\overrightarrow{AB}$ belongs
to the opposite side of t. (D50)

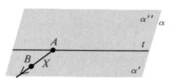

Diagram 50a

Proof

Let α denote the plane of point B and line t,
and let α' denote the B-side of t. Point A
is in t, and we want to show that all points
of $\overrightarrow{AB}$ are in α'. To do this, we will show
that any point X that is in $\overrightarrow{AB}$ also
must be in α'.

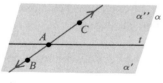

50b

First, since A and B are in plane α, the whole line AB is
in α. So, X is in α, and, therefore, X must belong to just one
of the sets α', α'', or t. If X were in t, it would be in both
t and AB. Hence, X would be A. But this is impossible since A
does not belong to the open ray $\overrightarrow{AB}$. So X is not in t. If X
were in α'', then X and B would be in opposite sides of t.

58

Then, by Axiom 8/2, $\overline{BX}$ would intersect t, and this intersection would have to be A. But then A would have to be between B and X. Then, by Corollary 5d/2, point X would have to belong to the open ray opposite $\overrightarrow{AB}$ and so could not be a point of $\overrightarrow{AB}$. Therefore, X is not in α''. Since X is not in t or in α'', X must be in α'.

Now let $\overrightarrow{AC}$ denote the open ray opposite $\overrightarrow{AB}$. Then C is a point of line AB, and C is in α. Since C and A are not the same point, C is not in t. Thus, C is in α' or in α''. But because B and C belong to opposite open rays, A is between B and C. Hence, A belongs to $\overline{BC}$. Because $\overline{BC}$ intersects t, points B and C are not in the same side of t. And because B is in α', point C must be in α''. Now the proof that $\overrightarrow{AC}$ is in α'' follows by the same argument that we used to show that $\overrightarrow{AB}$ was in α'.

Theorem 17/2 simply tells us that, in a plane, if we start from a point A in a line t and travel toward a point B in one side of t, then we always will stay in that side of t. If we start from A and travel in the opposite direction, then we always will stay in the opposite side of t.

Exercises

1 Assume that each set pictured in D51 consists of a bounded region of a plane. From the diagram, which of these sets appear to be convex sets and which do not?

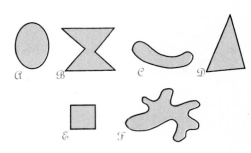

2 Let t denote a line in a plane α, and let α' and α'' denote the opposite sides of t. If A and B are two points in t, which of the following sets are convex? *Answer*

Diagram 51

  a $t \cup \alpha'$ **d** $\alpha' \cap t$

  b $\alpha' \cup \overrightarrow{AB}$ **e** $\alpha' \cup \overleftrightarrow{AB}$

  c $\alpha' \cup \alpha''$ **f** $\overrightarrow{AB} \cap \overrightarrow{BA}$

3 **a** Is the union of two noncollinear segments ever a convex set?

  b Is a set consisting of two points ever a convex set? *Answer*

4 Let t denote a coordinatized line, and let A denote the point of t whose coordinate is zero. Call the open ray whose points have positive coordinates the positive side of A, and call the open ray whose points have negative coordinates the negative side of A.

From this information, explain why each of the following statements is necessarily correct.

a If two points of *t* are in opposite sides of *A*, then their segment contains *A*. *Answer*

b If the segment determined by two points in *t* does not contain *A*, then the two points that determine the segment are in the same side of *A*.

c If *X* and *Y* are two points in the positive side of *A*, then all points of $\overline{XY}$ are in the positive side of *A*.

d If *U* and *V* are two points in the negative side of *A*, then all points of $\overline{UV}$ are in the negative side of *A*.

e The union of the set that consists of *A* and the sets that contain the two sides of *A* is the line *t*.

5 Each of the following statements combines two assertions. State each assertion separately. Then for each assertion, indicate whether it is true or whether it is false.

a A set is convex if and only if it is a segment. *Answer*

b The union of two sets is convex if and only if the sets intersect.

c The union of two collinear segments is convex if and only if the segments intersect.

6 From the information given in D52, which of the following statements appear to be correct? *Answer*

a *A* is in the *C*-side of *DB*.

b *D* is in the *C*-side of *AB*.

c $\overrightarrow{AD}$ intersects *CB*.

d $\overrightarrow{DC}$ is in the *C*-side of *DB*.

e $\overrightarrow{CA}$ is in the *D*-side of *CB*.

f $\overrightarrow{BD}$ is in the *C*-side of *BA*.

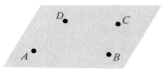

Diagram 52

7 Assume that the eight corner points of a cube are named as indicated in D53. From the information expressed by this diagram, which of the following statements seem correct?

a *H* and *C* are in the same side of $\alpha(E, F, B)$.

b *C* is a point of $\beta(A, E, G)$.

c The intersection of α and β, described in exercises 7a and 7b, is $\overline{AE}$.

d *G* and *A* are in the same side of $\gamma(D, B, H)$.

e In $\delta(A, B, C)$, $\overrightarrow{BD}$ is in the *C*-side of *AB*.

f $\overrightarrow{BH}$ is contained in a half-space of $\delta(A, B, C)$.

g $\overline{EG}$ and $\overline{HF}$ intersect.

h $\overrightarrow{AF}$ and $\overrightarrow{CH}$ are in opposite half-spaces of $\beta(A, E, G)$.

i $\overline{EC}$ and $\overline{BH}$ intersect.

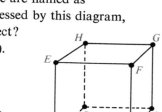

Diagram 53

◆ 8 The four points *A*, *B*, *C*, and *D* are coplanar with line *t* and none of these points is in *t*. If $\overline{AB}$ and $\overline{CD}$ intersect *t* and $\overline{AC}$ does not intersect *t*, show that $\overline{BD}$ cannot intersect *t*.

60

We now introduce *angles* into our system.

Definition 16/2 *Angle*
An angle is the union of two noncollinear closed rays that have
a common origin. The rays are the arms of the angle,
and their common origin is the vertex of the angle.

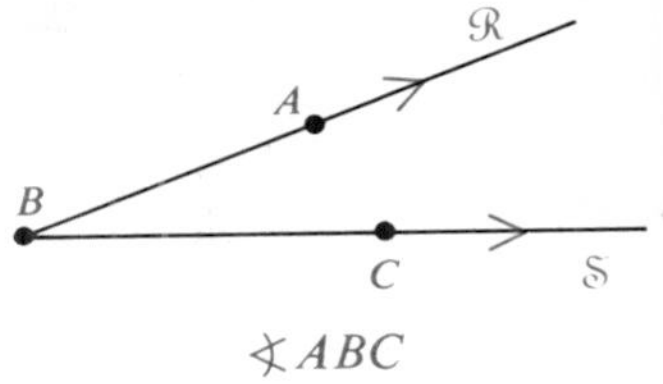

Conventions
If *B* is the common origin of two noncollinear
closed rays $\mathcal{R}$ and $\mathcal{S}$, and if *A* is any point of $\mathcal{R}$
other than *B* and *C* is any point of $\mathcal{S}$ other than *B*,
then the angle $\mathcal{R} \cup \mathcal{S}$ will be denoted by the
symbol $\measuredangle ABC$. Notice that the name of the vertex is
the middle letter in symbol $\measuredangle ABC$ (D54). When there
is no chance of confusion, we will denote the angle
by the symbol $\measuredangle B$. If rays $\mathcal{R}$ and $\mathcal{S}$ are not mentioned,
the symbol $\measuredangle ABC$ always will denote the angle whose arms are
the noncollinear closed rays $\overrightarrow{BA}$ and $\overrightarrow{BC}$. From the properties
of the union of sets, $\measuredangle ABC = \measuredangle CBA$.

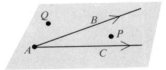

$\measuredangle ABC$

Diagram 54

Comment
An angle is contained in exactly one plane. (This is a
special case of Corollary 15/2.)

In D55, it is clear that, in some sense, *P* is inside, or in the
interior of, $\measuredangle BAC$, while *Q* is outside, or in the *exterior* of,
the angle.

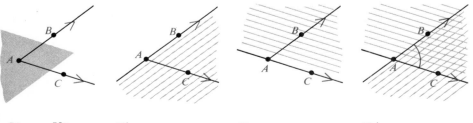

Diagram 55

We can give precise meaning to the interior and the exterior
of an angle in the following way. Let $\measuredangle BAC$ denote an angle
(D56a). In the plane of the angle, the line *AB* has a *C*-side, and

Diagram 56a   56b   56c   56d

the line AC has a B-side. If we shade a picture of each of these open half-planes, then there will be a doubly shaded region that corresponds to our natural idea of the interior of the angle. We will define the interior by this overlapping, or intersection, of half-planes. We then can define the exterior of the angle as that set consisting of all points of the plane that do not belong either to the angle or to its interior. Thus an angle will separate the plane into three parts: the angle itself, its interior, and its exterior.

Definition 17/2 *Interior of an angle, exterior of an angle*

The interior of $\angle BAC$ is the set in the plane of the angle that is the intersection of the C-side of line AB and the B-side of line AC. The exterior of $\angle BAC$ is the set of all points that are coplanar with the angle and do not belong either to the angle or to its interior.

The notion of an interior will occur again in connection with our study of triangles and general polygons. The interiors of these figures also will be defined by the intersection of open half-planes. Since by Axiom 8/2, these open half-planes are convex sets, it will be useful to establish the following property of convex sets.

Theorem 18/2

The intersection of any number of convex sets is a convex set.

Proof

Consider the set $\mathcal{A} \cap \mathcal{B} \cap \mathcal{C}, \ldots$, where each of the sets $\mathcal{A}, \mathcal{B}, \mathcal{C}, \ldots$ is a convex set. If there are no points or there is only one point common to all of the sets $\mathcal{A}, \mathcal{B}, \mathcal{C}, \ldots$, then the intersection set is convex by definition. If the intersection set has at least two points P and Q, then from the definition of intersection, both P and Q belong to each of the sets $\mathcal{A}, \mathcal{B}, \mathcal{C}, \ldots$. Since P and Q are in $\mathcal{A}$ and $\mathcal{A}$ is convex, segment $\overline{PQ}$ is contained in $\mathcal{A}$. By the same reasoning, $\overline{PQ}$ is contained in $\mathcal{B}$, in $\mathcal{C}$, and in each of the sets $\mathcal{A}, \mathcal{B}, \mathcal{C}, \ldots$. Therefore, $\overline{PQ}$ is in the intersection of all these sets. Thus, the intersection set contains every segment that joins two points in the set. Hence, the intersection set is a convex set.

In D57, Theorem 18/2 is illustrated for three particular convex sets.

We can now obtain the convexity of other familiar sets.

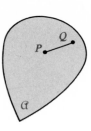
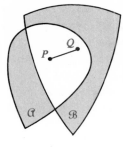
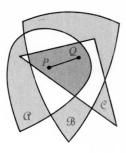

| Diagram 57a | 57b | 57c |

---

* Theorem 19/2

Each of the following sets is a convex set: a segment, an open ray, a closed ray, a line, an open half-plane, a closed half-plane, a plane, and the interior of an angle.

Exercises

1 Assume that $\mathcal{A} = \{A, B, C, D\}$, $\mathcal{B} = \{A, C, D, E, F\}$, and $\mathcal{C} = \{B, E, F, G, H\}$. Tabulate each of the following sets.

  a $\mathcal{A} \cap \mathcal{B}$ **d** $\mathcal{A} \cap (\mathcal{B} \cap \mathcal{C})$

  b $\mathcal{A} \cup \mathcal{C}$ **e** $\mathcal{B} \cap (\mathcal{A} \cup \mathcal{C})$

  c $(\mathcal{A} \cup \mathcal{B}) \cap \mathcal{C}$ *Answer*   **f** $\mathcal{C} \cup (\mathcal{A} \cap \mathcal{B})$

2 Why is each of the following statements false?

  a The union of any two noncollinear closed rays is an angle. *Answer*

  b The union of the noncollinear open rays $\overrightarrow{PA}$ and $\overrightarrow{PB}$ is an angle.

  c The union of $\overrightarrow{PA}$ and $\overrightarrow{PB}$ must be an angle.

3 Explain how it follows from Corollary 15/2 that an angle $\sphericalangle ABC$ is contained in exactly one plane.

4 From the information given in D58, name each angle that has point E as its vertex.

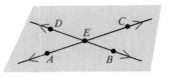

Diagram 58

5 In $\sphericalangle ABC$, point D belongs to $\overrightarrow{BA}$ and E belongs to $\overrightarrow{BC}$ (D59). Use Corollary 5c/2 to prove that $\sphericalangle ABC = \sphericalangle DBE$. *Answer*

6 By Axiom 8/2, an open half-plane is convex. How does this fact, together with Theorem 18/2, imply that the interior of an angle is convex?

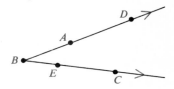

Diagram 59

7 Suppose that P and Q are two points interior to $\sphericalangle ABC$. Explain why $\langle P, R, Q \rangle$ implies that R is interior to $\sphericalangle ABC$. *Answer*

8 For each of the following cases, describe a pair of sets $\mathcal{R}$ and $\mathcal{S}$ that satisfy the given conditions.

  a $\mathcal{R}$, $\mathcal{S}$, and $\mathcal{R} \cup \mathcal{S}$ are all convex.

  b $\mathcal{R}$ and $\mathcal{S}$ are convex, but $\mathcal{R} \cup \mathcal{S}$ is not.

  c Neither $\mathcal{R}$ nor $\mathcal{S}$ is convex, but $\mathcal{R} \cup \mathcal{S}$ is convex.

63

9 Show that $\overline{AC}$ is not contained in $\not\subset ABC$ and, hence, that $\not\subset ABC$ is not a convex set. (Hint: Use Theorem 17/2 to show that a point P between A and C is interior to the angle.)

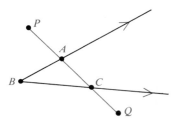

◆ **10** Show that there exist points P and Q in the exterior of $\not\subset ABC$ such that $\overline{PQ}$ intersects $\not\subset ABC$ (D60). Hence prove that the exterior of an angle is not a convex set.

◆ **11** If P is interior to $\not\subset ABC$ and Q is exterior to $\not\subset ABC$, prove that $\overline{PQ}$ intersects $\not\subset ABC$.

Diagram 60

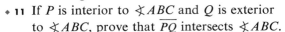

When we work with angles, it is convenient to have a definition of a ray that is between two other rays.

Definition 18/2 *Betweenness for rays*

A ray $\mathbb{S}$ is between rays $\mathcal{R}$ and $\mathcal{T}$ if the rays are related in the following way: The three rays have the same origin. The closed rays of $\mathcal{R}$ and $\mathcal{T}$ form an angle. The open ray of $\mathbb{S}$ is contained in the interior of the angle formed by $\mathcal{R}$ and $\mathcal{T}$. (D61)

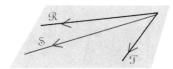

Diagram 61

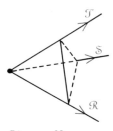

Diagram 62

The way that we have defined betweenness for rays allows us to speak of either the open ray or the closed ray of $\mathbb{S}$ as being between the closed rays of $\mathcal{R}$ and $\mathcal{T}$, between the open rays of $\mathcal{R}$ and $\mathcal{T}$, or between the open ray of one and the closed ray of the other. The definition also gives very particular requirements for betweenness. For example, consider the rays represented in D62. Ray $\mathbb{S}$ is not between $\mathcal{R}$ and $\mathcal{T}$ because the three sets are not coplanar. Therefore, the open ray of $\mathbb{S}$ is not in the interior of the angle formed by $\mathcal{R}$ and $\mathcal{T}$. Ray $\mathbb{S}$ is not between $\mathcal{R}$ and $\mathcal{T}$ in D63 because $\mathbb{S}$ has a different origin from that of $\mathcal{R}$ and $\mathcal{T}$. Nor is ray $\mathbb{S}$ between $\mathcal{R}$ and $\mathcal{T}$ in the following cases. In D64, $\mathcal{R}$ and $\mathcal{T}$ do not determine an angle. In D65, $\mathbb{S}$ is not in the interior of the angle determined by $\mathcal{R}$ and $\mathcal{T}$. Diagram 65 shows that, even if three rays are coplanar, have the same origin, and each two of them form an angle, one of them is not necessarily between the other two.

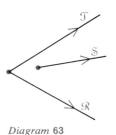

Diagram 63

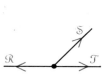

Diagram 64

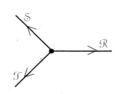

Diagram 65

To show more precisely what is implied by betweenness for rays, we need some simple order properties. A step-by-step, two-column proof of one of these properties is given next. This proof illustrates the kind of proofs that could be given for the other order properties.

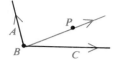

Diagram 66

Theorem 20/2

Point P is in the interior of $\sphericalangle ABC$ if and only if $\overrightarrow{BP}$ is between $\overrightarrow{BA}$ and $\overrightarrow{BC}$. (D66)

Proof

Statement	Reason

PART I

1 P is in the interior of $\sphericalangle ABC$.

1 Hypothesis

2 P is in the A-side of BC.

2 Statement 1 and the definition of the interior of an angle

3 $\overrightarrow{BP}$ is in the A-side of BC.

3 Theorem 17/2

4 P is in the C-side of BA.

4 Statement 1 and the definition of the interior of an angle

5 $\overrightarrow{BP}$ is in the C-side of BA.

5 Theorem 17/2

6 $\overrightarrow{BP}$ is in the interior of $\sphericalangle ABC$.

6 Statements 3 and 5 and the definition of the interior of an angle

7 Therefore, if P is in the interior of $\sphericalangle ABC$, the open ray $\overrightarrow{BP}$ is between $\overrightarrow{BA}$ and $\overrightarrow{BC}$.

7 Statements 1 and 6 and the definition of betweenness for rays

PART II

8 $\overrightarrow{BP}$ is between $\overrightarrow{BA}$ and $\overrightarrow{BC}$ of $\sphericalangle ABC$.

8 Hypothesis

9 $\overrightarrow{BP}$ is in the A-side of $\overrightarrow{BC}$.

9 Statement 8 and the definition of betweenness for rays

10 P is in the A-side of BC.

10 From statement 9, because P belongs to $\overrightarrow{BP}$

11 $\overrightarrow{BP}$ is in the C-side of BA.

11 Statement 8 and the definition of betweenness for rays

12 P is in the C-side of BA.

12 From statement 11, because P belongs to $\overrightarrow{BP}$

13 P is in the interior of $\sphericalangle ABC$.

13 Statements 10 and 12 and the definition of the interior of an angle

14 Therefore, if $\overrightarrow{BP}$ is between $\overrightarrow{BA}$ and $\overrightarrow{BC}$, then P is in the interior of $\sphericalangle ABC$.

14 Statements 8 and 13

Theorem 20/2 is a good example of a foundation theorem. There is nothing surprising about the facts of the theorem, but these facts need to be established. Proving foundation theorems is usually not difficult, but to do this carefully requires a considerable amount of time.

By using the same type of proof that was used for Theorem 20/2, we can establish the following theorems.

* Theorem 21/2

All points of $\overline{AC}$ between A and C are in the interior of $\sphericalangle ABC$.* (D67)

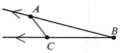

Diagram 67

* Theorem 22/2

Each ray between $\overrightarrow{BA}$ and $\overrightarrow{BC}$ intersects $\overline{AC}$ at a point between A and C. If P is in the interior of $\sphericalangle ABC$, then $\overrightarrow{BP}$ intersects $\overline{AC}$ at a point between A and C. (D68)

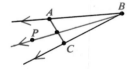

Diagram 68

By means of Theorems 20/2, 21/2, and 22/2, we now can obtain the following facts concerning betweenness for rays.

* Theorem 23/2

If ray $\mathcal{S}$ is between rays $\mathcal{R}$ and $\mathcal{T}$, then, in the plane of the rays, each two of the closed rays of $\mathcal{R}$, $\mathcal{S}$, and $\mathcal{T}$ form an angle; the open rays of $\mathcal{R}$ and $\mathcal{T}$ are in the opposite sides of the line of $\mathcal{S}$; $\mathcal{T}$ is not between $\mathcal{R}$ and $\mathcal{S}$, and $\mathcal{R}$ is not between $\mathcal{T}$ and $\mathcal{S}$. (D69)

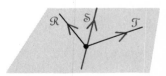

Diagram 69

* Theorem 24/2

If $\overrightarrow{AC}$ and $\overrightarrow{AD}$ are two open rays that are in an open half-plane of line AB, then one of the open rays $\overrightarrow{AC}$ and $\overrightarrow{AD}$ is between the other ray and $\overrightarrow{AB}$. (D70)

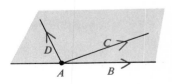

Diagram 70

* The set of points between A and C is sometimes called the *open segment* of $\overline{AC}$.

A natural idea associated with angles is the angle *opposite* a given angle. Since every ray has an opposite closed ray, the two arms of a given angle determine two opposite closed rays. It is natural to call the angle formed by these rays the *opposite angle*. (Many books call such a pair of angles *vertical angles*.)

Definition 19/2 *Opposite angles*

Two angles are opposite angles if the arms of one of the angles are the two closed rays opposite the arms of the other angle. (D71)

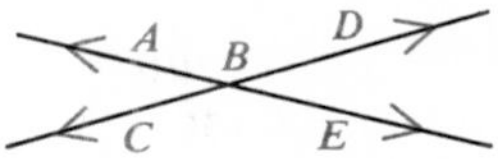

$\angle ABC$ and $\angle DBE$ are opposite angles.
$\angle ABD$ and $\angle CBE$ are opposite angles.

Diagram 71

* **Theorem 25/2**

Two opposite angles belong to the same plane. The interiors of the angles are in opposite sides of the line of each arm of the angles. If a ray is between the arms of one angle, then an opposite ray is between the arms of the opposite angle. (D72)

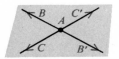

Diagram 72a

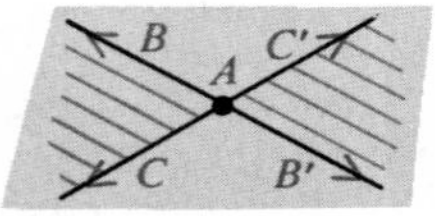

72b

72c

Exercises

1 Why is each of the following statements false?
   a If P is in the interior of $\angle BAC$, then $\overrightarrow{BP}$ is between $\overrightarrow{AB}$ and $\overrightarrow{AC}$.
   b If P is in the interior of $\angle BAC$, then $\overrightarrow{AP}$ is not between $\overrightarrow{AB}$ and $\overrightarrow{AC}$. *Answer*
   c If Q is not in either $\angle BAC$ or its exterior, then $\overrightarrow{AQ}$ must be between $\overrightarrow{AB}$ and $\overrightarrow{AC}$. *Answer*
   d If P belongs to $\alpha(A, B, C)$ but does not belong to $\angle BAC$, then $\overrightarrow{AP}$ must be between $\overrightarrow{AB}$ and $\overrightarrow{AC}$.
   e If P and Q are in the interior of $\angle BAC$ and $\overrightarrow{PQ}$ does not intersect $\angle BAC$, then $\overrightarrow{PQ}$ must be between $\overrightarrow{AB}$ and $\overrightarrow{AC}$.

2 If the two points P and Q are between the points B and C of $\angle BAC$, which of the following sets are in the interior of $\angle BAC$? In $\angle BAC$? In the exterior of $\angle BAC$?
   a P and Q *Answer*
   b $\overline{PQ}$
   c $\overrightarrow{AP}$
   d The open ray opposite $\overrightarrow{AQ}$
   e $\overleftrightarrow{BC} \cap \overline{PQ}$
   f $\overrightarrow{PQ}$

3 **a** If $\overrightarrow{AP}$ is in the interior of $\angle BAC$, does this imply $<B, P, C>$?

b If P and Q are in the interior of $\angle BAC$ and
if $<P, M, Q>$, is $\overrightarrow{AM}$ between $\overrightarrow{AB}$ and $\overrightarrow{AC}$? Is $\overrightarrow{AM}$
necessarily between $\overrightarrow{AP}$ and $\overrightarrow{AQ}$? Explain your answers.

c If $\overrightarrow{AB}$ is between $\overrightarrow{ED}$ and $\overrightarrow{EF}$, must $A = E$? *Answer*

d If P is in the interior of $\angle BAC$, must $\overline{BC}$ intersect $\overrightarrow{AP}$?

4 State Theorem 20/2 as two separate theorems.

5 If $\overrightarrow{EA}$ is between $\overrightarrow{ED}$ and $\overrightarrow{EF}$, which of the following
statements are necessarily correct?

a $\overrightarrow{ED}$ and $\overrightarrow{EF}$ are in opposite sides of EA.

b $\overrightarrow{EA}$ and $\overrightarrow{EF}$ form an angle.

c $\overrightarrow{ED}$ is between $\overrightarrow{EA}$ and $\overrightarrow{EF}$.

d $\overrightarrow{EA}$ is in $\alpha(D, E, F)$.

e $\overline{DF}$ intersects $\overrightarrow{EA}$ in some point Q.

6 If $\angle BAC$ and $\angle DAF$ are opposite angles and $<B, A, D>$,
name the angle that is opposite $\angle FAB$. *Answer*

7 Let γ denote the plane of $\angle BCA$. Also let $\overrightarrow{CD}$ denote
the open ray opposite $\overrightarrow{CA}$, and let $\overrightarrow{CE}$ denote the open ray
opposite $\overrightarrow{CB}$. Let α' and α'' respectively denote the B-side
and the E-side of AC. Let β' and β'' respectively denote
the A-side and the D-side of BC (D73).

a Is $\alpha' \cap \beta'$ the interior of $\angle BCA$?

b The interior of $\angle DCE$ is the intersection
of what two sets? *Answer*

c $\alpha'' \cap \beta'$ is the interior of which angle?

d If P belongs to $\alpha' \cap \beta'$ and if $<P, C, Q>$,
show that Q must belong to $\alpha'' \cap \beta''$.

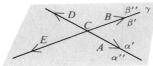

Diagram 73

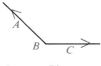

Diagram 74a

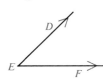

74b

As yet, we have said nothing about the size of angles. In D74,
$\angle ABC$ appears to be larger than $\angle DEF$, but in what way is it
larger and by how much? To answer these questions, we need a
way to find the size, or the measure, of each of these angles.

One scheme for finding the measure of an angle was devised
by the ancient Babylonians. This method, still commonly used,
can be described as follows. Suppose that we take a ray $\overrightarrow{OA}$ in
a plane (D75a) and suppose that we regard point O as a pivot.
We now let the ray turn in the plane, say in a counterclockwise

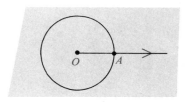

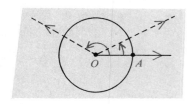

Diagram 75a   75b

68

direction, about point O. As the ray turns, or rotates, about point O, point A will follow the path of a circle. When point A has completed one rotation, the point will have returned to its starting position. At any position in the rotation, we can think of the ray as forming an angle with the ray in the starting position. Thus we can imagine that this angle becomes greater as the moving arm of the angle turns. That is, we can use the amount of turning to mean the size of the angle.

We also can use the circle traced by point A to give us a measure of this amount of turning. Again, suppose that we let point O be the center of the circle. We can start at point A in the circle and separate the curve into three hundred sixty equal "pieces" by using a succession of division points (D76). If we

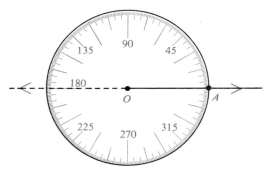

Diagram 76

number these points in the order in which A would intersect them and in such a way that A corresponds to zero and also to 360, then, to each of the numbers 1, 2, 3, . . . , 359, there corresponds a closed ray from point O to the point associated with that number. Then there is a closed ray from point O to the point with the number 1, which we can call *ray one*. Ray one is not $\overrightarrow{OA}$, but is the closed ray from point O through the point that corresponds with the number 1. Similarly, there is a ray two, a ray three, and so on. Clearly, ray one hundred eighty is the closed ray opposite $\overrightarrow{OA}$.

We can define the angle formed by $\overrightarrow{OA}$ and ray one as an angle of size one, the angle formed by $\overrightarrow{OA}$ and ray two as an angle of size two, and so on. The unit angle in physical geometry commonly is called an angle of *one degree* and is denoted by the symbol 1°. Thus, an angle of size twenty is an angle of twenty degrees and is denoted by the symbol 20°. A smaller unit angle, the *minute*, is obtained by separating an angle of 1° into sixty equal parts. A still smaller unit angle, the *second*, is obtained by separating an angle of one minute into sixty equal parts. An angle of one minute is denoted by the symbol 1′, and an angle of one second is denoted by the symbol 1″. Thus, one degree is sixty minutes, and one minute is sixty seconds. That is, 1° = 60′, and 1′ = 60″.

We can use the measuring circle to get the measure of any angle. Suppose, for example, that we want to find the measure of ∢BCD (D77a). We can place the vertex C on the measuring circle so that it coincides with point O. We can locate the closed ray $\overset{\cdot\rightarrow}{CD}$ so that it coincides with the closed ray $\overset{\rightarrow}{OA}$. Then $\overset{\cdot\rightarrow}{CB}$ intersects the circle at the point for one of our numbers, or at a point between two of them. Now we can assign a measure, or an approximation of the measure, to the angle. If we were to do this for two angles, then the angle assigned to the greater number, or greater measure, would be the larger angle, and the difference of the two numbers would be the difference in the size of the angles.

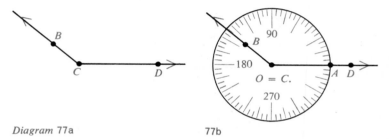

Diagram 77a   77b

Before we adapt this workable scheme for angle measure and build it into our geometry, we should observe its complications. First, this scheme would require us to change our definition of an angle. The definition would have to permit two opposite closed rays to form a 180° angle. Some books do this and call such an angle a *straight angle*. A line, then, contains many infinitely straight angles, since each point in the line determines two opposite closed rays.

Straight angles do have some advantages; but if we include these angles in our system, we cannot say either that every angle has a definite interior or that every angle is contained in exactly one plane. Furthermore, the measure of an angle depends upon its location with respect to the measuring circle. For example, consider ∢BCD represented in D78a. If we place $\overset{\rightarrow}{CD}$ along $\overset{\cdot\rightarrow}{OA}$,

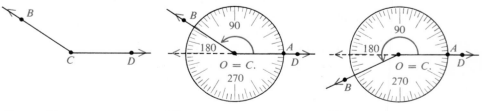

Diagram 78a   78b   78c

70

the open arm $\overrightarrow{CB}$ could fall in either side of line OA. Therefore, corresponding to the two cases, the angle would have two different sizes.

The possibilities just mentioned are useful in some parts of mathematics and its applications. In fact, in some situations, it is useful to think of an angle such as the one represented in D79a. The angle has been formed by rotating $\mathbb{S}$ about $\mathcal{R}$ more than twice. Thus, the size of the angle is greater than two times three hundred sixty.

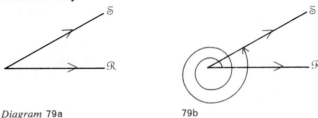

Diagram 79a   79b

Sometimes, it is useful to think of an angle as having a positive measure if the angle is regarded as a counterclockwise rotation of $\mathcal{R}$ onto $\mathbb{S}$, and as having a negative measure if the angle is regarded as a clockwise rotation of $\mathbb{S}$ onto $\mathcal{R}$ (D80).

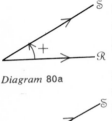

Diagram 80a

The situations just described simply point out that, in a mathematical system, the measure of an angle is what the system defines it to be. For our work in this book, we will not need the measure of an angle that permits all of the possibilities previously mentioned. Consequently, we will define the measure of an angle in a simple way. Later you will work with more general angle measures. These will not contradict our definition, but, instead, will include it as a special case.

80b

Instead of using the measuring circle, we can find the measure of a physical angle more easily by using a *semicircle*. That is, we can use one half of the measuring circle, the part that contains points from 0 through 180. Such an instrument is called a *protractor*. To measure an angle formed by rays $\mathcal{R}$ and $\mathbb{S}$ (D81a), the angle and the protractor are brought together in such a way that the angle vertex coincides with the center of the semicircle, one arm of the angle passes through point A, and the other arm passes

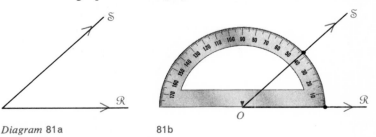

Diagram 81a   81b

through some point in the semicircle. This plan assigns to each angle just one number between 0 and 180. This number is the measure of the angle.

It is clear that, if a ray starts from the position $\overrightarrow{OA}$ and turns about point O in the plane of the protractor to the ray opposite $\overrightarrow{OA}$, then the ray sweeps out a closed half-plane with edge OA.

Just as the physical properties of a ruler do not prove anything in a mathematical sense, so the physical properties of a protractor do not prove anything. It is not clear, for example, just how we could separate a circle or a semicircle into a desired number of equal parts. The physical properties of a protractor suggest only that the following axiom in our system will give a single measure for an angle that corresponds to the measure of a physical angle.

Axiom 9/2

To each angle there corresponds a real number between 0 and 180 that is the measure of the angle.

Conventions

If an angle is denoted by the symbol ⊀BAC, then the measure of the angle will be denoted by the symbol ⊀$BAC°$, and will be read "the measure of ⊀BAC." Clearly, ⊀$BAC° = $ ⊀$CAB°$. We also will speak of the measure of an angle as its size, and we will say that one angle is larger or smaller than another according to whether its measure is greater than or less than that of the other.

The following is a standard way of classifying angles by their size.

Definition 20/2 *Acute angle, right angle, obtuse angle*

An angle is an acute angle if its measure is less than 90. An angle is a right angle if its measure is 90.* An angle is an obtuse angle if its measure is greater than 90. (D82)

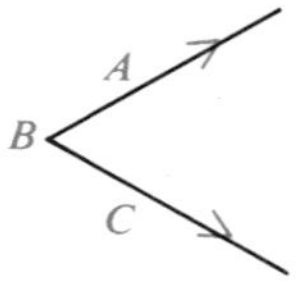

acute angle

Diagram 82a

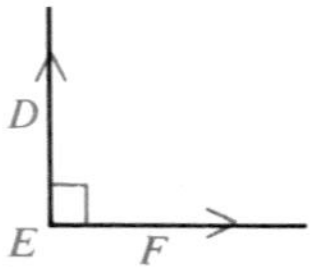

right angle

82b

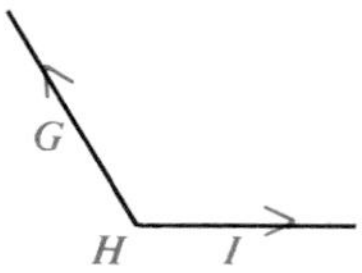

obtuse angle

82c

---

* In the picture of ⊀ DEF, the symbol beside the letter E indicates that ⊀ DEF is a right angle.

If $\overset{\rightarrow}{AB}$ is a closed ray in the edge of an
open half-plane α', there exists a one-to-one
correspondence between a set of open rays
in α' and the set of real numbers between
0 and 180 with the following properties.
For each open ray $\overset{\rightarrow}{AR}$ in α', there is just one
number r between 0 and 180 that is the measure
of $\sphericalangle BAR$. For each number r between 0
and 180, there is exactly one open ray $\overset{\rightarrow}{AR}$
in α' such that $\sphericalangle BAR$ has measure r. (D83)

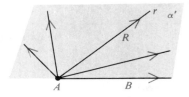

Convention
In Axiom 10/2, each number r corresponding to
a ray will be called a ray coordinate.
The closed ray $\overset{\rightarrow}{AB}$ in the edge of the half-plane
is the initial ray of the coordinate system.
(D83)

Diagram 83

For each open ray $\overset{\rightarrow}{AR}$ in α', Axiom 10/2 assigns a size to
$\sphericalangle BAR$. However, the axiom does not tell us anything about the
positions of two open rays $\overset{\rightarrow}{AP}$ and $\overset{\rightarrow}{AQ}$ in α' in relation to the sizes
of $\sphericalangle BAP$ and $\sphericalangle BAQ$. We can relate the order of the rays to the
size of the angles by introducing Axiom 11/2. This axiom gives
us a relation between ray coordinates in a half-plane and the
measure of angles that is similar to the relation we have for
coordinates in a line and the measure of distances.

Axiom 11/2 *Angle addition axiom*
If P is in the interior of $\sphericalangle BAQ$, then the
measure of $\sphericalangle BAQ$ is the sum of the
measures of $\sphericalangle BAP$ and $\sphericalangle PAQ$. That is, if P
is in the interior of $\sphericalangle BAQ$, then
$\sphericalangle BAQ° = \sphericalangle BAP° + \sphericalangle PAQ°$. (D84)

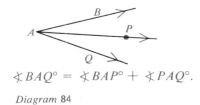

$$\sphericalangle BAQ° = \sphericalangle BAP° + \sphericalangle PAQ°.$$

Diagram 84

* Theorem 26/2

If $\overset{\rightarrow}{AX}$ and $\overset{\rightarrow}{AY}$ are two open rays in an
open half-plane α' and have
ray coordinates x and y respectively,
then $\sphericalangle XAY° = |x - y|$; $\sphericalangle XAY° = x - y$
if and only if $\overset{\rightarrow}{AY}$ is between $\overset{\rightarrow}{AX}$
and the initial ray of the coordinate system.
(D85)

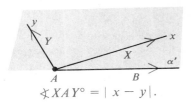

$$\sphericalangle XAY° = |x - y|.$$

Diagram 85

We now can establish a number of simple relations between
the sizes of certain angles and the positions of certain rays.

If point Q is in the plane of $\sphericalangle PAB$ and in the
same side of AB as P, then Q is
interior to, is in, or is exterior
to $\sphericalangle PAB$ according as the measure
of $\sphericalangle QAB$ is less than, equal to,
or greater than the measure of $\sphericalangle PAB$.
(D86)

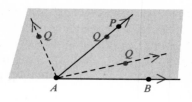

Diagram 86

From Axiom 11/2 and Theorem 27/2, we can obtain Corollary
27/2.

* Corollary 27/2

If $\overrightarrow{AQ}$ is between $\overrightarrow{AB}$ and $\overrightarrow{AP}$, then the
sum of the measures of $\sphericalangle QAB$ and
$\sphericalangle QAP$ is equal to the measure
of $\sphericalangle PAB$. In particular, each
of the measures of $\sphericalangle QAB$ and
$\sphericalangle QAP$ is less than the measure
of $\sphericalangle PAB$. (D87)

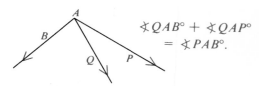

$\sphericalangle QAB° + \sphericalangle QAP°$
$= \sphericalangle PAB°.$

Diagram 87

Suppose that $\overrightarrow{AB}$ and $\overrightarrow{AC}$ are opposite closed rays and that
$\overrightarrow{AP}$ is a third closed ray (D88). It now can be proved, as one would
suppose, that the sum of the measures of $\sphericalangle PAB$ and $\sphericalangle PAC$ is
180. Two angles whose measures have a sum of 180 frequently
occur in geometry and are called *supplementary* angles.

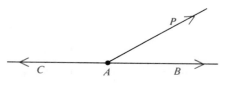

Diagram 88

Definition 21/2 *Supplementary angles*
Two angles are supplementary angles if the sum
of their measures is 180. Each of the two angles is a
supplement of the other.

** Theorem 28/2 *Angle supplement theorem*
If $\overrightarrow{AB}$ and $\overrightarrow{AC}$ are opposite closed rays and $\overrightarrow{AP}$ is a third
closed ray, then $\sphericalangle PAB$ and $\sphericalangle PAC$ are supplementary angles.
That is, $\sphericalangle PAB° + \sphericalangle PAC° = 180$.

By simple computation, we have the following relations.

* Theorem 29/2

A supplement of an acute angle is an obtuse angle.
A supplement of a right angle is a right angle.
A supplement of an obtuse angle is an acute angle.

The supplementary angles in D88 are a special case of angles that are called *adjacent* angles. We can define adjacent angles in the following way.

Definition 22/2 *Adjacent angles*

Two angles are adjacent angles if they are coplanar, have one arm in common, and their interiors do not intersect. (D89)

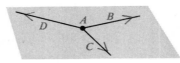

Each two of the three angles with vertex A are adjacent.

Diagram 89

The next theorem is a natural sort of opposite to the angle supplement theorem, Theorem 28/2.

* Theorem 30/2

If $\angle PAB$ and $\angle PAC$ are adjacent and supplementary, then $\overrightarrow{AB}$ and $\overrightarrow{AC}$ are opposite closed rays. (D90)

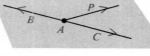

Diagram 90

It also is useful to have the following natural extension of the angle supplement theorem.

* Theorem 31/2

If point P is in the interior of $\angle QAB$ and $\overrightarrow{AC}$ is the closed ray opposite $\overrightarrow{AB}$, then Q is in the interior of $\angle PAC$, and $\angle BAP° + \angle PAQ° + \angle QAC° = 180$. (D91)

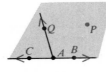

Diagram 91a

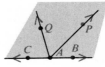

91b

Exercises

1 From the information given in D92, estimate each of the following.

a $\angle COA°$

b $\angle EOA°$

c $\angle HOD°$ *Answer*

d $\angle DOA°$

e $\angle COJ°$

f $\angle BOA° + \angle BOC°$

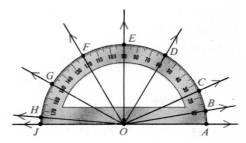

Diagram 92

75

g $\angle COD° + \angle FOG°$

h $\angle DOE° - \angle HOJ°$ *Answer*

2 Using a straightedge, draw angles with estimated measures of 90, 45, 60, 170, and 15 respectively. Then use a protractor to measure the approximate amount of error in each estimate.

3 Which of the following numbers could not be the measure of an angle in our system? In each case, give a reason for your decision.

a 78.99999 **e** $\frac{1}{789}$

b 180 **f** 360

c 0 **g** .0000000000000000001

d $\sqrt[3]{3}$ **h** $\sqrt{\pi}$

4 A plane α is separated into two open half-planes α' and α'' by a line t. Points R and S are in α but not in t. If the closed ray $\overrightarrow{AB}$ is contained in t, why are none of the following statements necessarily correct?

a If $\angle RAB° = r$ and $\angle SAB° = r$, then $R = S$.

b If $\angle RAB° = r$ and S is collinear with $\overrightarrow{AR}$, then $\angle SAB° = r$.

c For a given real number r, there is just one open ray $\overrightarrow{AP}$ in α' such that $\angle PAB° = r$.

d If R and S are in the same half-plane of t and $\angle RAB° = 179.9999999$, then $\overrightarrow{AS}$ must be between $\overrightarrow{AR}$ and $\overrightarrow{AB}$.

e If $0 < r < 180$, there is exactly one open ray $\overrightarrow{AR}$ in α such that $\angle BAR° = r$.

5 From the information expressed by D92, estimate the ray coordinate of each of the following rays.

a $\overrightarrow{OE}$ **b** $\overrightarrow{OC}$ **c** $\overrightarrow{OG}$ **d** $\overrightarrow{OJ}$

6 a If point A is in the interior of $\angle DEF$, what relationship exists between $\angle DEA°$, $\angle AEF°$, and $\angle DEF°$? *Answer*

b If $\angle AEF° + \angle AED° = \angle DEF°$, must A be in the interior of $\angle DEF$? Explain your answer.

7 In the edge of half-plane α', let $\overrightarrow{AB}$ denote the initial ray of a ray coordinate system. Let the open rays $\overrightarrow{AX}$ and $\overrightarrow{AY}$ in α' have coordinates x and y respectively.

a Find $\angle XAY°$, if $x = 92$ and $y = 36$.

b Find $\angle XAY°$, if $x = 130$ and $y = 18$. *Answer*

c Does $x < \frac{1}{2}y$ imply $\angle YAX° > \angle XAB°$?

d If $71 \leq x \leq 90$ and $3 \leq y \leq 37$, what is the maximum possible measure of $\angle XAY$? The minimum possible measure of $\angle XAY$?

e If $\angle XAY° = y - x$, must X be in the interior of $\angle YAB$?

8 Use the given conditions of Theorem 26/2 to prove the following parts of the theorem.

76

a If $\overrightarrow{AY}$ is between $\overrightarrow{AX}$ and the initial ray $\overrightarrow{AB}$, then $\sphericalangle XAY° = x - y$.

b If $\sphericalangle XAY° = x - y$, then $\overrightarrow{AY}$ is between $\overrightarrow{AX}$ and the initial ray $\overrightarrow{AB}$.

9 Let P denote the statement "Y belongs to $\sphericalangle XAB$"; let Q denote the statement "Y belongs to the exterior of $\sphericalangle XAB$"; and let R denote the statement "Y belongs to the interior of $\sphericalangle XAB$." Suppose that $\overrightarrow{AX}$ and $\overrightarrow{AY}$ with ray coordinates x and y respectively are open rays in an open half-plane determined by AB and that $\overrightarrow{AB}$ is the initial ray of the coordinate system. For each of the following assumptions, which of the statements P, Q, or R can be regarded as the correct conclusion?

a $x < y$. *Answer*
b $x > y$.
c $x = y$.
d $\overrightarrow{AY}$ is between $\overrightarrow{AX}$ and $\overrightarrow{AB}$.
e $\langle A, X, Y \rangle$.
f $\langle A, Y, X \rangle$. *Answer*
g $\langle B, X, Y \rangle$.
h $\sphericalangle XAB$ is acute, and $\sphericalangle BAY$ is obtuse.

10 Let α denote the plane of $\sphericalangle ABC$ and let r denote $\sphericalangle ABC°$.

a If $\overrightarrow{BA}$ is taken as the initial ray of a ray coordinate system for the C-side of AB, what must be the coordinate of $\overrightarrow{BC}$?

b If $\overrightarrow{BC}$ is taken as the initial ray of a ray coordinate system for the A-side of BC, what is the coordinate of $\overrightarrow{BA}$?

c If $\overrightarrow{BA'}$ opposite $\overrightarrow{BA}$ is the initial ray of the coordinate system in the C-side of AB, what is the coordinate of $\overrightarrow{BC}$?

♦ **11** In the plane of $\sphericalangle ABC$, let α' denote the A-side of BC, and let γ' denote the C-side of AB (D93). Let $\overrightarrow{BX}$ and $\overrightarrow{BY}$ denote two open rays between $\overrightarrow{BA}$ and $\overrightarrow{BC}$. In a ray coordinate system for α' with initial ray $\overrightarrow{BC}$, the coordinates of $\overrightarrow{BX}$ and $\overrightarrow{BY}$ are x and y respectively. In a ray coordinate system for γ' with initial ray $\overrightarrow{BA}$, the coordinates of $\overrightarrow{BX}$ and $\overrightarrow{BY}$ are x' and y' respectively.

a Explain why $|x - y|$ must equal $|x' - y'|$.

b Does $x > y$ imply $x' < y'$?

c Is $x + x' = y + y'$? Why?

d Does $x = y'$ imply $x' = y$?

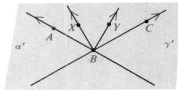

Diagram 93

Just as the midpoint of a segment bisects the segment, so there is a ray that bisects an angle. This ray is sometimes called the *midray* of the angle.

Definition 23/2 *Bisector of an angle*

The open ray $\overrightarrow{AP}$ and the closed ray $\overleftrightarrow{AP}$ are bisectors of $\sphericalangle BAC$ if P is in the interior of the angle and the measure of $\sphericalangle PAB$ equals the measure of $\sphericalangle PAC$. A line bisects an angle if it contains a ray that bisects the angle. (D94)

$\sphericalangle PAB^\circ = \sphericalangle PAC^\circ$.

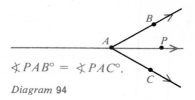

Diagram 94

* **Theorem 32/2**

For any angle, there is exactly one closed ray that bisects the angle.

Convention

The phrase "bisector of an angle" usually will refer to the line that bisects the angle.

Theorem 33/2

Opposite angles have the same measure. (D95)

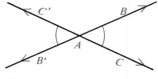

Diagram 95

Proof

Let $\sphericalangle B'AC'$ denote the angle opposite $\sphericalangle BAC$, with $\overrightarrow{AB'}$ opposite $\overrightarrow{AB}$ and $\overrightarrow{AC'}$ opposite $\overrightarrow{AC}$. By Theorem 28/2, $\sphericalangle BAC$ and $\sphericalangle BAC'$ are supplements, so

1 $\sphericalangle BAC^\circ = 180 - \sphericalangle BAC'^\circ$.

By Theorem 28/2, $\sphericalangle B'AC'$ and $\sphericalangle BAC'$ are also supplements, so

2 $\sphericalangle B'AC'^\circ = 180 - \sphericalangle BAC'^\circ$.

From statements 1 and 2, it follows that

3 $\sphericalangle BAC^\circ = \sphericalangle B'AC'^\circ$.

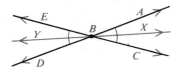

Diagram 96

* **Theorem 34/2**

If a ray bisects an angle, then the opposite ray bisects the opposite angle. (D96)

Another angle bisector property that will be very useful is the following one.

Theorem 35/2

If $\sphericalangle PAB$ is acute, then there exists an angle $\sphericalangle PAC$ such that $\overrightarrow{AB}$ is the bisector of $\sphericalangle PAC$. (D97)

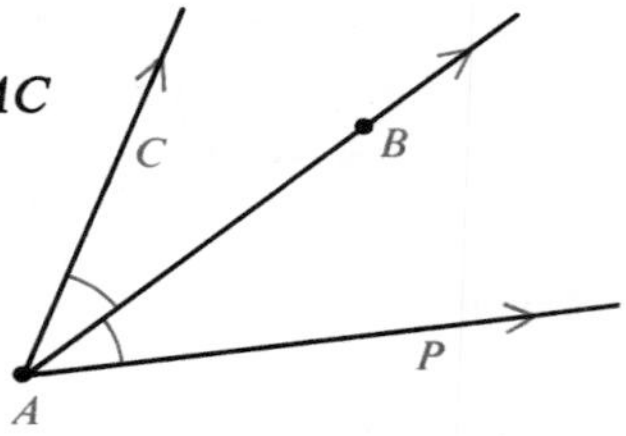

Proof

Since $\sphericalangle PAB$ is acute, $\sphericalangle PAB^\circ$ is less than 90. Thus $2(\sphericalangle PAB^\circ)$ is less than 180. Therefore, by Axiom 10/2, there exists, in the plane of $\sphericalangle PAB$, an open ray $\overrightarrow{AC}$ in the B-side of AP such that $\sphericalangle PAC^\circ = 2(\sphericalangle PAB^\circ)$. Because $\sphericalangle PAB^\circ < \sphericalangle PAC^\circ$, the closed ray $\overleftrightarrow{AB}$ is between $\overrightarrow{AP}$ and $\overrightarrow{AC}$. With the angle addition axiom, we then have $\sphericalangle PAB^\circ + \sphericalangle BAC^\circ = \sphericalangle PAC^\circ = 2(\sphericalangle PAB^\circ)$. So $\sphericalangle BAC^\circ = \sphericalangle PAB^\circ$, and $\overrightarrow{AB}$ bisects $\sphericalangle PAC$.

Diagram 97

We conclude this section with the notion of the angles formed by intersecting lines and the idea of perpendicular lines.

Convention

If two lines intersect, then the intersection point is the origin of two opposite closed rays in each line. In pairs, these four rays form exactly four angles. These angles will be called the angles formed by the two intersecting lines. (D98)

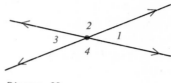

Diagram 98

*Theorem 36/2

If one of the four angles formed by two intersecting lines is a right angle, then all of the four angles are right angles. If all four of the angles formed by two intersecting lines have the same measure, then all four of the angles are right angles. (D99)

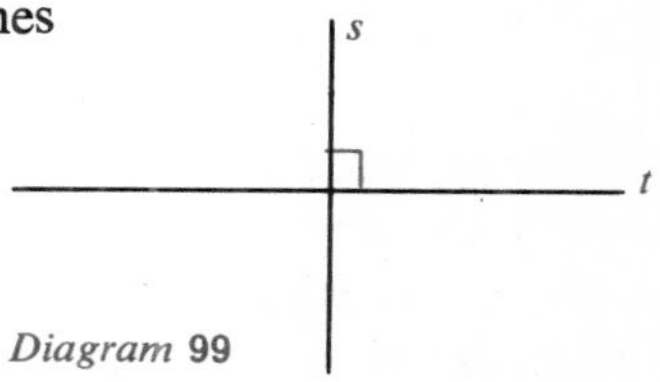

Diagram 99

Definition 24/2 *Perpendicular lines, rays, and segments*

Two lines are perpendicular if they intersect in such a way that one of the angles formed is a right angle. Two rays, two segments, and a ray and a segment are perpendicular if they intersect and if they belong to two lines that are perpendicular. Lines, rays, and segments that are perpendicular are perpendicular to each other at their point of intersection.

Convention

Perpendicularity will be denoted by the symbol ⊥. Thus, $s \perp t$, $\overleftrightarrow{AB} \perp \overleftrightarrow{CD}$, $\overline{EF} \perp \overline{GH}$, and $\overrightarrow{ML} \perp \overline{JK}$ are respective statements that two lines, two rays, two segments, and a ray and a segment are perpendicular to each other. (D100)

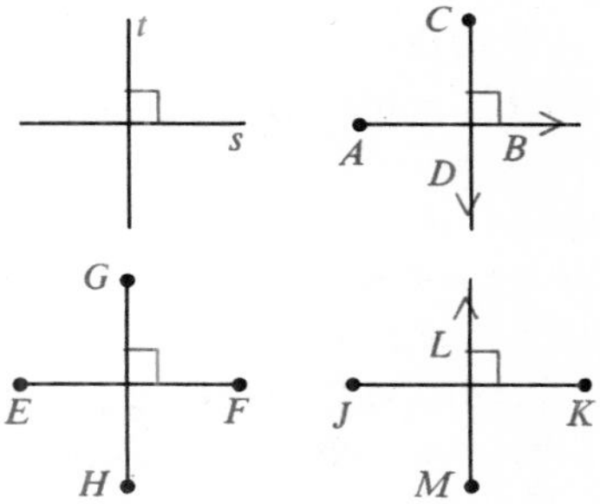

Diagram 100

Comment

$s \perp t \Longleftrightarrow t \perp s$; $\overleftrightarrow{AB} \perp \overleftrightarrow{CD} \Longleftrightarrow \overleftrightarrow{CD} \perp \overleftrightarrow{AB}$; $\overline{EF} \perp \overline{GH} \Longleftrightarrow \overline{GH} \perp \overline{EF}$; $\overrightarrow{ML} \perp \overline{JK} \Longleftrightarrow \overline{JK} \perp \overrightarrow{ML}$. (Symmetric properties for perpendicular lines, rays, and segments and for a ray and a segment that are perpendicular)

Theorem 37/2

If line s is in plane α, and A is a point of s, then there is exactly one line in α that is perpendicular to s at A. (D101)

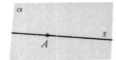

Diagram 101a

101b

Proof

Let B and B' denote two points of s such that point A is between them. Let α' and α'' denote

79

the opposite sides of s in α. By Axiom 10/2, there exists exactly one open ray $\overrightarrow{AC}$ in α' such that $\sphericalangle CAB° = 90$. By definition, AC is perpendicular to s at A. Also, AC is in α.

Next, let t denote a line in α that is perpendicular to s at A. Let $\overrightarrow{AQ}$ and $\overrightarrow{AQ'}$ denote the opposite open rays in t at A. By Theorem 17/2, either $\overrightarrow{AQ}$ or $\overrightarrow{AQ'}$ is in α'. We may suppose that the notation has been chosen so that $\overrightarrow{AQ}$ is in α'. Because $t \perp s$ at A, all four of the angles formed by s and t at A are right angles, so $\sphericalangle QAB° = 90$. But there is only one open ray in α' whose closed ray forms a right angle with $\overrightarrow{AB}$. Since $\overrightarrow{AC}$ is already such a ray, it follows that $\overrightarrow{AQ} = \overrightarrow{AC}$, and, hence, $t = AC$. Therefore, AC is the only line in α that is perpendicular to s at A.

Exercises

1 Four incorrect "if . . . then" statements are given in this exercise. For each statement, make a diagram in which the hypothesis is satisfied but the conclusion is not.

 a If $\overrightarrow{AP}$ is in the interior of $\sphericalangle BAC$, then $\overrightarrow{AP}$ bisects the angle.

 b If $\sphericalangle HJL° = \sphericalangle LJK°$, then $\overrightarrow{JL}$ bisects $\sphericalangle HJK$. *Answer*

 c If the line JL bisects $\sphericalangle HJK$, then $\overrightarrow{JL}$ is in the interior of $\sphericalangle HJK$.

 d If the line AD bisects an angle, then D is in the interior of the angle.

2 **a** If $\overrightarrow{AP}$ bisects $\sphericalangle BAC$ and $\overrightarrow{AQ}$ bisects $\sphericalangle CAB$, then what is true about $\overrightarrow{AP}$ and $\overrightarrow{AQ}$? *Answer*

 b If $\overrightarrow{AP}$ bisects $\sphericalangle BAC$ and $\overrightarrow{AP}$ also bisects $\sphericalangle DAE$, must $\sphericalangle BAC$ be the same angle as $\sphericalangle DAE$? Make a diagram that illustrates your conclusion.

3 The open rays $\overrightarrow{AB}$, $\overrightarrow{AC}$, and $\overrightarrow{AD}$ are in an open half-plane and have ray coordinates b, c, and d respectively. If $\overrightarrow{AD}$ is the bisector of $\sphericalangle BAC$, find the value of d for each of the following cases.

 a $b = 60$; $c = 30$. **d** $b = \sqrt{3}$; $c = 1$. *Answer*

 b $b = 20$; $c = 32$. **e** $b = \pi$; $c = 179$.

 c $b = 82$; $c = 16$. **f** $b = \sqrt{11}$; $c = \sqrt{10}$.

4 Using the information given in D102, name five pairs of angles for which the angles in each pair have the same measure.

5 For each of the following cases, use D102 to find the measures of $\sphericalangle 1$, $\sphericalangle 2$, $\sphericalangle 3$, $\sphericalangle 4$, $\sphericalangle 5$, and $\sphericalangle 6$.

 a $\sphericalangle CHE° = 20$, and $\sphericalangle AHF° = 37$.

 b $\sphericalangle AHD° = 44$, and $\sphericalangle FHD° = 37$.

 c $\sphericalangle EHB° = \pi$, and $\sphericalangle EHD° = \sqrt{31}$.

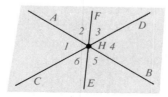

Diagram 102

d $\measuredangle EHB° = 50$, and $\overrightarrow{HD}$ bisects $\measuredangle FHB$.

e $\overrightarrow{HB}$ bisects $\measuredangle EHD$, and $\overrightarrow{HC}$ bisects $\measuredangle EHA$.

6 Let $\measuredangle ADB$ and $\measuredangle BDC$ denote two adjacent angles.

  a Are $\measuredangle ADB$ and $\measuredangle BDC$ coplanar? Do they have an arm in common? Do their interiors intersect? *Answer*

  b Are $\measuredangle ADB$ and $\measuredangle ADC$ coplanar? Do they have an arm in common? Are they adjacent angles? Explain your last answer.

  c If $\overrightarrow{DA}$ and $\overrightarrow{DC}$ are opposite rays, are $\measuredangle ADB$ and $\measuredangle BDC$ supplementary angles?

7 In Theorem 35/2, why is it necessary that $\measuredangle PAB$ be acute?

8 In Theorem 35/2, let $\overrightarrow{AB}$, $\overrightarrow{AP}$, and $\overrightarrow{AC}$ have ray coordinates $b, p,$ and c respectively.

  a What is c if $b = 30$ and $p = 15$? *Answer*

  b What is c if $b = 100$ and $p = 22$?

  c What is c if $b = \sqrt{93}$ and $p = \pi$?

  d What is the measure of $\measuredangle PAC$ if $b = 18$ and $p = 17$?

  e What is the measure of $\measuredangle PAC$ if $b = 8\sqrt{5}$ and $p = 3\sqrt{2}$?

9 Let A denote a point in a line t. When we develop the formal system further, what answers do you think we will establish to the following questions?

  a How many different planes contain t?

  b How many lines are perpendicular to t at A?

  c What is the nature of the union of all the lines perpendicular to t at A?

10 From the information given in D103, identify each of the following angles as acute, obtuse, or right.

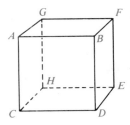

Diagram 103

  a $\measuredangle GHC$ **e** $\measuredangle BFC$

  b $\measuredangle ABF$ **f** $\measuredangle CDF$ *Answer*

  c $\measuredangle FAB$ **g** $\measuredangle CDA$

  d $\measuredangle CAF$ **h** $\measuredangle HDG$

11 We have not yet defined the perpendicularity of a line and a plane in the formal system. However, in D103, does it seem that FB should be perpendicular to $\alpha(A, B, C)$? That FA should be perpendicular to $\alpha(A, B, C)$? Try to formulate a definition for the perpendicularity of a line and plane that justifies your answers.

Definitions of 10/2

polygons and By now, you have seen many examples of foundation theorems
circles and their proofs. Although we need many more of these theorems, we want to include them with work in which you will take an active part. In the next two chapters, most of the theorems you will

prove will concern *circles* and other geometric figures called *polygons*. The main purpose of this section is to develop definitions for these figures.

We begin with the simplest and, in some ways, the most important of these figures, the *triangle*.

Definition 25/2 *Triangle*

A triangle is the union of the three segments determined by three noncollinear points. The three noncollinear points are the vertices of the triangle, and the three segments determined by the vertices are the sides of the triangle. An angle whose vertex is also a vertex of the triangle and each of whose arms contains a side of the triangle is an angle of the triangle.

Conventions

If A, B, and C are three noncollinear points, the triangle they determine will be denoted by the symbol $\triangle$ followed by the letters A, B, and C in any order, such as the symbol $\triangle ABC$. Thus $\triangle ABC = \triangle BCA = \triangle CBA$. A vertex and a side of a triangle are opposite each other if the side does not contain the vertex. Thus, in $\triangle ABC$, segment $\overline{AB}$ and vertex C are opposite each other. An angle of a triangle and a side are opposite each other if the angle does not contain the side. Also, when we refer to the angle between two sides, we will mean the angle of the triangle to which the two sides belong. When we refer to the side between two angles, we will mean the side that is contained in both angles and joins their vertices.

In $\triangle ABC$, the vertices are A, B, and C (D104); the sides are $\overline{AB}$, $\overline{BC}$, and $\overline{CA}$; the angles of the triangle are $\sphericalangle CAB$, $\sphericalangle ABC$, and $\sphericalangle BCA$. Notice that, since the arms of an angle are rays and the sides of a triangle are segments, an angle of a triangle is never contained in the triangle. In $\triangle ABC$, $\overline{AB}$ belongs to $\sphericalangle BAC$ and to $\sphericalangle ABC$, so $\overline{AB}$ is the side between these two angles.

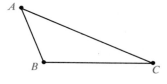

Diagram 104

---

* Theorem 38/2

A triangle is contained in exactly one plane.

We next define the interior and the exterior of a triangle in much the same way as we did for an angle.

Definition 26/2 *Interior of a triangle, exterior of a triangle*

The interior of $\triangle ABC$ is the set of points that is the intersection of the following three open half-planes: the C-side of AB, the B-side of AC, and the A-side of BC. The exterior of $\triangle ABC$ is the set of all points that are coplanar with the triangle and do not belong either to the triangle or to its interior. (D105)

Diagram 105a

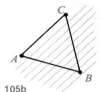

105b

Theorem 39/2

The interior of a triangle is a convex set.

Proof

The interior of a triangle is the intersection of three open half-planes. Open half-planes are convex sets, and the intersection of convex sets is a convex set. Therefore, the interior of a triangle is a convex set.

105c

105d

Clearly, neither a triangle nor its exterior can be a convex set. Notice points P and Q in D106. Points P and Q are in the exterior of the triangle, but these points are located in such a way that $\overline{PQ}$ is not contained in the exterior.

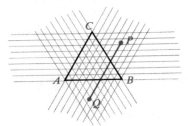

Diagram 106

The possibilities for the intersection of a triangle and a line in the plane of the triangle is given essentially by Theorem 40/2. The basic importance of this relationship was first pointed out by the mathematician Pasch (1843-1930). In some systems, the relationship is taken as an axiom, called the *Pasch axiom*. We include it in our system as a theorem. Its proof illustrates ways of dealing with a theorem that involves several cases.

83

Theorem 40/2 *Pasch theorem*

If a line in the plane of a triangle intersects the triangle, then the line intersects at least two sides of the triangle.

Proof

Let *t* denote a line that is in the plane of $\triangle ABC$ and that intersects the triangle in at least one point.

Case I Line *t* intersects the triangle at a vertex. We may assume the notation has been chosen so that *t* intersects the triangle at *A*. Then *t* intersects $\overline{AB}$ and $\overline{AC}$ at *A*. (D107a)

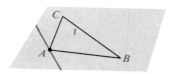

Diagram 107a

Case II Line *t* does not intersect the triangle at a vertex. Let *P* denote a point at which *t* intersects the triangle. Since *P* is in some side of the triangle, there is no loss of generality in supposing that *P* is between *A* and *B*. (D107b)

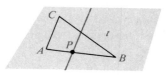

107b

   Since neither of the vertices *A* or *B* is in *t*, line $t \neq AB$. Because *P* is between *A* and *B*, points *A* and *B* are in opposite sides of *t*. Because vertex *C* is not in *t*, it is either in the *A*-side of *t* or in the *B*-side of *t*. Suppose that *C* is in the *A*-side of *t*. Then *B* and *C* are in opposite sides of *t*, so $\overline{BC}$ intersects *t*. Thus, *t* intersects both $\overline{AB}$ and $\overline{BC}$. In a similar way, it follows that, if *C* is in the *B*-side of *t*, then *t* intersects both $\overline{AC}$ and $\overline{AB}$.

Consider again the proof of Theorem 40/2. For Case I, the vertex of intersection could be *A*, *B*, or *C*. To avoid dealing with each of these possibilities, we have used the fact that we could always make *A* a vertex of intersection by relabeling the vertices of the triangle.

   For Case II, we have said that there is no loss of generality in supposing that *P* is between *A* and *B*. This means that any other case that could occur could be dealt with in the same way as the case we have selected.

   In the proof of Case II, the phrase "In a similar way" is used to avoid the necessity of repeating the argument.

   The methods that we have used in the last proof to take care of several possibilities at once are not without danger. We must take care, in selecting a particular case, that the case does not have some special property that would not be true in the other cases. In other words, these methods of proof obviously call for good judgment.

   The next properties are closely related to the Pasch theorem.

*Theorem 41/2

A line that is in the plane of a triangle
and passes through a point in the interior
of the triangle intersects the triangle in exactly
two points. (D108)

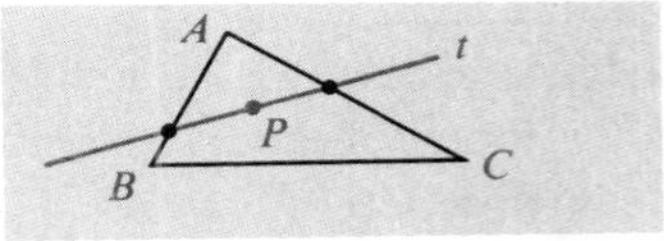

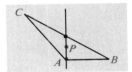

Diagram 108

* Corollary 41/2

A line that contains a vertex of a triangle
and a point in the interior of the triangle
intersects the side opposite the vertex at a point
between the other two vertices.* (D109)

Diagram 109

Another very useful notion is that of an *exterior angle* of a
triangle. In D110, ∢CBD is an exterior angle of △ABC at B. This
exterior angle is adjacent to ∢CBA of the triangle. Since $\overline{BA}$ and
$\overrightarrow{BD}$ are opposite rays, ∢CBD also is a supplement of ∢CBA.

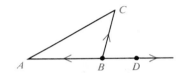

∢CBD is an exterior angle of △ABC.

Diagram 110

Definition 27/2 *Exterior angle of a triangle*
An angle is an exterior angle of a triangle if it is adjacent
to an angle of the triangle and is a supplement of that angle.
An exterior angle is exterior to a triangle at the vertex
that it has in common with an angle of the triangle.

Definition 28/2 *Perimeter of a triangle*
The sum of the lengths of the three sides of a triangle is
the perimeter of the triangle.

Exercises
1 Consider △PQR in answering each of the following.
  a Which three segments are the sides of the triangle?
  b Which side is opposite ∢QPR? *Answer*
  c Which vertex is opposite $\overline{QR}$?
  d Is ∢Q of the triangle also ∢PQR?
  e ∢R is between which two sides?
  f Which angle is opposite side $\overline{PR}$?
  g Which side is between ∢PRQ and ∢QPR?

* This corollary is also a special case of Theorem 22/2.

85

2 How does the meaning of intersection of sets imply that the intersection of three sets always is contained in the intersection of any two of the sets? For example, how does the intersection of sets imply that, if $\mathcal{A}$, $\mathcal{B}$, and $\mathcal{C}$ denote sets, then $\mathcal{A} \cap \mathcal{B} \cap \mathcal{C}$ is contained in $\mathcal{A} \cap \mathcal{B}$? *Answer*

3 With respect to $\triangle ABC$, let $\mathcal{A}$, $\mathcal{B}$, and $\mathcal{C}$ denote the A-side of BC, the B-side of CA, and the C-side of AB respectively. Use the property discussed in exercise 2 to show that the interior of $\triangle ABC$ is contained in the interior of each angle of the triangle.

4 a Show that, if point X is in the interior of any two angles of $\triangle ABC$, say $\sphericalangle A$ and $\sphericalangle B$, then X is in the interior of $\triangle ABC$.

b Use the results of exercises 3 and 4a to give a new definition of the interior of a triangle.

c Make a diagram to show that your new definition has the same meaning as Definition 26/2.

5 a If line t intersects $\triangle ABC$ only at point A, which two sides of $\triangle ABC$ does t intersect?

b Describe the possible intersections between a line and a triangle that are coplanar. *Answer*

c Can a line intersect the interior of a triangle without intersecting the triangle?

6 Make a diagram that illustrates a line intersecting one and only one side of a triangle.

7 Using D111, decide which of the following statements are true.

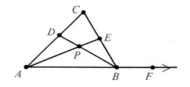

Diagram 111

a $\sphericalangle DPE$ is adjacent to $\sphericalangle DPA$.

b $\sphericalangle DPE$ and $\sphericalangle DPA$ are supplementary angles.

c $\sphericalangle BPE$ is an exterior angle of $\triangle DPA$.

d $\sphericalangle APB$ is an exterior angle of $\triangle DPA$.

e $\sphericalangle PDC$ is an exterior angle of $\triangle DPA$.

8 Judging from D111, why is each of the following statements false?

a $\sphericalangle EPB$ is an exterior angle of $\triangle DPA$.

b $\sphericalangle PBA$ is an exterior angle of $\triangle PEB$.

c $\sphericalangle CBF$ is an exterior angle of $\triangle PEB$.

d $\sphericalangle CBF$ is an exterior angle of $\triangle APB$.

e $\sphericalangle DPA° + \sphericalangle EPB° = 180$.

◆ 9 The sides of $\triangle ABC$ have lengths a, b, and c, and the perimeter of the triangle is p. In each of the following cases, some information is given concerning three of the four numbers a, b, c, and p. Give as much information as you can about the fourth number.

a $a = 11$; $b = 8$; $c = 9$. *Answer*

b $p = 12$; $a = |-4|$; $b = 5$.

c $p = 20$; $a = b = 6$.

d $a = 2\sqrt{3}$; $b = \sqrt{12}$; $c = \sqrt{27}$.

e $a < 6$; $b < 5$; $c < 7$. *Answer*

f $a > 1$; $b > 2$; $c > 3$.

g $a > 2$; $b > 3$; $p = 10$.

h $a < b < c < 30$.

Some basic properties of triangles have been listed first because they suggest properties that will be needed for polygons. The word "polygon" comes from the Greek word for "many angles." A triangle is a polygon with three angles and three sides. A polygon with n sides is called an n-*gon*, so a triangle is a *3-gon*. The particular class of *n*-gons that we want to define is a class of plane figures that have n vertices, n sides, n angles, and a convex interior.

As we know, three noncollinear points determine three segments, or a triangle. The special nature of triangles becomes clear if we next consider four noncollinear points. Four points do not determine four segments; instead, four points determine six segments. If we select only four of these segments, some of the figures we get are shown in D112.

Diagram 112

To make sense of the problem of defining a polygon, we need to borrow from logic the notion of an *ordered set*. That is, we need the idea of assigning one element of a set to be first, another to be second, another to be third, and so on. Suppose that $\{A, B, C, D\}$ is a set of four points. The notation $\{A, B, C, D\}$ is not meant to indicate any particular order of the points. Therefore, $\{A, B, C, D\} = \{B, C, A, D\}$. But suppose that we want to think of the points of this set in some particular successive order. For example, suppose that we want to consider the order in which B is first, A is second, D is third, and C is fourth. We will indicate the set in this order by the notation (B, A, D, C). Then the statement "$(A, B, C, D) = (B, C, A, D)$" is false because the two orderings of the set are different.

Diagram 113

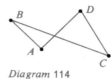

Diagram 114

Suppose that we next consider the successive segments $\overline{BA}$, $\overline{AD}$, and $\overline{DC}$ (D113). The union of these three segments forms a natural *segment path* from B to C through the ordered set (B, A, D, C). If we include the segment that joins the last point in (B, A, D, C) and the first point in this set, that is $\overline{CB}$, then the union of the four segments is a *segment circuit* through the ordered set (D114).

The polygons that we want are a particular kind of segment circuit. We will now add to the system the notions that we have been discussing and then see how we can specialize these ideas to obtain the definition of a polygon.

Convention

If $\mathbb{S} = \{A, C, H, \ldots, M\}$ is a set of n elements, where n is a positive integer, the notation $(B, K, L, \ldots, H)$ will denote the n elements of $\mathbb{S}$ as an ordered set in which B is the first element, K is the second, and so on, with H as the last and the nth element. [Thus if $\mathbb{S} = \{A, B, C, D\}$, an ordering of $\mathbb{S}$ in which D, B, A, and C are the first, second, third, and fourth elements respectively will be denoted by the symbol (D, B, A, C).]
If a set has two elements, an ordering of the set is called an ordered pair.
If a set has three elements, an ordering of it is called an ordered triple.
An ordering of n elements is called an *ordered n-tuple*.

In the convention just given, notice that we did not restrict the sets to sets of points. Later, we will want to use ordered sets of numbers.

To simplify the following definitions, we have used subscripts to name the elements of a set.

Definition 29/2 *Segment path, segment circuit*
If $(P_1, P_2, P_3, \ldots, P_n)$ is an ordered set of n points, where $n > 2$, then the union of the $n-1$ segments

$$\overline{P_1P_2}, \ \overline{P_2P_3}, \ \overline{P_3P_4}, \ \ldots, \ \overline{P_{n-1}P_n}$$

is a segment path from P_1 to P_n through the ordered set.
The union of the n segments

$$\overline{P_1P_2}, \ \overline{P_2P_3}, \ \overline{P_3P_4}, \ \ldots, \ \overline{P_{n-1}P_n}, \ \overline{P_nP_1}$$

is a segment circuit through the ordered set. The points $P_1, P_2, P_3, \ldots, P_n$ are the vertices of the circuit.

We now select the circuits whose segments do not cross each other. If we restrict these special circuits to a plane, we get figures that have an interior and an exterior.

Definition 30/2 *Simple segment circuit*

A segment circuit is a simple segment circuit if no point
other than a vertex belongs to two segments of the circuit
and each vertex belongs to exactly two of the segments.

Definition 31/2 *General polygon*

A simple segment circuit that is contained in a plane is
a general polygon. The segments of the circuit are the sides
of the polygon, and the vertices of the circuit are the
vertices of the polygon.

A general polygon is contained in exactly one plane, and it has
an interior and an exterior. But the interior of a general polygon
does not have to be convex, and each vertex does not have to be
the vertex of an angle (D115).

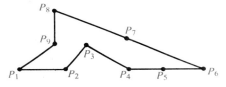

Diagram 115

We now consider a polygon with a convex interior.

Definition 32/2 *Convex polygon*

A general polygon is a convex polygon if each line that
contains a side of the polygon is the edge of a closed
half-plane that contains the polygon. (Thus, no two points
of a convex polygon are in opposite sides of a line
that contains a side.)

Finally, we add one more requirement that will give us the
polygons that we want.

Definition 33/2 *Properly convex polygon*

A convex polygon is a properly convex polygon if no three
of its vertices are collinear.

To understand why we need the preceding definitions, let us
look again at some possibilities for just four points and four
segments. The figure represented in D116 is not a circuit.

Diagram 116

89

Although the next figure is a segment circuit, it is not a simple circuit (D117).

Diagram 117

In D118, a simple segment circuit is shown. However, since the circuit is not a plane figure, it is not a general polygon.

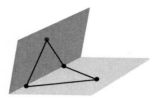

Diagram 118 ☐☐

The figure represented in D119 is a general polygon, but it is not a convex polygon.

Diagram 119

The next figure is a convex polygon, but it is not a properly convex polygon (D120).

Diagram 120

Finally, we get the figure that we want. A four-sided, properly convex polygon is shown in D121.*

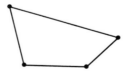

Diagram 121

---

* An important and unsolved problem is closely related to polygons. Suppose that n points in a plane represent cities and that a salesman is to travel a segment circuit that passes through each of these cities just once and returns to its starting point. No simple, general rule is known for determining which order of the points will give him the least distance to travel. However, it can be proved that the minimal circuit is always a polygon. If there is some order in which the points define a convex polygon (not necessarily a properly convex one), then there is no order in which they define a different polygon (convex or not). Therefore, when it exists, this convex polygon is always the minimal circuit.

The vertices of a given convex polygon can determine only the given polygon, while the vertices of a polygon that is not convex can define several different polygons. This fact explains why convexity plays such a natural part in the study of polygons.

90

Since we will be concerned primarily with properly convex polygons, we will make a special convention about them. We also will add to the system some definitions about polygons that correspond to those we have made for triangles.

Conventions

Unless otherwise stated, the word "polygon" will refer to a properly convex polygon. The notation $P_1P_2P_3 \ldots P_n$ commonly will be used to denote a polygon whose n vertices are $P_1, P_2, P_3, \ldots, P_n$ and whose n sides are

$$\overline{P_1P_2}, \ \overline{P_2P_3}, \ \overline{P_3P_4}, \ \ldots, \ \overline{P_{n-1}P_n}, \ \overline{P_nP_1}.$$

Definition 34/2 *Angle of a polygon, exterior angle of a polygon*

An angle that contains two sides of a polygon and whose vertex is also a vertex of the polygon is an angle of the polygon. An angle that is adjacent to an angle of a polygon and is a supplement of that angle is an exterior angle of the polygon. (D122)

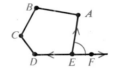

Diagram 122

Definition 35/2 *Interior of a polygon, exterior of a polygon*

Corresponding to each side of a polygon, there is an open half-plane that contains all but two of the vertices and whose edge contains the side. The intersection of all such open half-planes is the interior of the polygon. The set of all points in the plane of the polygon that are not either in the polygon or in its interior is the exterior of the polygon. (D123)

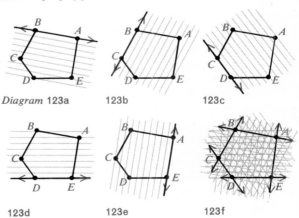

Diagram 123a   123b   123c

123d   123e   123f

We now add to the system some ideas about polygons that we did not state for triangles. The third idea in **Definition 36/2**, however, applies only to a polygon with more than three sides.

A segment that joins two points
of a polygon and is not contained
in a side of the polygon is a
chord of the polygon. A line
that contains a chord of a
polygon is a secant of the
polygon. A chord that joins
two vertices of a polygon is a
diagonal of the polygon. (D124)

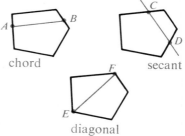

chord   secant

diagonal

Diagram 124

The following convention simply provides a convenient way
of referring to the parts of a polygon that are "next" to each other.

Conventions

Two vertices of a polygon are neighboring, or adjacent, vertices
if the segment joining them is a side. Two sides of a polygon
are neighboring, or adjacent, if they intersect at a vertex.
Two angles of a polygon are neighboring, but *not* adjacent,
if the segment joining their vertices is a side. Thus,
each vertex, each side, and each angle of a polygon
has two neighbors.

The next definitions give us a term for the distance around a
polygon and also some useful classifications of polygons.

Definition 37/2 *Perimeter of a polygon*

The sum of the lengths of the sides of a polygon is
the perimeter of the polygon.

Definition 38/2 *Equilateral polygon, equiangular polygon,*
regular polygon

A polygon whose sides all have the same length is an
equilateral polygon. A polygon whose angles all have
the same measure is an equiangular polygon. A polygon that is
both equilateral and equiangular is a regular polygon.

Definition 39/2 *Quadrilateral, rectangle, rhombus, square*

A 4-gon is a quadrilateral.
An equiangular quadrilateral
is a rectangle.
An equilateral quadrilateral
is a rhombus.
A regular quadrilateral
is a square. (D125)

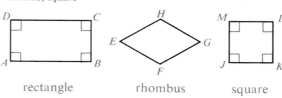

rectangle   rhombus   square

Diagram 125

Conventions

Two sides of a quadrilateral are opposite sides if they are not neighbors. Two angles of a quadrilateral are diagonally opposite if they are not neighbors.

Exercises

1 a One ordered set that can be formed from {*A, B, C*} is (*A, C, B*). What are the other possible ordered sets of {*A, B, C*}? *Answer*
  b How many different ordered sets can be formed from a set containing four points?

2 Reproduce D126 and then use your diagram to construct each figure described below.
  a The segment path for (*A, E, F, B, D, C*)
  b The segment circuit for (*A, B, C, D, E, F*)
  c The segment circuit for (*B, A, D, C, F, E*)

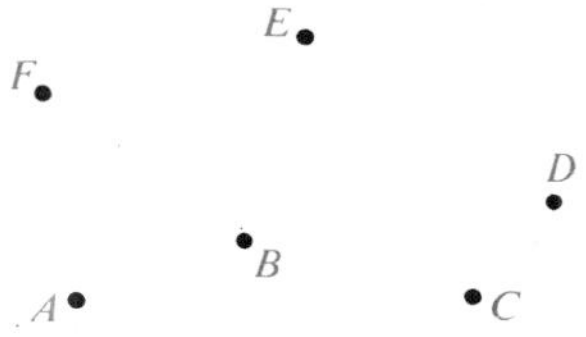

3 a Any segment path for a set of six noncollinear points will consist of how many segments? *Answer*
  b Any segment circuit for a set of six noncollinear points will consist of how many segments?

◆ **4** Two segment circuits are equivalent if they contain the same segments. For any ordering of *n* points, there are 2*n* − 1 other orderings such that each two of the 2*n* circuits are equivalent. Explain why this is so, and give the other seven orderings of {*A, B, C, D*} whose segment circuits are equivalent to the one determined by (*A, B, C, D*).

5 If *A, B,* and *C* are three collinear points, show that orderings exist of four points *A, B, C,* and *D* such that the corresponding circuits are not simple. *Answer*

6 If *D* is in the exterior of △*ABC* but in the interior of ⊰*A*, show that there must be an ordering of {*A, B, C, D*} such that the corresponding circuit is not a simple segment circuit.

7 Is every segment circuit through four noncoplanar points a simple circuit? Is there any relation of four coplanar points for which all the circuits through them are simple circuits?

8 Assume that each figure represented in D127 is a general polygon and that each dot represents a vertex.
  a Name the properly convex polygons.
  b Name the convex polygons that are not properly convex. *Answer*

Diagram 126

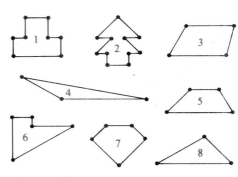

Diagram 127

93

9 Let $P_1P_2P_3 \ldots P_{56}$ denote a properly convex polygon with fifty-six vertices and fifty-six sides.

  a Name the arms of the angle of the polygon that has P_{32} as its vertex.

  b How many diagonals of the polygon have P_{10} as an endpoint? *Answer*

  c How many diagonals does the polygon have?

  d How many angles are exterior angles of the polygon at P_5?

10 Let $ABCDE$ denote a five-sided polygon (*pentagon*). By definition, the line that contains a side of the pentagon contains exactly two vertices of the pentagon, and the remaining three vertices are in the same side of the line. Explain why each of the following statements is true.

  a D and E are in the interior of $\sphericalangle ABC$.

  b D and B are in opposite sides of AC.

11 Quadrilateral $ABCD$ contains points R, S, T, and W as shown in D128. Identify each set of points below as a side, a chord, a diagonal, or a secant of the quadrilateral.

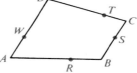

  a $\overline{WS}$ **f** $\overline{CB}$

  b WS **g** $\overline{CR}$

  c $\overline{RS}$ **h** $\overline{CA}$

  d $\overline{AB}$ **i** AC

  e $\overline{BD}$ *Answer*   **j** RT

Diagram 128

12 a Is every diagonal of a polygon also a chord of the polygon?

  b Is every chord of a polygon also a diagonal of the polygon?

  c Is every chord of a polygon a subset of some secant?

  d Sides of polygons join vertices. Are the sides of a polygon also diagonals of the polygon? Explain your answer.

  e Describe the intersection of a chord of a polygon and the secant that contains the chord.

  f Explain why two neighboring angles of a polygon are not called adjacent angles.

The most basic figures in plane geometry are polygons and circles. We now define circles in the formal system.

Definition 40/2 *Circle*

If point O is a point in a plane α and r is a positive real number, then the set of all points in α whose distance from point O is r is a circle.

94

Point *O* is the center of the circle, and *r* is the radius of the circle.

Convention

We will denote a circle with center *O* and radius *r* by the notation $C(O, r)$. (D129)

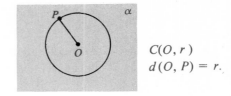

$C(O, r)$
$d(O, P) = r.$

Diagram 129

Definition 41/2 *Radial segment, chord, secant, diameter, tangent*

A segment joining the center and a point of the circle is a radial segment.* A segment joining two points of a circle is a chord of the circle. A line that contains a chord is a secant. A chord that contains the center of a circle is a diameter. A line that is in the plane of a circle and intersects the circle at just one point is a tangent. A circle and a tangent are tangent to each other at their intersection point. (D130)

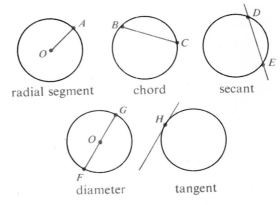

radial segment   chord   secant

diameter   tangent

Diagram 130

From Theorem 9/2, we know that every line in the plane of $C(O, r)$ that contains point *O* also contains two points at a distance *r* from *O*. Thus, we can obtain the following theorems.

* Theorem 42/2

A circle is contained in exactly one plane.

* Theorem 43/2

The center of a circle is the midpoint of every diameter of the circle.

* Theorem 44/2

In the plane of a circle, each line that passes through the center of the circle also contains a diameter of the circle.

Definition 42/2 *Interior of a circle, exterior of a circle*

The set consisting of the center of $C(O, r)$ and all points in the plane of $C(O, r)$ whose distance from point *O* is less than *r* is the interior of the circle. The set

---

* For simplicity, a radial segment also is often called a *radius*. Similarly, the number 2*r* often is called the diameter of the circle. The discussion always makes clear which is meant, a segment or a number.

95

of all points in the plane of the circle that are not either in the circle or in the interior of the circle is the exterior of the circle.

At this point, we can give a very good example of how difficult it may be to prove obvious facts. Suppose that A is in the interior of $C(O, r)$ and that B is in its exterior (D131). It should be the

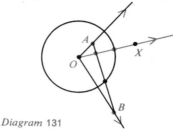

Diagram 131

case, then, that $\overline{AB}$ intersects the circle. This is easily shown if A, B, and O are collinear points. But if they are not collinear, we cannot yet establish the intersection of the circle and the segment, even though every closed ray $\overrightarrow{OX}$ between $\overrightarrow{OA}$ and $\overrightarrow{OB}$ must intersect both $\overline{AB}$ and the circle. Later in our work, we will be able to use other relations to get this intersection property in an easy way.

Exercises

1 Each side of square $ABCD$ has a length of 4, and its diagonals intersect at point P (D132). The following questions concern circles in the plane of square $ABCD$.

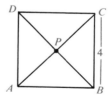

Diagram 132

a Which vertices of the square are in the circle $C(B, 4)$? *Answer*

b Is $C(D, 4) = C[D, d(A, B)]$?

c Which vertices of the square are common to $C(A, 4)$ and $C(D, 4)$?

d Which vertices of the square are inside $C(B, 4)$ and which are outside $C(B, 4)$?

e With respect to $C[P, d(P, A)]$, classify the following as chord, diameter, radial segment, or secant: $\overline{AB}$, $\overline{PB}$, $\overline{CD}$, and $\overline{AC}$.

f Name the two lines that each contain a side of the square and that are each tangent to $C(D, 4)$.

2 Assume that $C(P, 8)$ is contained in a plane α.

a If R is in α and $d(P, R) = 8$, must R be in the circle?

b If $d(P, Q) = 8$, must Q be in the circle? *Answer*

c If $\overline{PK}$ is a radius of $C(P, 8)$, what is $d(P, K)$?

96

3 Segment $\overline{AB}$ is a diameter of $C(O, 6)$, and point P is in the plane of the circle such that $d(A, P) = x$ and $d(B, P) = y$. For each of the following values of x and y, where must P be in relation to the circle?

  a $x = y = 6$.   **c** $x = 2; y = 10$. *Answer*

  b $x = 12; y = 0$.   **d** $x = 20; y = 8$.

4 Reword each of the following statements so that it is true.

  a If P is a point of $C(O, r)$, then PO is a radial segment. *Answer*

  b Line t that intersects $C(O, r)$ at just one point is tangent to the circle.

  c If X and Y are points of $C(O, r)$, then $\overline{XY}$ is a secant.

  d If P is in the interior of $C(O, r)$, then $d(O, P) > r$.

  e If $a < b$, then every point of $C(O, a)$ is in the interior of $C(O, b)$.

  f If $\overline{AB}$ is a chord of $C(O, r)$, then $<A, O, B>$.

5 In plane α, let O denote a point in line t. Also, in α, let $C(O, a)$ denote a circle with center O and radius a. Explain how you know that, in each side of t, there are infinitely many points in the circle. How does this result imply that α is the only plane containing $C(O, a)$?

6 Do you think that $C(A, x) = C(B, y)$ implies $A = B$ and $x = y$?

Chapter review

1 Explain what each of the following notations represents.

  a $\beta(F, G, H)$ **e** $\overline{EF}$ **i** $\measuredangle HJK°$

  b RT **f** $\mathcal{R}$ **j** $\{A, B, C, D, E\}$

  c $d(H, J), H \neq J$ **g** $<R, S, T>$.   **k** (A, B, C, D, E)

  d $<r, s, t>$.   **h** $\overrightarrow{MN}$ **l** $ABCDE$

2 Points A and B in a line t have coordinates 6 and -4 respectively. Which of the following numbers is the distance from A to B?

  a $|6 - 4|$ **d** $|6 + 4|$

  b $|4 - 6|$ **e** 2

  c $|-4 - 6|$ **f** 10

3 Three collinear points A, B, and C have coordinates a, b, and c respectively. For each of the following statements indicate, if possible, which of the points A, B, or C is between the other two. Otherwise, write the word "indeterminate" for the statement.

  a $b > a > c$.

  b $d(A, C) + d(A, B) = d(C, B)$.

  c $|a| < |b| < |c|$.

d $c < |b| < a.$

e $|c| < b < |a|.$

f $d(B, A) = d(C, A) + d(B, C).$

4 The coordinates of points G, H, J, and K in line t are -2, -1, 3, and 8 respectively. Let x denote the coordinate of point X in t.

a What are the possible values of x if point X is contained in $\overrightarrow{HK}$? In $\overrightarrow{HG}$?

b Are $\overrightarrow{HG}$ and $\overrightarrow{JK}$ opposite rays? Are they oppositely directed rays?

c Are $\overrightarrow{HJ}$ and $\overrightarrow{HK}$ like-directed rays?

d What are the coordinates of the two points in t that are at distance 23 from G?

5 Which of the following sets are convex?

a $\overline{AF}$ **g** $\{A\}$

b $\measuredangle ABC$ **h** The set consisting of

c $C(P, r)$ the two points A and B

d The half-plane α'' **i** The interior of $\triangle ABC$

e Space   **j** $\alpha' \cup \alpha''$

f $\overrightarrow{AB} \cap \overrightarrow{BA}$ **k** $AB \cap CD$

6 If the two lines AB and CD intersect at point X such that $\langle A, X, B \rangle$ and $\langle C, X, D \rangle$, which of the following statements are necessarily correct?

a The two angles $\measuredangle AXD$ and $\measuredangle DXB$ are opposite angles.

b $\measuredangle CXA° = \measuredangle BXD°.$

c $\measuredangle AXD° + \measuredangle CXB° = 180.$

d $\measuredangle AXC° + \measuredangle CXB° = 180.$

e If $\measuredangle AXD° = \measuredangle CXB°$, then $AB \perp CD.$

7 The three points A, B, and C are in the edge of the opposite open half-planes α' and α'', and point B is between A and C.

a Is there an open ray $\overrightarrow{AX}$ in α' such that the measure of $\measuredangle XAC$ is 14?

b Is there an open ray $\overrightarrow{BY}$ in α' such that $\measuredangle YBC° = 14$?

c Is there an open ray $\overrightarrow{BW}$ in α'' such that its ray coordinate is $\frac{17}{3}\sqrt{1010}$?

8 Line BA is the edge of an open half-plane α'. If the open rays $\overrightarrow{BC}$, $\overrightarrow{BD}$, $\overrightarrow{BE}$, $\overrightarrow{BF}$, $\overrightarrow{BG}$, and $\overrightarrow{BX}$ in α' have ray coordinates 40, 135, 100, 170, 80, and x respectively, which of the following statements are necessarily correct?

a The angles $\measuredangle FBC$, $\measuredangle EBG$, and $\measuredangle FBG$ are obtuse, acute, and right angles respectively.

b $\measuredangle DBE° = |110 - 135|.$

c If X is in the interior of $\measuredangle GBC$, then $\measuredangle GXB° + \measuredangle BXC° = \measuredangle GXC°.$

d If $x > 110$, then X is in the exterior of $\angle EBA$.

e The angles $\angle EBG$ and $\angle DBG$ are adjacent.

f If $BX \perp BE$, then X is in the interior of $\angle CBA$.

9 Let $\mathcal{S}$ denote the intersection of line t and $\triangle HJK$, and let P denote a point interior to the triangle.

   a Can $\mathcal{S}$ be the empty set?

   b Can $\mathcal{S}$ be $\{H\}$?

   c Can $\mathcal{S}$ be $\{H, J\}$?

   d If t contains P, can $\mathcal{S}$ be the empty set?

   e If Q is a second point interior to the triangle, must the intersection of $\overline{PQ}$ and $\triangle HJK$ be the empty set?

10 a When is the sum of the measures of two angles not the measure of an angle?

   b What are the finite convex sets to which point A belongs?

11 Which of the following relations have been established in the formal system?

   a The open rays $\overrightarrow{BA}$ and $\overrightarrow{BC}$ are opposite rays if and only if B is between A and C.

   b If point P is not in line t, then there is exactly one line through P that is perpendicular to t.

   c The three angles of a triangle have measures whose sum is 180.

   d The supplement of an obtuse angle is an acute angle.

   e The interior of a triangle is a convex set.

   f If two planes intersect, their intersection is a line.

   g If P is not in line t, there exists a line through P that is coplanar with t but that does not intersect t.

12 Indicate whether each of the following statements is necessarily true (T), possibly true (P), or necessarily false (F).

   a A polygon is a quadrilateral.

   b All quadrilaterals are polygons.

   c A rhombus is an equiangular quadrilateral.

   d Any square is a rhombus.

   e A rectangle is a regular 4-gon.

   f All polygons are segment circuits.

   g Point P is in the circle $C(P, r)$.

   h If $d(P, X) = 3$, then X is in the circle $C(P, 3)$.

   i If P is a point in the circle $C(O, r)$, then PO is a radial segment.

   j The intersection of a circle and a secant of the circle is a chord.

   k The intersection of a circle and a tangent to the circle is a convex set.

   l If a line intersects a circle in exactly one point, the line is a tangent to the circle.

13 Which of the following statements are necessarily correct?

a If plane α contains the point H and the point J, then line HJ exists and is contained in α.

b The union of two opposite half-planes is a plane.

c If $d(A, B) = 0$, then neither point A nor point B exists.

d If $d(A, B) = 5$, then there exists a coordinate system for the line AB such that the coordinate of A is -3 and the coordinate of B is 77.

e If point P is in the segment $\overline{AB}$, then P is between A and B.

f If point P is not in $\overline{AB}$, then there is exactly one plane that contains P, A, and B.

g The intersection of eighty-five open half-spaces is a convex set.

h If A and B are in a set, and $\overline{AB}$ is also in the set, then the set is convex.

i If $\overline{AB}$ is not in a set, and A and B are in the set, then the set is not convex.

j The angle $\measuredangle ABC$ is contained in $\triangle ABC$.

k If P is not between A and C, then $\overrightarrow{BP}$ is not in the interior of $\measuredangle ABC$.

l Two opposite angles are not adjacent.

m Two adjacent angles are supplements.

The notion of 11/3
congruence In everyday conversation, we commonly talk of two objects (a pair of dice, for example) as being the same in size and shape. This notion, that one thing may be a copy of another, is one that we want to introduce into our formal system. The mathematical term for "the same in size and shape" is "congruent." Thus, each die of a pair is congruent to the other.

In this chapter, we first define the notion of congruence for very simple figures, such as segments, angles, and triangles. Then, later, we extend the notion to more complicated figures. For two plane figures, that is, for figures we could cut out of cardboard, congruence clearly relates to the physical fact that one figure can be placed on the other so that they are an "exact fit." Since we always can fit one stick on another if both have the same length or fit one physical angle on another if both have the same measure, we make the following definitions.

Definition 43/3 *Congruence of segments*
A segment $\overline{AB}$ and a segment $\overline{CD}$ are congruent if they have the same length. That is, $\overline{AB}$ and $\overline{CD}$ are congruent if $d(A, B) = d(C, D)$.

101

Convention

That $\overline{AB}$ and $\overline{CD}$ are congruent will be
denoted by $\overline{AB} \cong \overline{CD}$. (D133)

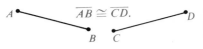

Diagram 133

Comment

$\overline{AB} \cong \overline{CD}$ implies and is implied by each
of the relations $\overline{CD} \cong \overline{AB}$, $\overline{AB} \cong \overline{DC}$, and $d(A, B) = d(C, D)$.

Definition 44/3 Congruence of angles

An $\sphericalangle ABC$ and an $\sphericalangle DEF$ are congruent if they have the same measure.
That is, $\sphericalangle ABC$ and $\sphericalangle DEF$ are congruent if $\sphericalangle ABC° = \sphericalangle DEF°$.

Convention

That $\sphericalangle ABC$ is congruent to $\sphericalangle DEF$ will be denoted
by $\sphericalangle ABC \cong \sphericalangle DEF$. (D134)

Comment

$\sphericalangle ABC \cong \sphericalangle DEF$ implies and is implied
by each of the relations $\sphericalangle DEF \cong \sphericalangle ABC$,
$\sphericalangle CBA \cong \sphericalangle DEF$, and $\sphericalangle ABC° = \sphericalangle DEF°$.

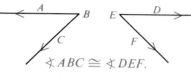

Diagram 134

Comment

A segment is congruent to itself, and an angle is congruent
to itself.

* Theorem 45/3

Two right angles are congruent.

If point B is between A and C and if we know the lengths of
two of the three segments $\overline{AB}$, $\overline{BC}$, and $\overline{AC}$, then we can find the
length of the third segment by using either the sum or the differ-
ence of the two known lengths. It will be convenient to have this
simple idea stated in the following form. For reference, we will
call it the *segment addition theorem*.

* Theorem 46/3 *Segment addition theorem*

If B is between A and C and if E is between D and F,
then the following congruences are
such that each two of them imply the third:
$\overline{AB} \cong \overline{DE}$, $\overline{BC} \cong \overline{EF}$, and $\overline{AC} \cong \overline{DF}$. (D135)

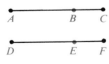

Diagram 135

A similar theorem about angle measures follows from the
angle addition axiom.

* Theorem 47/3 *Angle addition theorem*

If $\overrightarrow{BX}$ is between $\overrightarrow{BA}$ and $\overrightarrow{BC}$ and if $\overrightarrow{EY}$
is between $\overrightarrow{ED}$ and $\overrightarrow{EF}$, then the
following congruences are such that
each two of them imply the third:
$\sphericalangle ABX \cong \sphericalangle DEY$, $\sphericalangle CBX \cong \sphericalangle FEY$,
and $\sphericalangle ABC \cong \sphericalangle DEF$. (D136)

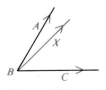 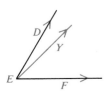

Diagram 136

102

Supplements of congruent angles are congruent.

We next want a mathematical way of expressing the fact that two triangles have the same shape and size. One rather natural way to do this is to make use of six parts of a triangle, that is, the three sides and the three angles. If two triangles are the same in shape and size, it always is possible to set up a correspondence between these six parts of one and the same six parts of the other so that sides of the same length correspond to each other and angles of the same size correspond to each other. This kind of correspondence is what we obtain, in a physical way, if we place one triangle on top of another in an exact fit.

We can set up many different one-to-one correspondences between two sets of six things. Consequently, we first need to define the particular kind of correspondence between the sides and angles in which we are interested. When we fit one triangle on another, the way we put sides on sides forces the way in which angles fit on angles. Because of this, we not only want sides to correspond to sides and angles to correspond to angles, but we also want more than this. We want the correspondence to be such that, if two sides in one triangle correspond to a particular pair of sides in the other triangle, then the angle between the first pair corresponds to the angle between the second pair.

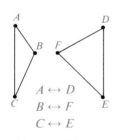

$A \leftrightarrow D$

$B \leftrightarrow F$

$C \leftrightarrow E$

Diagram 137

We can select the correspondence we want by making use of a correspondence between the vertices of the triangles. Suppose that we want to compare $\triangle ABC$ and $\triangle DEF$. Suppose also that we choose a pairing of the vertices, say A with D, B with F, and C with E (D137). We can indicate this one-to-one correspondence by the notation $A \leftrightarrow D$, $B \leftrightarrow F$, and $C \leftrightarrow E$. Then we can select a one-to-one correspondence of the angles by the condition that two angles correspond if the vertices of the angles are also corresponding vertices of the triangles. This gives us the following one-to-one correspondence of the angles: $\angle A \leftrightarrow \angle D$, $\angle B \leftrightarrow \angle F$, and $\angle C \leftrightarrow \angle E$.

Next, we can select a one-to-one correspondence of sides by the condition that two sides correspond if they are opposite corresponding vertices of the triangles. For example, because $A \leftrightarrow D$, the side opposite A, namely, $\overline{BC}$, corresponds to the side opposite D, which is $\overline{FE}$. Thus we get the following one-to-one correspondence of sides: $\overline{AB} \leftrightarrow \overline{DF}$, $\overline{BC} \leftrightarrow \overline{FE}$, and $\overline{AC} \leftrightarrow \overline{DE}$. Now it is easy to see that the angles that are between pairs of corresponding sides also correspond.

Finally, we can use the pairing of vertices, the pairing of angles, and the pairing of sides to define a *correspondence of the triangles.* We can indicate the one-to-one correspondence between these nine parts of one triangle and the same nine parts of the other by the notation $ABC \leftrightarrow DFE$.

A correspondence of two triangles, by itself, does not tell us anything about how the corresponding sides compare in length or how the corresponding angles compare in size. A correspondence is just a special way of selecting the parts to be compared. But now we can use the correspondence of triangles to express the "exact fit," or congruence notion, of triangles. A correspondence of the triangles is a *congruence of the triangles* if corresponding sides and corresponding angles are congruent. The condition that two triangles have the same shape and size is just the condition that a correspondence of the triangles exists that is a congruence.

Let us put these ideas into the system.

Definition 45/3 *Correspondence of triangles*

A correspondence of $\triangle ABC$ and $\triangle DEF$ is a one-to-one correspondence between the vertices of $\triangle ABC$ and the vertices of $\triangle DEF$, between the angles of $\triangle ABC$ and the angles of $\triangle DEF$, and between the sides of $\triangle ABC$ and the sides of $\triangle DEF$ with the following properties. The vertices of the corresponding angles are also corresponding vertices of the triangles. The corresponding sides are opposite the corresponding vertices of the triangles.

Convention

The notation $ABC \leftrightarrow DEF$ will be used to denote the correspondence of $\triangle ABC$ and $\triangle DEF$ in which the correspondence of vertices is $A \leftrightarrow D$, $B \leftrightarrow E$, and $C \leftrightarrow F$, the correspondence of angles is $\angle A \leftrightarrow \angle D$, $\angle B \leftrightarrow \angle E$, and $\angle C \leftrightarrow \angle F$, and the correspondence of sides is $\overline{AB} \leftrightarrow \overline{DE}$, $\overline{BC} \leftrightarrow \overline{EF}$, and $\overline{AC} \leftrightarrow \overline{DF}$.

Comment

A particular correspondence of $\triangle ABC$ and $\triangle DEF$ may be expressed in more than one way. That is, different notations can be used if they do not denote a change in the pairs of elements that correspond to each other. Thus $ABC \leftrightarrow DEF$ is the same correspondence as $DEF \leftrightarrow ABC$ and as $BAC \leftrightarrow EDF$.

Definition 46/3 *Congruence of triangles*

A correspondence of $\triangle ABC$ and $\triangle DEF$ is a congruence of the triangles if the corresponding sides are congruent and the corresponding angles are congruent. Two triangles are congruent if there is a correspondence of the triangles that is a congruence.

Conventions

That the correspondence $ABC \leftrightarrow DEF$ of $\triangle ABC$ and $\triangle DEF$ is a congruence of the triangles will be denoted by

$\triangle ABC \cong \triangle DEF$. Just as there are different ways of expressing the same correspondence of two triangles, so there are different ways of expressing the same congruence of the triangles. The congruence expressed by the sentence $\triangle ABC \cong \triangle DEF$ also is expressed by the sentences $\triangle DEF \cong \triangle ABC$, $\triangle ACB \cong \triangle DFE$, and $\triangle BAC \cong \triangle EDF$. (D138)

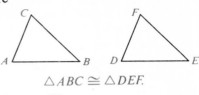

$\triangle ABC \cong \triangle DEF$.

Diagram 138

We purposely have made definitions of a correspondence and a congruence of $\triangle ABC$ and $\triangle DEF$ that will permit the possibility that $\triangle ABC$ and $\triangle DEF$ could be the same triangle. Different congruences of a triangle with itself correspond physically to the different ways that a triangle can be picked up and put down in the same place without having all of the vertices in the same position as they were. The statement $\triangle ABC \cong \triangle ABC$ is always correct. It simply corresponds physically to putting the triangle back in the same place, with each vertex where it was before.

The notation $\triangle ABC \cong \triangle DEF$ is convenient for indicating not only that the triangles are congruent but also that $ABC \leftrightarrow DEF$ is a congruence of the triangles. On the other hand, we often want to express the fact that two triangles are congruent without saying which correspondence of the triangles is a congruence. We, therefore, make the following conventions.

Conventions

The statement "$\triangle ABC$ and $\triangle DEF$ are congruent" will mean that there is a congruence of the triangles, but not necessarily the congruence $ABC \leftrightarrow DEF$. The statement "$\triangle ABC$ and $\triangle DEF$ are congruent *in that order*" will mean that $\triangle ABC \cong \triangle DEF$.

Finally, notice that, in our definition of a correspondence and of a congruence of triangles, nothing is said that requires the triangles to be in the same plane.

Exercises

1 Indicate whether each of the following statements is true (T) or false (F). Correct each false statement by adding to or deleting from the statement.

  a If $\overline{AB} \cong \overline{CD}$, then $\overline{AB} = \overline{CD}$. *Answer*
  b If $d(A, B) = d(C, D)$ and $A \neq B$, then $\overline{AB} \cong \overline{CD}$.
  c If point M is the midpoint of $\overline{AB}$, then $\overline{AM} = \overline{MB}$ and $d(A, M) \cong d(M, B)$.
  d If $\overline{AB} = \overline{CD}$, then $A = C$ and $B = D$.
  e If $\overline{AB} = \overline{CD}$, then $\overline{AB} \cong \overline{CD}$.

2 Apply the instructions for exercise 1 to the following statements.

 a If $\angle ABC° = \angle DEF°$, then $\angle ABC \cong \angle DEF$.

 b If $\angle ABC = \angle DEF$, then $\angle ABC \cong \angle DEF$. *Answer*

 c If $\angle ABC \cong \angle DEF$, then $\angle ABC = \angle DEF$. *Answer*

 d If $\angle ABC° = 90$, then any angle that is a supplement of $\angle ABC$ is congruent to $\angle ABC$.

 e $\angle ABC \cong \angle BCA$.

3 Use the correspondence $RST \leftrightarrow HJK$ of $\triangle RST$ and $\triangle HJK$ in connection with this exercise (D139).

 a Which part of $\triangle RST$ corresponds to $\overline{HJ}$ of $\triangle HJK$?

 b Which part of $\triangle HJK$ corresponds to $\angle R$ of $\triangle RST$?

 c Side $\overline{ST}$ of $\triangle RST$ corresponds to which part of $\triangle HJK$? *Answer*

 d Vertex J of $\triangle HJK$ corresponds to which part of $\triangle RST$?

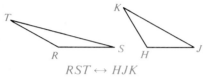

$RST \leftrightarrow HJK$

Diagram 139

4 Let $SRT \leftrightarrow JHK$ denote a particular correspondence between $\triangle RST$ and $\triangle HJK$. This same correspondence could be expressed by the notation $TRS \leftrightarrow \sim\sim$, $RTS \leftrightarrow \sim\sim$, or $\sim\sim \leftrightarrow KJH$. *Answer*

5 In each of the following, some part of either $\triangle ABC$ or $\triangle DEF$ is named (D140). Using $ABC \leftrightarrow FDE$ for each case, identify the corresponding part in the other triangle.

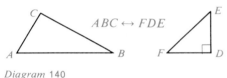

$ABC \leftrightarrow FDE$

Diagram 140

 a Point B of $\triangle ABC$

 b $\angle A$ of $\triangle ABC$

 c $\overline{DE}$ of $\triangle DEF$

 d The side opposite $\angle E$

 e $\overline{AC}$

 f $\angle FED$ *Answer*

 g Vertex E

 h The angle opposite $\overline{FE}$

6 Let $ABC \leftrightarrow BAC$ denote a one-to-one correspondence of $\triangle ABC$ with itself.

 a Side $\overline{AB}$ corresponds to which side?

 b The vertex A corresponds with which vertex?

 c $\angle ABC$ corresponds to which angle?

7 Assume that the correspondence $ABC \leftrightarrow DEF$ is a congruence, that is, $\triangle ABC \cong \triangle DEF$. Use this information to complete each of the following.

 a $A \leftrightarrow \sim\sim$

 b $\sim\sim \leftrightarrow \angle FED$

 c $\overline{CB} \leftrightarrow \sim\sim$ *Answer*

 d $\angle B \cong \sim\sim$.

 e $\sim\sim = \angle F°$.

 f $\overline{AB} \cong \sim\sim$.

 g $\sim\sim = d(F, D)$.

 h $\sim\sim = \angle FDE°$.

 i $\angle EDF \cong \sim\sim$.

 j $\triangle CBA \cong \sim\sim$.

 k $\sim\sim \cong \overline{DF}$.

 l $\angle A \cong \sim\sim$.

 m $\overline{FE} \cong \sim\sim$.

 n $\sim\sim \cong \triangle FDE$. *Answer*

 o $\triangle BAC \cong \sim\sim$.

 p $\sim\sim = d(D, E)$.

8 Base your answers to the following questions
on the cube represented in D141 and your opinion
about the properties of a cube.

a Is $\overline{AD} \cong \overline{GF}$? Is $\overline{DC} \cong \overline{FB}$?

b Is the diagonal $\overline{AC}$ congruent to the diagonal $\overline{GB}$?

c Are $\sphericalangle ADC$ and $\sphericalangle GFB$ right angles? Are they
congruent angles? *Answer*

d What is the measure of $\sphericalangle DAC$? The measure
of $\sphericalangle FGB$?

e Is $\sphericalangle DAC \cong \sphericalangle FGB$?

f Is $\sphericalangle DCA \cong \sphericalangle FBG$?

g Is $\triangle ADC \cong \triangle GFB$? *Answer*

h Name two congruence correspondences of $\triangle ADC$ and $\triangle GBF$.

i Are $\triangle ADC$ and $\triangle GBF$ coplanar?

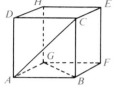

Diagram 141

9 If $\triangle MRK \cong \triangle FHP$, name the three pairs of
corresponding angles and the three pairs of corresponding sides.

10 Suppose that $\triangle ABC \cong \triangle DEF$ and $\triangle DEF \cong \triangle XYZ$.
Do you think that $BCA \leftrightarrow YZX$ is also a congruence?

11 How many different correspondences of $\triangle ABC$ and $\triangle RPQ$
match $\sphericalangle A$ with $\sphericalangle P$? How many match $\overline{AB}$ and $\overline{PQ}$?

12 Use a protractor and a ruler to draw a triangle, $\triangle ABC$,
such that $\sphericalangle A° = 35$, $d(A, B) = 3$, $d(B, C) = 5$. From
your drawing, is it possible to find the approximate measures
of $\sphericalangle B$, $\sphericalangle C$, and $\overline{AC}$? Can you draw a second triangle,
$\triangle PQR$, such that $\sphericalangle P° = 35$, $d(P, R) = 3$, and $d(R, Q) = 5$
but such that $d(A, C) \neq d(P, Q)$? What does this
suggest about $\triangle ABC$ and $\triangle PQR$?

We now have a language and a notation for describing the
congruence of triangles and all the different orders in which they
might be congruent. But as yet, we have no conditions, aside from
the definition, that tell us when two triangles are congruent. To
get such conditions, we need another axiom. The following discussion suggests an axiom that seems reasonable.

Consider $\triangle ABC$ and $\triangle DEF$ represented in D142. The small
marks in the pictures indicate the parts of one triangle that are
congruent to parts of the other. That is, we suppose that
$\overline{AB} \cong \overline{DE}$, $\overline{BC} \cong \overline{EF}$, and $\sphericalangle B \cong \sphericalangle E$. Physically, it seems obvious
that we could place B on E so that $\overline{BA}$ would be on $\overline{ED}$ and

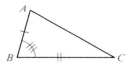

Diagram 142

107

$\overline{BC}$ on $\overline{EF}$. Then, A would be on D, and C would be on F. In other words, the given congruence of certain parts implies that the correspondence $ABC \leftrightarrow DEF$ is a congruence. We can't prove this congruence from the facts that we now have in the system, so we make it a *congruence axiom*.

Axiom 12/3 *Side, angle, side (s.a.s.) congruence axiom*
If a correspondence of two triangles or of a triangle with itself is such that two sides and the angle between them are respectively congruent to the corresponding two sides and the angle between them, then the correspondence is a congruence of the triangles.

Notice that Axiom 12/3 gives conditions that imply congruence of two triangles in space as well as of two triangles in the same plane.

Exercises

1 Complete the following statement so that it will be a summary of Axiom 12/3.
If the correspondence $ABC \leftrightarrow DEF$ between $\triangle ABC$ and $\triangle DEF$ is such that $\overline{AB} \cong \overline{DE}$, $\angle B \cong \angle E$, and $\overline{BC} \cong \overline{EF}$, then the correspondence is a ∿ and $\triangle ABC \cong$ ∿.

2 In each of the following, two pairs of congruent sides of $\triangle ABC$ and $\triangle DEF$ are given. For each, name a pair of angles whose congruence, together with the s.a.s. axiom, would imply a congruence of the triangles. Then state the congruence.
   a $\overline{AC} \cong \overline{DF}$ and $\overline{BC} \cong \overline{FE}$. *Answer*
   b $\overline{AB} \cong \overline{FE}$ and $\overline{AC} \cong \overline{DE}$.
   c $\overline{AC} \cong \overline{DE}$ and $\overline{BC} \cong \overline{FD}$.

3 Eight pairs of triangles are represented in D143 and some of their congruent parts are indicated by identical dash marks. From the given information, which pairs of triangles are congruent by the s.a.s. axiom? *Answer*

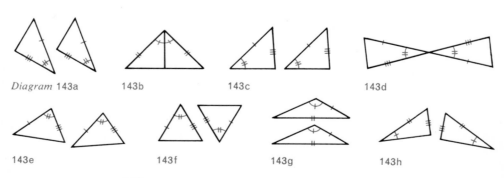

Diagram 143a   143b   143c   143d

143e   143f   143g   143h

4 Segment $\overline{AC}$ intersects $\overline{DE}$ at B so that $\overline{AB} \cong \overline{BE}$ and $\overline{DB} \cong \overline{BC}$ (D144). A proof that $\sphericalangle ADB \cong \sphericalangle ECB$ is outlined below. Copy the proof and supply the missing reasons.*

Statements	Reasons
1 $\overline{AB} \cong \overline{BE}$.	1 Given condition
2 $\overline{DB} \cong \overline{BC}$.	2 ~~~
3 $\sphericalangle ABD \cong \sphericalangle EBC$.	3 ~~~
4 $\triangle ABD \cong \triangle EBC$.	4 ~~~
5 $\sphericalangle D \cong \sphericalangle C$.	5 ~~~

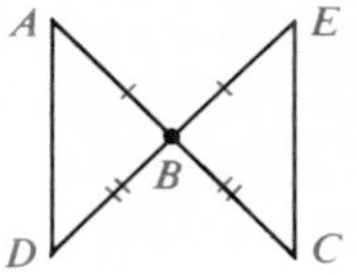

Diagram 144

5 Segments $\overline{AB}$ and $\overline{CD}$ bisect each other at E (D145). Copy and complete the following proof that $\overline{AC} \cong \overline{DB}$.

Statements	Reasons
1 $\overline{AB}$ and $\overline{CD}$ bisect each other at E.	1 Hypothesis
2 $\overline{AE} \cong \overline{EB}$ and $\overline{CE} \cong \overline{ED}$.	2 ~~~
3 $\sphericalangle AEC \cong$ ~~~.	3 Opposite angles have the same measure.
4 $\triangle AEC \cong$ ~~~.	4 ~~~
5 $\overline{AC} \cong \overline{DB}$.	5 ~~~

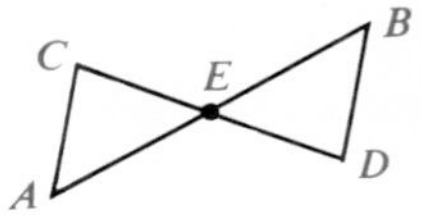

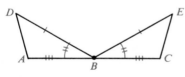

Diagram 145

6 For exercise 5, what correspondence between $\triangle ACE$ and $\triangle EBD$ is a congruence? *Answer*

7 In exercise 5, how does the given information imply that $\overline{AB}$ and $\overline{CD}$ have no endpoint in common? If you interchange the labels of A and B in D145, you change the picturing of $\triangle AEC$ and $\triangle BED$. Does the relabeling change the reasoning of the proof?

8 Given: B is the midpoint of $\overline{AC}$; $\sphericalangle DBA \cong \sphericalangle EBC$; $\overline{DB} \cong \overline{BE}$. (D146)
Prove: $\sphericalangle ADB \cong \sphericalangle BEC$.

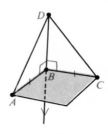

Diagram 146

9 Given: $\overrightarrow{DB} \perp \overline{AB}$, $\overrightarrow{DB} \perp \overline{BC}$, and $\overline{AB} \cong \overline{BC}$. (D147)
Prove: $\overline{AD} \cong \overline{DC}$. *Answer*

10 Is your proof for exercise 9 valid if $C = A$? If $\langle A, B, C \rangle$?

Diagram 147 ⌐◼

---

* In proofs involving congruent triangles, you will often use the fact that two angles or two segments are congruent because they are corresponding parts of congruent triangles as the reason for a step in the proof. You can use the notation C.p. $\cong \triangle$s to indicate that the justification for a step in a proof is that the angles or segments are corresponding parts of congruent triangles.

11 Given: Square $ABCD$; R is the midpoint of $\overline{AB}$;
$<C, Q, B>$; $<A, F, D>$; $\overline{DF} \cong \overline{CQ}$. (D148)
Prove: $\overline{RF} \cong \overline{RQ}$.
(Hint: By definition, the sides and the
angles of a square are congruent.)

Diagram 148

12 Given: $\overrightarrow{AB}$ bisects $\sphericalangle CAD$; $\overline{AC} \cong \overline{AD}$;
$<A, B, E>$. (D149)
Prove: $\sphericalangle CBE \cong \sphericalangle DBE$.

13 In geometry, it often is necessary
to work with intersecting figures
like those represented in D150a.
In these situations, it sometimes is
helpful to represent the figures separately as

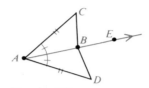

Diagram 149

shown in D150b. Use the congruent parts indicated in the
diagrams to determine the congruence correspondence
between $\triangle ABC$ and $\triangle ABD$. *Answer*

Diagram 150a   150b

14 Given: $\overline{AB}$ intersects $\overline{AC}$ at A; $\overline{BE}$ intersects $\overline{AC}$ at E
such that $<A, E, C>$; $\overline{CD}$ intersects $\overline{AB}$ at D such that
$<B, D, A>$; $\overline{AB} \cong \overline{AC}$; $\overline{AD} \cong \overline{AE}$. (D151)
Prove: $\overline{CD} \cong \overline{BE}$.

Diagram 151

15 We ordinarily interpret the statement "$\overline{AB}$ intersects $\overline{AC}$
at A" to mean that A is the only intersection point
of $\overline{AB}$ and $\overline{AC}$. But one could interpret the statement to mean
simply that A is a point common to $\overline{AB}$ and $\overline{AC}$. If we use
this second interpretation, does the conclusion in exercise 14
still follow if $\overrightarrow{AB}$ and $\overrightarrow{AC}$ are opposite open rays? If $\overrightarrow{AB}$ and
$\overrightarrow{AC}$ are the same ray? Make diagrams to illustrate your answers.

16 Prove that the diagonals of a square $ABCD$ are
of equal length. *Answer*

◆ **17** Given: Point A is not in BE; points C and D
are in $\overline{BE}$ such that $<B, C, D>$ and $<C, D, E>$;
$\overline{BC} \cong \overline{ED}$; $\overline{AC} \cong \overline{AD}$; $\sphericalangle ACE \cong \sphericalangle ADB$. (D152)
Prove: $\triangle ACE \cong \triangle ADB$.

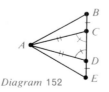

Diagram 152

Obviously, the side, angle, side axiom, Axiom 12/3, does not
give the only set of conditions that will force two triangles to be
congruent. However, we do not need to assume these other
conditions. We can prove them by using Axiom 12/3.

In D153, the marks in the pictures of $\triangle ABC$ and $\triangle DEF$ indicate that two angles and the side between them in one triangle are respectively congruent to two angles and the side between them in

 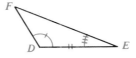

Diagram 153

the other triangle. If we were to move $\triangle ABC$ so that A was at D in $\triangle DEF$ and B was at E, we could make $\overline{AC}$ lie along $\overline{DF}$ because $\measuredangle A$ and $\measuredangle D$ are the same size. Then $\overline{BC}$ would lie along $\overline{EF}$ because $\measuredangle B$ and $\measuredangle E$ are the same size. This would cause C to fall on F. Thus, the two triangles must be congruent. Let us see how Axiom 12/3 allows us to reach the same conclusion without talking about "moving" one of the triangles.

Theorem 49/3 *Angle, side, angle (a.s.a.) congruence theorem*

If a correspondence of two triangles or of a triangle with itself is such that two angles and the side between them are respectively congruent to the two corresponding angles and the side between them, then the correspondence is a congruence of the triangles. (D154)

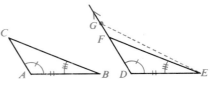

Diagram 154

Proof

Statements	Reasons
1 Let $ABC \leftrightarrow DEF$ denote a correspondence of triangles in which $\measuredangle A \cong \measuredangle D$, $\overline{AB} \cong \overline{DE}$, and $\measuredangle B \cong \measuredangle E$.	1 Given conditions
2 In $\overrightarrow{DF}$ there is a point G such that $d(A, C) = d(D, G)$.	2 Corollary 9/2: there is exactly one point of a ray at a given distance r from the origin of the ray.
3 In the correspondence $CAB \leftrightarrow GDE$, $\overline{CA} \cong \overline{GD}$, $\measuredangle A \cong \measuredangle D$, and $\overline{AB} \cong \overline{DE}$.	3 Statements 1 and 2
4 $\therefore \triangle CAB \cong \triangle GDE$.*	4 From statement 3 and Axiom 12/3, $CAB \leftrightarrow GDE$ is a congruence.

---

* The symbol "$\therefore$" is read "therefore."

111

5 $\therefore \sphericalangle ABC \cong \sphericalangle DEG.$	5 Corresponding angles in a congruence are congruent.
6 $\sphericalangle ABC \cong \sphericalangle DEF.$	6 From statement 1
7 $\therefore \sphericalangle DEF \cong \sphericalangle DEG.$	7 By statements 5 and 6, both angles are the same size as $\sphericalangle ABC.$
8 $\overrightarrow{EF} = \overrightarrow{EG}.$	8 By Theorem 14/2, statement 7 implies that G is in $\overrightarrow{EF}.$
9 G is the intersection of lines DF and $EF.$	9 From statement 2, G is in DF and from statement 8, G is in $EF.$
10 $G = F.$	10 F obviously is the intersection of lines DF and $EF.$ By statement 9, G also is their intersection. And from Theorem 1/2, there is only one intersection point.
11 $\therefore \triangle CAB \cong \triangle FDE.$	11 Restatement of statement 4, since $G = F$

In step 7 of the proof just given, it was argued that two angles are congruent because they are each congruent to the same third angle. When some simple property, such as this one, occurs over and over again in different situations, it is typical of mathematicians to pick out the property and name it as a type of *general property* of relations. Being aware of these properties helps us to see the unity of mathematics, so let us consider a few of them.

Let us invent a symbol, say the symbol $\bowtie$, to represent some relation that might exist between two objects in a class of objects $\{\mathcal{A}, \mathcal{B}, \mathcal{C}, \ldots\}$. The objects might be numbers and the relation could be "greater than." Three basic classifications for any such relation $\bowtie$ are the following:

Identity property, or *reflexive property*: The relation $\bowtie$ has the identity property if $\mathcal{A} \bowtie \mathcal{A}$ is always true.

Symmetric property: The relation $\bowtie$ has the symmetric property if $\mathcal{A} \bowtie \mathcal{B} \leftrightarrow \mathcal{B} \bowtie \mathcal{A}$ is always true.

Transitive property: The relation $\bowtie$ has the transitive property if $\mathcal{A} \bowtie \mathcal{B}$ and $\mathcal{B} \bowtie \mathcal{C}$ always imply $\mathcal{A} \bowtie \mathcal{C}.$

A relation that has all three of the above properties often is called an *equivalence relation*. Clearly, equality is an equivalence relation, since $\mathcal{A} = \mathcal{A}$, $\mathcal{A} = \mathcal{B} \leftrightarrow \mathcal{B} = \mathcal{A}$, and $\mathcal{A} = \mathcal{B}$ and $\mathcal{B} = \mathcal{C}$

imply $\mathcal{Q} = \mathcal{C}$. Congruence of segments, as well as congruence of angles, also has all three of these properties. For example, $\angle A \cong \angle A$ and $\angle A \cong \angle B \Longleftrightarrow \angle B \cong \angle A$. Also, $\angle A \cong \angle B$ and $\angle B \cong \angle C$ imply $\angle A \cong \angle C$. We used the transitive property for congruence of angles to obtain statement 7 of our last proof. Also, because we defined congruence by equality of measures, the three properties for equality give us these same properties for congruence of triangles.

Since the properties of an equivalence relation belong to logic rather than to geometry, we can use them in our system without formally stating them. The following two theorems, however, are useful to have in the system.

---

* Theorem 50/3

The relation of a congruence of segments and the relation of a congruence of angles have the identity, the symmetric, and the transitive properties.

* Theorem 51/3

The relation of a congruence between triangles has the identity, the symmetric, and the transitive properties.

Theorem 51/3 simply says that a congruence of a triangle with itself always exists; that, if there is a congruence of a first triangle with a second triangle, then there is a congruence of the second with the first; that a congruence between a first triangle and a second triangle, together with a congruence between the second and a third, always implies that there is a congruence between the first and the third.

Exercises

1 Consider two points R and S.
  a What does the symbol $d(R, S)$ denote?
  b Is the distance between R and S some positive real number r?
  c Is there a point G in a given $\overrightarrow{MN}$ such that $d(M, G) = d(R, S) = r$?
  d If G is in $\overrightarrow{MN}$ and $d(M, G) > d(M, N)$, which of the points M, N, and G is between the other two? *Answer*
  e If G is in $\overrightarrow{MN}$ and $d(M, G) = d(M, N)$, must $G = N$?
2 Assume that in the plane of $\angle PAB$, point Q is in the P-side of AB.
  a Does $\angle QAB° < \angle PAB°$ imply that Q is in the B-side of PA?
  b What must be the relation between the measures of $\angle PAB$ and $\angle QAB$ if Q is a point in the exterior of $\angle PAB$? *Answer*

c Does $\sphericalangle QAB° = \sphericalangle PAB°$ imply $\overrightarrow{AP} = \overrightarrow{AQ}$?

d If $\overrightarrow{AP} = \overrightarrow{AQ}$, must P belong to $\overrightarrow{AQ}$? Must Q belong to $\overrightarrow{AP}$? Must $P = Q$?

3 From the information given in D155, which two segments must be congruent if $\triangle MNP \cong \triangle RST$ by the a.s.a. theorem?

Diagram 155

4 In each of the following, pairs of congruent parts of $\triangle DEF$ and $\triangle XYZ$ are named (D156). In each case, name a pair of sides or a pair of angles whose congruence, together with those given, would imply $\triangle DEF \cong \triangle XYZ$ by the a.s.a. theorem.

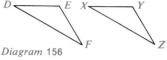

Diagram 156

a $\sphericalangle D \cong \sphericalangle X, \sphericalangle F \cong \sphericalangle Z.$ **d** $\sphericalangle D \cong \sphericalangle X, \sphericalangle E \cong \sphericalangle Y.$

b $\sphericalangle E \cong \sphericalangle Y, \overline{DE} \cong \overline{XY}.$ **e** $\sphericalangle F \cong \sphericalangle Z.$

c $\overline{EF} \cong \overline{YZ}.$ *Answer*   **f** $\sphericalangle D \cong \sphericalangle X, \overline{DF} \cong \overline{XZ}.$

5 Ten pairs of triangles are represented in D157 with corresponding congruent parts indicated.

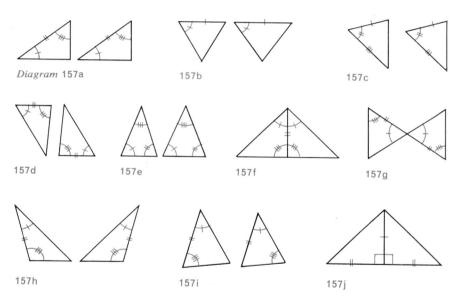

Diagram 157a   157b   157c

157d   157e   157f   157g

157h   157i   157j

For each pair of triangles, decide if the given information implies that there is a congruence of the triangles, and if so, indicate whether a proof could be obtained directly from the s.a.s. axiom or from the a.s.a. theorem.

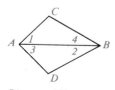

6 Given: $\triangle ACB$ and $\triangle ADB$ such that $\sphericalangle 1 \cong \sphericalangle 3$* and $\sphericalangle 4 \cong \sphericalangle 2$. (D158)

Prove: $\triangle ACB \cong \triangle ADB.$ *Answer*

Diagram 158

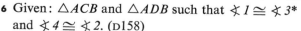

* Mathematical conditions often are indicated by diagrams such as D158; however, the same information could be given without a diagram. For example, we could speak of $\sphericalangle CAB$ instead of $\sphericalangle 1$, and, for this reason, such an exercise is a part of the formal system.

114

7 Given: $\overline{CD}$ bisects $\overline{AB}$ at point E, and $\sphericalangle DBA \cong \sphericalangle CAB$. (D159)
Prove: $\overline{DE} \cong \overline{CE}$.

8 Given: Points A and E are in opposite sides of BD; $\overline{AB} \perp \overline{BD}$; $\overline{ED} \perp \overline{BD}$; $\overline{AB} \cong \overline{DE}$; $\overline{AE}$ intersects $\overline{BD}$ at C such that $\sphericalangle BAC \cong \sphericalangle DEC$. (D160)
Prove: $\overline{BC} \cong \overline{DC}$.

Diagram 159

9 Given: The line AB with $\langle A, P, B \rangle$; C and D in opposite sides of AB; $\sphericalangle CAB \cong \sphericalangle DAB$; $\sphericalangle CPB \cong \sphericalangle DPB$. (D161)
Prove: $\sphericalangle ACP \cong \sphericalangle ADP$.

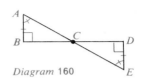

Diagram 160

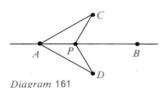

Diagram 161

10 Given: Points D and E in segments $\overline{BC}$ and $\overline{AC}$ respectively such that $\sphericalangle CAD \cong \sphericalangle CBE$ and $\overline{BC} \cong \overline{AC}$. (D162)
Prove: $\overline{BE} \cong \overline{AD}$.

Diagram 162

11 Given: Points D and E in segments $\overline{BC}$ and $\overline{AC}$ respectively such that $\overline{CE} \cong \overline{CD}$ and $\overline{CA} \cong \overline{CB}$.
Prove: $\overline{BE} \cong \overline{AD}$.

12 Given: Points C and D in BE such that $\langle B, C, D \rangle$ and $\langle C, D, E \rangle$. Point A is not in BE; $\sphericalangle BAC \cong \sphericalangle DAE$; $\overline{AB} \cong \overline{AE}$; $\sphericalangle ABC \cong \sphericalangle AED$. (D163)
Prove: $\sphericalangle ACD \cong \sphericalangle ADC$.

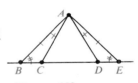

Diagram 163

13 Given: $\triangle ABC \cong \triangle DEF$; the bisector of $\sphericalangle A$ intersects $\overline{BC}$ at P; the bisector of $\sphericalangle D$ intersects $\overline{EF}$ at Q.
Prove: $\overline{AP} \cong \overline{DQ}$.

14 Given: $C(O, r)$ and two diameters $\overline{AC}$ and $\overline{BD}$. (D164)
Prove: $\overline{AB} \cong \overline{CD}$.

15 Consider the polygons $ABCDE$ and $P_1 P_2 \dots P_{20}$.
a What two triangles are congruent if $\sphericalangle C \cong \sphericalangle P_{17}$, $\overline{BC} \cong \overline{P_{16}P_{17}}$, and $\overline{CD} \cong \overline{P_{17}P_{18}}$? *Answer*
b If $\overline{P_8 P_{10}} \cong \overline{DA}$, what two pairs of corresponding angles must be congruent to imply $\triangle P_8 P_9 P_{10} \cong \triangle DEA$ by the a.s.a. theorem? *Answer*

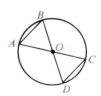

Diagram 164

16 Is the information that the polygons ABC and DEF are regular 3-gons sufficient to imply that these polygons are congruent?

17 If $AMPQ$ is a rhombus, can we prove, by either the s.a.s. axiom or the a.s.a. theorem, that $\sphericalangle M \cong \sphericalangle Q$? (D165) *Answer*

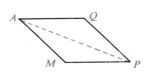

Diagram 165

18 Given: Point A in the interior of $\sphericalangle CBD$ with E and F in BC and BD respectively and such that $\sphericalangle 1 \cong \sphericalangle 4$, $\sphericalangle 2 \cong \sphericalangle 3$, and $\overline{AC} \cong \overline{AD}$. (D166)

Prove: $\sphericalangle AEB \cong \sphericalangle AFB$.

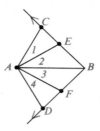

Diagram 166 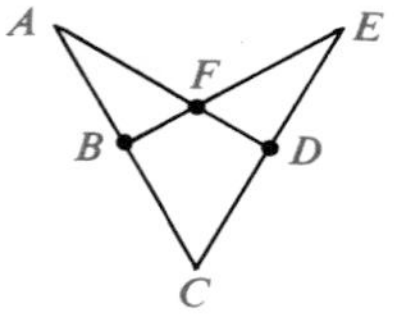   Diagram 167

19 Given: Points B and D of $\overline{AC}$ and $\overline{EC}$ respectively such that $\overline{AD}$ intersects $\overline{EB}$ at F with $\overline{AF} \cong \overline{FE}$ and $\overline{FB} \cong \overline{FD}$. (D167)

Prove: $\triangle ADC \cong \triangle EBC$.

20 Given: $\triangle ABC$ with $<B, E, C>$ and $<A, D, E>$ such that $\sphericalangle 1 \cong \sphericalangle 2$ and $\sphericalangle 3 \cong \sphericalangle 4$. (D168)

Prove: $\sphericalangle AEC \cong \sphericalangle AEB$.

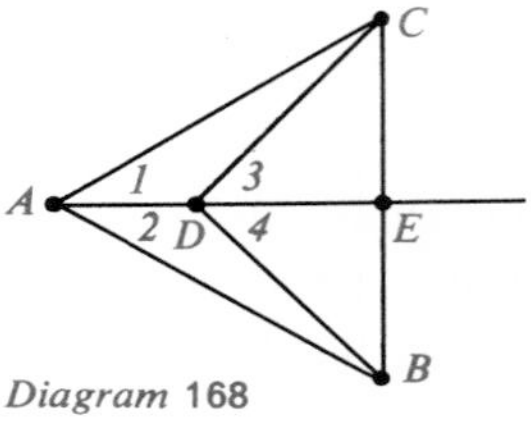

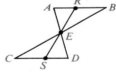

Diagram 168

21 Using the information given in exercise 20, can it be proved that $\sphericalangle AEC$ and $\sphericalangle AEB$ are right angles? If so, prove it.

22 Given: $\overline{AD}$ intersects $\overline{BC}$ at E and $\overline{AB} \cong \overline{CD}$. Also, $\sphericalangle BAD \cong \sphericalangle CDA$; $\sphericalangle CBA \cong \sphericalangle BCD$; $<A, R, B>$; $<C, S, D>$; $<R, E, S>$. (D169)

Prove: $\overline{RE} \cong \overline{SE}$.

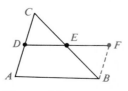

Diagram 169

◆ 23 Given: $\triangle ABC$ with D and E points of $\overline{AB}$ and $\overline{AC}$ respectively such that $\sphericalangle 1 \cong \sphericalangle 2$ and $\sphericalangle 3 \cong \sphericalangle 4$. (D170)

Prove: $\overline{BE} \cong \overline{CD}$ and $\overline{AD} \cong \overline{AE}$.

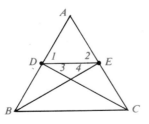

Diagram 170

24 Given: $\triangle ABC$ with D and E midpoints of $\overline{AC}$ and $\overline{BC}$ respectively, and point F in line DE such that $<D, E, F>$ and $\overline{DE} \cong \overline{EF}$. (D171)

Prove: $\overline{AD} \cong \overline{BF}$.

Diagram 171

116

◆ **25** Given: $\triangle PAB$ and $\triangle QAB$ are in different planes, and $\triangle PAB \cong \triangle QAB$. Point X is any point of $\overline{AB}$ such that $\langle A, X, B \rangle$. (D172)
Prove: $\overline{QX} \cong \overline{PX}$. (Is the condition $\langle A, X, B \rangle$ necessary?)

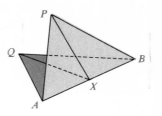

26 If the midray of an angle of a triangle is perpendicular to the opposite side, prove that this midray bisects the side and that the triangle has two congruent sides.

Diagram 172 ⌫▣

27 If a point is in a line and the line is the perpendicular bisector of a segment, prove that this point is equidistant from the endpoints of the segment.

28 Use the five relations of real numbers named below in connection with the following exercises. *Answer*

1) $=$ 2) $\neq$ 3) $<$ 4) $>$ 5) $\cong$

  a Which relations have the identity property?
  b Which relations have the symmetric property?
  c Which relations have the transitive property?
  d Which relations have all three properties, and, thus, are equivalence relations?

The method of 12/3

congruent We now have reached a turning point in the book. From here on,
triangles we expect that you will be proving many of the theorems in the system. In some cases, the statement of a theorem will be followed by a *proof outline*. This outline will suggest one way that you can develop a proof. For other theorems, we will leave the proof entirely to you. It is not intended that you must follow a proof outline, and you should see if you can find other proofs. When a theorem is not followed by a proof outline, we usually will indicate some notation to be used in the proof. We will do this either in the statement of the theorem, or in a suggestion for the proof. Our purpose in indicating the notation is simply to make it easier for you to compare proofs.

The side, angle, side axiom and the angle, side, angle congruence theorem suggest a method for attacking geometric problems. In a given geometric figure, we may be able to find certain segments of equal length or angles of equal size that imply the congruence of certain triangles. From the congruence of the triangles, we know the congruence of all the corresponding parts, and some of these congruences may be *new* information about the figure. This new information may be sufficient to prove some desired property of the figure or to obtain the congruence of still other triangles. These properties, in turn, may give us more new

117

information. This method of using congruent triangles is a powerful one, as we shall see. It neither solves all problems nor gives any
simple rule for solving problems. However, every proof must have
some sort of a bridge between known facts and unknown facts.
The congruence of triangles gives us one of these bridges.

With the use of congruent triangles, we now can prove a key
theorem in the structure of our geometry. This theorem states
that an exterior angle of a triangle is larger than either of the
nonadjacent angles of the triangle. Thus, $\angle CBD$ is larger than
either $\angle A$ or $\angle C$ (D173).

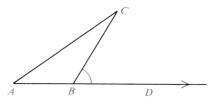

Diagram 173

We can easily guess that this conclusion in regard to $\angle CBD$ is
correct. If we think of the closed ray $\overrightarrow{BD}$ turning about B toward
$\overrightarrow{BC}$ and through the interior of $\angle DBC$ (D174), it seems that $\overrightarrow{BD}$
should reach a position $\overrightarrow{BX}$ that is parallel to $\overrightarrow{AC}$. At this position,
it appears that $\angle XBD$ is congruent to $\angle A$ and that $\angle XBC$ is
congruent to $\angle C$. Thus, we would expect the measure of angle
$\angle CBD$ actually to be equal to the sum of the measures of $\angle A$
and $\angle C$.

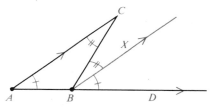

Diagram 174

At this point, we cannot prove the equality just mentioned
because it depends on properties of *parallelism*. And without the
proper choice of an axiom about parallelism, the equality is not
necessarily correct. That is, there are geometries in which the
equality is not true. Using the information we have, however, we
can prove the weaker theorem stated above. That is, we can prove
that $\angle CBD°$ is greater than $\angle A°$ and is greater than $\angle C°$. We
can do this by selecting $\overrightarrow{BX}$ in a different way and, when we make
this selection, we do not need to use parallelism.

Let M denote the midpoint of $\overline{BC}$ (D175). Also let segment $\overline{AM}$
be extended through M to P so that M also is the midpoint
of $\overline{AP}$. Now $\overrightarrow{BP}$ plays a role similar to that of $\overrightarrow{BX}$ in D174.

118

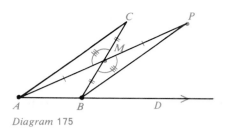

Diagram 175

From the congruence of $\overline{MA}$ and $\overline{MP}$ and of $\overline{MC}$ and $\overline{MB}$ and because $\sphericalangle CMA$ and $\sphericalangle BMP$ are congruent opposite angles, $\triangle CMA \cong \triangle BMP$ by the s.a.s. axiom. Therefore, $\sphericalangle C$ is congruent to $\sphericalangle MBP$. However, $\sphericalangle MBP$ is smaller than the exterior angle $\sphericalangle CBD$ because $\overrightarrow{BP}$ is between $\overrightarrow{BC}$ and $\overrightarrow{BD}$. So $\sphericalangle C$ is smaller than the exterior angle $\sphericalangle CBD$.

The heart of this argument is that the way in which P is defined forces P to be in the interior of $\sphericalangle MBD$. Therefore, it requires $\overrightarrow{BP}$ to be between $\overrightarrow{BC}$ and $\overrightarrow{BD}$. We will establish this fact by a *lemma*. A lemma is a theorem that is proved separately to simplify the proof of some other theorem. Usually, then, a lemma is not of great interest in itself but is a "helping" theorem. In this particular case, the lemma that we will prove will help us establish the theorem concerning the relation of an exterior angle of a triangle to the angles of the triangle.

Lemma 52/3

Given $\sphericalangle MBD$, if $\overrightarrow{BA}$ is the closed ray opposite $\overrightarrow{BD}$ and if $\overrightarrow{MP}$ is the closed ray opposite $\overrightarrow{MA}$, then P is in the interior of $\sphericalangle MBD$. (D176)

Proof

Because $\overrightarrow{BA}$ and $\overrightarrow{BD}$ are opposite rays, A and D are in opposite sides of line BM (Theorem 17/2). Because $\overrightarrow{MA}$ and $\overrightarrow{MP}$ are opposite rays, A and P are in opposite sides of BM. Thus, P is in the side of BM opposite the A-side. So

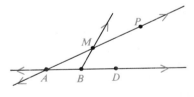

Diagram 176

1   P is in the D-side of BM.

By Theorem 17/2, $\overrightarrow{AM}$ is in the M-side of line BD because M is in this side. Since $\overrightarrow{MA}$ and $\overrightarrow{MP}$ are opposite rays, M is between A and P (Corollary 5d/2). Therefore, by the definition of closed ray $\overrightarrow{AM}$, P belongs to ray $\overrightarrow{AM}$. Hence,

2   P is in the M-side of BD.

From statements 1 and 2, it follows that P is in the interior of $\sphericalangle MBD$.

Theorem 52/3

An exterior angle of a triangle is greater than either of the angles of the triangle that are not adjacent to it.

Proof

Let $\sphericalangle DBC$ denote an exterior angle of $\triangle ABC$ at B with $\overrightarrow{BD}$ opposite $\overrightarrow{BA}$. (D177a) There is a midpoint M in $\overline{BC}$ (Corollary 11/2). In $\overrightarrow{AM}$, there is a point P such that M is the midpoint of $\overline{AP}$ (Theorem 13/2).

Because M is the midpoint of $\overline{BC}$ and of $\overline{AP}$,

1 $\overline{MB} \cong \overline{MC}$ and $\overline{MP} \cong \overline{MA}$.

Because $\sphericalangle BMP$ is opposite $\sphericalangle CMA$, then, by Theorem 33/2,

2 $\sphericalangle BMP \cong \sphericalangle CMA$.

From statements 1 and 2 and Axiom 12/3 (side, angle, side axiom),

3 $\triangle BMP \cong \triangle CMA$.

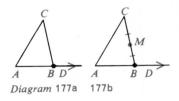

Diagram 177a 177b

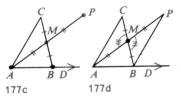

177c   177d

Therefore, as corresponding parts of congruent triangles,

4 $\sphericalangle MBP \cong \sphericalangle MCA$.

Statement 4 can be restated as

5 $\sphericalangle CBP° = \sphericalangle BCA°$.

Since M is between A and P, $\overrightarrow{MP}$ and $\overrightarrow{MA}$ are opposite open rays. So, by the previous lemma, P is in the interior of $\sphericalangle MBD$, and, therefore,

6 P is in the interior of $\sphericalangle CBD$.

From statement 6 and Theorem 27/2, it follows that

7 $\sphericalangle CBD° > \sphericalangle CBP°$.

Combining statements 5 and 7, we have

8 $\sphericalangle CBD° > \sphericalangle BCA°$; that is, $\sphericalangle CBD° > \sphericalangle C°$.*

From statement 8 it has been established that

9 An exterior angle is greater than that nonadjacent angle of the triangle whose vertex is in the exterior angle.

Now let $\overrightarrow{BE}$ be the ray opposite $\overrightarrow{BC}$, so $\sphericalangle EBA$ is also an exterior angle of $\triangle ABC$ at B, and A is in $\sphericalangle EBA$. (D178) Then from statement 9, it follows that

10 $\sphericalangle EBA° > \sphericalangle BAC°$; that is, $\sphericalangle EBA° > \sphericalangle A°$.

But because $\sphericalangle EBA$ is opposite $\sphericalangle CBD$,

11 $\sphericalangle CBD° = \sphericalangle EBA°$.

Statements 10 and 11 together imply

12 $\sphericalangle CBD° > \sphericalangle A°$.

Diagram 178

The proof of Theorem 52/3, including the proof of its lemma, is a good example of how our proofs depend on the foundations

---

* Here we are using the property of real numbers that, if $x = y$ and $z > x$, then $z > y$.

120

that we have built. This proof also raises an important question that is bound to occur to you as you write your own proofs. Just how much detail is necessary in a proof? For example, in our proof of Theorem 52/3, there is no statement that A, M, and C are three noncollinear points. So one could ask, "How do you know that A, M, and C define $\triangle AMC$?" Now, because M is the midpoint of $\overline{BC}$, it is clear that $M \neq C$. Because it is given that A is not in line BC, then A is neither M nor C and A is not collinear with M and C. So it is not difficult to answer the question. But should the facts of this answer have been stated in the proof itself?

There is no simple, clear-cut answer to this question. If every proof gave the statement and the justification for every possible detail, proofs would get longer and longer and more and more clumsy. In practice, the writer avoids this awkwardness by leaving out details that he judges will be clear to the reader without an explanation. Since this matter requires judgment and experience, it could trouble you at the start.

At this stage of your work, we advise you not to worry too much about including reasons for every detail of your proofs. It is far more important that you learn to find the *main* relations in a given geometric figure and to *express your arguments clearly*. By concentrating on these objectives, you occasionally may overlook a necessary part of a proof and make the error of assuming that some major part of an argument is true just because it seems to be so in a drawing. But your judgment in selecting the major steps of a proof will improve, in a natural way, with practice and without your worrying about it.

Consider Theorem 52/3 again. We can get the following fact immediately from the exterior angle property.

Theorem 53/3

If one angle of a triangle is not acute, then the other two angles of the triangle are acute. (D179)

Proof

Let $\triangle ABC$ denote a triangle in which $\measuredangle C$ is not acute.

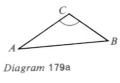

Diagram 179a

Then

1   $\measuredangle C° \geqq 90$.

Let $\measuredangle DCA$ denote an exterior angle of $\triangle ABC$ at C. Because, by definition, $\measuredangle C$ and $\measuredangle DCA$ are supplements,

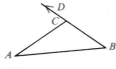

179b

2   $\measuredangle C° = 180 - \measuredangle DCA°$.

    Substituting from statement 2 in statement 1 yields

3   $180 - \measuredangle DCA° \geqq 90$.

Hence,

4   $90 \geqq \measuredangle DCA°$.

121

By the exterior angle property of Theorem 52/3,

5 $\angle DCA° > \angle A°$,

and

6 $\angle DCA° > \angle B°$.

Combining statements 4 and 5 yields

7 $90 > \angle A°$.

The combination of statements 4 and 6 implies that

8 $90 > \angle B°$.

Therefore, both $\angle A$ and $\angle B$ are acute.

Corollary 53a/3

If point P is not in a line t, then there is at most one line through P that is perpendicular to t. (D180)

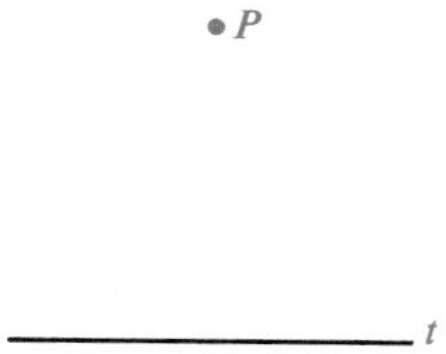

Proof

Two lines that pass through P and are perpendicular to t imply the existence of a triangle with two right angles. This contradicts Theorem 53/3.

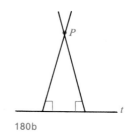

Diagram 180a   180b

Because of Theorem 53/3, the following classification of triangles commonly is used.

Definition 47/3 *Acute triangle, right triangle, obtuse triangle*

A triangle is an acute triangle if all three of its angles are acute. A triangle is a right triangle if one of its angles is a right angle. A triangle is an obtuse triangle if one of its angles is an obtuse angle. (D181)

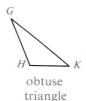

acute triangle   right triangle   obtuse triangle

Diagram 181

Convention

In a right triangle, the side opposite the right angle is called the hypotenuse. The other two sides are called the legs of the right triangle. (D182)

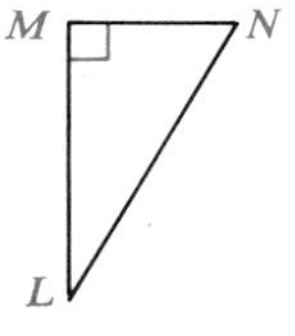

$\overline{LN}$ is the hypotenuse of $\triangle LMN$.

$\overline{LM}$ and $\overline{MN}$ are the legs of $\triangle LMN$.

Diagram 182

Corollary 53b/3

In a right triangle, the angle opposite each leg is acute.

Exercises

1 For each of the following cases, which of the given points is in the interior of the angle mentioned in the statement?

a Open ray $\overrightarrow{BX}$ is opposite $\overrightarrow{BC}$ of $\angle ABC$; $\overrightarrow{AD}$ is opposite $\overrightarrow{AX}$.

b Open ray $\overrightarrow{SW}$ is opposite $\overrightarrow{ST}$ of $\angle RST$; $\langle S, H, R \rangle$; open ray $\overrightarrow{HW}$ is opposite $\overrightarrow{HK}$.

c Open ray $\overrightarrow{EL}$ is opposite $\overrightarrow{EF}$ of $\measuredangle DEF$; $<L, M, E>$; open ray $\overrightarrow{DM}$ is opposite $\overrightarrow{DP}$.

2 Three lines t_1, t_2, and t_3 intersect at the three points A, B, and C, forming $\measuredangle 1, \measuredangle 2, \ldots, \measuredangle 9$ (D183).

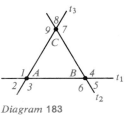

Diagram 183

  a Name the exterior angles of $\triangle ABC$.

  b Which angle of $\triangle ABC$ is adjacent to $\measuredangle 1$? To $\measuredangle 4$? To $\measuredangle 8$? *Answer*

  c Which angle of $\triangle ABC$ is congruent to $\measuredangle 2$? To $\measuredangle 8$? To $\measuredangle 3$?

  d Which angles of $\triangle ABC$ are not adjacent to $\measuredangle 7$? To $\measuredangle 1$? To $\measuredangle 5$?

3 Use the information given in exercise 2 to decide which of the following statements are necessarily valid. *Answer*

  a $\measuredangle 1° > \measuredangle ABC°$ and $\measuredangle 1° > \measuredangle ACB°$.

  b $\measuredangle 4$ is greater than $\measuredangle A$ and $\measuredangle B$ of $\triangle ABC$.

  c $\measuredangle 1$ and $\measuredangle 2$ are both greater than $\measuredangle B$ and $\measuredangle C$ of $\triangle ABC$.

  d $\measuredangle 1$ is greater than $\measuredangle B$ of $\triangle ABC$ and $\measuredangle B$ is congruent to $\measuredangle 5$, so $\measuredangle 1$ is greater than $\measuredangle 5$.

4 Assume that $\measuredangle CBD$ is an exterior angle of $\triangle ABC$ at B (D184).

  a What does $\measuredangle CBD° = 90$ imply about the measure of $\measuredangle C$? *Answer*

  b What does $\measuredangle CBD° > 120$ imply about $\measuredangle A°$?

  c What does $\measuredangle CBD° < 60$ imply about the measure of $\measuredangle C$?

  d What does $\measuredangle C° = 24$ imply about the measure of the exterior angle $\measuredangle CBD$?

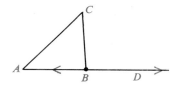

Diagram 184

  e What does $\measuredangle C° > 30$ imply about $\measuredangle CBD°$?

  f What does $\measuredangle CBD° = r$ imply about the value of $(\measuredangle A° + \measuredangle C°)$?

  g What does $\measuredangle ABC° = 83$ imply about the measure of $\measuredangle C$? *Answer*

5 Given: $\triangle ABC$ with $\measuredangle A \cong \measuredangle B$ and point D such that $<C, D, B>$. (D185)

  Prove: $\measuredangle CDA$ is greater than $\measuredangle CAD$.

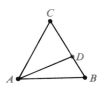

Diagram 185

6 If a triangle has two congruent exterior angles, must the triangle itself have two congruent angles? If so, prove it.

7 Complete each of the following statements about real numbers so that each statement is valid.

  a If $a > b$ and $b > c$, then $a \sim\!\!\sim c$.

  b If $a = b$ and $b > c$, then $a \sim\!\!\sim c$.

  c If $a > b$ and $b = c$, then $a \sim\!\!\sim c$.

123

d If $a > b$ and $b \geq c$, then a ~~~ c.

e If $a < b$ and $b < c$, then ~~~. *Answer*

f If $a \leq b$ and $b \leq a$, then ~~~.

g If $a > b$ and $c > a$, then ~~~.

h If $z \leq x$ and $x \leq y$, then ~~~.

i If $a > b$, then $a + 10$ ~~~ $b + 10$.

j If $a = b$, then $a + 10$ ~~~ $b + 6$.

In section 4/1, we mentioned that some exercises in this book would be stated as theorems. The word "Theorem" will introduce each exercise of this kind and will indicate that you should write a proof of the theorem in as careful and as formal a way as possible. Exercise 8 below is the first exercise of this kind.

8 *Theorem*

The sum of the measures of each two angles of a triangle is less than 180.

9 Prove Theorem 53/3 as a corollary of the theorem stated in exercise 8.

10 Assume that the three angles of $\triangle ABC$ and one exterior angle are labeled as indicated in D186.

For each of the following cases, classify, if possible, $\angle 1$, $\angle 2$, $\angle 3$, $\angle 4$, and $\triangle ABC$ as acute, right, or obtuse.

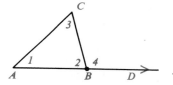

Diagram 186

a $\angle 2° = 90$. *Answer*

b $\angle 4° = 20$.

c $\angle 1 \cong \angle 2 \cong \angle 3$; $\angle 4° = 120$.

d $\angle 3° = 40$.

e $\angle 1° = 160$.

f $\angle 1 \cong \angle 2$; $\angle 4° = 100$.

11 a If $\angle A$ of $\triangle ABC$ is a right angle, which side is the hypotenuse? Name the two legs of the triangle.

b Name the legs and the hypotenuse of $\triangle DEF$, if $\angle F° = 90$.

c Is it possible to have a right triangle with two congruent sides? Would the congruent sides be the legs of the triangle?

d What relation exists between the length of the hypotenuse and the length of each leg in a right triangle?

e If $\angle A$ of $\triangle ABC$ is a right angle, identify $\angle B$ and $\angle C$ as right angles, acute angles, or obtuse angles.

12 Assume that point P is not in line t.

a If $PA \perp t$ at H and $PB \perp t$ at J, what relation exists between H and J? Between PA and PB? Must $\overline{PA}$ and $\overline{PB}$ be congruent?

124

b If the points A and B of exercise 12a are in t, what relation exists between $d(P, A)$ and $d(P, B)$? *Answer*

◆ **13** *Theorem (angle, angle, side theorem)*

If a correspondence of two triangles is such that two angles in one triangle are respectively congruent to their corresponding angles and if a pair of corresponding sides are congruent, then the correspondence is a congruence.

◆ **14** Make a diagram to show why a side, side, angle congruence cannot be expected to determine a congruence of two triangles.

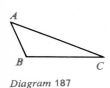

Diagram 187

Suppose that we draw a triangle in which the sides have different lengths (D187). Our diagram suggests that, if one side is longer than another side, then the angle opposite the longer side is larger than the angle opposite the other side. We want to establish this angle, side order in two ways. That is, we want to establish it so that, if we know which of two sides of a triangle is longer, then we know which of the two opposite angles is larger, and *conversely*.*

We begin the study of the side, angle order relations of the triangle with the special case in which two of the sides are congruent. Such a triangle plays so basic a part in Euclidean geometry that it is given a separate name.

Definition 48/3 *Isosceles triangle*

A triangle is an isosceles triangle if two of its sides are congruent. (D188)

Conventions

The two congruent sides of an isosceles triangle commonly are called the sides of the triangle, and the third side is called the base of the triangle. The angle of an isosceles triangle that is opposite the base is called the vertex angle, and the other two angles are called the base angles of the triangle.

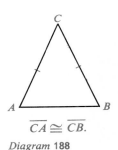

$CA \cong CB.$

Diagram 188

One side, angle relation of triangles now can be stated in the following form.

---

* "Conversely" is a convenient term for expressing a kind of opposite in known and unknown conditions. If you interchange one of the given conditions of a given theorem with one of the conclusions, the new statement is often called a converse of the given theorem. The two statements are said to be converses of each other. The converse of a theorem may not be a theorem. Even if the converse is a theorem, it requires a proof of its own.

125

Theorem 54/3

The base angles of an isosceles triangle are congruent. (D189)

First proof of Theorem 54/3

Let $\triangle ABC$ denote an isosceles triangle in which $\overline{CA} \cong \overline{CB}$.
Then, by Axiom 12/3, the correspondence $ABC \leftrightarrow BAC$
of the triangle with itself is a congruence,
since, from the given conditions,

1 $\overline{CA} \cong \overline{CB}$.

From the identity property,

2 $\angle ACB \cong \angle BCA$.

Also, from the given conditions,

3 $\overline{CB} \cong \overline{CA}$.

The base angles $\angle CAB$ and $\angle CBA$ are corresponding parts
in the congruence; hence, they are congruent to each other.

Corollary 54/3

The three angles of an equilateral triangle are mutually
congruent. (D190) (An equilateral triangle is equiangular.)

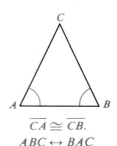

$\overline{CA} \cong \overline{CB}.$

$ABC \leftrightarrow BAC$

Diagram 189

Diagram 190

In proving theorems, we often use properties of some parts of
the figure that are not mentioned in either the hypothesis or the
conclusion of the theorem. These parts are called *auxiliary parts*
of the figure involved in the theorem. Deciding which auxiliary
parts such as points, lines, or angles have properties that would
be useful is an important step in inventing a proof. In a second
proof of Theorem 54/3, which is given next, we use the closed
ray $\overrightarrow{CP}$ as an auxiliary part of $\triangle ABC$.

Second proof of Theorem 54/3

Let $\triangle ABC$ denote an isosceles triangle in which $\overline{CA} \cong \overline{CB}$. (D191a)

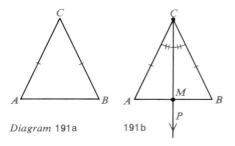

Diagram 191a   191b

Let $\overrightarrow{CP}$ denote the closed ray bisecting $\angle C$ (Theorem 32/2).
Then $\overrightarrow{CP}$ intersects $\overline{AB}$ at a point M
between A and B (Theorem 22/2). In the
correspondence $ACM \leftrightarrow BCM$, it is given that

1 $\overline{CA} \cong \overline{CB}$.

Because $\overrightarrow{CM}$ is the bisector of $\angle ACB$,
2 $\angle ACM \cong \angle BCM$.
From the identity property,
3 $\overline{CM} \cong \overline{CM}$.
By the side, angle, side axiom (Axiom 12/3), it follows
that $\triangle ACM \cong \triangle BCM$. As corresponding parts in a congruence,
4 $\angle A \cong \angle B$,
and
5 $\overline{AM} \cong \overline{BM}$.
Hence, M is the midpoint of $\overline{AB}$. Also, as corresponding parts
in a congruence,
6 $\angle AMC \cong \angle BMC$.

Because M is between A and B, the closed rays $\overrightarrow{MA}$ and $\overrightarrow{MB}$
are opposite rays (Corollary 5d/2). So by the
angle supplement theorem (Theorem 28/2), the sum of
the measures of $\angle AMC$ and $\angle BMC$ is 180. Since these angles
have equal measures, it follows, by statement 6, that
7 $\angle AMC° = \angle BMC° = 90$.
Therefore, line CM is perpendicular to $\overline{AB}$ at M. Combining
this fact with statement 5, we then have the following fact.
8 The line bisecting $\angle C$ also is the perpendicular
bisector of side AB.

But there is only one line that bisects $\angle C$, and there is
only one line in the plane of $\triangle ABC$ that is perpendicular
to AB at M (Theorem 37/3). Therefore, in the plane of $\triangle ABC$,
we have the following relation.
9 The perpendicular bisector of $\overline{AB}$ is also the bisector
of $\angle C$.

───────────

In our second proof of Theorem 54/3, we also have proved
the following theorem.

───────────

* Theorem 55/3
In the plane of an isosceles triangle, the perpendicular
bisector of the base is also the bisector of the vertex angle.
(D192)

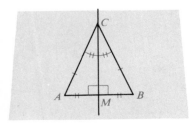

Diagram 192

127

It hardly is necessary to observe that, while our first proof of Theorem 54/3 was the simpler, our second proof yielded much more information. This result is one reason why new proofs are often developed for theorems that have already been proved. Theorem 55/3, which we got from the second proof, will be very important in many other proofs. We also will make use of the following corollary of Theorem 55/3.

* Corollary 55/3

The line through the midpoint of the base of an isosceles triangle and the opposite vertex is perpendicular to the base and bisects the vertex angle.

We next establish the converse of Theorem 54/3.

Theorem 56/3

If two angles of a triangle are congruent, then the sides opposite these angles are congruent. (D193)

Proof

Let $\triangle ABC$ denote a triangle in which

1 $\angle A \cong \angle B$.

This also implies that

2 $\angle B \cong \angle A$.

By the symmetric property for distance,

Diagram 193

3 $\overline{AB} \cong \overline{BA}$.

So, from statements 1, 2, and 3 and the angle, side, angle theorem, $ABC \leftrightarrow BAC$ is a congruence of $\triangle ABC$ with itself.

4 $\therefore \overline{AC} \cong \overline{BC}$

as corresponding parts of a congruence.

Corollary 56/3

If three angles of a triangle are mutually congruent, then the three sides are mutually congruent. (An equiangular triangle is equilateral.)

Theorem 57/3

If two sides of a triangle are not congruent, then the angle opposite the greater of these two sides is greater than the angle opposite the lesser of the two sides. (D194)

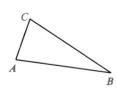

Diagram 194a   194b

Proof

Let $\triangle ABC$ denote a triangle in which $d(C, B) > d(C, A)$.
Then there exists a point D in $\overrightarrow{CB}$ such that $d(C, D) = d(C, A)$.
Since $d(C, D) < d(C, B)$, point D is between C and B.

128

Therefore, $\overrightarrow{AD}$ is between $\overrightarrow{AB}$ and $\overrightarrow{AC}$ and

1 $\angle A° > \angle CAD°$.

By the choice of D, $\overline{CA} \cong \overline{CD}$. Hence,

2 $\angle CAD° = \angle CDA°$.

Since $\angle CDA$ is an exterior angle of $\triangle ADB$, we also have

3 $\angle CDA° > \angle B°$.

Now, combining statements 1, 2, and 3 gives

4 $\angle A° > \angle CDA° > \angle B°$.

From statement 4 and the transitive property of "greater than,"

5 $\angle A° > \angle B°$.

Therefore, $\angle A$, opposite the greater side $\overline{CB}$, is greater than $\angle B$, opposite the lesser side $\overline{CA}$.

The following angle, side order property of triangles now follows easily.

Theorem 58/3

If two angles of a triangle are not congruent, then the side opposite the greater of the two angles is greater than the side opposite the lesser of the two angles.

Proof

Let $\triangle ABC$ denote a triangle in which $\angle A° > \angle B°$. For the two numbers $d(C, B)$ and $d(C, A)$, exactly one of the following relations must be true:

1) $d(C, B) = d(C, A)$;

2) $d(C, B) < d(C, A)$;

3) $d(C, B) > d(C, A)$.

From Theorem 54/3, statement 1 implies $\angle B° = \angle A°$, which is false. Therefore, statement 1 is false. From Theorem 57/3, statement 2 implies $\angle B° > \angle A°$, which is false. Hence statement 2 is false. Thus statement 3 is the only alternative and must be true. Thus side $\overline{CB}$, opposite the greater angle, $\angle A$, is greater than side $\overline{CA}$, opposite the lesser angle, $\angle B$.

Corollary 58/3

The hypotenuse of a right triangle is greater than each of the other two sides of the triangle.

Proof

The hypotenuse is opposite a right angle. By Corollary 53b/2, each leg is opposite an acute angle. Hence, by Theorem 58/3, the hypotenuse is greater than each leg.

Exercises

1 a Name the base angles of the isosceles triangle $\triangle DEF$ if the congruent sides are $\overline{DE}$ and $\overline{EF}$.

b Name the vertex of the isosceles triangle $\triangle GHT$ if $\overline{GT} \cong \overline{HT}$.

c Name the sides of the isosceles triangle $\triangle RST$ if $\angle R \cong \angle T$. *Answer*

d Name the base of the isosceles triangle $\triangle DFG$ if $\angle F \cong \angle D$.

2 Given: $\triangle AHR$ with $\langle A, B, F \rangle$ and $\langle B, F, H \rangle$ such that $\overline{AB} \cong \overline{FH}$ and $\overline{BR} \cong \overline{FR}$. (D195)

Prove: $\triangle ABR \cong \triangle HFR$. *Answer*

3 Given: $\triangle AHR$ with $\langle A, B, F \rangle$ and $\langle B, F, H \rangle$ such that $\overline{AB} \cong \overline{FH}$ and $\angle ABR° = \angle HFR°$. (D195)

Prove: $\angle ARB° = \angle FRH°$. *Answer*

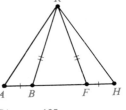

Diagram 195

4 Let $\triangle ABC$ denote an isosceles triangle with congruent sides $\overline{AB}$ and $\overline{AC}$. Euclid proved our Theorem 54/3, that is, that $\angle B \cong \angle C$ (D196) in the following way. Give the answer to each "Why?" in this proof.

There exist points D and E such that $\langle A, B, D \rangle$, $\langle A, C, E \rangle$, and $\overline{BD} \cong \overline{CE}$. Then $\triangle ACD \cong \triangle ABE$ (Why?). So $\overline{CD} \cong \overline{BE}$, and $\angle CDA \cong \angle BEA$. Therefore, $\triangle CDB \cong \triangle BEC$ (Why?). Then, from $\angle ACD \cong \angle ABE$ and $\angle BCD \cong \angle CBE$, it follows that $\angle ACB \cong \angle ABC$ (Why?).*

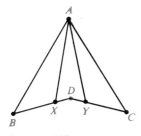

Diagram 196

5 Given: Point D is in the interior of $\angle BAC$ with $\langle B, X, D \rangle$ and $\langle D, Y, C \rangle$ such that $\overline{AB} \cong \overline{AC}$, $\overline{DB} \cong \overline{DC}$, and $\angle BAX \cong \angle XAY \cong \angle YAC$. (D197)

Prove: $\overline{AX} \cong \overline{AY}$.

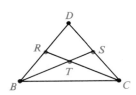

Diagram 197   *Diagram 198*

6 Given: $\triangle BCD$ with R and S the midpoints of $\overline{BD}$ and $\overline{DC}$ respectively. Segments $\overline{BS}$ and $\overline{RC}$ intersect at T, and $\overline{DB} \cong \overline{DC}$. (D198)

Prove:

a T is in the interior of $\triangle BCD$.

b $\triangle BTC$ is isosceles.

---

* Because the diagram for this theorem has the appearance of an old style bridge and because beginners found this proof difficult, the theorem was called the *pons asinorum*, or the *bridge of asses*.

c $\overrightarrow{DT}$ bisects $\measuredangle D$.

d $\overrightarrow{DT}$ bisects $\overline{BC}$.

e $\overrightarrow{DT} \perp \overline{BC}$.

7 a In $\triangle DMP$, if $d(D, M) > d(M, P) > d(D, P)$, then which angle of $\triangle DMP$ is the largest? The smallest? *Answer*

b In $\triangle ABC$, if $d(A, B) = \frac{22}{7}$, $d(B, C) = \pi$, and $d(A, C) = \sqrt{10}$, then which angle of $\triangle ABC$ is the largest? The smallest? *Answer*

8 a In $\triangle CAT$, if $\measuredangle C° > \measuredangle T° > \measuredangle A°$, which side of $\triangle CAT$ is the longest? The shortest?

b In $\triangle AXE$, if $\measuredangle A° = \frac{65}{21}$, $\measuredangle X° = \frac{89}{28}$, and $\measuredangle E° = \pi$, which side of $\triangle AXE$ is the longest? The shortest?

9 If $\overline{DE}$ is the base of isosceles triangle $\triangle DEF$, and G is between D and E, prove that the length of $\overline{FG}$ is less than the length of $\overline{FD}$.

10 Assume that point P is in the interior of $\triangle ABC$.

a Prove that $\measuredangle APB° > \measuredangle ACB°$.

b If $\measuredangle ACB$ is obtuse, prove that $d(A, B) > d(A, P)$.

◆ **11** *Theorem*

If two sides in one triangle are respectively congruent to two sides in a second triangle and the angle between the two sides in the first triangle is larger than that between the corresponding sides in the other triangle, then the side opposite this larger angle is longer than the side opposite the corresponding smaller angle.

◆ **12** *Theorem* (*modified side, side, angle congruence theorem*)

In a correspondence of two triangles, if two sides of one triangle and the angle opposite the longer of these two sides are congruent respectively to their corresponding parts in the second triangle, then the correspondence is a congruence.

Let us look for a moment at the pattern of what we are doing. Because triangles will appear as subsets of nearly every geometric figure we study, the basic facts about triangles will be extremely useful. We began by using a congruence condition to obtain the exterior angle inequality. We then combined this fundamental triangle property with congruences to establish the basic angle, side order relations of triangles and the important symmetric property of isosceles triangles (Theorem 55/3). With these relations to help us, we now can obtain still other congruence conditions. First, however, we add to the system the following rather obvious, but necessary, fact about triangles.

The sum of the lengths of any two sides of a triangle is greater than the
length of the third side. (D199)

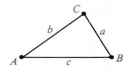

Proof

Let $\triangle ABC$ denote a triangle in which $d(A, B) = c$,
$d(B, C) = a$, and $d(C, A) = b$. In $\overset{\longrightarrow}{AC}$, there is a point P
such that C is between A and P, and
$d(C, P) = d(B, C) = a$. Then,

1 $d(A, P) = d(A, C) + d(C, P) = b + a$.

Because C is between A and P, the closed ray $\overset{\cdot\cdot\longrightarrow}{BC}$ is
between $\overset{\cdot\longrightarrow}{BA}$ and $\overset{\cdot\cdot\longrightarrow}{BP}$, so

Diagram 199a

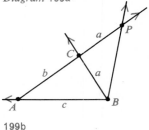

199b

2 $\sphericalangle ABP° > \sphericalangle CBP°$.

But $\triangle BPC$ is isosceles, since $\overline{BC}$ and $\overline{PC}$ each have
length a. Therefore, by Theorem 54/3,

3 $\sphericalangle CBP° = \sphericalangle BPC°$.

Combining statements 2 and 3 gives

4 $\sphericalangle ABP° > \sphericalangle BPC°$.

But $\sphericalangle BPC$ is also $\sphericalangle BPA$, so statement 4 says that,
in $\triangle ABP$, $\sphericalangle B$ is greater than $\sphericalangle P$. So, by Theorem 58/3,
side $\overline{AP}$ opposite B is greater than side $\overline{AB}$ opposite P.
That is,

5 $d(A, P) > d(A, B)$, or $a + b > c$.

By the same kind of argument, $b + c > a$ and $c + a > b$.
Therefore, the sum of the lengths of any two sides
of a triangle is greater than the length
of the third side.

We now can simplify the conditions for "betweenness" of
points.

If A, B, and C are three points such that
$d(A, C) = d(A, B) + d(B, C)$, then B is between A and C.

Proof

The three points cannot be the vertices of a triangle because
the length of AC is not less than the sum of the lengths
of $\overline{AB}$ and $\overline{BC}$. Therefore, the three points are collinear,
and so they satisfy the definition that B
is between A and C.

We turn now to further congruence properties and first establish two special congruence theorems for right triangles. Our proof
of Theorem 60/3 is a slightly modified type of column proof.

In a correspondence of right triangles, if the hypotenuse of one corresponds and is congruent to that of the other and if one pair of corresponding acute angles are congruent angles, then the correspondence is a congruence. (D200)

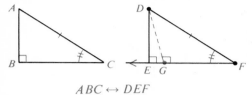

$$ABC \leftrightarrow DEF$$

Diagram 200

Proof

Let $ABC \leftrightarrow DEF$ denote a correspondence of right triangles in which ⊀B and ⊀E are corresponding right angles and in which

1 $\overline{AC} \cong \overline{DF}$.	1 Given
2 ⊀$C \cong$ ⊀F.	2 Given

Let G denote a point in $\overrightarrow{FE}$ such that

3 $\overline{FG} \cong \overline{CB}$.	3 Corollary 9/2

Then,

4 $\triangle ABC \cong \triangle DGF$.	4 Statements 1, 2, 3 and the side, angle, side axiom (Axiom 12/3)
5 ∴ ⊀$DGF \cong$ ⊀B.	5 Corresponding angles of a congruence

Since ⊀B is a right angle, it follows, from statement 5, that ⊀DGF is a right angle and, hence, that line DG is perpendicular to line FE. But there is at most one line through D that is perpendicular to EF (Corollary 53a/3). Because ⊀DEF is a given right angle, DE is perpendicular to EF. Therefore,

6 $DG = DE$.	6 Stated above
7 ∴ $G = E$.	7 Two lines intersect in at most one point.
8 $\triangle ABC \cong \triangle DFE$.	8 Restatement of statement 4, since $G = E$

Theorem 61/3 *Hypotenuse, side congruence theorem*

In a correspondence of right triangles, if the hypotenuse of one corresponds and is congruent to that of the other and if one of the other pairs of corresponding sides are congruent sides, then the correspondence is a congruence.

Proof

Let $\triangle ABC$ and $\triangle DEF$ denote right triangles (D201a), with B and E the vertices of right angles, such that

1 $\overline{AC} \cong \overline{DF}$

and

2 $\overline{AB} \cong \overline{DE}$.

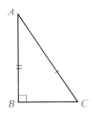 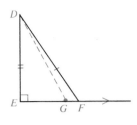 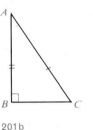 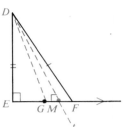

Diagram 201a　　　　　　　　　　　　　　201b

In the open ray $\overrightarrow{EF}$, there is a point G such that

3 $\overline{BC} \cong \overline{EG}$.

　　From statements 2 and 3 and the congruence of the right angles at B and E, the side, angle, side congruence axiom implies that

4 $\triangle ABC \cong \triangle DEG$.

Therefore, as corresponding parts in a congruence,

5 $\overline{AC} \cong \overline{DG}$.

Statement 5, with statement 1, implies that

6 $\overline{DF} \cong \overline{DG}$.

　　Now assume that

7 $F \neq G$.

Then, from statement 6, $\triangle DFG$ is an isosceles triangle with base $\overline{FG}$ and vertex D. (D201b) The line t through D and the midpoint M of base $\overline{FG}$, therefore, is perpendicular to the line of the base; that is, $DM \perp EF$ (Theorem 55/3). But there is at most one line through D that is perpendicular to EF, and line DE is given as such a line. Therefore, t must be line DE, and so

8 $M = E$.

But F and G belong to the open ray $\overrightarrow{EF}$. Therefore, M, between F and G, is in this open ray. And because an open ray does not contain its endpoint,

9 $M \neq E$.

　　The contradiction of statements 8 and 9 implies that the assumption in statement 7 is false. Therefore, the contradiction implies that

10 $F = G$.

Consequently, statement 4 may be restated as

11 $\triangle ABC \cong \triangle DEF$.

134

Exercises

1 The triples listed below consist of three real numbers.
Which triples could represent the lengths of the sides
of a triangle? *Answer*

a 1, 2, 3   e 4, 4, 4
b 4, 5, 6   f 7, 7, 14
c 15, 15, 1   g 5, 1, 8
d 8, 20, 12   h $\sqrt{3}, \sqrt{4}, \sqrt{5}$

2 The following triples are in the order a, b, c where
$a = d(B, C)$, $b = d(A, C)$, and $c = d(A, B)$. In each case,
tell whether the segments $\overline{AB}$, $\overline{AC}$, and $\overline{BC}$ form a triangle,
are collinear, or cannot exist with these lengths
and endpoints. If the segments are collinear, tell
which point is between the other two.

a 7, 3, 10 *Answer*   d 5, 4, 1
b 10, 8, 6   e 11, 11, 23
c 2, 6, 10   f 10, 100, 100

3 The lengths of two sides of a triangle are 7 and 3.
Therefore, the length of the third side must be
greater than ∼∼∼ and less than ∼∼∼.

4 If a number x is not greater than a number b, in other
words, if $x \leq b$ is correct, then b is said to be an
upper bound to x. Similarly, if x is not less than a,
that is, if $a \leq x$ is correct, then a is called a
lower bound to x. The numbers a and b in $a \leq x \leq b$
are said to be *bounds* to x. If x is actually
between bounds a and b, then $a < x < b$. The numbers
in each of the following triples are the measures
of the sides of a triangle. One of the measures
is denoted by the letter x. In each case, tell what
bounds x must be between.

a 3, 4, x *Answer*   d π, 5, x
b 10, x, 21   e x, 54, 39
c x, 8, 8   f 1, x, 1

◆ 5 a If a and b denote the lengths of two sides of a
triangle and a is greater than b, then the length x
of the third side must be between what bounds? *Answer*
b If a, b, and c denote the lengths of the sides
of a triangle, show that, in any case, $|a - b| < c$.

◆ 6 If C is a point in the interior of $\triangle ABD$, prove that
$d(A, C) + d(C, B) < d(A, D) + d(D, B)$.
(Hint: Since C is in the interior of $\triangle ABD$,
the open ray $\overrightarrow{AC}$ must intersect $\overline{BD}$ at some point E.)

7 Seven pairs of triangles are represented in D202, and,
in each case, certain parts of the two triangles

135

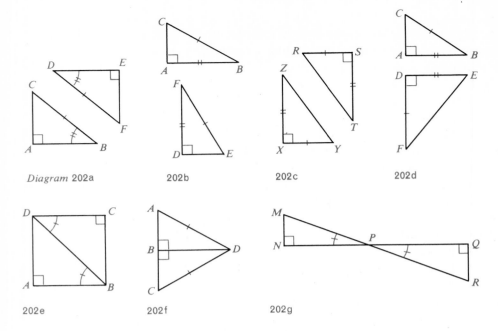

Diagram 202a   202b   202c   202d

202e   202f   202g

are indicated as congruent. First decide if this information is sufficient to imply that the triangles are congruent. Then state a congruence condition (s.a.s. and so on) that could be used to prove directly that a congruence of the triangles exists.

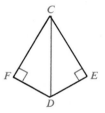

Diagram 203

8 Given: Quadrilateral *CFDE* with $\angle F° = \angle E° = 90$, and *CD* bisects $\angle C$. (D203)

Prove: $\overline{FC} \cong \overline{EC}$. *Answer*

9 Given: $\triangle ABC$ with $<A, D, C>$ and $<C, E, B>$ such that $AE \perp CB$, $BD \perp AC$, and $\overline{AE} \cong \overline{BD}$. Also, $\overline{AE}$ intersects $\overline{BD}$ at *F*. (D204)

Prove:

a $\triangle ABD \cong \triangle BAE$. *Answer*

b $\overline{FD} \cong \overline{FE}$.

c $\triangle ABC$ is isosceles.

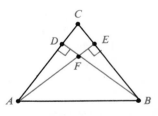

Diagram 204

10 Given: $\triangle ABC$ with $\overline{AC} \cong \overline{BC}$. Lines *BD* and *AE* are perpendicular respectively to *AC* and *BC* with $<D, C, A>$ and $<B, C, E>$.

Prove: $\overline{BD} \cong \overline{AE}$.

11 Is the conclusion of exercise 10, that $\overline{BD} \cong \overline{AE}$, correct if neither of the conditions $<D, C, A>$ and $<B, C, E>$ is given?

12 If *A, B,* and *C* are noncollinear and if $<A, P, B>$, $<B, Q, C>$, and $<C, R, A>$, prove that the perimeter of $\triangle ABC$ is greater than that of $\triangle PQR$. (D205)

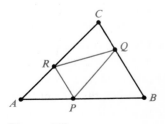

Diagram 205

136

We now take up the last of the major congruence theorems. Later, we will see that this congruence condition is, in some ways, the most important one.

Theorem 62/3 *Side, side, side (s.s.s.) congruence theorem*
If a correspondence of triangles is such that three sides of one triangle are congruent respectively to the three corresponding sides of the other triangle, then the correspondence is a congruence of the triangles.

Proof
Let $ABC \leftrightarrow DEF$ denote a correspondence of triangles such that $\overline{AB} \cong \overline{DE}$, $\overline{AC} \cong \overline{DF}$, and $\overline{BC} \cong \overline{EF}$. (D206a) Since $\angle BAC°$ is a

 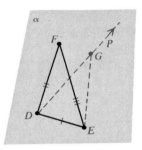  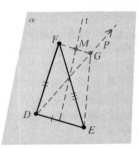

Diagram 206a 206b

number between 0 and 180, then, by Axiom 10/2, there is exactly one open ray $\overrightarrow{DP}$ in the plane α of $\triangle DEF$ such that $\overrightarrow{DP}$ is in the F-side of line DE and $\angle PDE° = \angle CAB°$. In $\overrightarrow{DP}$, there is a point G such that
1 $d(D, G) = d(A, C)$, that is, $\overline{AC} \cong \overline{DG}$.
We also are given
2 $\overline{AB} \cong \overline{DE}$,
and, because $\angle PDE$ is also $\angle GDE$,
3 $\angle CAB \cong \angle GDE$.
Thus, the correspondence $ABC \leftrightarrow DEG$ is a congruence (Axiom 12/3). That is,
4 $\triangle ABC \cong \triangle DEG$.
Because $\overline{DG}$ was chosen congruent to $\overline{AC}$ and $\overline{DF}$ was given congruent to $\overline{AC}$, then
5 $\overline{DG} \cong \overline{DF}$.
Also, since $\overline{EG} \cong \overline{BC}$, as corresponding parts in a congruence, and $\overline{EF} \cong \overline{BC}$ is a given condition, then
6 $\overline{EG} \cong \overline{EF}$.
    Now assume that
7 G is not in either $\overrightarrow{DF}$ or $\overrightarrow{EF}$.

137

Then, from statement 5, $\triangle DFG$ is an isosceles triangle with base $\overline{FG}$ and vertex D. (D206b) From statement 6, $\triangle EFG$ also is an isosceles triangle with base $\overline{FG}$ but with vertex E. Let M denote the midpoint of $\overline{FG}$. From the property of an isosceles triangle given in Theorem 55/3, the line t in α, which is the perpendicular bisector of base $\overline{FG}$, must pass through both the vertices D and E. Therefore, line t must be the line DE. And since M is in t,

8 M is in line DE.

But F and G are in an open half-plane with edge DE. So M, between F and G, belongs to this open half-plane.

9 $\therefore$ M is not in line DE.

The contradiction of statements 8 and 9 shows that statement 7 is false. The denial of statement 7, then, is that G must be in at least one of the open rays $\overrightarrow{DF}$ and $\overrightarrow{EF}$. But in a ray, there cannot be two points at the same distance from the ray's origin (Corollary 9/2). If G is in $\overrightarrow{DF}$, then, by statement 5, G and F are at the same distance from D. So $G = F$. If G is in $\overrightarrow{EF}$, then, by statement 6, G and F are the same distance from E. So $G = F$. Because G must be in at least one of the rays, it follows that

10 $G = F$.

Therefore, statement 4 can be restated as

11 $\triangle ABC \cong \triangle DEF$.

In the proof of Theorem 62/3, the following fact was established.

Corollary 62/3

In the plane of $\triangle DEF$ and in the F-side of DE, point F is the only point whose distances from D and E are the numbers $d(F, D)$ and $d(F, E)$ respectively.

Exercises

1 First tell which of the pairs of triangles represented in D207 are congruent. Then for each congruent pair, state a congruence and a congruence condition (s.a.s. and so on) that could be used to prove directly that the congruence exists.

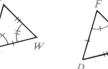

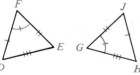

Diagram 207a   207b   207c

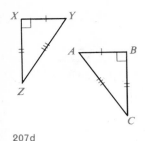

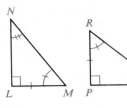

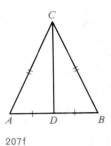

207d   207e   207f

2 Given: Polygon $ABCD$ with $\overline{AB} \cong \overline{CD}$ and $\overline{AD} \cong \overline{BC}$.
The diagonals $\overline{AC}$ and $\overline{BD}$ intersect at E. (D208)
Prove:

  a $\triangle ABD \cong \triangle CDB$.

  b $\triangle BEC \cong \triangle DEA$. *Answer*

  c $\overline{AC}$ and $\overline{BD}$ bisect each other.

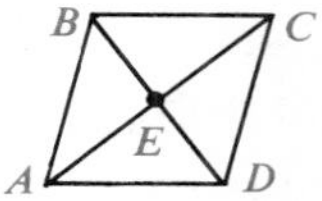

Diagram 208

3 Given: Segments $\overline{BC}$ and $\overline{AD}$ intersect at O such
that $\overline{AC} \cong \overline{DB}$ and $\overline{BC} \cong \overline{AD}$. (D209)
Prove:

  a $\triangle ABC \cong \triangle BAD$.   **b** $\overline{CO} \cong \overline{DO}$.

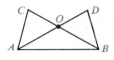

Diagram 209

4 Given: Points A, R, S, and C in line t such that
$<A, R, S>$, $<R, S, C>$, and $\overline{AR} \cong \overline{CS}$. Points B and D
not in t such that $\overline{AB} \cong \overline{CD}$ and $\overline{BS} \cong \overline{DR}$.
Prove: $\measuredangle BSA \cong \measuredangle DRC$. *Answer*

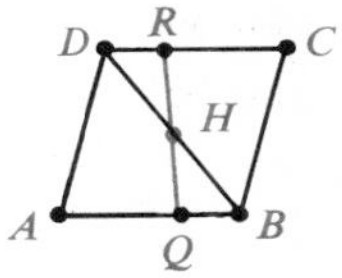

5 For exercise 4, must all of the points be coplanar?
Is $\measuredangle BSA \cong \measuredangle DRC$ if $B = D$?

Diagram 210

6 Given: Polygon $ABCD$ with $\overline{AD} \cong \overline{BC}$ and $\overline{DC} \cong \overline{AB}$.
Also, $<D, R, C>$ and $<A, Q, B>$ such that RQ bisects
diagonal $\overline{DB}$ at H. (D210)
Prove: $\overline{QH} \cong \overline{HR}$.

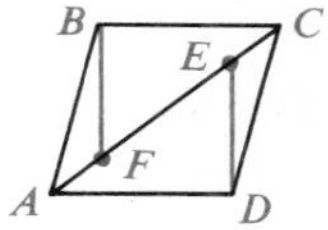

Diagram 211

7 Given: Polygon $ABCD$ with points F and E
in diagonal $\overline{AC}$ such that $<A, F, E>$ and
$<F, E, C>$. Also, $\overline{AF} \cong \overline{EC}$; $\overline{AB} \cong \overline{DC}$; $\overline{BC} \cong \overline{AD}$. (D211)
Prove: $\overline{BF} \cong \overline{ED}$.

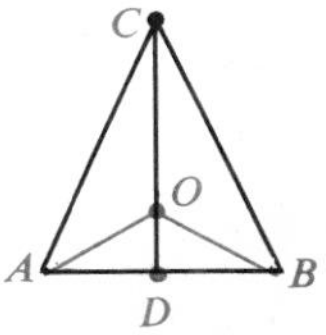

8 Given: Isosceles triangle $\triangle ABC$ with vertex angle $\measuredangle C$.
Point D is the midpoint of $\overline{AB}$,
and $<C, O, D>$. (D212)
Prove: $\overline{AO} \cong \overline{OB}$.

Diagram 212

◆ **9** Given: $\triangle JKL$ and $\triangle XYZ$ with
$<L, F, K>$ and $<Z, Q, Y>$ such that
$\overline{JK} \cong \overline{XY}$, $\overline{JL} \cong \overline{XZ}$, $\overline{ZQ} \cong \overline{QY}$,
$\overline{LF} \cong \overline{FK}$, and $\overline{XQ} \cong \overline{JF}$. (D213)
Prove: $\triangle JKL \cong \triangle XYZ$.

Diagram 213

10 Show that, if point P is not in line t, there is,
in the plane of P and t, a line that contains P
and does not intersect t. *Answer*

◆ 11 Show that the perimeter of the polygon *ABCD* is greater than the sum of the lengths of its two diagonals.

◆ 12 Given: In $\sphericalangle BAC$, point D is between B and A, point E is between C and A, and $\overline{AB} \cong \overline{AC}$ and $\overline{AD} \cong \overline{AE}$. Point F is the intersection point of $\overline{BE}$ and $\overline{DC}$. (D214) Prove: AF bisects $\sphericalangle A$. (Notice that this gives a procedure for constructing an angle bisector.)

Diagram 214

Perpendicularity 13/3
of a line and a plane

Our general plan in building the foundations was to work from the line to a plane to space. In keeping with that plan, we now want to begin the foundations of solid geometry. In particular, we want to establish the perpendicularity relations of lines with planes. Again, to save time, we will make some use of starred theorems. We also will make partial exercises out of some proofs, that is, we will ask you to supply the reasons for the statements in some of the proofs.

In this section, we will be working with congruent triangles that are in different planes. Some of you may find it difficult to visualize three-dimensional figures and to "see" different relations between parts of such figures. The ability to see things in "the mind's eye" differs greatly from person to person. This may be why people seem to divide more sharply in liking or in not liking geometry than they do about most other subjects. But everyone is visually minded to some extent, and developing one's ability in this regard is valuable in many ways quite apart from its value in geometry.

In Axioms 2/2 and 3/2, assumptions were made concerning relations between points and a plane and also between lines and a plane. For example, by Axiom 3/2, a line is contained in a plane if two of its points are in the plane. From this axiom, we have the following rather obvious theorem.

---

* Theorem 63/3

A line that is not contained in a plane intersects the plane in at most one point.

As yet, we have no assumptions or theorems concerning the possible relations of one plane to another. To get a start with such relations, we introduce a new axiom about the intersection properties of planes. The practice of introducing an axiom as we need it, rather than introducing a group of them at the start, allows you to see more clearly the part played in the system by each axiom.

140

If two planes intersect, then their intersection is a line.
(D215)

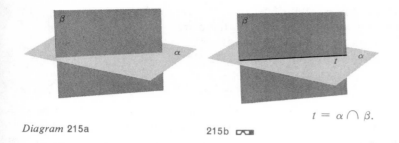

$$t = \alpha \cap \beta.$$

Diagram 215a   215b ▱▪

If we combine the intersection property of Axiom 13/3 with facts already in the system, we now can obtain the following existence property.

Theorem 64/3

If A is a point in a plane α, there exist infinitely many lines in α that pass through A. (D216)

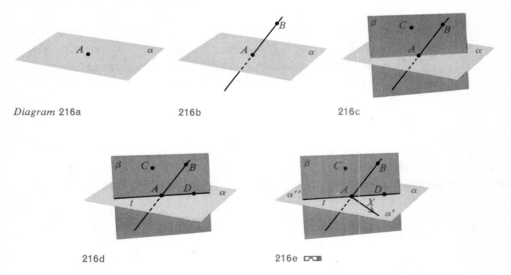

Diagram 216a   216b   216c

216d   216e ▱▪

Proof

Space is not contained in α (Axiom 4/2), so there exists a point B not in α. Space is not contained in line AB (Axiom 4/2), so there exists a point C not in line AB. There is a plane $\beta(A, B, C)$ by Axiom 2/2. Plane β is not α, since B is not in α. From Axiom 13/3, it follows that the

intersection of α and β is a line t. Since A belongs
to both α and β, the line t passes through A.
By the existence properties of the ruler axiom, Axiom 6/2, there
are infinitely many points in t, and so there is a point D in t
that is not A. By the separation axiom, Axiom 8/2,
the sides of t in α exist. That is, α' and α'' exist.
And from the existence properties in Axiom 10/2, there are
infinitely many open rays $\overrightarrow{AX}$ in α' that correspond
to the ray coordinate system with initial ray $\overrightarrow{AD}$.
Thus there are infinitely many lines AX in α.

The proof of Theorem 64/3 shows how much detail can be
involved in the proof of a seemingly simple theorem, and it
illustrates again how much time could be used in developing
foundations for our system if we did not make use of the agreement about starred theorems.

By an argument quite similar to that for Theorem 64/3, we
can show that the following statement is true.

---

* Theorem 65/3

Each line is contained in infinitely many planes.

Our axioms about coordinates in a line gave us the separation
of a line into two opposite rays. The separation of a plane by a
line was obtained by Axiom 8/2. Now, with Axiom 13/3 and
relations previously established, the separation of space by a plane
can be proved. Although we will not give the proof, we will state
the separation as a theorem.

---

* Theorem 66/3 *Space separation theorem*

For a plane α, there exist two nonempty,
convex sets $\mathcal{R}'$ and $\mathcal{R}''$ that
do not intersect each other or α.
Space is the union of $\mathcal{R}'$ and $\mathcal{R}''$
with α, and any segment that joins
a point of $\mathcal{R}'$ and a point of $\mathcal{R}''$
intersects α. (D217)

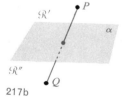

Diagram 217a   217b

Definition 49/3 *Open and closed half-spaces*

If space is the union of a plane α and two sets $\mathcal{R}'$ and $\mathcal{R}''$,
and if $\mathcal{R}'$ and $\mathcal{R}''$ are nonempty, convex sets that do not
intersect each other or α, then each of the sets $\mathcal{R}'$ and $\mathcal{R}''$ is
an open half-space. Each of these open half-spaces also is a
side of α, and the two open half-spaces are opposite sides
of α. Plane α is the face of each half-space, and $\alpha \cup \mathcal{R}'$
and $\alpha \cup \mathcal{R}''$ are *closed half-spaces*.

142

Convention

If A is not in α, we will speak of the open half-space
to which A belongs as the A-side of α.

A number of familiar relations now follow quite simply from
the fact that a half-space is convex.

* Theorem 67/3

Two points belong to the same side of a plane if and only if
the segment joining them does not intersect the plane.

* Theorem 68/3

If line t is in plane α and P is not
in α, then, in the plane β of P and t,
the P-side of line t is contained
in the P-side of plane α, and the
opposite open half-plane of β is
contained in the opposite side of α.
(D218)

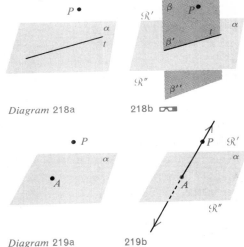

Diagram 218a   218b

* Theorem 69/3

If A is a point of plane α and P
is not a point of α, then the
open ray $\overrightarrow{AP}$ is contained in the P-side
of α, and the opposite open ray
is contained in the opposite side of α.
(D219)

Diagram 219a   219b

Exercises

1 Which of the following statements are correct? *Answer*

a If the two points A and B are contained in the plane α,
then the line AB is contained in α.

b If the line AB is in the plane α, then A and B are in α.

c If the line AB is not contained in the plane α,
then A is not in α and B is not in α.

d If the line AB intersects the plane α in the two points
C and D, then the line AB is contained in α.

e If the line AB intersects the plane α, then AB
intersects α either in exactly one point or in
infinitely many points.

2 The three open rays $\overrightarrow{AB}$, $\overrightarrow{AC}$, and $\overrightarrow{AD}$ are in the plane α
and points B, C, and D are collinear (D220).
If the open ray $\overrightarrow{AE}$ is not contained in α,
describe the intersection of each of the following.

a AE and plane α

b The plane of A, B, and E and plane α *Answer*

c $\theta(A, D, E)$ and $\beta(A, B, E)$

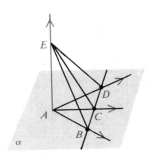

Diagram 220

143

d AC and DE

e The plane of A, B, and C and plane α

f $\not\triangleleft DCE$ and α

g AD, AC, and AB

h $\beta(A, B, E)$ and $\triangle DEB$

i $\overrightarrow{AD}$, $\overrightarrow{AC}$, and α *Answer*

3 Plane α separates space into two open half-spaces $\mathscr{R}'$
and $\mathscr{R}''$ (D221). Point B is in the A-side of α,
and the two points C and D are in the non-A-side
of plane α. Which of the following statements are valid?

a The segment $\overline{AC}$ intersects α.

b The segment $\overline{BC}$ intersects α.

c The segment $\overline{AB}$ intersects α.

d The half-space $\mathscr{R}''$ is a convex set.

e The union of $\mathscr{R}'$ and $\mathscr{R}''$ is a convex set.

f The plane of A, B, and D must contain point C.

g The face of $\mathscr{R}'$ is $\theta(A, B, C)$.

h If point G is in the B-side of α and point H is
in the C-side of α, then $\overline{GH}$ intersects α.

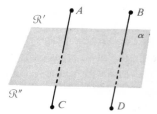

Diagram 221

4 Which of the following statements are necessarily true? *Answer*

a If $\overline{AB}$ does not intersect the plane α, then A and B
are in the same side of α.

b If A and B are not in the same side of α, then $\overline{AB}$
intersects α.

c If $\overrightarrow{AB}$ intersects α, then A and B are in opposite sides
of α.

d If A and B are in opposite sides of α, then $\overrightarrow{AB}$
intersects α.

e If A and B are in the same side of α, then $\overrightarrow{AB}$ cannot
intersect α.

f If A is contained in α, then the open ray $\overrightarrow{AB}$ cannot
intersect α.

♦ 5 Let S denote the following statement: "If two planes
intersect, then their intersection contains at least
two points." Prove that statement S is equivalent
to Axiom 13/3. In other words, prove that
$S \Longleftrightarrow$ Axiom 13/3.

We now turn to the main purpose here, that of establishing
some perpendicularity relations. We begin with a notion closely
related to perpendicularity. When we talk about the height of a
lighting fixture above the floor of a room, for example, we have
in mind the idea of the distance from a point P (the light) to a
plane α (the floor). By the distance from P to α, we mean the
distance between P and a point F in α that is less than the distance

from P to any other point Q in α (D222). Thus we mean the shortest distance from P to the plane, and we think of the line PF as being perpendicular to the plane. We sometimes even speak of this distance as the *perpendicular* distance.

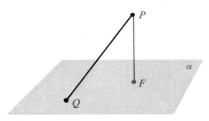

Diagram 222

We can use the natural ideas in this example of perpendicularity to define what we mean by the distance of a point P from a general set S. At the same time, it also will be convenient to introduce a term for the point, or points, of S that are closest to P.

Definition 50/3 *Foot of a point*
A point F in set S is called a foot in S of P if point P is not in S and if no point of S is closer to P than F is. That is, F is a foot in S of P if $d(P, F) \leq d(P, Q)$ for all points Q in S. Point F is the unique foot in S of point P if every other point of S is farther from P than F is. That is, F is *the* foot in S of P if $d(P, Q) > d(P, F)$ for all points Q that are in S and different from F.

Definition 51/3 *Distance between a point and a set*
The distance between point P and set S is $d(P, F)$ if F exists as a foot in S of P.

Convention
The distance between a point P and a set S sometimes will be indicated by the notation $d(P, S)$ and also will be called the distance from P to S or from S to P.

Comment
If a point P has any foot F in set S, then $d(P, S)$ exists and is the positive number $d(P, F)$. This positive number then must be the distance from P to any other foot in S of point P.

The definitions we have just put into our system give us a simple and definite language for talking not only about the distance from a point to a plane but also about the distance from a point to a square, a line, a circle, or any set.

It is easy to see that a point may have more than one foot in a set. For example, every point of a circle is a foot in the circle of the circle's center (D223). The center point of a square has four feet in the square. One easily can think of other examples though we do not as yet have proofs for them.

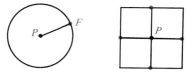

Diagram 223

It is not necessary, however, for a point to have any foot in a set. The origin P of the open ray $\overrightarrow{PQ}$ does not belong to the open ray, but it has no foot in the open ray. For if F is any point of the open ray, then F is not P. Consequently, there are points of the ray between P and F, and these points are closer to P than F is. Thus, F cannot be a foot in $\overrightarrow{PQ}$ of P. Since F is *any* point, no point of the open ray is a foot of P.

We now can describe the hardest problem of this section, using the following geometric language: "If P is not in a plane α, what is the *locus* in α of the feet of P?" The word "locus" is just the Latin word for "location," or "place." Thus, the locus problem is simply the question "Where, in α, are the feet of P?" We expect, of course, that the solution should be a single point F and that the line PF will give us a perpendicular to the plane α. A proof of the locus problem has two parts. First we will have to show that there is a point F in α that is a foot of P. Then we will have to show that every foot of P is F. In other words, we will have to show that F is the only foot of P.

Before we take up the plane locus problem, we first will consider a simpler question: "If P is not in line t, what is the locus in t of the feet of P?" We can get the answer to this question as a corollary of the following existence theorem for perpendicular lines.*

Theorem 70/3

If point P is not in line t, then there is exactly one line through P that is perpendicular to t.

Proof

Let α denote the plane determined by P and t, and let A denote a point of t. In α, there is a line s that is perpendicular to t at A (Theorem 37/2).

Case I If P belongs to s, then s is a line through P that is perpendicular to t.

---

* The proof of this theorem does not depend on Axiom 13/3, and the theorem could have been put into the system earlier. However, we purposely left it to be part of this general discussion of perpendicularity.

146

Case II If *P* does not belong to *s*, then *P* is in the interior of one of the angles formed by *s* and *t*, say $\sphericalangle BAE$, where $\overrightarrow{AB}$ is in *t* and $\overrightarrow{AE}$ is in *s*. (D224a)

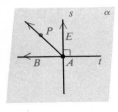 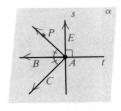 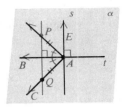

Diagram 224a   224b   224c

Because $\overrightarrow{AP}$ is between the arms $\overrightarrow{AB}$ and $\overrightarrow{AE}$ of a right angle, $\sphericalangle PAB$ is acute. So by Theorem 35/2, there exists a closed ray $\overrightarrow{AC}$ such that $\overrightarrow{AB}$ is the bisector of $\sphericalangle PAC$. Since, by the definition of a bisector of an angle, $\overrightarrow{AC}$ must be coplanar with $\overrightarrow{AB}$ and $\overrightarrow{AP}$, then $\overrightarrow{AC}$ is in α. In $\overrightarrow{AC}$, there is a point *Q* such that $d(A, Q) = d(A, P)$. Then $\overline{AP}$ and $\overline{AQ}$ are the sides of the isosceles triangle $\triangle PAQ$, and the bisector of the vertex angle of the triangle, $\sphericalangle A$, is perpendicular to the base $\overline{PQ}$ (Theorem 55/3). Since *t* is the bisector of $\sphericalangle A$, line *t* is perpendicular to *PQ*. Therefore, *PQ* is a line through *P* that is perpendicular to *t*.

From Case I and Case II, it follows that there is a line through *P* that is perpendicular to *t*. By Corollary 53a/3, there is at most one such line. Therefore, there is exactly one such line.

Corollary 70/3
If point *P* is not in line *t*, there is exactly one point in *t* that is the foot of *P*. This point is the intersection of *t* and the line through *P* that is perpendicular to *t*.

Proof
Let *F* denote the intersection point of *t* and the line through *P* that is perpendicular to *t*. Let *Q* denote any point of *t* other than point *F*. Then $\overline{PQ}$ is the hypotenuse of the right triangle $\triangle PFQ$. Hence, the length of $\overline{PQ}$ is greater than the length of the leg $\overline{PF}$. Since $d(P, Q) > d(P, F)$ for all *Q* in *t* distinct from *F*, point *F* is the unique foot in *t* of point *P*.

Exercises
1 Assume that three points *A*, *B*, and *C* in line *t* have coordinates 2, 3, and 7 respectively (D225).
  a Is *C* in $\overline{AB}$?
  b Which point of $\overline{AB}$ is closer to *C* than any other point of $\overline{AB}$? *Answer*

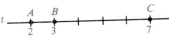

Diagram 225

147

c Is B in $\overline{AB}$?

d Is B a foot in $\overline{AB}$ of C?

e Is B the foot in $\overline{AB}$ of C?

f What is the distance between C and $\overline{AB}$?

g Which point in $\overline{BC}$ is the foot of A? *Answer*

h What is the distance between A and $\overline{BC}$?

i Let $\mathcal{S}$ denote the set consisting of the two points A and C; that is, let $\mathcal{S} = \{A, C\}$. What is the foot in $\mathcal{S}$ of B?

j What is the distance between B and $\mathcal{S}$?

2 Assume that legs $\overline{AB}$ and $\overline{BC}$ of right triangle $\triangle ABC$ have lengths 3 and 4 respectively and that the length of hypotenuse $\overline{AC}$ is 5 (D226).

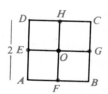

Diagram 226

a What is the foot in $\overline{AB}$ of C?

b What is the distance from $\overline{AB}$ to C?

c If $\mathcal{R} = BC$, what is $d(A, \mathcal{R})$? *Answer*

d Is A the foot in $\overline{AC}$ of B? Is C the foot in $\overline{AC}$ of B?

e Is the foot in $\overline{AC}$ of B some point in $\overline{AC}$ that is between A and C? Why? *Answer*

f Suppose that Q is the foot in $\overline{AC}$ of B and that P is any point of $\overline{AC}$ other than Q. Then which is correct, $d(B, Q) < d(B, P)$ or $d(B, P) < d(B, Q)$?

3 The points $E, F, G,$ and H are the respective midpoints of the sides $\overline{DA}, \overline{AB}, \overline{BC},$ and $\overline{CD}$ of square $ABCD$. The chords $\overline{EG}$ and $\overline{HF}$ intersect at point O. Each side of $ABCD$ has length 2 (D227).

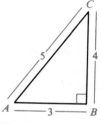

Diagram 227

a What are the feet in $ABCD$ of point O? *Answer*

b Why is $d(C, AB) = 2\,d(G, CD)$ a correct statement?

c If point Q is the midpoint of $\overline{OG}$, name a foot in $ABCD$ of Q.

d Name a foot of D in $\measuredangle CBA$. Is this point *the* foot of D in $\measuredangle CBA$?

e Name a foot of H in $\measuredangle CBA$. Is this point both *a* foot and *the* foot of H?

f Which point is the foot in $\overline{AF}$ of C? *Answer*

g If M is the foot in line EH of C, which of the three points $E, H,$ and M is between the other two?

h If $\mathcal{S}$ is the set consisting of the one point H, name the foot in $\mathcal{S}$ of B.

i Name a foot in the open ray $\overrightarrow{AB}$ of C. By definition, what is the distance from C to $\overrightarrow{AB}$?

j Name a foot in $\overrightarrow{AB}$ of D. What is the distance from D to $\overrightarrow{AB}$?

k Is there a foot in $\overrightarrow{OH}$ of F? Does a distance from F to $\overrightarrow{OH}$ exist?

148

4 Sets $\mathcal{R}$ and $\mathcal{S}$ can be such that every point of $\mathcal{R}$ is at the same distance from $\mathcal{S}$, while points of $\mathcal{S}$ are at different distances from $\mathcal{R}$. There are obvious examples if $\mathcal{R}$ consists of a single point and $\mathcal{S}$ does not. Give an example in which $\mathcal{R}$ and $\mathcal{S}$ are polygons.

◆ **5** In the plane of a circle $C(O, 3)$, point P is at a distance 8 from point O. Prove that the intersection of $C(O, 3)$ and $\overline{OP}$ is the foot in $C(O, 3)$ of point P.

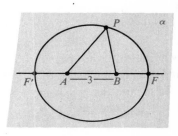

◆ **6** Two points A and B are 3 units apart in plane α (D228). The set of all points P in α such that $d(A, P) + d(P, B) = 7$ is called an *ellipse*. Show that the foot of B in the ellipse is the intersection of the ellipse with $\overrightarrow{AB}$.

Diagram 228

◆ **7** Assume that $\overline{AB}$ and $\overline{AC}$ are noncollinear, noncongruent segments. Make a diagram that shows the nature of the set of points P in $\alpha(A, B, C)$ such that $d(P, \overline{AB}) = d(P, \overline{AC})$.

We now define perpendicularity for a line and a plane.

Definition 52/3 *Perpendicular line and plane*

A line t and a plane α are perpendicular if their intersection is point P and if t is perpendicular to every line of α through P. Line t and plane α are perpendicular to each other at their point of intersection. A segment or a ray is perpendicular to a plane if it intersects the plane and its line is perpendicular to the plane. (D229)

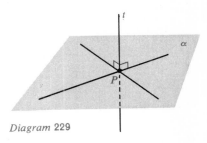

Diagram 229

Comment

The symbol $\perp$ also is used to denote perpendicularity of lines and planes. $t \perp \alpha \Longleftrightarrow \alpha \perp t$. (Symmetric property for perpendicularity of a line and a plane)

Our next perpendicularity property in space follows from known facts about perpendicularity in a plane.

Theorem 71/3

Corresponding to a point P and a plane α, there is at most one line that passes through P and is perpendicular to α. (D230)

Proof

Assume that there are two lines t and t' passing through P and perpendicular to α. Let β denote the plane determined by t and t'.

149

From the definition of a line
perpendicular to a plane, neither t
nor t' is in α, so $\beta \neq \alpha$. Also,
by definition, t and t' intersect α.
So β intersects α, and by Axiom 13/3,
the intersection is a line s.
Then $t \perp s$ and $t' \perp s$.
But by Theorem 37/3 and by
Corollary 53a/3, there cannot be
two lines in β that pass through P
and are perpendicular to s. Therefore, the assumption
is false, and there is at most one line that passes through P
and is perpendicular to α.

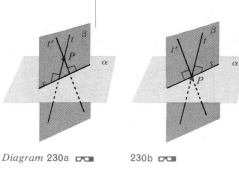

Diagram 230a   230b

We proved Theorem 71/3 by using the fact that in a plane
there cannot be two intersecting lines that are both perpendicular
to a third line of the plane. The same fact can be used, in much the
same way, to prove a companion theorem.

* Theorem 72/3
Corresponding to a point P and a line t, there is at most one
plane that passes through P and is perpendicular to t.

We now know that there cannot be two lines through a point
P that are perpendicular to a plane α. We need to show that at
least one line (hence, exactly one line) exists that passes through
P and is perpendicular to α. Though the fact seems clear, proving
it is not at all obvious. Such a situation is typical in working with
foundation properties. Actually, we can find a quite simple proof
if we detour slightly and first solve a different problem.

Suppose there is a line t through point P that is perpendicular
to plane α at M (D231a). Let Q denote the point in the opposite

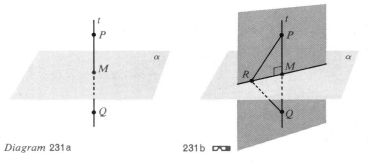

Diagram 231a   231b

side of α from P and such that M is the midpoint of $\overline{PQ}$. If R is
any point of α other than M, then $\triangle PQR$ is in a plane that intersects α in the line RM. So, if t is perpendicular to α, we have

150

$t \perp RM$. And because M is the midpoint of $\overline{PQ}$, it is clear that $\triangle PQR$ is an isosceles triangle with base $\overline{PQ}$ and $d(R, P) = d(R, Q)$.

The previous argument suggests a simple relation that one would expect. It suggests that α is not only the plane that is perpendicular to t at M but that it also is the set of points, or the locus of points, such that each point is the same distance from P as it is from Q. In our example, we obtained the equidistant property from the perpendicularity of t and α. This suggests that perhaps we could work the other way around. That is, perhaps we could obtain the perpendicularity property from the equidistant property. This, in fact, is possible, and proving the equidistant property first is the detour we spoke of earlier.

Suppose that the locus of points equidistant from two given points P and Q is a plane α (D232). Then all the points of any line s in α must be equidistant from P and Q. But s is determined by any two of its points, say A and B. So it should be true that, if two points A and B are equidistant from P and Q, then every point of line AB is equidistant from P and Q. This gives us a starting point.

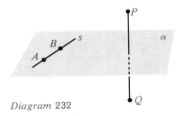

Diagram 232

In the proof of our next theorem, we have not included the reason for each statement. In other words, these parts of the proof have been left to you.

Theorem 73/3

If two points A and B are each equidistant from two points P and Q, then every point of line AB is equidistant from P and Q. (D233)

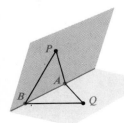
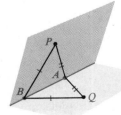
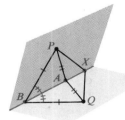

Diagram 233a   233b   233c

151

Proof

Because P is not Q and $d(A, P) = d(A, Q)$, point A is neither P nor Q. Similarly, $d(B, P) = d(B, Q)$ implies that B is neither P nor Q.

Line PQ has only one point, the midpoint of $\overline{PQ}$, that is equidistant from P and Q, while line AB has at least two points that are equidistant from P and Q. Consequently, line PQ is not line AB. Therefore, at least one of the points P and Q, say, point P, is not in line AB. Then A, B, and P determine a triangle so the three lengths $d(A, B)$, $d(A, P)$, and $d(B, P)$ are such that the sum of each two is greater than the third (Theorem 59/3). Since $d(A, B)$, $d(A, Q)$, and $d(B, Q)$ are respectively the same lengths, the sum of each two also is greater than the third. Therefore, no one of the points A, B, and Q is between the other two, so Q is not in line AB, either.

Now let X denote any point of line AB that is different from points A and B. From the fact that A and B are equidistant from P and Q, we have

1 $\triangle PAB \cong \triangle QAB.$ 1 〜〜

Therefore,

2 $\angle PBA \cong \angle QBA;$ 2 〜〜

3 $\angle PAB \cong \angle QAB.$ 3 〜〜

Since X is in line AB, it belongs to the open ray $\overrightarrow{BA}$, the open ray $\overrightarrow{AB}$, or to both. If X belongs to $\overrightarrow{BA}$, then

4 $\triangle PBX \cong \triangle QBX.$ 4 〜〜

So

5 $d(P, X) = d(Q, X).$ 5 〜〜

If X belongs to $\overrightarrow{AB}$, then

6 $\triangle PAX \cong \triangle QAX.$ 6 〜〜

Hence,

7 $d(P, X) = d(Q, X).$ 7 〜〜

Thus, in all cases, X is equidistant from P and Q. Therefore, every point of line AB is equidistant from P and Q.

For the next theorem, congruences of triangles are not necessary.

Theorem 74/3

If three noncollinear points A, B, and C are each equidistant from two points P and Q, then every point in the plane $\alpha(A, B, C)$ is equidistant from P and Q. (D234)

Proof

Let X denote a point in the plane $\alpha(A, B, C)$.
By Theorem 73/3, each of the lines AB, BC,
and CA consists of points equidistant
from P and Q. So if X is in one of these
lines, it is equidistant from P and Q.
Now let Y denote a point that is not X
and that is in the interior of $\triangle ABC$.
By the Pasch property in Theorem 41/2,
the line XY through a point in the
interior of the triangle must intersect
the triangle in two points D and E.
Because all points of the triangle are
equidistant from P and Q, each of the points
D and E, and, hence, the whole line DE,
is equidistant from P and Q. Therefore,
X in line DE is equidistant from P and Q.

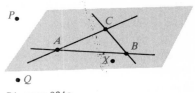

Diagram 234a

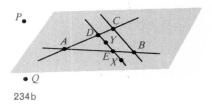

234b

 Since, in all cases, X is equidistant from P and Q,
the whole plane α is equidistant from P and Q.

 We still have not solved the entire locus problem. We still
must show that the points of α are the *only* points that are equidistant from P and Q. This fact, together with the perpendicularity property, is established in Theorem 75/3.

Theorem 75/3

The set of all points equidistant from two points P and Q is
a plane that is perpendicular to line PQ at the midpoint M
of segment $\overline{PQ}$.

Proof

Let β and γ denote two planes through line PQ. (D235a)

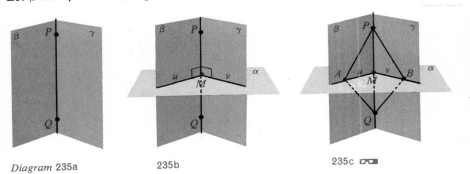

Diagram 235a   235b   235c

In β, let u denote the line perpendicular to PQ at M. In γ,
let v denote the line perpendicular to PQ at M. Let α
denote the plane of u and v. Let A and B, different

153

from M, denote points in u and v respectively so that α also is the plane of A, B, and M.

From the congruences $\triangle AMP \cong \triangle AMQ$ (Why?) and $\triangle BMP \cong \triangle BMQ$ (Why?), it follows that A and B, as well as M, are equidistant from P and Q (Why?). Then, by Theorem 74/3, all points of α are equidistant from P and Q.

To show that α is perpendicular to line PQ at M, let s in α denote any line that passes through M, and let D denote a point of s different from M. (D236a)

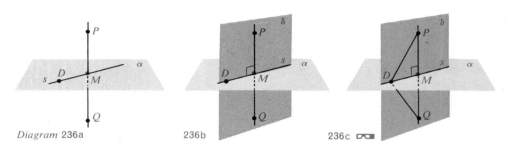

Diagram 236a   236b   236c

Lines s and PQ determine a plane δ (Why?). In δ, $\triangle PQD$ is an isosceles triangle (Why?). The line s that joins the vertex D to the midpoint of the base $\overline{PQ}$, therefore, is perpendicular to the base. So $s \perp PQ$. Thus PQ is perpendicular at M to every line of α through M. Hence $PQ \perp \alpha$.

All that remains to be shown is that any point equidistant from P and Q is in α. Let X denote a point equidistant from P and Q and assume that

1 X is not a point of α. (D237a)

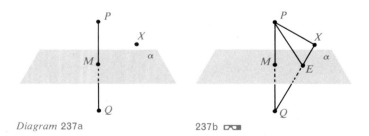

Diagram 237a   237b

Then X is not M, and so X is not in line PQ. Since X is not in α, it belongs to one side of α. We may suppose that the notation has been chosen so that X is in the P-side of α. Since X and Q are in opposite sides of α, segment $\overline{QX}$ intersects α at a point E (space separation theorem, Theorem 66/3). Then X and E are both equidistant from P

154

and Q, and so the whole line XE is equidistant from P and Q.
But Q is in line XE, and Q is not equidistant from P and Q.
Therefore, assumption 1 is false, and the set of all points
equidistant from P and Q is plane α.

Corollary 75a/3

A line that is perpendicular to each of two intersecting lines
is perpendicular to the plane of the two lines.

Proof

Let t denote a line that is perpendicular to each of the lines
u and v at their intersection point M. In t, there exist
points P and Q such that M is the midpoint of PQ.
By using the same argument that was used in the proof
of Theorem 75/3, it follows that t is perpendicular
to the plane α of u and v.

Corollary 75b/3

If P and Q are two points in a plane δ, the set of all points
in δ that are equidistant from P and Q is the line in δ
that is the perpendicular bisector of $\overline{PQ}$.

Proof

The set of all points equidistant from P and Q form a plane α
that is perpendicular to PQ at its midpoint M. Therefore,
the points of δ equidistant from P and Q are the points of δ
that are in α. The intersection of δ and α is a line s
through M. Since PQ is perpendicular to α at M,
it is perpendicular to s at M.

We could, of course, have proved Corollary 75b/3 much
earlier in the system. But since space properties often are obtained
from properties of the plane, it is interesting to see that the procedure can work the other way around, that is, that properties of
the plane can be obtained from space properties.

Exercises

1 If line m is contained in plane β, which of the
following statements are necessarily correct? *Answer*

a If line t is perpendicular to line m, then $t \perp \beta$.

b If line t is perpendicular to β, then $t \perp m$.

c If line t intersects m and is not perpendicular to m,
then t is not perpendicular to β.

d If P is in m and $t \perp \beta$ at P, then $t \perp m$.

e If P is in m and $t \perp m$ at P, then $t \perp \beta$.

f If line n in β intersects m at P and t is perpendicular
at P to n and m, then t is perpendicular to β.

g If t intersects β at P and is perpendicular
to every line in β that contains P, then $t \perp \beta$.

2 If point A is not in plane α and lines AB and AC are perpendicular to α, which of the following statements are necessarily correct?

  a Points B and C are in α.

  b $d(A, B) = d(A, C)$.

  c $AB = AC$.

  d $\overrightarrow{AB} = \overrightarrow{AC}$.

  e $\overline{AB} \cong \overline{AC}$.

3 If point A is in plane α and lines BA and CA are perpendicular to α, with C in the B-side of α, which of the following statements are correct?

  a Points B and C are not in α.

  b $\overline{BA} \cong \overline{CA}$.

  c $\overrightarrow{AC} = \overrightarrow{AB}$.

  d $AC = AB$.

  e $\langle A, C, B \rangle$ or $\langle A, B, C \rangle$.

◆ 4 Prove Theorem 72/3.

5 Let P denote a point and let α denote a plane. Which of the following statements are valid conclusions from Theorem 71/3? *Answer*

  a One and only one line passes through P and is perpendicular to α.

  b There is one line that contains P and is perpendicular to α.

  c There are not two or more lines passing through P that are perpendicular to α.

  d There is only one line that contains P and is perpendicular to α.

  e There is not more than one line that contains P and is perpendicular to α.

6 If A, B, C, and D are four points of plane β and if $EB \perp \beta$, which of the following angles must be right angles (D238)?

  a $\angle ABE$ **d** $\angle CBE$

  b $\angle EBD$ **e** $\angle ABC$

  c $\angle CBD$ **f** $\angle ABD$

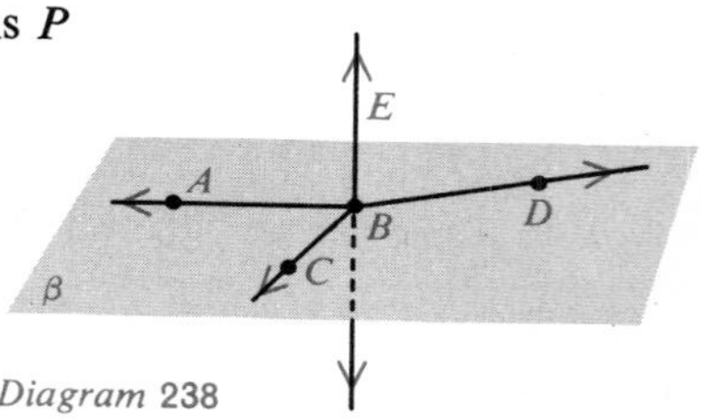

Diagram 238

7 If F is the foot in t of point P and if Q is any point of PF other than F, prove that F is the foot in t of Q. *Answer*

8 The five points A, B, C, D, and E are noncoplanar (D239). If $AB \perp \alpha(D, A, C)$ and $AB \perp \beta(D, A, E)$, which of the following statements are correct?

  a $\angle DAE^\circ = 90$.   **d** $AB \perp \theta(E, A, C)$.

  b $\alpha = \beta$.   **e** $\angle CAB^\circ = 90$.

  c $\langle E, A, C \rangle$.

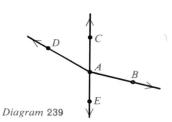

Diagram 239

156

9 Let A and B denote two points of a plane α that are equidistant from a point P not in α.

a If F is the midpoint of $\overline{AB}$, prove that $d(P, F) < d(P, A)$.

b How does the property in exercise 9a imply that P cannot have two feet in α?

c If P has a foot G in α and if line t in α passes through G, why must G be the foot in t of P? How does this imply that PG must be perpendicular to α?

10 Assume that points A and B are in opposite sides of plane β and that every point in β is equidistant from A and B (D240).

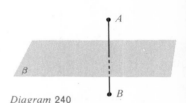

a If C is in β, is $d(C, A) = d(C, B)$?

b If $d(P, A) = d(P, B)$, is P in β? *Answer*

c If $d(A, C) = \frac{1}{2}d(A, B)$, must C be in β?

d If $\overline{AX} \cong \overline{BX}$, must X be in β?

e If $d(A, C) + d(C, B) = d(A, B)$, must C be in β?   *Diagram 240*

11 Assume that M is the midpoint of a segment $\overline{AB}$.

a If $PM \perp \overline{AB}$ and $QM \perp \overline{AB}$, must $Q = P$? Must $PM = QM$? *Answer*

b If $PM \perp \overline{AB}$, is $\overline{PA} \cong \overline{PB}$?

c If $\overline{QA} \cong \overline{QB}$ with $Q \neq M$, is $QM \perp \overline{AB}$?

d If $\overline{PM} \perp \overline{AB}$ and $\overline{QM} \perp \overline{AB}$, is the plane of Q, M, and P perpendicular to $\overline{AB}$ at M?

e What is the locus of all points equidistant from A and B?

12 Two points A and B are each equidistant from two points P and Q, and point C is a third point of line AB.

a Is $\overline{CP} \cong \overline{CQ}$? Why?

b Must $\overline{PB}$ be congruent to $\overline{PA}$?

c Could $\overline{PB}$ be congruent to $\overline{PA}$?

d Must line AB intersect line PQ? *Answer*

e Must line CA bisect $\angle PCQ$?

f Prove that $\triangle CPB \cong \triangle CQB$.

Since it will be convenient to have a simple term to identify the plane equidistant from two points, we add the following convention to our system.

Convention

The midplane of two points means the plane consisting of all points that are equidistant from the two points.

Theorem 76/3

Corresponding to a point P and a line t, there is exactly one plane β that passes through P and is perpendicular to t. If P is not in t, then the point at which β and t are perpendicular is the foot in t of P.

Proof

If P is in t, then, by Theorem 9/2, there exist two points A
and B that are in t and are equidistant from P.
By Theorem 75/3, the midplane β of A and B is perpendicular
to $\overline{AB}$ at the midpoint P.

If P is not in t, then P has a foot F in t (Corollary 70/3),
and there exist two points A and B that are in t and are
equidistant from F (Theorem 9/2). (D241a)

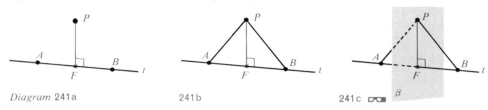

Diagram 241a   241b   241c

The congruence of right triangles, $\triangle PFA \cong \triangle PFB$, implies that
$\overline{PA} \cong \overline{PB}$ (s.a.s. axiom). Hence P, as well as F, is equidistant
from A and B. Therefore, P is in the midplane β of A and B,
and, by Theorem 75/3, plane β is perpendicular to AB at F.
Consequently, β is perpendicular to t at F.

By Theorem 72/3, there is at most one plane through P
that is perpendicular to t, so β is the only plane
through P that is perpendicular to t.

Corollary 76/3

The union of all lines that are perpendicular to a line t
at a point M in t is a plane that is perpendicular to t at M.

We now have the existence of planes that are perpendicular to
a given line. Next we turn to the converse problem. We want to
show that there are lines perpendicular to a given plane. The
proof for the existence of these lines shows how we can make use
of the symmetric property of the perpendicularity relation.

Theorem 77/3

For each point A in a plane α, there exists exactly one line
that is perpendicular to α at A. (D242)

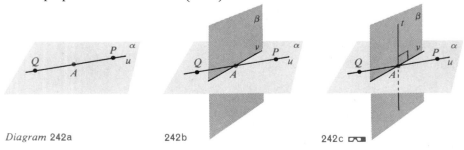

Diagram 242a   242b   242c

Proof

Let *u* denote a line that is in α and that passes through *A*.
In *u*, there are points *P* and *Q* such that *A* is the midpoint
of $\overline{PQ}$. Let β denote the midplane of *P* and *Q*, and let *v*
denote the line of intersection of β and α. In β, there is
a line *t* that is perpendicular to *v* at *A*. Because *u* ⊥ β,
we have *u* ⊥ *t*. Therefore, *t* ⊥ *u*. Since *t* ⊥ *u* and *t* ⊥ *v*,
line *t* is perpendicular to the plane of *u* and *v*, which is
the plane α.

That *t* is the only line perpendicular to α at *A* follows
from Theorem 71/3.

The next theorem will be of importance later, when we deal
with parallels in space.

Theorem 78/3

If two lines are perpendicular to the same plane, there is one
and only one plane that contains both lines. (D243)

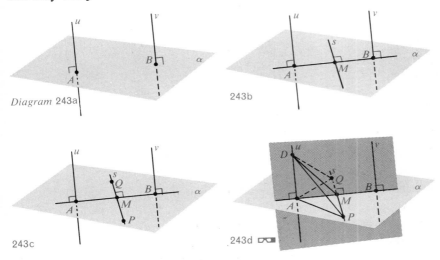

Diagram 243a

243b

243c

243d

Proof

Let *u* and *v* denote two lines that are perpendicular to a
plane α at points *A* and *B* respectively. Then, by Theorem 77/3,
A ≠ *B*. Let *s* denote the line in α that is perpendicular
to $\overline{AB}$ at its midpoint *M*. In *s*, there are points *P* and *Q*
such that *M* is also the midpoint of $\overline{PQ}$. Since, in α, line *AB*
is the perpendicular bisector of $\overline{PQ}$, point *A* is equidistant
from *P* and *Q*. Let *D* denote any point of *u* other than *A*.
Then the congruence of right triangles, △*DAP* ≅ △*DAQ*
(Why?), gives $\overline{DP} \cong \overline{DQ}$. So *D* is equidistant from *P* and *Q*.
Hence, line *AD* = *u* is equidistant from *P* and *Q* (Theorem 73/3).

Therefore, u is in the midplane of P and Q. By the same reasoning, v is in the midplane of P and Q. Therefore, u and v are coplanar.

Since there is only one plane containing A and v, the midplane of P and Q is the only plane containing both u and v.

Now we finally can complete the proof of the statement that, for each point and each plane, there is just one line through the point that is perpendicular to the plane.

Theorem 79/3

If P is not in plane α, there is exactly one line through P that is perpendicular to α. The intersection of this line with α is the unique foot in α of point P.

Proof

Let A denote a point of α, and let s denote the line perpendicular to α at A. If P is in s, then there is a line through P that is perpendicular to α.

If P is not in s, let β denote the plane of P and s. (D244a)

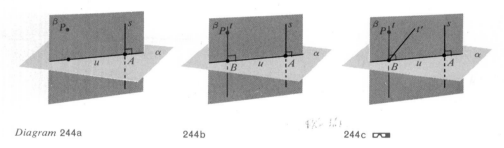

Diagram 244a   244b   244c

Let u denote the line of intersection of α and β. In plane β, there is a line t through P that is perpendicular to u at some point B. Let t' denote the line that is perpendicular to α at B. Then there is just one plane containing t' and s. This is the plane that contains B and line s, and this plane, therefore, is plane β. Hence t' is in β. But in β, there is only one line that is perpendicular to u at B. Therefore, $t' = t$, and t is a line through P that is perpendicular to α.

In all cases then, there is a line through P that is perpendicular to α, and, by Theorem 71/3, there is just one such line.

If F is the intersection of α and the line through P that is perpendicular to α, and if Q is any other point of α, then $\overline{PQ}$ is the hypotenuse of right triangle $\triangle PFQ$. Hence $\overline{PQ}$ is longer than $\overline{PF}$. Therefore, F is the unique foot in α of point P.

Corollary 79/3

If *t* is a line of plane *α* and if *P* is not in *α*, then the plane through *P* and perpendicular to *t* contains the foot in *α* of *P*.

Proof

Let *F* denote the foot in *α* of *P*, and let *G* denote the foot in *t* of *P*. If *G* = *F*, the theorem is trivially correct by Theorem 76/3. If *G* ≠ *F*, let *u* denote the line that is perpendicular to *α* at *G* (Theorem 77/3). (D245a)

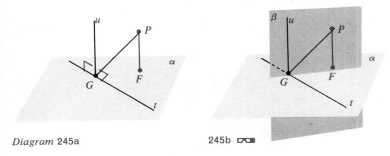

Diagram 245a   245b ▭

Then *u* and *PF* are in a plane *β* (Theorem 78/3) that contains *PG*. From *t* ⊥ *u* and *t* ⊥ *PG*, it follows, by Corollary 75a/3, that *t* ⊥ *β*. Therefore, *F* is in the plane through *P* that is perpendicular to *t*.

Exercises

1 If *F* is the foot in plane *α* of point *P* and if *Q* is any point of line *PF* other than *F*, show that *F* is the foot in *α* of *Q*. *Answer*

◆ **2** *Theorem*

If plane *β* contains a line *t* that is perpendicular to a plane *α* and if *r* is the intersection of *α* and *β*, then every line *s* of *α* that is perpendicular to *r* is also perpendicular to *β*. (D246)

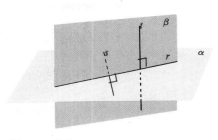

Diagram **246** ▭

3 If *F* is the foot in plane *α* of point *P* and *C(F, r)* is a circle in *α*, prove that all points of the circle are equidistant from *P*. (D247)

4 Let $\overline{AB}$ and $\overline{CD}$ denote two diameters of circle *C(F, r)* in plane *α*. If point *P* is equidistant from *A, B, C,* and *D*, prove either that *P* = *F* or that *F* is the foot in *α* of *P*.

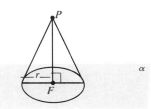

Diagram 247

161

◆ **5** *Theorem*

If line *t* intersects plane α but is not perpendicular
to α, then there is exactly one line in α that is
perpendicular to *t*. (D248)

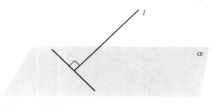

Diagram 248

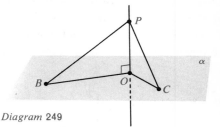

Diagram 249

6 Line *PO* is perpendicular to plane α at *O*, and *B* and *C* are
two other points of α (D249). Prove the
following statements.

a $d(O, B) > d(O, C)$ implies $d(P, B) > d(P, C)$.
b $d(P, B) > d(P, C)$ implies $d(O, B) > d(O, C)$.

7 *Theorem*

There is no line that is perpendicular to each of two
intersecting planes. (Hint: Let α and β denote
two planes that intersect in line *s*. Assume that line *t*
is perpendicular to α at *A* and that *t* is perpendicular
to β at *B*.)

8 Given: The plane α(*A, Q, C*) is the
midplane of the two points *R* and *R'*
with $<R, Q, R'>$. (D250)
Prove:

a $\triangle RAC \cong \triangle R'AC$.
b $\angle RCQ \cong \angle R'CQ$.

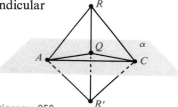

Diagram 250

9 Which of the following statements are true (T) and
which are false (F)?

a If a line is perpendicular to two lines in a plane,
it is perpendicular to the plane. *Answer*
b If three lines are perpendicular to the same line
at the same point, the three lines are coplanar.
c More than one plane can pass through a given point
and yet be perpendicular to a given line.
d Through a point not in a plane, there can be
one and only one line that is perpendicular to the plane.
e There is one and only one line that is perpendicular
to two intersecting planes.
f If two lines are perpendicular and one of them is
perpendicular to a plane, then the other line is
also perpendicular to the plane.

162

10 Assume that line AB is perpendicular to plane β at B.

  a Name the foot in β of A.

  b If $BC \perp \beta$, is C in β? Is $AB = AC$?

  c If $AH \perp \beta$, must H be in β? Must H be in AB? *Answer*

  d If D is contained in β and $D \neq B$, is $d(A, B) < d(A, D)$?

  e If $GH \perp \beta$ and $GH \neq AB$, are GH and AB coplanar?
Must $\sphericalangle ABH$ be congruent to $\sphericalangle GHB$?

11 If point P has foot F in plane α and has foot G in line t
in α, then G is the foot in t of F. Explain how
the preceding statement follows from Corollary 79/3. *Answer*

12 Line s intersects plane α at A and line t intersects α
at B, $A \neq B$. If $s \perp AB$, $t \perp AB$, and s and t are coplanar,
must s and t be perpendicular to α?

13 What is the locus of all the lines that are perpendicular
bisectors of $\overline{AB}$?

14 Point H is the midpoint of the base $\overline{AC}$
of isosceles triangle $\triangle ABC$ in plane α.
Line PH is perpendicular to line AC,
and P is not in α (D251).

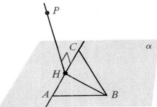

  a Is $\sphericalangle PHB$ necessarily a right angle?

  b Must $d(P, B)$ be greater than $d(P, H)$?

  c Is AC perpendicular to $\beta(P, H, B)$?

Diagram 251

15 Given line PQ, what is the locus of all
points X such that Q is the foot in PQ of point X? *Answer*

16 Lines AB and CD are perpendicular to plane γ at the
two points B and D respectively. If EF is perpendicular
to plane γ at F, and F is in BD, prove that EF is
in the plane determined by AB and CD. *Answer*

◆ 17 Lines AB and CD are perpendicular to plane γ at the two
points B and D respectively. Point E is not in BD,
but is in the plane determined by AB and CD. Prove that
the foot in γ of E is in the line BD.

◆ 18 If A, B, and F are three points in plane α and if F is
the foot in α of P, prove that $\sphericalangle PAF° \leqq \sphericalangle PAB°$.

Chapter review

  1 Which of the following are implied by the fact that
$RST \leftrightarrow LMJ$ is a correspondence of $\triangle RST$ and $\triangle LMJ$?

    a $S \leftrightarrow M$ **d** The correspondence $SRT \leftrightarrow MLJ$ is

    b $\overline{ST} \leftrightarrow \overline{JM}$ the same as the given correspondence.

    c $\sphericalangle R \cong \sphericalangle L.$ **e** $\triangle RST \cong \triangle LMJ.$

  2 Information about five pairs of triangles is given in D252.
For each pair of triangles, decide if the given
information implies, by one of our congruence axioms
or theorems, that the triangles are congruent. Then,

for each pair of congruent triangles, name the axiom
or theorem on which the congruence depends and give
a correspondence of the triangles that is a congruence.

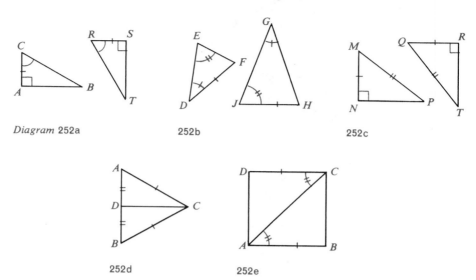

Diagram 252a   252b   252c

252d   252e

3 Point *D* is between points *A* and *C* such that $d(A, C) = a$
and $d(A, D) = b$. Suppose that $BD \perp DC$ and that *E*
between *B* and *D* is such that $d(B, E) = a - b$. Is $\triangle ADE$
congruent to $\triangle BDC$?

4 Triangle $\triangle ABC$ is isosceles and *M* is the midpoint
of the base $\overline{AB}$. If $<A, X, C>$ and $<B, Y, C>$, which
of the following statements must be correct?

a $\angle A \cong \angle B$.   **f** $\angle MXC \cong \angle CYM$.

b $\angle A \cong \angle XMA$.   **g** $\overline{XC} \cong \overline{CY}$.

c $\overline{XM} \cong \overline{YM}$.   **h** $\angle C \cong \angle XMY$.

d $\overline{XY} \cong \overline{AM} \cong \overline{MB}$.   **i** $\triangle ABC \cong \triangle BAC$.

e $\overline{AX} \cong \overline{XC}$.   **j** $\overline{MA} \cong \overline{MB}$.

5 Let *a*, *b*, *c*, *d*, and *e* denote the measures
of the angles of $\triangle ABC$ and $\triangle ACD$ represented in
D253. If $a > b$ and $c > d > e$, which side
of the two triangles is the shortest? Why?

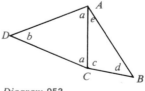

Diagram 253

6 If line *DE* separates plane α into open half-planes α'
and α'', what is the locus of each of the following sets
of points?

a All points *F* in α' such that $d(D, F) = d(E, F)$

b All points *F* in α such that $d(D, F) = d(E, F)$

c All points *F* in space such that $d(D, F) = d(E, F)$

7 Segments $\overline{AB}$ and $\overline{AC}$ of $\triangle ABC$ are respectively congruent
to $\overline{A'B'}$ and $\overline{A'C'}$ of $\triangle A'B'C'$, and $\angle B \cong \angle B'$. Indicate

whether each of the following statements is necessarily true (T), possibly true (P), or necessarily false (F).

a $\triangle ABC \cong \triangle A'B'C'$.

b $AC \perp BC$.

c If $AB \perp BC$, then $\triangle ABC \cong \triangle A'B'C'$.

d If $d(A, C) \geq d(A, B)$, then $\triangle ABC \cong \triangle A'B'C'$.

e If $t = BC$, then $d(A, t) > d(A, C)$.

8 Assume that the three open rays $\overrightarrow{OA}$, $\overrightarrow{OB}$, and $\overrightarrow{OC}$ are noncoplanar.

a Identify the intersection of $\alpha(A, O, C)$ and $\beta(C, O, B)$.

b Describe the intersection of OB and $\alpha(A, O, C)$.

c What is the intersection of $\overrightarrow{OA}$ and $\beta(C, O, B)$?

d Which of the angles $\angle COA$, $\angle AOB$, and $\angle BOC$ must be right angles if $CO \perp \gamma(B, O, A)$?

e If $\alpha(A, O, C)$ is perpendicular to $\beta(C, O, B)$, how many lines in α are perpendicular to β?

9 The coordinates of points A, B, and C in line t are -11, -3, and 8 respectively.

a What is the foot of B in the set $\{A, C\}$?

b Does a foot of C in $\{A, B, C\}$ exist? Explain your answer.

c If the distance from A to $\overrightarrow{BC}$ exists, find this distance.

d If the coordinate of P in t is -7, what are the feet in $\{A, B, C\}$ of P?

10 a If $t \perp \alpha$ at point P and if X is a point of α other than P, must t be perpendicular to PX?

b If line t is perpendicular to two lines in plane α, must t be perpendicular to α?

c If A, B, and C are three points in plane β and each of these points is equidistant from the two points P and Q, must every point of β be equidistant from P and Q?

d If $t \perp \alpha$ and s is in α, must t be perpendicular to s?

e If s is in α but t is not, and if line t is perpendicular to line s, must t be perpendicular to α?

f If lines r, s, and t are perpendicular to line u at the same point, must r, s, and t be coplanar?

g If $t \perp s$ and $t \perp \alpha$, must s be in α?

h If two points A and B are each equidistant from the two points P and Q, must AB be the perpendicular bisector of $\overline{PQ}$?

i If $r \perp \alpha$ and $s \perp \alpha$, must r and s be coplanar?

j If $PF \perp \alpha$ at F, must $d(P, F)$ equal $d(P, \alpha)$?

11 Which of the following statements are true?

a If a foot of point P in a set $\mathbb{S}$ exists, then P is not in the set $\mathbb{S}$.

165

b If point P has F and G as two feet in a set S, then P, F, and G are noncollinear.

c If point P has foot F in a set R and if F belongs to $R \cap S$, then P has F as a foot in $R \cap S$.

d Perpendicularity of lines is a symmetric relation but is neither reflexive nor transitive.

e If $R \oplus S$ is defined to mean that the intersection of set R and set S is nonempty, then, for sets that are triangles, the relation $\oplus$ is reflexive and symmetric but not transitive.

Cumulative review

1 If t, α, $\overline{AB}$, β'', and $\overrightarrow{CD}$ denote respectively a line, a plane, a segment, an open half-plane, and an open ray in space, why is $t \cap \alpha \cap \overline{AB} \cap \beta'' \cap \overrightarrow{CD}$ a convex set?

2 Are two adjacent supplementary right angles with a common arm necessarily coplanar?

3 If line AP bisects $\angle BAC$, must P be in the interior of $\angle BAC$?

4 If AB and CD are perpendicular, must $\overline{AB}$ and $\overline{CD}$ be perpendicular? Explain your answer.

5 Use the polygon $P_1P_2P_3 \ldots P_{34}$ in connection with this exercise.

a Name two angles of the polygon that each contain segment $\overline{P_{20}P_{21}}$.

b The polygon has how many sides? How many vertices?

c Describe an open half-plane that contains the points $P_2, P_3, P_4, \ldots, P_{33}$. Name three angles that are adjacent to $\angle P_7P_{11}P_{12}$.

6 Which of the following statements are correct?

a The length of any chord of a polygon is less than or equal to the length of any diagonal of the polygon.

b Vertices A and E of polygon $ABCDE$ are adjacent vertices.

c If each vertex, side, and angle of an n-gon has $(n - 2)$ neighbors, then $n = 4$.

d There are fourteen exterior angles of the polygon $P_1P_2P_3 \ldots P_7$.

7 The closed ray $\overrightarrow{YA}$ is the ray opposite $\overrightarrow{YZ}$ of $\angle XYZ$, and $\overrightarrow{XB}$ is the ray opposite $\overrightarrow{XA}$. Which of the following statements are necessarily correct?

a Point B is interior to $\angle XYZ$.

b Point A is interior to $\angle BXY$.

c The two angles $\angle XYA$ and $\angle XYZ$ are supplements.

d The angles $\angle BXY$ and $\angle AYX$ are adjacent.

e The open ray $\overrightarrow{YB}$ bisects $\angle XYZ$.

8 For exercise 7, must $\sphericalangle XYZ$ be greater than $\sphericalangle XAY$? Explain your answer.

9 Point M is the midpoint of $\overline{PQ}$. The two points A and B are equidistant from P and Q, and neither A nor B is in PQ.

  a Must $\triangle APQ$ be congruent to $\triangle BPQ$?

  b Must $\triangle PAB$ be congruent to $\triangle QAB$?

  c If plane β contains AB, must β be perpendicular to PQ?

  d Must $\triangle BPQ$ be isosceles?

  e Must $\overline{MB}$ be shorter than $\overline{BQ}$?

10 Which of the following statements are necessarily true if β is the midplane of points A and B?

  a $d(A, \beta) = d(B, \beta)$.

  b $AB \perp \beta$.

  c If M is in β, then $\overline{AM} \cong \overline{MB}$.

  d If $\overline{AQ} \cong \overline{BQ}$, then Q is in β.

  e If HJ is in β, then $\overline{AH} \cong \overline{AJ}$.

  f If $AC \perp \beta$ and $BD \perp \beta$, then $C = D$.

  g If $RS \perp AB$, then RS is in β.

11 If side $\overline{AC}$ of $\triangle ABC$ is greater than $\overline{AB}$, and the midrays of $\sphericalangle B$ and $\sphericalangle C$ intersect at D, which one of the following statements is necessarily false?

  a If $\triangle ABC$ is a right triangle and $\sphericalangle A° \neq 90$, then $\sphericalangle B° = 90$.

  b If $d(B, C) = 3$, then $d(A, C) > 3$.

  c $d(D, C) > d(D, B)$.

  d If $\sphericalangle A° < \sphericalangle B°$, then $\sphericalangle A° < \sphericalangle C°$.

  e $d(B, C) \geqq 2\,d(A, C)$.

12 Which of the following statements have been established in the formal system?

  a The measure of an exterior angle of a triangle is the sum of the measures of the two nonadjacent angles of the triangle.

  b The measure of an exterior angle of a triangle is greater than the measure of either of the two nonadjacent angles of the triangle.

  c The sum of the measures of the angles of a triangle is 180.

  d In a rectangle, each angle is a right angle.

  e If $\overrightarrow{AB}$ and $\overrightarrow{AC}$ are opposite closed rays and $\overrightarrow{AP}$ is a third closed ray, then $\sphericalangle PAB° + \sphericalangle PAC° = 180$.

Parallel lines 14/4

There are four basic geometric ideas that we have not yet put into our formal system. These are the notions of *parallelism* of lines and of planes; *similarity* of figures (figures of the same shape, but not necessarily the same size); the idea of *area* for plane figures; and, finally, the notion of *volume* for solid figures. The first two of these notions, parallelism and similarity, are very closely related. We will study parallelism in this chapter, and we will consider similarity in Chapter 5.

We begin by defining parallel lines.

Definition 53/4 *Parallel lines*

Two lines are parallel if they are coplanar and do not intersect. A segment or a ray in one line is parallel to a ray or a segment in another line if the two lines are parallel.

Convention

That lines r and s are parallel to each other will be indicated by the notation $r \parallel s$. That $\overrightarrow{AB}$ and $\overrightarrow{CD}$ are parallel to each other will be indicated by the notation $\overrightarrow{AB} \parallel \overrightarrow{CD}$.
This notation also indicates that line AB is parallel to line CD.

Comment

$r \parallel s \Longleftrightarrow s \parallel r$. (Symmetric property of parallel lines)

Parallel lines are required to be coplanar because, in space, two lines can fail to intersect and yet be nothing like our intuitive notion of parallel lines. Two such lines, for example, r and s (D254), are called *skew* lines.

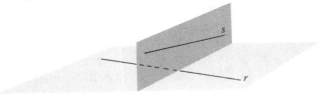

Diagram 254

Definition 54/4 *Skew lines*
Two noncoplanar lines are *skew* lines.

The basic part played by parallelism in the structure of a formal geometry can be indicated in the following way. In choosing axioms for the formal system and in seeking to establish different properties, we have been guided by our feelings about the geometric properties of physical space. It might seem, at this point, that we have imposed enough conditions to force our mathematical space to have all the obvious properties we associate with physical space. But such is not the case.

As we mentioned in the first chapter, the mathematician Lobachevsky discovered that one can define a geometry (call it an L-geometry) that has all of the axioms and properties of our system so far, but one that also has properties quite unlike those we think of as natural. For example, the following statement is a theorem in an L-geometry.

"If r and s are parallel lines in a plane α, then there exists a line t in α that is perpendicular to r and is parallel to s."

Suppose that you say, "Draw a picture to illustrate this statement." One reply might be, "For a convincing picture, the point at which t is perpendicular to r has to be at least a million miles from s, and so large a picture cannot be drawn." You might then say, "Well, draw it to scale, letting an inch, for example, represent 500,000 miles." But the answer to this is, "In an L-geometry, there are no similar figures, that is, there are no figures with the same shape but with different size. So, in a small scale drawing, the lines would not have all of the properties of the original lines."

The fairly obvious fact is that, if drawings could show, in a convincing way, the odd properties of an L-geometry, then such a geometry undoubtedly would have been found nearly as soon as Euclid's geometry. So, without going into a long discussion, we can say only that an L-geometry is a *logical* possibility.

So far, our geometry is both a Euclidean geometry and an L-geometry. That is, so far, we have built the same kind of a geometric space and have proved the same kind of beginning theorems as both Euclid and Lobachevsky proved. Now we are at the point where we must consider the following problem. Suppose that t is a line in a plane α and that point P in α is not in t (D255). Then how many lines in α pass through P and do not intersect t?

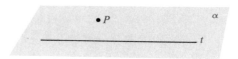

Diagram 255

Euclid made one decision concerning this problem, and, two thousand years later, Lobachevsky made a different decision. First Euclid easily showed that there had to be at least one such line. His proof was based on the exterior angle property of triangles, and the reasoning was as follows.

Theorem 80/4

If the open rays $\overrightarrow{PA}$ and $\overrightarrow{QB}$ at the endpoints of segment $\overline{PQ}$ are coplanar and are in opposite sides of line PQ and if $\angle APQ \cong \angle BQP$, then lines PA and QB are parallel. (D256)

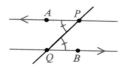

Diagram 256a   256b

Proof

Assume that lines PA and QB are not parallel. Since PA and QB are coplanar and are not parallel, they intersect at point W, which cannot be P or Q. Hence W is not in line PQ. Then W is either in the A-side of PQ or in the B-side of PQ. If W is in the A-side, then $\angle BQP$ is an exterior angle of $\triangle QPW$ at Q. So $\angle BQP° > \angle APQ°$, which is a contradiction of the given conditions. If W is in the B-side of PQ, then $\angle APQ$ is an exterior angle of $\triangle PQW$ at P. So $\angle APQ° > \angle BQP°$, which also is a contradiction.

170

Since all possibilities lead to a contradiction, the assumption that lines *PA* and *QB* are not parallel is false.

Therefore, lines *PA* and *QB* are parallel.

Corollary 80a/4

If *P* is not in line *t*, then there exists a line through *P* that is parallel to *t*.* (D257)

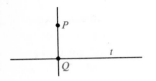

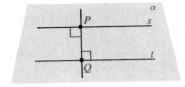

Diagram 257a   257b

Proof

Let *Q* denote the foot of *P* in line *t*. In the plane α of *P* and *t*, let *s* denote the line that is perpendicular to line *PQ* at *P*. Since all four angles at *P* and all four angles at *Q* are right angles, it follows, from Theorem 80/4, that *s* is parallel to *t*.

Corollary 80b/4

Two lines in a plane that are both perpendicular to a third line in the plane are parallel to each other.

___

Now we can restate, in a different form, the problem that we considered earlier. If *P* is not in line *t*, is there more than one line through *P* that is parallel to *t*? Euclid said "No." Because he could not prove his answer, he made it an axiom. In other words, in Euclidean geometry, by assumption, there is exactly one line through *P* that is parallel to *t*. Others agreed with Euclid, but they thought his parallel axiom could be proved and so was a theorem rather than an axiom. The matter was settled centuries later by Lobachevsky. He took, as an axiom, the statement that there always are two lines through *P* parallel to *t*. Using this axiom, he constructed the first non-Euclidean geometry. Lobachevsky, therefore, showed that Euclid was correct in making his answer an axiom but that Euclid was wrong if he believed this was the only axiom that would work.

It would be interesting to see what would happen from here on if we were to adopt Lobachevsky's axiom. But this would take us too far afield and would not get us to the more interesting parts

___

* Geometries do exist that have some of the properties of ours but are such that each two (straight) lines in a (flat) plane intersect each other. However, these geometries, which were first noted by the mathematician Riemann, cannot satisfy all of the axioms that we now have in our system. This is evident from Corollary 80a/4.

of Euclidean geometry. We, therefore, will make our space a
Euclidean one by adding the following assumption.

Axiom 14/4 *Parallel axiom*

Corresponding to a line *t* and a point *P* not in *t*, there is
exactly one line through *P* that is parallel to *t*.

Axiom 14/4 immediately forces, in our space, the existence of
a great many different relations, and we have a choice in the order
of proving these relations. First we will establish the basic properties of the "sameness in direction" of parallel lines. Then we
will work with the "betweenness" and the "equidistance" notions
of parallels. Many of the theorems in this section will just be
statements of foundation properties about parallel lines. But in
following sections, we will apply these properties to circles, triangles, and quadrilaterals. We will leave most of the proofs of
these later theorems to you.

For reference, we first state some obvious but necessary facts.

---

* Theorem 81/4

Two parallel lines belong to exactly one plane.

* Corollary 81/4

Each of the following pairs of sets belong to exactly one plane:
two parallel segments, two parallel rays, and a ray and
a segment that are parallel.

The next relations are simple consequences of the parallel
axiom that will be useful in our system.

---

* Theorem 82/4

In the plane of two intersecting lines, a line
that is parallel to one of the intersecting lines
is not parallel to the other. (D258)

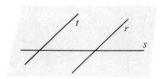

Diagram 258

* Corollary 82/4

In the plane of two parallel lines, a third line
that intersects one of the parallel lines also intersects the other.

Because a line is not parallel to itself, parallelism of lines does
not have the identity property. Parallelism of lines, however,
does have a weak form of transitivity. That is, for three different
lines *r*, *s*, and *t*, if *r* ∥ *s* and *s* ∥ *t*, then *r* ∥ *t*. We will call this
property the *weak transitivity* of parallels.*

---

* The relation of lines, such that lines with the relation are either parallel or identical, is transitive. It also is an equivalence relation.

172

Theorem 83/4

Two lines perpendicular to the same plane are parallel. (D259)

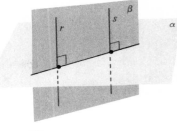

Proof

If two lines r and s are both perpendicular to a plane α, they are coplanar in a plane β (Theorem 78/3). Both r and s are perpendicular to the intersection line of α and β. Therefore, by Corollary 80b/4, lines r and s are parallel.

Diagram 259

Theorem 84/4

A plane that is perpendicular to one of two parallel lines is perpendicular to both of these parallel lines. (D260)

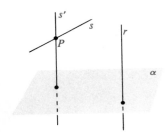

Diagram 260

Proof

Let r and s denote two parallel lines, and let α denote a plane perpendicular to r. Let P denote a point in s, and let s' denote the line through P that is perpendicular to α. Since s' and r are perpendicular to α, these lines are parallel to each other. Then both s' and s are lines through P that are parallel to r. But by Axiom 14/4, there is only one line through P that is parallel to r. Consequently, $s' = s$. Therefore, s is perpendicular to α.

Theorem 85/4 *Weak transitivity of parallels*

Two lines that are each parallel to a third line are parallel to each other. (D261)

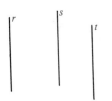

Diagram 261a   261b

Proof

Let *r* and *s* denote two lines such that each is parallel
to a third line *t*. There exists a plane α that
is perpendicular to *t*. Therefore, by Theorem 84/4, plane α
also is perpendicular to *r* and *s*. Since *r* and *s* are
both perpendicular to α, they are parallel to each other
(Theorem 83/4).

Exercises

1 Explain why two skew lines are neither parallel
nor intersecting.

2 Which of the following statements are correct
without exception?

a If two lines do not intersect, they are parallel.

b If line *r* is parallel to line *s*, then *r* and *s* are coplanar.

c If *r* and *s* are not parallel, then they are not coplanar.

d Parallelism of lines is a relationship having
the reflexive property. *Answer*

e If $\overline{AB} \parallel \overrightarrow{CD}$, then $\overrightarrow{BA} \parallel \overline{CD}$.

f In space, coplanar lines that do not intersect are
called skew lines.

g If *r* ∥ *s* and *s* ∥ *t*, then *r* ≠ *t*. *Answer*

♦ 3 Use Theorem 85/4 as an axiom to prove Axiom 14/4
as a theorem. (Hint: Make use of Corollary 80a/4,
whose proof did not depend on Axiom 14/4.)

♦ 4 Use Corollary 82/4 as an axiom to prove Axiom 14/4
as a theorem. (Hint: Use Corollary 80a/4.)

5 Prove Corollary 80b/4.

6 Which of the following statements are necessarily correct? *Answer*

a If *r* ⊥ *s*, *t* ⊥ *s*, and *r* ≠ *t*, then *r* ∥ *t*.

b If *r* ∥ *t* and *r* ⊥ *s*, then *t* ⊥ *s*.

c If the two lines *r* and *s* are in plane α,
and if *r* ⊥ *t* and *s* ⊥ *t*, then *r* ∥ *s*.

d If *r* ∥ *s* and *r* is in plane α, then *s* is in α.

e If *r* is contained in β and if *r* ∥ *s* and *s* intersects β,
then *s* is contained in β.

f If $\overrightarrow{AB}$ and $\overrightarrow{CD}$ are nonintersecting, coplanar rays,
then *AB* ∥ *CD*.

7 Assume that two intersecting lines *m* and *t*
determine a plane β (D262).

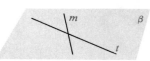

Diagram 262

a If *r* is in β, must *r* intersect either *m* or *t*?

b If *s* ∥ *t*, must *s* intersect *m*? *Answer*

c If *s* is in β and *s* ∥ *m*, must *s* intersect *t*?

d If *h* is not parallel to *t*, must *h* intersect *t*?

e If line *k* intersects both *t* and *m*, must *k* be in β?

8 Assume that two points A and B are in a plane α
and lines AC and BD are perpendicular to α (D263).

a Do AC and BD have a point in common? Why?

b Are AC and BD in α? Are they coplanar?

c Which line in α is perpendicular to both AC
and BD?

d Does $d(A, C) = d(B, D)$? Is $\overleftrightarrow{AC} \parallel \overrightarrow{BD}$? *Answer*

e Is $CD \perp BD$? Is $AB \perp BD$?

f If $EF \parallel AC$, must EF intersect α? Must EF
intersect either BD or AB?

g If GH is in the plane of AC and BD, must $GH \perp \alpha$?
Must GH intersect AB?

Diagram 263

9 Is skewness of pairs of lines a transitive relation?
Explain.

10 Show that the following corollary of Theorem 84/4 follows
from the symmetric property of perpendicularity:
If a line r is perpendicular to a plane α, then
any line s parallel to r is also perpendicular to α.

♦ 11 Line PA intersects plane α at A (D264).
If the foot F in α of P is not A,
show that each of the following statements
is true.

a Point G, the foot in AP of F, is between A
and P.

b Point H, the foot in α of G, is between A
and F.

c Lines HG and PF are parallel.

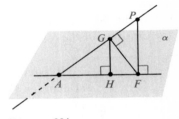

Diagram 264

We next want to introduce the "same direction" notion for
parallel lines. Since there actually are two directions in a line,
the natural things to talk about are parallel rays. In both pictures
of D265, the rays $\mathcal{R}$ and $\mathcal{S}$ are parallel, since the lines of the rays

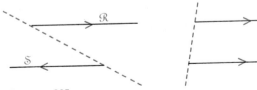

Diagram 265

are parallel. But it is clear that, in the first case, we think of the
rays as having opposite directions; while in the second case, we
think of them as having the same direction. The dotted lines that
join the origins of the rays suggest how to make this difference
perfectly definite.

Definition 55/4 *Like-directed and oppositely directed noncollinear rays*
Two noncollinear rays $\mathcal{R}$ and $\mathcal{S}$ have the same direction or are like-directed rays if they are parallel and if, in their plane, the open rays of $\mathcal{R}$ and $\mathcal{S}$ are in the same side of the line through the origins of the rays.
The noncollinear rays have opposite direction or are oppositely directed if they are parallel and if, in their plane, the open rays of $\mathcal{R}$ and $\mathcal{S}$ are in opposite sides of the line through their origins. (D266)

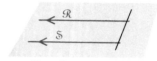

like-directed rays   oppositely directed rays

Diagram 266

Convention
If two rays are like directed, we will say that each ray has the direction of the other.

By our previous definition of like-directed collinear rays (Definition 11/2), a ray has the same direction as itself. "Sameness of direction" for rays, therefore, has the identity property. Also, sameness of direction is clearly a symmetric relation, and, as one would expect, it is a transitive relation. We will not develop proofs of these properties, but we will simply take the following theorems as foundation properties.

*** Theorem 86/4**
If $\mathcal{R}$ denotes a ray and P a point, then there is exactly one closed ray with origin P that has the same direction as $\mathcal{R}$ and there is exactly one closed ray with origin P that has the opposite direction to $\mathcal{R}$. These two closed rays are opposite rays.

*** Theorem 87/4**
If $\mathcal{R}$, $\mathcal{S}$, and $\mathcal{T}$ denote rays and if $\mathcal{R}$ and $\mathcal{S}$ are like directed and $\mathcal{S}$ and $\mathcal{T}$ are like directed, then $\mathcal{R}$ and $\mathcal{T}$ are like directed.

*** Corollary 87/4**
If $\mathcal{R}$, $\mathcal{S}$, and $\mathcal{T}$ denote rays and if $\mathcal{R}$ and $\mathcal{S}$ are like directed and $\mathcal{S}$ and $\mathcal{T}$ are oppositely directed, then $\mathcal{R}$ and $\mathcal{T}$ are oppositely directed.

Exercises

1 Which of the following statements imply that
the open rays $\overrightarrow{AB}$ and $\overrightarrow{CD}$ are parallel?

  a $\overline{AB} \parallel \overline{CD}$.

  b $AB \parallel CD$.

  c $A = C$.

  d $\overrightarrow{AB}$ and $\overrightarrow{CD}$ are collinear, but they do not intersect.

  e $\overrightarrow{AB}$ and $\overrightarrow{CD}$ are perpendicular to $\overline{BD}$. *Answer*

2 Which of the following statements are correct if $\mathcal{R}$ and $\mathcal{S}$
are collinear rays? *Answer*

  a $\mathcal{R}$ and $\mathcal{S}$ have either the same direction or
opposite directions.

  b If $\mathcal{R}$ contains $\mathcal{S}$, then $\mathcal{R}$ and $\mathcal{S}$ have opposite directions.

  c If $\mathcal{R}$ does not contain $\mathcal{S}$, then $\mathcal{R}$ and $\mathcal{S}$ have
opposite directions.

  d If $\mathcal{R}$ and $\mathcal{S}$ are like directed, then either $\mathcal{R}$ contains $\mathcal{S}$
or $\mathcal{S}$ contains $\mathcal{R}$.

  e The ray $\mathcal{R}$ has the same direction as the ray $\mathcal{R}$.

3 In which of the following cases must the noncollinear,
parallel, open rays $\overrightarrow{AB}$ and $\overrightarrow{CD}$ be like directed?

  a Point B is in the D-side of line AC. *Answer*

  b Point C is in the B-side of AD.

  c Points B and D are in opposite sides of AC.

  d $AC \parallel BD$.

  e Points B and C are in opposite sides of AD.

  f The open ray $\overrightarrow{BA}$ has the direction of the open ray $\overrightarrow{DC}$.

4 If point P is not in the line AB, then, by Axiom 14/4,
there exists only one line, say CD, that contains P
and is parallel to AB. For each of the following questions,
assume that P is between C and D.

  a How many closed rays with origin P have the direction
of $\overrightarrow{AB}$?

  b How many open rays with origin P have the direction
of $\overrightarrow{BA}$?

  c How many rays with origin P have the direction
of $\overrightarrow{AB}$? *Answer*

  d How many closed rays have the direction of $\overrightarrow{BA}$?

  e If $\overrightarrow{PD}$ and $\overrightarrow{AB}$ are like directed, name three closed rays
that are like directed to $\overrightarrow{PD}$.

  f If $\overrightarrow{PD}$ and $\overrightarrow{BA}$ are like directed, are $\overrightarrow{CP}$ and $\overrightarrow{AB}$
like directed?

  g Can $\overrightarrow{AC}$ and $\overrightarrow{DB}$ be like directed? Why?

  h If $\overrightarrow{PD}$ and $\overrightarrow{BA}$ are like directed, why are $\overrightarrow{PC}$ and $\overrightarrow{BA}$
oppositely directed?

  i If $\overrightarrow{CP}$ and $\overrightarrow{AB}$ are like directed, why are $\overrightarrow{CD}$ and $\overrightarrow{AB}$ like directed?

It is useful to have a special term for a line that intersects a set of lines.

Definition 56/4 *Transversal*

A line that intersects every line of a set of lines but is itself not in the set is a transversal of the set of lines.

If a transversal of two coplanar lines intersects these two lines at different points, then the parallelism or the nonparallelism of the two lines depends upon the nature of the angles that are formed by the two lines and the transversal. To simplify the reference to different angles, the following definitions commonly are used.

Definition 57/4 *Alternate interior angles*

If a transversal t of two coplanar lines r and s intersects r at P and intersects s at a different point Q, then there are four angles at P formed by r and t and four angles at Q formed by s and t. Each of these angles has one arm (called the transversal arm) contained in transversal t and another arm contained in a closed half-plane of t.

    An angle at P and an angle at Q are a pair of alternate interior angles if they have the following properties. Their transversal arms are oppositely directed and intersecting rays. Their other arms are in opposite closed half-planes of t. (D267)

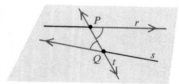 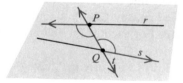

Diagram 267

Definition 58/4 *Corresponding angles*

An angle at P and an angle at Q are corresponding angles if their transversal arms are like directed and if their other arms are contained in the same closed half-plane of t. Each of the two angles corresponds to the other. (D268)

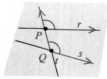 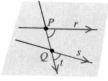 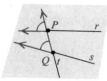 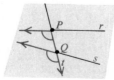

Diagram 268

We can now restate Theorem 80/4 as part of a more general theorem.

Theorem 88/4

If a transversal t of two coplanar lines r and s intersects them at different points, then r is parallel to s if and only if each two alternate interior angles are congruent.

Proof

Let α denote the plane of the lines. Let P denote the intersection of t with r, and let Q denote the intersection of t with s. In r, there are two opposite open rays $\overrightarrow{PA}$ and $\overrightarrow{PD}$. In s, there are two opposite open rays $\overrightarrow{QB}$ and $\overrightarrow{QC}$. Assume that the notation has been chosen so that $\overrightarrow{PA}$ and $\overrightarrow{QC}$ are in the same side of t.

Part I A pair of alternate interior angles are congruent, say $\angle QPA \cong \angle PQB$. Then, by Theorem 80/4, r is parallel to s.

Part II The lines r and s are parallel. (D269)
Since $\angle PQB$ exists, its measure, $\angle PQB°$, is a number between 0 and 180. By Axiom 10/2, therefore, there exists an open ray $\overrightarrow{PA'}$ in α and in the C-side of t such that $\angle QPA'° = \angle PQB°$. Then, by Theorem 80/4, line PA' is parallel to s. It is given that line PA is parallel to s; but, by Axiom 14/4, there is only one line through P that is parallel to s. Therefore, $PA' = PA$. And since $\overrightarrow{PA'}$ and $\overrightarrow{PA}$ are in the same side of t, it follows that $\overrightarrow{PA'} = \overrightarrow{PA}$. So $\angle QPA' \cong \angle PQB$ also is the congruence $\angle QPA \cong \angle PQB$, which is the congruence of two alternate interior angles.

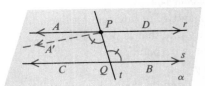

Diagram 269

The other pair of alternate interior angles, $\angle PQC$ and $\angle QPD$, also are congruent. This follows from a similar argument or from the fact that these angles are supplements of the first pair of congruent alternate interior angles.

Corollary 88a/4

The lines r and s are parallel if and only if each two corresponding angles are congruent.

Proof

By the definition of corresponding angles, one and only one of them contains the transversal arm of the other. And this one of the pair has for its alternate interior angle the angle that is opposite the corresponding angle.

179

Since opposite angles are congruent, it follows that
two corresponding angles are congruent if and only if
two alternate interior angles are congruent. Therefore,
two corresponding angles are congruent if and only if
r and *s* are parallel.

Corollary 88b/4

A line that is in the plane of two parallel lines and is perpendicular
to one of them is perpendicular to the other. (D270)

Proof

If *t* is in the plane of two parallel lines *r* and *s*
and if *t* is perpendicular to *r*, then *t*
intersects *r* and so intersects *s* (Corollary 82/4).
The angles formed by *t* and *s* are right angles,
since they are congruent to the corresponding
angles formed by *t* and *r*. Therefore, $t \perp s$.

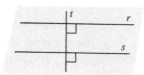

Diagram 270

> The following fact is also useful to have for reference in our
> system.

Theorem 89/4

If *r* and *s* are intersecting lines, then, in their plane,
every line that is perpendicular to *r* intersects every line
that is perpendicular to *s*. (D271)

Proof

Let α denote the plane of *r* and *s*, and let *r'*
and *s'* denote lines in α that are perpendicular
to *r* and *s* respectively. If *r'* and *s'* did not
intersect, they would be parallel. Then *r*,
being perpendicular to *r'*, would also be
perpendicular to *s'* (Corollary 88b/4). Then *r*
and *s*, being two lines that are perpendicular
to *s'*, would be parallel (Corollary 80b/4).
This contradicts the given fact that *r* and *s*
intersect. Therefore, *r'* and *s'* must intersect.

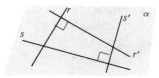

Diagram 271

Exercises

1 Lines *a* and *d* intersect between the parallel lines
b and *c*, and neither *a* nor *d* is parallel to *b*
(D272). If the four lines are coplanar,
which of the following statements are true?

  a Line *a* is a transversal of lines *b* and *c*.
  b Line *a* is a transversal of lines *b*, *c*, and *d*.
  c Line *b* is a transversal of lines *a*, *c*, and *d*.
  d Line *d* is a transversal of line *a*.
  e Line *c* is a transversal of lines *a* and *d*.

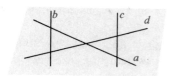

Diagram 272

2 Assume that line AB intersects the coplanar lines CD and EF at A and B respectively and that points A through H are located as shown in D273.

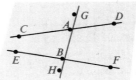

Diagram 273

  a Which angle corresponds to ⊀HBF? *Answer*
  b Which angle is the alternate interior angle to ⊀DAB?
  c Name the transversal arm of ⊀FBA.
  d Which of the corresponding angles ⊀CAB and ⊀HBE contains the transversal arm of the other?
  e Explain why the pair of angles ⊀DAG and ⊀HBF are neither alternate interior angles nor corresponding angles.

3 In the situation considered in exercise 2, a pair of angles such as ⊀CAG and ⊀HBF are sometimes called *alternate exterior angles*.
  a Give a definition for such a pair of angles.
  b Would the congruence of the alternate exterior angles ⊀CAG and ⊀HBF imply $CD \parallel EF$? Why?

4 Assume that lines AB and CD are parallel, that lines AC and BD are parallel, and that the sixteen angles formed by their intersections are numbered as shown in D274.
  a A pair of alternate interior angles are ⊀4 and ⌇⌇⌇. *Answer*
  b A pair of corresponding angles are ⊀11 and ⌇⌇⌇, or ⊀11 and ⌇⌇⌇.
  c Are ⊀3 and ⊀6 alternate interior angles? *Answer* Are they corresponding angles?
  d Are ⊀7 and ⊀9 alternate interior angles? Are they corresponding angles?
  e Are ⊀5 and ⊀9 alternate interior angles? Are they corresponding angles?

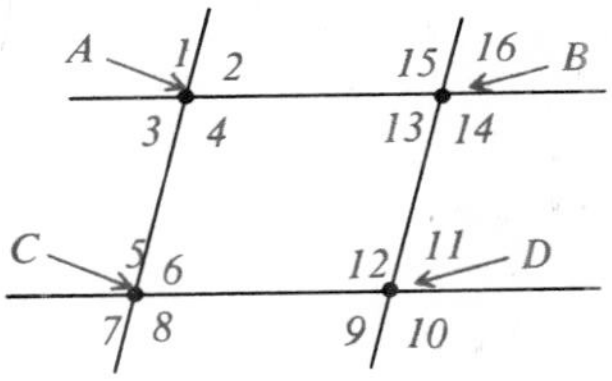

Diagram 274

5 Use the conditions of exercise 4 and D274 to decide which of the following statements are correct. Then explain why they are correct.
  a ⊀$3 \cong$ ⊀6.
  b ⊀$8 \cong$ ⊀10.
  c ⊀$6 \cong$ ⊀12.
  d ⊀$4 \cong$ ⊀15.
  e ⊀$11 \cong$ ⊀9.
  f ⊀$9 \cong$ ⊀15.
  g ⊀$1 \cong$ ⊀8.
  h ⊀$5 \cong$ ⊀12.
  i ⊀$10 \cong$ ⊀5.
  j ⊀$12 \cong$ ⊀8.

6 The steps of a proof that ⊀10 and ⊀1, represented in D274, are congruent are given below. Give the reason for each step of the proof.
  1 ⊀$10 \cong$ ⊀14.
  2 ⊀$14 \cong$ ⊀15.
  3 ⊀$15 \cong$ ⊀1.
  4 ∴ ⊀$10 \cong$ ⊀1.

181

7 Which of the following statements are necessarily correct if line *r* is in the plane of the parallel lines *a* and *b*?

a If $r \perp a$, then $r \perp b$.

b If *r* is not perpendicular to *a*, then *r* is not perpendicular to *b*.

c If $r \parallel a$, then $r \parallel b$. *Answer*

d If $r \parallel a$ and $r \parallel b$, then $r \neq a$ and $r \neq b$.

e If *r* does not intersect either *a* or *b*, then $r \parallel a$ and $r \parallel b$.

8 Lines *AB* and *CD* are parallel, and $\overline{AD}$ and $\overline{BC}$ intersect at point *M* (D275). Prove that, if *M* is the midpoint of $\overline{AD}$, it is also the midpoint of $\overline{BC}$. *Answer*

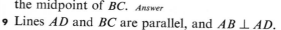

Diagram 275

9 Lines *AD* and *BC* are parallel, and $AB \perp AD$.

a If $\overline{AC} \cong \overline{BD}$, prove that $\overline{AD} \cong \overline{CB}$.

b Is *DC* necessarily parallel to *AB*? If so, prove it.

◆ 10 a If $\mathcal{S}$ is the set of all lines in plane α that pass through point *P* in α, prove that no line of α is a transversal of $\mathcal{S}$.

b If $\mathcal{S}$ is the set of all lines through *P*, prove that there is no transversal of set $\mathcal{S}$.

11 If a line is in the plane of two intersecting lines and is perpendicular to one of these lines, prove that it is not perpendicular to the other.

12 Assume that line *EF* is coplanar with the pair of perpendicular lines *CA* and *AB*.

a If $EF \perp BC$, must *EF* intersect *AC*? Why? *Answer*

b If $EF \perp AB$, must *EF* intersect *AC*? Why?

c If *EF* contains *A* and is perpendicular to *BC* at *G*, is *G* between *B* and *C*?

d If $EF \perp AC$, must *EF* intersect *BC*? Why?

e Name the foot in *AB* of *C*. What is the distance from *C* to *AB*? Name the longest side of $\triangle ABC$. *Answer*

13 Line *r* is parallel to side $\overrightarrow{AB}$ of $\triangle ABC$ and intersects the open rays $\overrightarrow{CA}$ and $\overrightarrow{CB}$ at *D* and *E* respectively (D276). Prove that $CAB \leftrightarrow CDE$ is a correspondence of triangles in which corresponding angles are congruent.

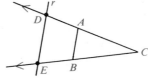

Diagram 276

14 *Theorem*

If two coplanar angles are such that the arms of one are respectively like directed to the arms of the other, then the angles are congruent.

a Illustrate the theorem by diagrams for the following three possible cases: (1) One of the two vertices is in the other angle. (2) One of the vertices is

182

in the interior of the other angle. (3) Neither vertex
is in the other angle nor in its interior.

b Prove case 1, as stated in exercise 14a.

◆ **15** *Theorem*

If two coplanar angles are such that the arms of one are
respectively oppositely directed to the arms of the other,
then the angles are congruent.

Prove this theorem using Corollary 87/4 and the theorem
of exercise 14. What case has to be considered
other than the three that were considered in exercise 14?

◆ **16** *Theorem*

If two coplanar angles are such that each angle has an arm
that is like directed to an arm of the other and an arm
oppositely directed to an arm of the other, then
the angles are supplements.

Prove this theorem using Theorem 28/2, Corollary 87/4,
and the theorem of exercise 15.

Now that we have the congruence of alternate interior angles
from Theorem 88/4, we can establish one of the most basic facts
of Euclidean geometry. This is the fact that the angles of a triangle
have measures whose sum is 180. We can also obtain the complete exterior angle property that we noticed in the last chapter.
In establishing these properties, we will use a simple fact that we
now state as a theorem.

---

* Theorem 90/4

In the plane of two parallel lines, all points
of one line are in the same side of the
other line. (D277)

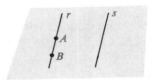

Diagram 277

Convention

Because of Theorem 90/4, if *r* and *s* are
two parallel lines, we can speak of the *r*-side
of *s* as the side of *s* that contains *r*.

Theorem 91/4 *Angle-sum theorem*

The sum of the measures of the angles
of a triangle is 180. (D278)

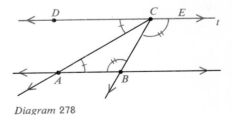

Diagram 278

Proof

Through the vertex *C* of △*ABC*, there
exists a line *t* that is parallel to line *AB*
(parallel axiom, Axiom 14/4).* In *t*,

---

* A proof must depend upon the parallel axiom because in an L-geometry the sum of the
measures of the angles in a triangle is always less than 180.

there is a closed ray $\overset{\rightarrow\cdot}{CD}$ with the direction of $\overset{\rightarrow\cdot}{BA}$ and an opposite closed ray $\overset{\rightarrow\cdot}{CE}$ with the direction of $\overset{\rightarrow\cdot}{AB}$. Because $AB \parallel CD$, both A and B are in the same side of line CD. Thus A is in the B-side of CD. And because $\overset{\rightarrow\cdot}{CD}$ and $\overset{\rightarrow\cdot}{BA}$ are like directed, A is in the D-side of BC. Therefore, A is in the interior of $\angle DCB$, and $\overset{\rightarrow\cdot}{CA}$ is between $\overset{\rightarrow\cdot}{CD}$ and $\overset{\rightarrow\cdot}{CB}$. Then, by the extension of the angle supplement theorem, Theorem 28/2,

1 $\angle DCA° + \angle ACB° + \angle BCE° = 180.$

Each of the lines AC and BC is a transversal of the parallel lines t and BA. Therefore, as congruent alternate interior angles at C and A,

2 $\angle DCA° = \angle BAC°.$

Also, as congruent alternate interior angles at C and B,

3 $\angle BCE° = \angle ABC°.$

Substituting statements 2 and 3 in statement 1 gives

4 $\angle BAC° + \angle ACB° + \angle ABC° = 180$

or

5 $\angle A° + \angle C° + \angle B° = 180.$

Corollary 91a/4

In an equiangular triangle, the measure of each angle is 60.

Corollary 91b/4

The measure of an exterior angle of a triangle is the sum of the measures of the two nonadjacent angles of the triangle. (D279)

Diagram 279

Proof

Let $\angle DAC$ denote an exterior angle of $\triangle ABC$ at A. Since this angle is a supplement of $\angle A$ in the triangle,

1 $\angle DAC° = 180 - \angle A°.$

By the angle-sum theorem,

2 $\angle B° + \angle C° = 180° - \angle A°.$

Comparing statements 1 and 2, we have

3 $\angle DAC° = \angle B° + \angle C°.$

Another corollary of Theorem 91/4 is the fact that the sum of the measures of the two acute angles in a right triangle must be 90. Because of the importance of right triangles and the frequent appearance of pairs of angles whose measures have a sum of 90, such pairs of angles are given the special name *complements*.

Definition 59/4 *Complementary angles*

Two angles are complementary angles if the sum of their measures is 90. Each of the two angles is the complement of the other.

184

The acute angles of a right triangle are complements.

_____

For reference, we also state the following fact, which follows from arithmetic.

_____

* Theorem 92/4
Complements of congruent acute angles are congruent.

Exercises

1 Assume that the parallel lines *AB* and *CD* determine the plane β.

 a Is *C* in the *D*-side of *AB*?

 b Is *B* in the *A*-side of *CD*?

 c If point *P* is in the plane β, must *P* be in the *C*-side of *AB* or in the *B*-side of *CD*?

 d Does the *A*-side of *CD* contain the points that are not in the *D*-side of *AB*?

 e Are there any points in both the *C*-side of *AB* and the *A*-side of *CD*? *Answer*

2 In each of the following cases, the measures of two angles of a triangle are given. Find the measure of the third angle.

 a 21 and 77

 b 170 and 3

 c *x* and *x*

 d *y* and *z* *Answer*

 e 6 and $6 + \pi$

 f $2(3 + x)$ and $2(3 - x)$

 g $|76|$ and $|-35|$

 h 179 and 0.999

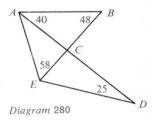

Diagram 280

3 In D280, the measures of some of the angles of a figure have been indicated. Give the numerical value of each of the following.

 a $\angle EAC°$

 b $\angle ACB°$

 c $\angle ACE°$

 d $\angle CED°$ *Answer*

 e $\angle ECD°$

 f $\angle BCD°$

4 The lines *AB* and *DE* are parallel; $\langle A, C, E \rangle$; $\langle B, C, D \rangle$. If $\angle 5° = 135$ and $\angle 7° = 55$, find the measures of the other numbered angles represented in D281.

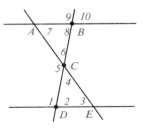

Diagram 281

5 *Theorem*

If a correspondence exists between two triangles such that two pairs of corresponding angles are congruent, then the third pair of corresponding angles also are congruent.

6 If $\triangle ABC \cong \triangle DEF$, point *B* is the foot in *BC* of *A*, and $\angle D° = 20$, what is $\angle C°$? *Answer*

7 If one angle of an isosceles triangle has a measure of 100, what are the measures of the other angles of the triangle?

8 a What are the measures of $\angle A$ and $\angle B$ if the measure of $\angle A$ is 40 less than four times that of $\angle B$ and if $\angle B$ is the complement of $\angle A$? *Answer*

b What are the measures of $\angle C$ and $\angle D$ if they are congruent and complementary?

c Find the measures of the angles of $\triangle ABC$, where $\angle B$ and $\angle A$ are complementary and $\angle C$ is three times the measure of $\angle A$. *Answer*

d The measure of the complement of $\angle A$ is $(70 + x)$; the measure of the complement of $\angle B$ is $(70 - x)$; $\angle A \cong \angle B$. What is the value of x?

e Find the measures of the angles of the equilateral triangle $\triangle ABC$.

9 In the proof of Theorem 91/4, the statement is made that, in t, there is a closed ray $\overrightarrow{CD}$ with the direction of $\overrightarrow{BA}$. Justify the existence of a closed ray such as $\overrightarrow{CD}$ and the fact that it is in t.

10 If $\overrightarrow{BD}$ bisects the exterior angle $\angle EBC$ of $\triangle ABC$ and if $BD \parallel AC$, prove that $\overline{AB} \cong \overline{BC}$ (D282).

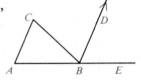

Diagram 282

11 Prove that the bisector of an exterior angle at the vertex of an isosceles triangle is parallel to the base of the triangle.

12 For polygon $EFGH$, if x and y are the measures of the exterior angles at E and G respectively, prove that $\angle H° + \angle F° = x + y$.

13 Assume that point Q is the midpoint of $\overline{BC}$ in $\triangle ABC$ (D283).

a If $d(A, Q) = \frac{1}{2}d(B, C)$, prove that $\triangle ABC$ is a right triangle with hypotenuse $\overline{BC}$.

b If $\triangle ABC$ is a right triangle with hypotenuse $\overline{BC}$, prove that $d(A, Q) = \frac{1}{2}d(B, C)$. *Answer*

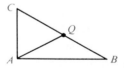

Diagram 283

14 *Theorem*

If the acute angles of a right triangle have measures of 30 and 60 respectively, then the shortest side of the right triangle (the side opposite the angle of measure 30) has a length that is one half the length of the hypotenuse. (Hint: Use exercise 13b.)

15 Prove that, if one side of a right triangle has a length that is one half the length of the hypotenuse, then the angle opposite this side has a measure of 30 and the other acute angle has a measure of 60. (Hint: Use exercise 13b.)

♦ 16 Two right triangles $\triangle ADB$ and $\triangle DCB$ are coplanar and congruent with $\angle A° = \angle C° = 90$. If $\angle ADC° = 60$ and B is in the interior of $\angle ADC$, prove that $d(A, B) + d(B, C) = d(D, B)$.

17 As indicated in D284, $AC \perp CB$; $CD \perp AB$; $DE \perp AC$; $EF \perp AD$; $FG \perp AE$. If $\sphericalangle B° = 30$, what is the value of $\dfrac{d(A, G)}{d(A, B)}$? *Answer*

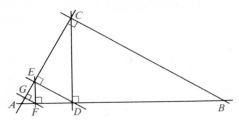

Diagram 284

18 If point M is the midpoint of segment $\overline{DE}$ of $\triangle DEF$ (D285), prove the following.
  a If $d(F, M) < \frac{1}{2}d(D, E)$, then $\sphericalangle DFE$ is obtuse.
  b If $d(F, M) > \frac{1}{2}d(D, E)$, then $\sphericalangle DFE$ is acute.

19 Points E and D are in the exterior of $\triangle ABC$ and in the interiors of $\sphericalangle CAB$ and $\sphericalangle CBA$ respectively (D286).

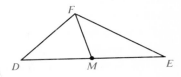

Diagram 285

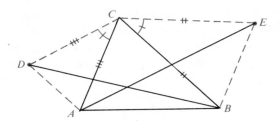

Diagram 286

If $\sphericalangle BCE \cong \sphericalangle ACD$, $\overline{CB} \cong \overline{CE}$, and $\overline{AC} \cong \overline{CD}$, prove that $\triangle DBC \cong \triangle AEC$.

We now take up a new form of betweenness, the kind we intend when we speak of some object as being between two railroad tracks. From past experience, it is now clear how to define this *strip* between two parallel lines.

Definition 60/4 *Strip between two parallel lines*

The strip between two parallel lines r and s is the intersection of the r-side of s and the s-side of r. The lines r and s are the opposite edges of the strip, and the union of the strip with both edges is the closed strip of the parallel lines. (D287)

Diagram 287

187

Definition 61/4 *Points between two parallel lines*

A point (or a set of points) is between two parallel lines
if it is contained in the strip between them.*

* Theorem 93/4

A line that is between two parallel lines is parallel to both of them.

* Theorem 94/4

Exactly one of three parallel lines in a plane is between the other two.

* Theorem 95/4

If line s is parallel to lines r and t and is
between them, then r and t are in opposite sides
of s and every transversal of the parallel lines
intersects s at a point between the intersections
with r and t. (D288)

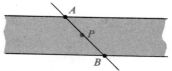

Diagram 288

* Theorem 96/4

If A and B are in opposite edges of a strip
between two parallel lines, then a point P
of line AB is between A and B if and only if P
is between the parallel lines. (D289)

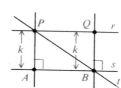

Diagram 289

Finally, we want to establish the natural property that a strip
between parallels has a constant width, that is, that the edges of
the strip are *equidistant*. What we mean by two parallel lines r
and s being equidistant is that all points of r are the same distance
from s, all points of s are the same distance from r, and the distance of a point in s from r is the same as the distance of a point
in r from s.

Theorem 97/4

If r and s are parallel lines, then there exists one number k
such that every point of r is at distance k from s, and every
point of s is at distance k from r. (D290)

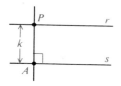

Diagram 290a   290b   290c

Proof

Let P denote a point of r and let A denote the foot in s of P.
Then k, defined by $k = d(P, A)$, is the distance from P to s,
and line PA is perpendicular to s.

---

* Notice, from Definition 60/4, that the strip we have defined is the *open* strip and does not
contain the edges.

Let Q denote any second point in r, and let B denote its foot in s so that QB is perpendicular to s. Line QB is not PA, because Q is not in PA. And because PA and QB are both perpendicular to s, they are parallel to each other (Corollary 80b/4). Therefore, line $t = PB$ is a transversal of the parallel lines PA and QB and also of the parallel lines r and s.

Points B and Q are in the same side of line PA (Theorem 90/4), and points A and B are in the same side of r (Theorem 90/4). Hence $\overrightarrow{PQ}$ and $\overrightarrow{AB}$ are like directed, and $\overrightarrow{PA}$ and $\overrightarrow{QB}$ are like directed. We have, therefore,

1 $\angle ABP \cong \angle QPB.$ 1 Alternate interior angles of parallel lines are congruent (Theorem 88/4).

2 $\angle APB \cong \angle QBP.$ 2 Alternate interior angles of parallel lines are congruent.

3 $\overline{PB} \cong \overline{PB}.$ 3 Identity property

4 $\therefore \triangle ABP \cong \triangle QPB.$ 4 Angle, side, angle congruence theorem (Theorem 49/3)

5 $\therefore \overline{PA} \cong \overline{BQ}.$ 5 Corresponding parts of a congruence

6 $d(P, A) = k = d(Q, B).$ 6 From statement 5 and the definition of k

Since P is at distance k from s and since any other point Q of r is at distance k from s, every point of r is at distance k from s.

Because line PA is perpendicular to s, it also is perpendicular to the parallel line r (Corollary 88b/4). Thus P is the foot in r of A. Therefore, $k = d(A, P)$ also is the distance of A from r. The proof that every other point in s is at this same distance from r is similar to the proof that every point of r is the same distance from s as P.

Definition 62/4 *Distance between parallel lines*
The distance between two parallel lines is the distance from any point in one of the lines to the other line.

Convention
If r and s are parallel lines, the distance between them will be denoted by $d(r, s)$. From Theorem 97/4, if P is in r, then $d(r, s) = d(P, s)$.

Theorem 98/4
In the plane of two parallel lines, the locus of points equidistant from the two lines is a third line that is parallel to both of them and is between them.

Let α denote the plane of two parallel lines r and s,
and let A denote any point of r. (D291a)

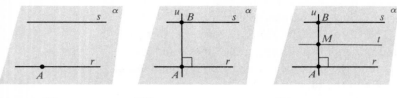

Diagram 291a   291b   291c

In α, there is a line u that is perpendicular to r at A.
By Corollary 88b/4, line u also is perpendicular to s
at a point B. Let M denote the midpoint of $\overline{AB}$. By the
parallel axiom, there is a line t through M that is parallel
to r. Because M is in neither r nor in s, line t containing
M is neither r nor s. So t is parallel to both r and s since
it is parallel to r (Theorem 85/4). And because M is
between r and s, line t is between r and s.

Point A is the foot in r of M. Also, since t is parallel
to r, it follows, by Theorem 97/4, that
1 $d(M, A) = d(M, r) = d(t, r)$.
Point B is the foot in s of M. And since t is parallel
to s, Theorem 97/4 also implies that
2 $d(M, B) = d(M, s) = d(t, s)$.
Because M is the midpoint of $\overline{AB}$,
3 $d(M, A) = d(M, B)$.
Substituting in statement 3 from statements 1 and 2 yields
4 $d(t, r) = d(t, s)$.
Thus all points of t are equidistant from r and s.

Now let X denote any point in α that is equidistant
from r and s. (D292a)

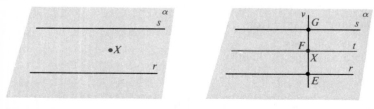

Diagram 292a   292b

There is a line v through X that is perpendicular to r, t,
and s at points E, F, and G respectively. Because E is
the foot in r of F and because G is the foot in s of F,
it follows from statement 4 that
5 $d(F, E) = d(F, G)$.

Because X is equidistant from r and s, point X is not in r or in s.* Consequently, E also is the foot in r of X, and G is the foot in s of X. Therefore, the fact that X is equidistant from r and s implies that

6 $d(X, E) = d(X, G)$.

But in line v, there is only one point equidistant from E and G (Theorem 11/2), so statements 5 and 6 imply that

7 $X = F$.

Therefore, X is in t.

From the two parts of the proof, it follows that t is the locus of all points in α that are equidistant from r and s.

Convention

The line in the plane of two parallel lines that is equidistant from both of these parallel lines will be called their midparallel.

The usefulness of midparallels can be seen in the property stated in Theorem 99/4.

Theorem 99/4

If r and s are parallel lines, then their midparallel bisects every segment that has one endpoint in r and one endpoint in s.
(D293)

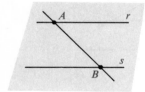

Diagram 293a   293b   293c

Proof

Let r and s denote parallel lines. Let $\overline{AB}$ denote a segment such that A is in r and B is in s. If t denotes the midparallel of r and s, then t must intersect line AB (Corollary 82/4) at a point M between A and B (Theorem 95/4). Through M, there is a line u that is perpendicular to r at C and perpendicular to s at D. And because t is equidistant from r and s,

1 $\overline{MC} \cong \overline{MD}$.

---

* We have not defined the distance between a line and a point in the line. This is inconvenient at times, but so is a zero distance inconvenient at times. It is a matter of choice, and many books use zero as a distance.

If u is the line AB, then $\overline{MC}$ is $\overline{MA}$, $\overline{MB}$ is $\overline{MD}$, and statement 1 shows that t bisects $\overline{AB}$.

If u is not line AB, then $\measuredangle AMC$ is opposite $\measuredangle BMD$. Then, from the congruence of opposite angles,

2 $\measuredangle AMC \cong \measuredangle BMD$.

Since all right angles are congruent,

3 $\measuredangle MCA \cong \measuredangle MDB$.

By the angle, side, angle congruence theorem,

4 $\triangle AMC \cong \triangle BMD$.

Therefore, as corresponding parts of a congruence,

5 $\overline{AM} \cong \overline{BM}$,

which shows that t bisects $\overline{AB}$.

We leave to you the proofs of some corollaries to Theorem 99/4.

Corollary 99a/4

If r and s are parallel lines and if A is in r and B is in s, then the line t that passes through the midpoint M of $\overline{AB}$ and is parallel to r is the midparallel of r and s. (D294)

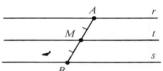

Diagram 294

Corollary 99b/4

A line that passes through the midpoint of one side of a triangle and is parallel to a second side bisects the third side. (D295)

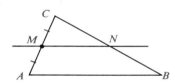

Diagram 295

Corollary 99c/4

The segment that joins the midpoints of two sides of a triangle is parallel to the third side, and its length is one half the length of the third side. (D296)

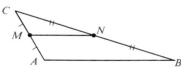

Diagram 296

Exercises

1 Assume that point P is in the strip between the parallel lines AB and CD in plane α.
  a Is P in the AB-side of CD? In the CD-side of AB?
  b Must P be in α?
  c If point X is between A and D, is X in the strip?
  d If $\overline{AQ} \cong \overline{CQ}$ and Q is in α, must Q be in the strip?
  e If M is in the interior of $\triangle ABC$, must M be in the strip?
  f If point N is in the interior of $\measuredangle ABD$, must N be in the strip? *Answer*
  g Is the segment $\overline{AD}$ in the strip? In the closed strip?

192

2 Prove that the strip between two parallel lines AB and CD is a nonempty, nonlinear, convex set. (Hint: Use Theorems 18/2, 19/2, and 96/4.)

3 If point X is in the strip between the parallel lines AB and CD, prove that $\overrightarrow{CX}$ intersects AB. *Answer*

4 If $AB \parallel CD$, prove that there are infinitely many lines between AB and CD. (Hint: Show that, for each X such that $\langle A, X, C \rangle$, there is a line t through X such that t is between AB and CD.)

5 Which of the following statements are necessarily correct?

a If line r is parallel to the two lines m and n, then one of the three lines must be between the other two.

b If r is between the parallel lines m and n, then r is parallel to m and r is parallel to n.

c If $AB \parallel CD$ and $\langle A, G, C \rangle$, then G is between AB and CD.

d The closed ray $\overrightarrow{AB}$ is in the closed strip between the parallel lines AB and CD.

e The closed ray $\overrightarrow{AC}$ is in the closed strip between the parallel lines AB and CD.

f If G is between A and B, then G is in the closed strip of the parallel lines AB and CD.

6 If a transversal intersects the parallel lines r and s at C and D respectively, under what conditions is $d(r, s) = d(C, D)$? Could $d(r, s) < d(C, D)$? Could $d(r, s) > d(C, D)$? *Answer*

7 If line $r = AB$ is parallel to line $s = CD$, are all of the equalities in the following sequence correct?
$$d(AB, CD) = d(r, s) = d(A, s) = d(C, r) = d(B, CD) = d(D, AB).$$

8 The three lines AB, CD, and EF are such that the two lines AB and CD are parallel and determine the plane α. From this information, decide which of the following statements are not necessarily correct and make a diagram to illustrate your reason for deciding that a statement is not necessarily correct.

a If $\overline{AE} \cong \overline{EC}$ and $\overline{BF} \cong \overline{FD}$, line EF is parallel to AB and CD. *Answer*

b If $\overline{AE} \cong \overline{EC} \cong \overline{BF} \cong \overline{FD}$, line EF is parallel to AB and CD.

c If $\langle A, E, C \rangle$ and $\langle B, F, D \rangle$, line EF is parallel to AB and CD.

d If E and F are in α and are such that $\overline{AE} \cong \overline{EC}$ and $\overline{BF} \cong \overline{FD}$, line EF is parallel to AB and CD, and EF is the midparallel of these lines.

e If EF is the midparallel of AB and CD, point E is the same distance from AB as it is from CD, and EF is in α.

193

9 If line EF is the midparallel of lines AB and CD, $<C, E, B>$, and $<A, F, D>$, which of the following statements are necessarily correct? *Answer*

a $\overline{AF} \cong \overline{FD}$.

b $\overline{CE} \cong \overline{FD}$.

c $\overline{CB} \cong \overline{AD}$.

d $d(C, E) = \dfrac{d(C, B)}{2}$.

e $d(D, F) \leqq d(C, B)$.

f If $\overline{AG} \cong \overline{GD}$, then G is in EF.

g If G is in EF, then $\overline{AG} \cong \overline{GD}$.

h $\measuredangle AFB \cong \measuredangle CED$.

i Any point in EF is equidistant from AB and CD.

j If X is in EF such that $<A, X, C>$, then $\overline{AX} \cong \overline{XC}$.

10 Prove that any two points of a line m are the same distance apart as their feet in any parallel line n.

11 Prove Corollary 99a/4.

12 Prove Corollary 99b/4.

13 Prove Corollary 99c/4. *Answer*

14 In $\triangle ABC$, point D is the midpoint of $\overline{AB}$ (D297), and E is that point in $\overline{BC}$ such that $DE \parallel AC$. If F in $\overline{AC}$ is such that $\overline{FC} \cong \overline{DE}$, prove that $\overline{DB} \cong \overline{EF}$ and that $\measuredangle BDE \cong \measuredangle EFC$.

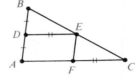

Diagram 297

15 In $\triangle ABC$, point D is the midpoint of $\overline{AC}$ and E is that point in $\overline{CB}$ such that $DE \parallel AB$. If point F is the point in $\overline{AB}$ such that $EF \parallel AC$, prove that $\overline{DF} \cong \overline{EB}$ (D298).

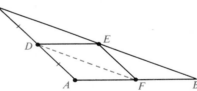

Diagram 298

16 In $\triangle ABC$, points D, E, and F are the midpoints of the sides opposite A, B, and C respectively. ($\triangle DEF$ is called the *midpoint triangle* of $\triangle ABC$.) Prove that $\triangle AFE \cong \triangle EDC \cong \triangle FBD \cong \triangle DEF$.

17 Suppose that $\triangle_1$ (read "triangle sub-one") is the midpoint triangle of $\triangle ABC$, that $\triangle_2$ is the midpoint triangle of $\triangle_1$, that $\triangle_3$ is the midpoint triangle of $\triangle_2$, and so on. What is the ratio of the parallel midpoint segments in $\triangle ABC$ and $\triangle_8$? In $\triangle ABC$ and $\triangle_n$? *Answer*

18 The line CD is between the parallel lines AB and EF, and the points are such that $<A, C, E>$ and $<B, D, F>$ (D299).

a If $d(A, C) = 8$, $d(C, E) = 4$, and $d(B, D) = 6$, what is the length of $\overline{DF}$? (Hint: Draw a diagram that shows the midparallel of AB and CD.)

b If $d(A, C) = 6$, $d(A, E) = 9$, and $d(B, F) = 24$, find the lengths of $\overline{BD}$ and $\overline{DF}$.

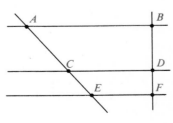

Diagram 299

• **c** If $d(A, C) = 6$, $d(C, E) = 4$, and $d(B, F) = 24$, what are the lengths of $\overline{BD}$ and $\overline{DF}$?

• **19** Assume that point D is not in the plane of $\triangle ABC$ (D300). (Figure $DABC$ is called a *tetrahedron*, or a *triangular pyramid*.) If points E, F, and G are the midpoints of $\overline{DA}$, $\overline{DB}$, and $\overline{DC}$ respectively, prove that $\measuredangle E$, $\measuredangle F$, and $\measuredangle G$ of $\triangle EFG$ are respectively congruent to $\measuredangle A$, $\measuredangle B$, and $\measuredangle C$ of $\triangle ABC$.

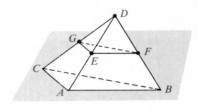

Diagram 300

Properties of 15/4
quadrilaterals In our formal system, we now have enough information about the relations of segments, rays, lines, and planes to prove a great number of theorems about different special figures. In this section and the next two, we will give typical examples of such theorems for circles, triangles, and quadrilaterals. The proofs of most of these theorems will be left to you.

In this section, remember that by "quadrilateral" we mean a properly convex polygon with four sides. Throughout this section, we will denote a quadrilateral by four capital letters, such as $ABCD$ (D301). This notation is meant to imply that $\overline{AB}$ and $\overline{DC}$ are opposite sides, $\overline{BC}$ and $\overline{DA}$ are opposite sides, and $\overline{AC}$ and $\overline{BD}$ are the two diagonals of the quadrilateral.

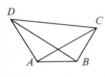

Diagram 301

By the convexity property of polygons, each diagonal is in a ray between the arms of an angle. With this property, together with the angle addition axiom and the angle-sum theorem of triangles, you can easily establish our next theorem.

---

* Theorem 100/4

The sum of the measures of the angles of a quadrilateral is 360. (D302)

* Corollary 100/4

In a rectangle, each angle is a right angle.*

Definition 63/4 *Parallelogram*

A quadrilateral in which pairs of opposite sides are parallel is a parallelogram.

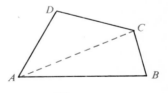

Diagram 302

From Corollary 99c/4, we can obtain a general property of all quadrilaterals.

---

* By definition, a rectangle is an equiangular quadrilateral.

The midpoints of the sides of a quadrilateral are the vertices
of a parallelogram. (D303)

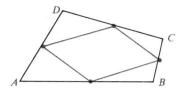

Diagram 303

The theorems that we consider next are of two types. In one
type, the theorem asserts that if a figure belongs to a particular
class of figures, then it has certain properties that are not stated in
the definitions of such figures. For example, if a figure is a
parallelogram, then its diagonals bisect each other. The second
type of theorem asserts that if a figure has certain properties, then
it must belong to a particular class of figures. For example, if two
opposite sides of a quadrilateral are parallel and congruent, then
the quadrilateral must be a parallelogram.

Theorem 102/4
Opposite sides of a parallelogram are congruent.
(D304)

Proof idea
Show that $\triangle ABC \cong \triangle CDA$.

Diagram 304

Theorem 103/4
Diagonally opposite angles of a parallelogram are congruent.

Theorem 104/4
Two neighboring angles of a parallelogram
are supplements.*

Theorem 105/4
If two opposite sides of a quadrilateral are
parallel and congruent, the quadrilateral
is a parallelogram. (D305)

Diagram 305

Proof idea
Show that if $\overline{AB} \cong \overline{CD}$ and
$\overline{AB} \parallel \overline{CD}$, then $\triangle ABD \cong \triangle CBD$.

Theorem 106/4
The diagonals of a parallelogram bisect
each other. (D306)

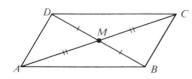

Diagram 306

* Neighboring angles are such that the join of their vertices is a side.

196

Theorem 107/4

If the diagonals of a quadrilateral bisect each other,
the quadrilateral is a parallelogram.

Theorem 108/4

Every rectangle is a parallelogram.

Theorem 109/4

The diagonals of a rectangle are congruent.

Theorem 110/4

If the diagonals of a parallelogram are congruent, the
parallelogram is a rectangle.

Theorem 111/4

Every rhombus is a parallelogram.*

Theorem 112/4

A parallelogram is a rhombus if and only if its
diagonals are perpendicular. (D307)

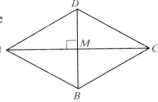

Diagram 307

Proof idea

Show that, if $\sphericalangle AMB° = 90$, then $\overline{AB} \cong \overline{AD}$. Also
show that, if $\overline{AB} \cong \overline{AD}$, then $\sphericalangle AMD° = 90$.

Next we define another special type of quadrilateral.

Definition 64/4 *Trapezoid*

A quadrilateral in which one pair of opposite sides are parallel
and the other pair of opposite sides are not parallel is a
trapezoid. The two parallel sides of a trapezoid are its bases.
Each pair of angles that contains the same base is a pair
of base angles. The median of a trapezoid is the segment
joining the midpoints of the nonparallel sides. If the
two opposite, nonparallel sides are congruent, then
the trapezoid is an isosceles trapezoid. (D308)

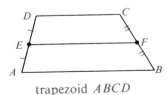

trapezoid *ABCD*

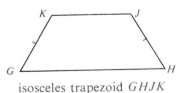

isosceles trapezoid *GHJK*

Diagram 308

Convention

The two nonparallel sides of a trapezoid are often referred to
as the sides of the trapezoid.

---

* All four sides of a rhombus are congruent.

197

Theorem 113/4

Each base angle of the shorter base of a trapezoid
is larger than its diagonally opposite angle. (D309)

Proof idea

Show that $\angle D° > \angle B°$.

Diagram 309

Corollary 113/4

In a trapezoid, the sum of the measures of the
base angles of the shorter base is greater than 180.

Theorem 114/4

The longer base of a trapezoid and the
intersection point of the lines of the sides
are in opposite sides of the line of the shorter
base. (D310)

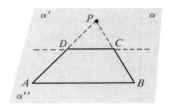

Diagram 310

Theorem 115/4

Each pair of base angles in an isosceles trapezoid
consists of two congruent angles.

Exercises

1 According to our definition and conventions for a
quadrilateral, which of the following statements are
correct for quadrilateral $MNPQ$? *Answer*
   a $\overline{MN}$ is the side opposite $\overline{PQ}$.
   b $\overline{MP}$ is a diagonal.
   c Diagonal $\overline{NQ}$ is in a ray between the arms of $\angle N$.
   d $\angle PNQ° + \angle QNM° = \angle N°$.
   e $\overline{QP}$ and $\overline{MN}$ must be parallel.

2 The sum of the measures of the angles of a triangle is
   180. The sum of the measures of the angles of a 4-gon,
   or quadrilateral, is 2(180). Show that the sum
   of the angle measures of a 5-gon, or pentagon,
   is 3(180). What is the sum of the angle measures
   of a 6-gon, or hexagon? What formula do these results
   suggest for the sum of the angle measures of an n-gon? *Answer*

3 Prove Theorem 101/4.

4 a Prove Theorem 102/4. *Answer*   c Prove Theorem 104/4.
   b Prove Theorem 103/4.   d Prove Theorem 106/4.

5 a Prove Theorem 105/4.
   b Prove Theorem 107/4.

6 a Show that an equiangular polygon need not be equilateral.
   b What is a quadrilateral called that is equilateral but
   not necessarily equiangular?

7 Use $(n - 2)180$ for the angle sum of an n-gon to answer each
   of the following questions.
   a What is the measure of each angle of a regular hexagon?

b What is the measure of each exterior angle of a regular pentagon? *Answer*

c How many sides does a regular polygon have if the measure of each angle is 120? 140? 160? 179?

d How many sides does a regular polygon have if each exterior angle has a measure of 10?

8 a Prove Theorem 108/4. *Answer*   **c** Prove Theorem 110/4.

   b Prove Theorem 109/4.   **d** Prove Theorem 111/4.

9 Prove Theorem 112/4.

10 Prove that each diagonal line of a rhombus bisects two angles of the rhombus.

11 If one of the diagonals of a quadrilateral is the perpendicular bisector of the other, then the quadrilateral is called a "kite."

   a Is every rhombus a kite? *Answer*

   b Is every kite a rhombus?

   c Can a kite be a rectangle?

12 a What is the measure of each angle of a parallelogram if the measure of one of its angles is 117?

   b What is the measure of each angle of a parallelogram if the measure of one of its angles is greater by 20 than three times the measure of another angle? *Answer*

13 Prove: For parallelogram $ABCD$, if the diagonal line AC bisects either $\angle A$ or $\angle C$, then the parallelogram is a rhombus.

14 Quadrilateral $ABCD$ is a rhombus whose diagonals intersect at M (D311). The length of $\overline{DC}$ is 8, and the measure of $\angle D$ of $ABCD$ is 120. Find the measure of each of the following segments and angles.

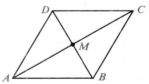

Diagram 311

   a $\overline{AD}$ **f** $\overline{DM}$

   b $\angle C$ **g** $\overline{MB}$

   c $\angle MDC$ *Answer*   **h** $\overline{DB}$

   d $\angle MCD$ **i** $\angle DAC$

   e $\angle DMC$ **j** $\angle ABC$

15 Prove Theorem 113/4.

16 a Prove Theorem 114/4. *Answer*

   b Prove Theorem 115/4.

17 The shorter base of the trapezoid $RSTW$ is $\overline{WT}$ (D312). If $d(W, T) > d(S, T)$, prove that $d(R, S) > d(R, W)$.

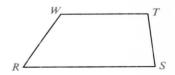

Diagram 312

18 Assume that point M is the midpoint of the larger base $\overline{AB}$ of the isosceles trapezoid $ABCD$ (D313). Prove each of the following.

   a $\triangle MAD \cong \triangle MBC$.

   b $\angle CDM \cong \angle DCM$.

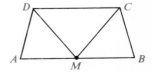

Diagram 313

19 *Theorem*

The median of a trapezoid is parallel to the bases of the trapezoid and the length of the median is one half the sum of the lengths of the bases.

◆**20** Segment $\overline{EF}$ is the median of the trapezoid $ABCD$ whose smaller base is $\overline{DC}$ (D314). Point G is the foot in $\overline{AB}$ of C, and $\overleftrightarrow{CG}$ and $\overline{EF}$ intersect at H. If $d(D, C) = 4$, $d(A, B) = 6$, $\angle A° = 90$, and $\angle B° = 60$, what are the measures of the following sets?

a $\overline{EF}$ e $\overline{HF}$

b $\overline{GB}$ f $\overline{EH}$

c $\angle GCB$ g $\overline{CF}$ *Answer*

d $\overline{BC}$

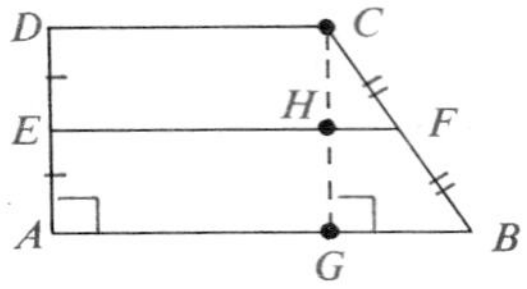

Diagram 314

◆**21** Prove that the two diagonals from the vertex of a regular pentagon trisect the angle at that vertex. (An angle is trisected by two rays that separate the given angle into three congruent angles.)

Basic 16/4

constructions The next theorems we will work with concern triangles and circles. These theorems will be more interesting and more easily understood if they are checked in a physical way by accurate drawings rather than by rough sketches. To make these accurate drawings, you need only a few simple methods of using a compass and a straightedge (an unmarked ruler). These methods, called *constructions*, are probably familiar to you, but it may help to review some of the most basic ones.

Though constructions are not part of our formal geometry, every compass and straightedge construction is related to a mathematical theorem about the existence and intersection properties of certain mathematical lines and circles. That is, one can always restate a compass and straightedge construction as a mathematical theorem. For the constructions that we now will review, the corresponding theorems in the system involve intersection properties of circles and of lines and circles. Although we haven't yet established these theorems, it is interesting to see the relation of the constructions to both the theory that we already have developed and the theory that we will need.

The first basic construction we will consider is the following.

1) The construction of the line t that is the perpendicular bisector of a given segment $\overline{AB}$

200

This basic construction means that we are given segment $\overline{AB}$ marked on a paper (the paper corresponds to a plane α). We wish to construct a line t that will be perpendicular to $\overline{AB}$ at the midpoint M of $\overline{AB}$ (D315). We know, from Corollary 75b/3, that t is

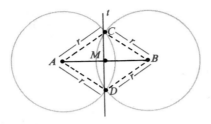

Diagram 315

the locus of points in α that are equidistant from A and B. Since t is determined by any two of its points, we can draw t with a straightedge if we can find two points C and D that are equidistant from A and B. One way to find two such points is to construct a circle $C(A, r)$ with center A and any radius r greater than $\frac{1}{2}d(A, B)$. Then the circle $C(B, r)$ with the same radius, but with center B, will intersect $C(A, r)$ in two points, C and D.* Since both of the points C and D are at distance r from A and B, line $t = CD$ is the desired perpendicular bisector of $\overline{AB}$.

We now can use construction 1 to make a second construction.

2) The construction of the line t that passes through a given point P and is perpendicular to a given line s

Whether or not P is in s (D316), we can draw a circle $C(P, r)$ that intersects s at two points A and B.† Because P is equidistant from

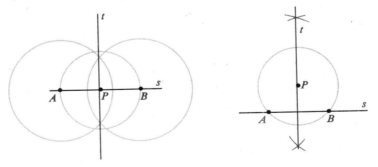

Diagram 316

A and B, it is in the perpendicular bisector of $\overline{AB}$. This bisector of $\overline{AB}$ is, therefore, the desired line t that can be drawn by using

---

* This intersection property has not yet been proved in the system.
† Again recall that this intersection property has not yet been proved for P not in s.

construction 1. (Notice that, in the picture at the right, the entire circles with centers A and B have not been drawn. Only small portions of these two circles are drawn to indicate the points of intersection.)

3) The construction of the line t that is the bisector of a given angle $\sphericalangle XCY$

We can draw a circle $C(C, r)$ that intersects the closed rays $\overrightarrow{CX}$ and $\overrightarrow{CY}$ at points A and B respectively (D317). Since C is equidistant from A and B, it is in line t, which is the perpendicular bisector of $\overline{AB}$. Therefore, we can construct line t. And because $\overline{AB}$ is the base of the isosceles triangle $\triangle ABC$, line t is also the bisector of the vertex angle $\sphericalangle C$ (Theorem 55/3).

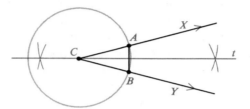

Diagram 317

As a last example, we consider the following construction.

4) The construction of an angle that has a given arm $\overrightarrow{DW}$ and is congruent to a given angle $\sphericalangle XCY$

A circle $C(C, r)$, constructed with center C, intersects $\overrightarrow{CX}$ at a point A and intersects $\overrightarrow{CY}$ at a point B (D318). A circle with the

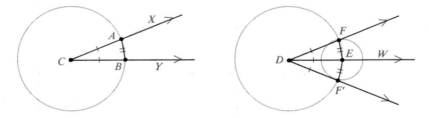

Diagram 318

same radius as $C(C, r)$ but with center D intersects $\overrightarrow{DW}$ at a point E. Now the circle with center E and radius $d(A, B)$ intersects the second circle $C(D, r)$ at two points F and F'. By the side, side, side congruence theorem, $\triangle ACB$ is congruent to both $\triangle FDE$ and $\triangle F'DE$. Thus $\sphericalangle XCY$ is congruent to both of the angles $\sphericalangle FDE$ and $\sphericalangle F'DE$, and both of these angles have $\overrightarrow{DW}$ as one arm.

202

In these constructions, we have made use of a principle that is worth special attention. Suppose that you want to determine the nature of a set $\mathcal{S}$ that is the set of all points that satisfy certain given conditions, say, conditions P, Q, and R. Suppose that $\mathcal{P}$ is the set of all points that satisfy condition P, that $\mathcal{Q}$ is the set of those points that satisfy Q, and that $\mathcal{R}$ is the set of points that satisfy R. Then, clearly, $\mathcal{S}$ must be the set of points common to all three of the sets $\mathcal{P}$, $\mathcal{Q}$, and $\mathcal{R}$, that is, $\mathcal{S} = \mathcal{P} \cap \mathcal{Q} \cap \mathcal{R}$. (Of course, $\mathcal{S}$ could be empty.)

To see how we used this principle, consider again our first construction. To find two points C and D, each equidistant from A and B, we seek two points, each at a selected distance r from both A and B. Since $C(A, r)$ is the set of all points in the plane α at distance r from A and $C(B, r)$ is the set of all points at distance r from B, the intersection of the circles consists of all points at distance r from both A and B. Consequently, the intersection set contains the two points C and D.

To give a different example, suppose that, in a plane α, point A is in line t and that point B is not in t (D319). And suppose that the

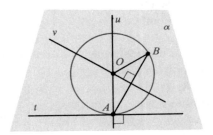

Diagram 319

problem is to find, or to prove the existence of, all the circles in α that pass through B and are tangent to t at A. If we draw a picture of a possible solution, it appears that, for a circle $C(O, r)$ to be tangent to t at A, point A must be the foot in t of O. And if $C(O, r)$ passes through both A and B, then, by the definition of a circle, O must be equidistant from A and B. Thus, the possible centers in α must have A as a foot in t and be equidistant from A and B. The set of all points in α that have A as a foot in t is, except for A, the line u perpendicular to t at A. And the set of all points in α equidistant from A and B is the line v, which is the perpendicular bisector of $\overline{AB}$. Thus, there is one and just one point that satisfies both conditions. This point is the intersection point O of the nonparallel lines u and v. The radius r must be the common length $d(O, A) = d(O, B)$, so there is one and just one circle in α that satisfies the given conditions.

In the following problems, you are to use only a straightedge and a compass. No use is to be made of a protractor or the markings on a ruler. For some of these problems, you are simply asked to carry out a physical experiment. For other problems, you are asked to *explain* a construction. The following example illustrates an explanation of a construction.

Problem

Given segment $\overline{AC}$, *explain* a construction for a square $ABCD$ that has $\overline{AC}$ as a diagonal.

Solution 1

Construct line t (D320) that is the perpendicular bisector of $\overline{AC}$ at the midpoint M of $\overline{AC}$ (basic construction). The circle $C(M, r)$, with $r = d(M, A)$, intersects t at the desired points B and D. Because $\overline{AC} \perp \overline{BD}$, the figure $ABCD$ is a rhombus. By the s.a.s. axiom, $\triangle AMB \cong \triangle BMC \cong \triangle CMD \cong \triangle DMA$. Hence, $\overline{AB} \cong \overline{BC} \cong \overline{CD} \cong \overline{DA}$. Because the diagonals are congruent, the figure is a square rhombus.

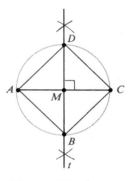

Diagram 320

Solution 2

An angle $\sphericalangle EFG$ with measure 45 can be constructed (D321), since a right angle can be constructed and bisected (basic construction). At A, construct rays $\overrightarrow{AX}$ and $\overrightarrow{AY}$ in opposite sides of AC and such that $\sphericalangle CAX \cong \sphericalangle CAY \cong \sphericalangle EFG$ (basic construction). Construct the line CZ perpendicular to AX, and let D be the point of perpendicularity (basic construction). Construct line CW perpendicular to AY at B. Because $\sphericalangle CAX$ and $\sphericalangle CAY$ are acute, D is in $\overrightarrow{AX}$ and B is in $\overrightarrow{AY}$. In the right triangle $\triangle ACD$, $\sphericalangle C$ is the complement of $\sphericalangle A$. Since $\sphericalangle A° = 45$, then $\sphericalangle C° = 45$. Similarly, $\triangle ACB$ is an isosceles right triangle. Since $\sphericalangle DAB° = 2(\sphericalangle DAC°) = 90$ and, similarly, $\sphericalangle DCB° = 90$, figure $ABCD$ is a rectangle. Because $\overline{CD} \cong \overline{DA}$, the figure is also a square.

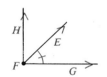

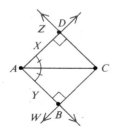

Diagram 321

1 a Construct the perpendicular bisectors of the sides of an acute triangle, a right triangle, and an obtuse triangle.

b Check that, in each case, the three bisectors constructed for exercise 1a intersect at a common point P. (The lines are said to be *concurrent* at P, and P is called the *circumcenter* of the triangle.)

c Check that, in each case, the circle that has center P and that passes through one vertex also passes through the other vertices. (This circle is called the *circumcircle* of the triangle.)

d From your constructions, decide what property is suggested concerning the location of P in relation to the type of triangle.

2 For a point P and a line t that does not contain P, explain a construction for each of the following.

a An isosceles right triangle $\triangle PAB$ that has $\angle A° = 90$ and side $\overline{AB}$ in t *Answer*

b An isosceles right triangle $\triangle PAB$ that has hypotenuse $\overline{AB}$ in t

3 A line that passes through a vertex of a triangle and is perpendicular to the line of the opposite side is an *altitude line*. Construct the three altitude lines of an acute triangle, a right triangle, and an obtuse triangle. Check that, in each case, the three lines are concurrent (that is, check that all three lines intersect) at a point P. (A point such as P is called the *orthocenter* of the triangle.) What property is suggested by the three cases for the location of P?

4 Use a construction to check that the three angle bisectors of a triangle are concurrent at a point I, called the *incenter* of the triangle. Find the foot F of I in the line of one side, and construct the circle $C(I, r)$, where $r = d(I, F)$. This circle, called the *incircle* of the triangle, should be tangent to all three sides of the triangle.

5 Explain how our basic constructions imply that one can construct angles with the following measures.

a 45   **e** 135
b 60   **f** 105
c 15   **g** 165
d 75 *Answer*   **h** 150

6 For a point P and a closed ray $\overrightarrow{AB}$ such that P is not in $\overleftrightarrow{AB}$, explain a construction for a closed ray $\overrightarrow{PX}$ that is like directed to $\overrightarrow{AB}$ and a closed ray $\overrightarrow{PY}$ that is oppositely directed to $\overrightarrow{AB}$.

7 Suppose that point D in line t and $\triangle ABC$ are given (D322). The s.a.s. axiom can be used as follows to construct a triangle that has a vertex D, a side in t, and that is congruent to $\triangle ABC$: Mark off $\overline{DE}$ in t so that $\overline{DE} \cong \overline{AB}$. (Use the setting $d(A, B)$ on a compass to mark off $\overline{DE}$.) Copy $\angle A$

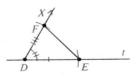

Diagram 322

at D by constructing $\angle EDX \cong \angle BAC$. In $\overrightarrow{DX}$ mark
off $\overline{DF}$ so that $\overline{DF} \cong \overline{AC}$. Then $\triangle EDF \cong \triangle BAC$
by the s.a.s. axiom.

   a Explain how you could obtain the desired $\triangle DEF$
by using the ideas of the a.s.a. theorem.

   b Assuming circle intersection, explain how
you could base the construction on the s.s.s. theorem.

8 Given two segments $\overline{AB}$ and $\overline{CD}$, explain a construction for each
of the following.

   a A parallelogram whose diagonals are respectively
congruent to $\overline{AB}$ and $\overline{CD}$

   b A parallelogram that has the property of exercise 8a and
has diagonals that intersect at angles of measures 60 and 120

   c A parallelogram that has the property of exercise 8a
and that also is a rhombus

9 Use points P, A, and C, with P not in AC, to explain a
construction for the following.

   a Point B such that $PACB$ is a parallelogram

   b Line t such that t is the midparallel of PB and AC,
where B is as determined in exercise 9a

10 Construct the circumcircle of an equilateral triangle $\triangle ABC$.
Check that, if point D is in the circle and in the interior
of $\angle BAC$, then $d(A, D) = d(B, D) + d(D, C)$.
(Hint: See exercise 1c.)

11 Use a circle $C(O, r)$ and point P in the circle
to construct a circle $C(P, x)$, where $x < 2r$ and
such that $C(P, x)$ intersects $C(O, r)$ at points A
and B (D323). Construct a circle $C(A, x)$ that
intersects $C(O, r)$ at C, where $C \neq P$, and
that intersects $C(P, x)$ at D in the interior
of $C(O, r)$. Construct line CD, and let E denote
the intersection of CD and $C(O, r)$.
Check that $d(D, E) = r$.

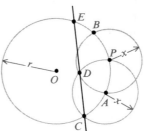

Diagram 323

Properties of 17/4
triangles and It will be convenient to have the following convention in our
circles system as we study properties of triangles and circles.

Convention
If there is a point P in the intersection of two or more sets,
then the sets are said to be *concurrent* and to be *concurrent*
at P. This language is most commonly used in connection
with a set of lines or a set of planes. (D324)

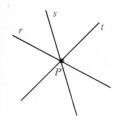

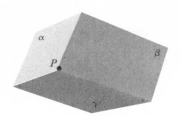

lines *r*, *s*, *t*
concurrent at *P*

planes α, β, γ
concurrent at *P*

Diagram 324

Definition 65/4 *Circumcircle of a polygon*
A circle that passes through all the vertices of a polygon
is the circumcircle of the polygon. The center
of the circle is a circumcenter of the polygon.
The polygon is said to be inscribed in the circumcircle,
and the circumcircle is said to be circumscribed
about the polygon. (D325)

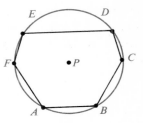

Diagram 325

Theorem 116/4
In the plane of $\triangle ABC$, there is exactly one point *P*
that is equidistant from the three vertices *A*, *B*, and *C*.

Proof idea
Let *u*, *v*, and *w* be the sets of points in the plane of the triangle
that are equidistant from *A* and *B*, from *B* and *C*, and from *C*
and *A* respectively. Use Corollary 75b/3 and Theorem 89/4
to show that the intersection of *u*, *v*, and *w* is a single point *P*.

From the proof idea suggested for Theorem 116/4, you can
get the following corollaries.

Corollary 116a/4
The three lines that are in the plane of a triangle and are
the perpendicular bisectors of the sides of the triangle
are concurrent. (D326)

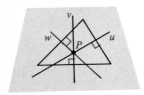

Diagram 326

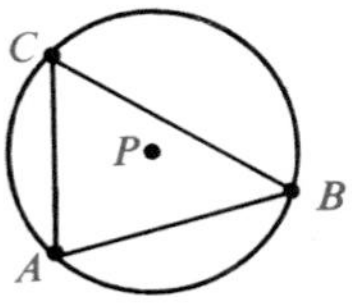

Diagram 327

Corollary 116b/4
There is exactly one circumcircle of a given triangle. (D327)

207

Since any circumcircle of a polygon is also a circumcircle of each triangle determined by three vertices of the polygon, Corollary 116b/4 gives us another corollary.

Corollary 116c/4

For any polygon, there is at most one circumcircle.

Since the diagonals of a rectangle are the same length and bisect each other, we now also have Theorem 117/4.

* Theorem 117/4

The circumcenter of a rectangle $ABCD$ exists and is the intersection point of the diagonals $\overline{AC}$ and $\overline{BD}$. (D328)

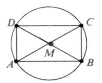

Diagram 328

There now are several ways to prove Theorem 118/4.

* Theorem 118/4

The circumcenter of a right triangle $\triangle ABC$ is the midpoint M of the hypotenuse $\overline{AB}$. (D329)

Diagram 329

An interesting fact suggested by Theorem 118/4 is stated in the next theorem.

Theorem 119/4

If $\overline{AB}$ is a diameter of circle $C(O, r)$ and P is any point in the plane of the circle and distinct from A and B, then P belongs to $C(O, r)$ if and only if $\measuredangle APB$ is a right angle. (D330)

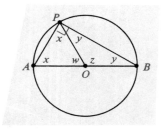

Diagram 330

Proof idea

If $\measuredangle APB$ is a right angle, it can be shown, from Theorem 118/4, that $C(O, r)$ must be the circumcircle of right triangle $\triangle APB$

208

and, so, passes through P. If P is in the circle $C(O, r)$, it cannot be in line AB (Why?). Hence $\triangle APB$ exists. Define the measures x, y, z, and w shown in D330 and prove the indicated congruence of angles. Then, from $z = 2x$ and $w = 2y$, get $x + y = \angle P° = 90$.

Exercises

1 Assume that line PA is perpendicular to the plane $\alpha(A, B, C)$.

 a Name three lines concurrent at A.

 b Name three planes concurrent at C. *Answer*

 c Are the three planes named in exercise 1b concurrent at any other point?

 d Could three planes be concurrent at a point P and also at a second point Q? In the same manner, could three lines be concurrent? Could three circles be concurrent?

2 a If a circumcircle exists for polygon $ABCDE$ (a pentagon), why must the circumcircle also be the circumcircle of $\triangle ACE$ and quadrilateral $BCDE$?

 b Can a circumcircle ever exist for a planar figure that is not a properly convex polygon?

 c Suppose that a circumcircle of a given polygon exists. Do all of the figures obtained from different orders of the vertices of the given polygon also have a circumcircle? *Answer*

 d Explain a construction for a quadrilateral $ABCD$ that has no circumcircle.

3 Explain a construction for inscribing each of the following in a given circle.

 a A regular hexagon (6-gon)

 b An equilateral triangle

 c A square

 d A regular octagon (8-gon)

4 Use Corollary 75b/3 to prove each of the following.

 a *Theorem*

 In the plane of a circle, the perpendicular bisector of every chord of the circle passes through the center of the circle. *Answer*

 b *Corollary*

 If a chord of a circle is not a diameter, then the center of the circle has the midpoint of the chord as its foot in the line of the chord.

 c *Theorem*

 A polygon $P_1 P_2 P_3 \ldots P_n$ in a plane α has a circumcircle if and only if the lines in α that are the perpendicular bisectors of the sides of the polygon are concurrent.

5 Prove Theorem 116/4.

6 Assume that a pentagon *ABCDE* has a circumcenter *P*. For each of the following locations of *P*, explain a construction for *ABCDE*.

  a *P* is interior to the pentagon.

  b *P* is in the pentagon.

  c *P* is exterior to the pentagon.

7 Prove that a parallelogram has a circumcircle if and only if it is a rectangle. (Hint: Use Theorems 106/4, 110/4, and 117/4.)

8 Angle *B* of △*ABC* is a right angle; ⦞*A*° = 60; *d*(*A*, *B*) = 4 (D331). If point *M* is the midpoint of $\overline{AC}$ and *P* is the foot of *M* in $\overline{CB}$, find the measure of each of the following segments and angles.

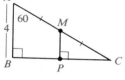

Diagram 331

  a ⦞*BCA*

  b $\overline{AC}$

  c $\overline{MA}$

  d The radius of the circumcircle of △*ABC* *Answer*

  e $\overline{MP}$

  f ⦞*PMB*

  g The radius of the circumcircle of △*PMB*

♦ 9 Prove that, if *P* is interior to circle *C*(*O*, *r*) and is not in diameter $\overline{AB}$, then ⦞*APB* is obtuse.

10 If *A* is in circle *C*(*O*, *r*), prove that the locus of the midpoints of all the chords from *A* is a circle with point *A* removed. (Hint: Consider the corollary proved in exercise 4b and Theorem 119/4.)

11 Assume that polygon *ABCDEF* is a regular hexagon inscribed in circle *C*(*O*, *r*). Prove that △*ACE* is an equilateral triangle. *Answer*

12 Segment $\overline{AB}$ is a diameter of circle *C*(*O*, *r*). Points *D* and *E* are in *C*(*O*, *r*) but not in $\overline{AB}$. If $\overline{AD} \cong \overline{BE}$, prove that $\overline{BD} \cong \overline{AE}$.

13 Quadrilateral *ABCD* is inscribed in circle *C*(*O*, *r*). Segment $\overline{AB}$ is a diameter of the circle, and $\overline{AD} \cong \overline{BC} \cong \overline{CD}$. Prove that *ABCD* is an isosceles trapezoid whose sides and shorter base have length *r*.

♦ 14 Let *ABCD* denote a trapezoid whose bases $\overline{AB}$ and $\overline{CD}$ have midpoints *M* and *N* respectively. Prove each of the following statements.

  a If *MN* is perpendicular to both bases, then the trapezoid is isosceles. *Answer*

  b If the trapezoid is isosceles, then *MN* is perpendicular to both bases.

♦ 15 Prove that a trapezoid has a circumcircle if and only if the trapezoid is isosceles.

Another set of concurrent lines associated with a triangle is the set of *altitude lines*. First we define an *altitude* of a triangle.

Definition 66/4 *Altitude of a triangle*
The segment that joins a vertex of a triangle to its foot
in the line of the opposite side is an altitude of the triangle.
The line containing an altitude is an altitude line
of the triangle.

Convention
If F is the foot in line AB of vertex C
in $\triangle ABC$, point F is called the foot
of the altitude $\overline{CF}$ (D332). Segment $\overline{CF}$
is called the altitude from C to side $\overline{AB}$.
(Segment $\overline{CF}$ is the altitude from C to
side $\overline{AB}$, even if $\overline{CF}$ and $\overline{AB}$ do not intersect.)

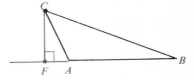

Diagram 332

We easily can obtain the concurrence of the three altitude lines of a triangle by first introducing the notion of a *midpoint triangle*.

Definition 67/4 *Midpoint triangle*
The three points that are the midpoints of the sides of $\triangle ABC$
are the vertices of the midpoint triangle of $\triangle ABC$.

We already know that the perpendicular bisectors of the sides of a triangle $\triangle ABC$ are concurrent (D333). These concurrent lines

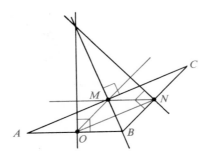

Diagram 333

are the perpendiculars at the midpoints M, N, and O. But these lines also are the altitude lines of the midpoint triangle, $\triangle MNO$. This fact suggests that perhaps the converse could be true, that is, perhaps the altitude lines of any triangle also are always the perpendicular bisectors of the sides of some other triangle and, hence, are concurrent. To follow this suggestion, we need to show that any triangle is the midpoint triangle of another triangle.

211

Corresponding to $\triangle ABC$, there is a triangle $\triangle A'B'C'$ such that its midpoint triangle is $\triangle ABC$, and $AB \parallel A'B'$, $BC \parallel B'C'$, and $CA \parallel C'A'$. (D334)

Proof idea

Let r denote the line through A that is parallel to BC; let s denote the line through B that is parallel to CA; let t denote the line through C that is parallel to AB. Show that r and s intersect in a point C', that s and t intersect in a point A', and that t and r intersect in a point B'. (Use Theorem 82/4.) Show that A, B, and C are midpoints of the segments thus determined.

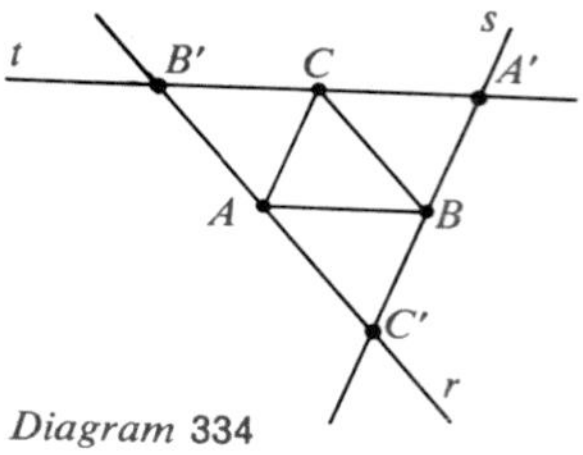

Diagram 334

We now can prove that the altitude lines of a triangle are concurrent.

Theorem 121/4

The three altitude lines of $\triangle ABC$ are concurrent. (D335)

Proof idea

Let u, v, and w denote the altitude lines through A, B, and C respectively, and let $\triangle A'B'C'$ denote the triangle whose midpoint triangle is $\triangle ABC$. Consider the relation of u, v, and w to $\triangle A'B'C'$.

Definition 68/4 *Orthocenter of a triangle*

The orthocenter of a triangle is the intersection point of the three altitude lines of the triangle.

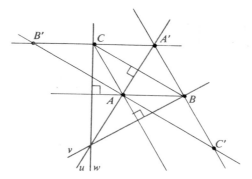
Diagram 335

Theorem 122/4

The circle that is in the plane of a triangle and has a side of the triangle as a diameter passes through the feet of two of the altitudes.

Proof idea

Use Theorem 119/4.

Exercises

1 Indicate which of the following statements are true (T) and which are false (F).

a If $\overline{AB} \perp \overline{BC}$, then $\overline{AB}$ is an altitude of $\triangle ABC$.

b If B is the foot in line BC of A, then $\sphericalangle ACB^\circ = 90$. *Answer*

c If B is the foot in line BC of A, then $\overline{BC}$ is an altitude of $\triangle ABC$.

d If AF is an altitude line of $\triangle RST$, then at least one of the points R, S, or T is in line AF.

e If HJ is an altitude line of $\triangle HKM$, then HJ must be perpendicular to line KM.

2 Explain why each of the following statements is false.

a If a segment is an altitude of a triangle, then it is perpendicular to a side of the triangle. *Answer*

b If $\measuredangle B$ of $\triangle ABC$ is a right angle, then $\overline{AB}$ and $\overline{AC}$ are altitudes of $\triangle ABC$.

c If CD is an altitude line of $\triangle ABC$, then segment $\overline{CD}$ must be an altitude of $\triangle ABC$.

d If S is the foot in segment $\overline{ST}$ of R, then segment $\overline{RS}$ is an altitude of $\triangle RST$.

3 Prove that the altitude line BD of $\triangle ABC$ bisects $\measuredangle B$ if and only if $\overline{AB} \cong \overline{BC}$.

4 If point O is the orthocenter of $\triangle ABC$, prove each of the following statements.

a If $\triangle ABC$ is a right triangle, then point O belongs to the triangle. *Answer*

b If one angle, say $\measuredangle A$, is obtuse, then $C \neq O$; the altitude line through C does not intersect $\overline{AB}$; point O is in the exterior of the triangle.

c If the triangle is acute, then the foot of A in BC is between B and C; the foot of B in AC is between A and C; point O is in the interior of the triangle.

d Use exercises 4a, 4b, and 4c to prove that, if O is in the triangle, then the triangle is a right triangle; if O is in the exterior of the triangle, then the triangle is obtuse; and if O is in the interior of the triangle, then the triangle is acute.

5 Prove that, if a triangle is not a right triangle, then at least two of its altitudes are shorter than any of the three sides of the triangle. *Answer*

6 Prove that, if two altitudes of an acute triangle are congruent, then the sides that contain the feet of these altitudes are congruent, and the triangle is isosceles.

7 Prove that, if two altitudes of any triangle are congruent, then the sides that are in the lines containing the feet of these altitudes are congruent, and the triangle is isosceles.

8 a Prove that, if a triangle is isosceles, then the altitudes to the congruent sides are congruent. (This is a converse of the theorem in exercise 7.)

b State the results of exercises 7 and 8a as a single theorem.

9 What theorem about the three altitudes of an equilateral triangle is a natural corollary of the theorem that you gave for exercise 8b?

10 Assume that points E, F, and G are the respective midpoints of segments $\overline{AB}$, $\overline{AC}$, and $\overline{BC}$ of $\triangle ABC$ (D336).

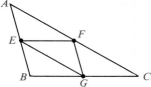

a Name the midpoint triangle of $\triangle ABC$.

b Line EF is parallel to which line?

c Segment $\overline{EG}$ is congruent to what two other segments? *Answer*

d Is there a triangle $\triangle XYZ$ such that its midpoint triangle is $\triangle ABC$? If $\triangle XYZ$ exists, is it unique?

e Is there a midpoint triangle of $\triangle EFG$? If so, is it unique?

Diagram 336

11 Assume that the midpoint triangle of $\triangle ABC$ is $\triangle RST$. If the measures of the angles labeled *1*, *2*, and *3* in D337 are x, y, and z respectively, what are the measures of the angles labeled *4* through *12* in terms of x, y, and z?

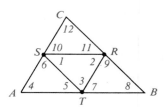

Diagram 337

12 Five triangles are represented in D337. Prove that the four triangles distinct from $\triangle ABC$ are congruent to each other.

13 Points E, F, and G are in the sides $\overline{AB}$, $\overline{BC}$, and $\overline{CA}$ respectively of $\triangle ABC$, and none of these points are vertices of $\triangle ABC$. If $GF \parallel AB$, $EF \parallel AC$, and $GE \parallel BC$, prove that $\triangle EFG$ is the midpoint triangle of $\triangle ABC$.

◆14 Prove Theorem 121/4.

15 If A, B, and C are three noncollinear points in plane α, what is the locus of all lines in α that are equidistant from all three points?* *Answer*

◆16 The triangular pyramid, or tetrahedron, shown in D338 is determined by $\triangle ABC$ in plane α and the three segments joining A, B, and C to a point D not in α. The altitude of the pyramid is the segment $\overline{DF}$, where F is the foot in α of D. Let R, S, and T denote the feet of D in lines AB, BC, and CA respectively. Let r, s, and t denote the lines in α that are perpendicular to AB at R, BC at S, and CA at T respectively. Prove that r, s, and t are concurrent at F.

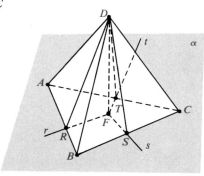

Diagram 338

---

* Though we always have used the term "locus" for point sets, the answer to a locus problem may be a set of lines or planes.

◆ 17 Assuming the results of exercise 16, suppose that six segments are given that correspond to and are respectively congruent to the six edges of the tetrahedron *ABCD*. Explain a construction for a segment congruent to the altitude $\overline{DF}$. (Hint: Note that, if a paper pyramid were cut along the edges to *D* and the triangular faces were folded out flat in the base plane α (D339),

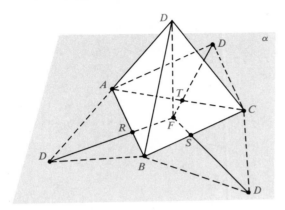

Diagram 339 👓

then the altitude lines *DR*, *DS*, and *DT* of exercise 16 would intersect at *F*.)

We now can show the existence of circles that are tangent to all three lines of the sides of a triangle. Recall that we defined a line to be a tangent to a circle if it is in the plane of the circle and intersects the circle at just one point. The circle and the line are then said to be tangent to each other at that point.

The next two theorems give the basic relation of a circle and a tangent.

Theorem 123/4
If *F* is the foot in line *t* of point *P*, then, in the plane of *P* and *t*, the circle with center *P* and radius $d(P, F)$ is tangent to *t* at *F*. (D340)

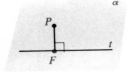

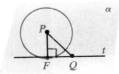

Diagram 340a   340b   340c

Proof

Let α denote the plane of P and t. The circle in α with
center P and radius $r = d(P, F)$ intersects t at F
since F is at the radius distance from P. If Q is any
point of t other than F, $d(P, Q) > d(P, F)$ since F is
the foot in t of P. Therefore, Q is not in the circle.
Since the circle and t intersect only at F, they are tangent at F.

Corollary 123/4

In the plane of a circle, a line that is perpendicular to a
radial segment at its endpoint in the circle is tangent to the circle.

Theorem 124/4

A line t that is tangent to circle $C(O, r)$ at point P is
perpendicular to the radial segment $\overline{OP}$.

Proof

Assume that
1 t is not perpendicular to $\overline{OP}$. (D341a)

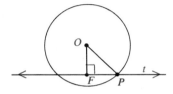

Diagram 341a   341b

Then O has a foot F in t that is not P. In the ray opposite $\overset{\cdot\cdot\rightarrow}{FP}$,
there is a point P' such that $d(F, P') = d(F, P)$, so
2 $\overline{FP} \cong \overline{FP'}$.
As right angles,
3 $\measuredangle PFO \cong \measuredangle P'FO$.
Statements 2 and 3 with
4 $\overline{OF} \cong \overline{OF}$
imply that
5 $\triangle FPO \cong \triangle FP'O$,
by the side, angle, side axiom. Therefore,
6 $\overline{OP} \cong \overline{OP'}$,
since they are corresponding parts in a congruence. But
from statement 6, P' is in $C(O, r)$, so t intersects the
circle twice, and, therefore, is not a tangent. This
contradiction shows that statement 1 is false and,
therefore, that t is perpendicular to $\overline{OP}$ at P.

Exercises

1 Decide which of the following statements are false. Then
   state conditions that would make each such statement true.
   a A point X must be in the circle $C(O, r)$ if $d(O, X) = r$. Answer
   b If X is in the circle $C(O, r)$, then $d(O, X) = r$.

216

c If line t and circle $C(O, r)$ have just one point in common, then t must be tangent to the circle.

d If line t is coplanar with circle $C(O, r)$ and is perpendicular to the radial segment $\overline{OA}$, then t is tangent to the circle.

e If line t is coplanar with $C(O, r)$ and is perpendicular to the chord $\overline{AB}$ at B, then t cannot be tangent to the circle.

f If line t is tangent to $C(O, r)$ at P, then t is perpendicular to line OP.

2 Explain and illustrate a construction that determines each of the following.

a The unknown center of a given circle (Because of this construction, it is customary to regard the center of any known circle as also being known.) *Answer*

b The line tangent to a given circle at a specified point in the circle

c The circle that has a given point as center and is tangent to a given line (When is this case not possible?)

3 Point P is exterior to the circle $C(O, r)$ in plane α. Assume the fact (as yet unproved) that the circle in α with diameter $\overline{OP}$ intersects $C(O, r)$ at two points A and B. Prove that the lines PA and PB are tangent to the circle $C(O, r)$ at A and B respectively and that $\overline{PA} \cong \overline{PB}$.

4 If point A is in line t, what is the locus of all the centers of circles with radius 3 that are tangent to t at A? That are tangent to t at some point? Explain and illustrate your answers.

5 a Prove that a line that is perpendicular to a tangent of a circle at the point of tangency and is in the plane of the circle passes through the center of the circle.

b Prove that a line that passes through the center of the circle and is perpendicular to a tangent of the circle also passes through the point of tangency.

6 Let $C(O, r)$ and n denote a given circle and a line in the same plane. Explain and illustrate a construction that determines each of the following.

a A line that is tangent to $C(O, r)$ and is parallel to n

b A line that is tangent to $C(O, r)$ and is perpendicular to n

7 The four collinear points A, B, C, and D, in that order, are successive points in a line t, that is, $<A, B, C>$ and $<B, C, D>$. For each of the following cases, describe the possible positions of a point X in the line t.

a X belongs to $\overrightarrow{BD}$ and $\overrightarrow{CA}$.   **c** X is not in $\overrightarrow{CA}$. *Answer*

b X belongs to $\overrightarrow{BD}$ and $\overrightarrow{BA}$.   **d** X is not in $\overline{BC}$.

From the perpendicularity property in Theorem 124/4, we can obtain the following facts.

If point O is in the plane of two lines s and t, then O is the center of a circle tangent to both s and t if and only if O is equidistant from s and t. (p342)

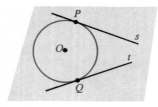 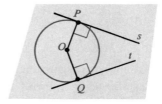

Diagram 342a   342b

Proof

If there is a circle $C(O, r)$ tangent to s at P and tangent to t at Q, then, because $\overline{OP} \perp s$ and $\overline{OQ} \perp t$, point P is the foot in s of O and Q is the foot in t of O. Since $r = d(O, P) = d(O, Q)$, point O is equidistant from s and t.

On the other hand, if O is equidistant from s and t, then O is not in s or in t* and $d(O, F) = d(O, G)$, where F is the foot of O in s and G is the foot of O in t. The circle $C(O, r)$ with $r = d(O, F) = d(O, G)$ passes through F and G, and the circle is tangent to s and t because s is perpendicular to $\overline{OF}$ at F and t is perpendicular to $\overline{OG}$ at G.

Theorem 125/4 raises the question "In a plane, what is the locus of points that are equidistant from two lines?" We know that, for two parallel lines, the answer to this question is their midparallel. For intersecting lines, such as r and s (D343), a

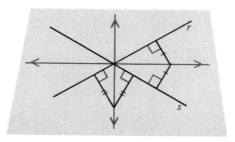

Diagram 343

---

* By the definition we have made, the distance between a point and a line does not exist if the point is in the line.

218

natural guess is that the answer should be the four rays that bisect the angles formed by the intersecting lines.

To help us prove the previous guess, we first establish two lemmas. You will recall that a lemma is a theorem that is proved separately to simplify the proof of another theorem.

Lemma 126a/4

If $\angle ABC$ is acute and if P is in the open ray $\overrightarrow{BC}$, then the foot of P in line AB is in the open ray $\overrightarrow{BA}$. (D344)

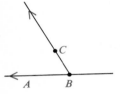
Diagram 344a

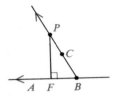
344b

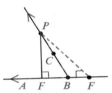
344c

Proof

The foot F of P in line AB is not B because PB is not perpendicular to AB. ($\angle PBA$ is acute.) If F were in the open ray opposite $\overrightarrow{BA}$, then the acute $\angle PBA$ would be an exterior angle at B of the right triangle $\triangle PBF$. Hence $\angle PBA$ would be greater than the right angle at F. This is impossible, so F must be in $\overrightarrow{BA}$.

Lemma 126b/4

If P is in the interior of $\angle ABC$ and is equidistant from lines BA and BC, then the feet of P in BA and BC are in the open rays $\overrightarrow{BA}$ and $\overrightarrow{BC}$. (D345)

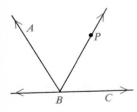
Diagram 345a

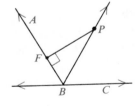
345b

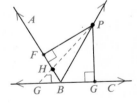
345c

Proof

Both of the measures $\angle ABP°$ and $\angle CBP°$ cannot be as great as 90 because, if they were, their sum, which is $\angle ABC°$, would be as great as 180. One of the measures, therefore, is less than 90, and we may suppose that $\angle ABP$ is an acute angle. Then, by Lemma 126a/4, the foot F of P in line AB

219

is in the open ray $\overrightarrow{BA}$. Let G denote the foot in line BC of point P. Since P is equidistant from BA and BC, $d(P, F) = d(P, G)$. Then G is not B, since $\overline{PB}$ is longer than $\overline{PF}$ (because $B \neq F$). If $\overrightarrow{BG}$ were the open ray opposite $\overrightarrow{BC}$, then G and P would be in opposite sides of line AB, so $\overline{PG}$ would intersect AB at a point H between P and G. Then, from $d(P, G) > d(P, H)$ and $d(P, H) \geq d(P, F)$ (since F is the foot of P), we would have the contradiction that $d(P, G) > d(P, F)$. Therefore, G is neither B nor in the ray opposite $\overrightarrow{BC}$. Hence, G belongs to the open ray $\overrightarrow{BC}$.

Now we can use these two lemmas to prove Theorem 126/4.

Theorem 126/4

The set of all points that are in the interior of $\sphericalangle ABC$ and are equidistant from lines BA and BC is the open ray that bisects $\sphericalangle ABC$.

Proof

Let $\overrightarrow{BD}$ denote the open ray bisecting $\sphericalangle ABC$, and let $\mathcal{R}$ denote the set of points in the interior of $\sphericalangle ABC$ that are equidistant from lines BA and BC.

Part I Let P denote a point of the bisector ray $\overrightarrow{BD}$. (D346a)

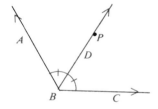

Diagram 346a   346b

Then $\sphericalangle PBA$ and $\sphericalangle PBC$ are both acute angles (Why?). Therefore, by Lemma 126a/4, the foot F of P in BA is in $\overrightarrow{BA}$, and the foot G of P in BC is in $\overrightarrow{BC}$. Then $\triangle PBF \cong \triangle PBG$ (Why?). Therefore, $d(P, F) = d(P, G)$, so P is equidistant from lines BA and BC. Hence the open ray $\overrightarrow{BD}$ is contained in $\mathcal{R}$.

Part II Let Q denote a point of $\mathcal{R}$, that is, a point in the interior of $\sphericalangle ABC$ that is equidistant from BA and BC. (D347a)

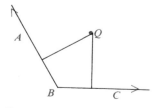

Diagram 347a   347b

Then by Lemma 126b/4, the foot E in BA of point Q is in $\overrightarrow{BA}$
and the foot H in BC of point Q is in $\overrightarrow{BC}$. Then, because Q
is in $\mathcal{R}$, $\overline{QE} \cong \overline{QH}$, and $\triangle QBE \cong \triangle QBH$ (Why?). Therefore,
$\sphericalangle EBQ \cong \sphericalangle HBQ$, and $\overrightarrow{BQ}$ is the bisector of $\sphericalangle ABC$ (Why?).
But there is only one open ray that bisects $\sphericalangle ABC$.
Thus, $\overrightarrow{BQ} = \overrightarrow{BD}$, and Q is in $\overrightarrow{BD}$. Therefore, $\mathcal{R}$ is contained
in $\overrightarrow{BD}$.

From Parts I and II of the proof, it follows that $\mathcal{R} = \overrightarrow{BD}$.

Theorem 127/4
In the plane of two intersecting lines s and t, the set $\mathcal{R}$
of all points that are equidistant from s and t is the union
of the four open rays that bisect the angles formed by s
and t. (D348)

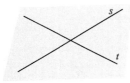
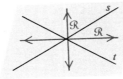

Diagram 348a   348b

Proof
Any point of $\mathcal{R}$ is equidistant from s and t and, so, is not in s
or in t. Any point in $\mathcal{R}$, therefore, is in the interior
of an angle formed by s and t and so, by Theorem 126/4,
is in the open ray that bisects that angle.

Any point in one of the open ray angle bisectors is in
the interior of an angle formed by s and t. Therefore,
by Theorem 126/4, any point in one of these angle bisectors is
equidistant from s and t and, hence, belongs to $\mathcal{R}$.

_____

A useful fact suggested by D348b is stated in Theorem 128/4.

_____

Theorem 128/4
If lines s and t intersect, then the two lines that bisect
the angles formed by s and t are perpendicular. (D349)

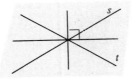

Diagram 349a   349b

_____

We now leave to you the details in the proofs of the following
concurrence theorems.

Theorem 129/4

The three lines that bisect the angles
of △ABC are concurrent at a point I
that is in the interior of the triangle
and is equidistant from the three lines
AB, BC, and CA. (D350)

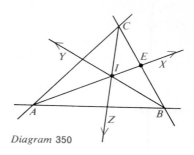

Proof idea

Let $\overrightarrow{AX}$, $\overrightarrow{BY}$, and $\overrightarrow{CZ}$ be the open rays that
bisect the angles at A, B, and C
respectively. First show that $\overrightarrow{AX}$ must
intersect $\overline{BC}$ at E between B and C
and that $\overrightarrow{BY}$ must intersect $\overline{AE}$ at I between
A and E. Next show that I is in the
interior of the triangle and, therefore,
in the interior of ∢C. Finally, show
that I is also equidistant from AB, BC,
and CA and, therefore, that I is
in $\overrightarrow{CZ}$. Then the lines AX, BY, and CZ
are also concurrent at I.

Diagram 350

Corollary 129/4

The circle whose center is I and whose
radius is the common distance of I
from AB, BC, and CA is tangent to all
three of these lines. (D351)

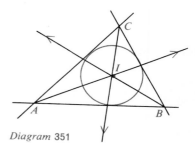

Definition 69/4 *Incircle of a triangle, incenter of a triangle*

The circle that is tangent to the three lines
containing sides of a triangle and whose center
is interior to the triangle is the incircle
of the triangle. The center of the incircle
is the incenter of the triangle.

Diagram 351

* Theorem 130/4

Two lines that are bisectors of exterior angles of
△ABC are concurrent at point E with the bisector
of the third angle of the triangle, and E is
equidistant from lines AB, BC, and CA. (D352)

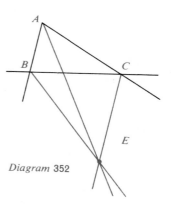

Diagram 352

Corollary 130/4

The circle with center E whose radius is the
common distance of E from lines AB, BC, and CA
is tangent to all three lines.

Definition 70/4 *Excircle of a triangle, excenter of a triangle*

The circle that is tangent to the three lines containing
sides of a triangle and whose center is exterior to
the triangle is an excircle of the triangle. The center
of an excircle is an excenter of the triangle. (D353)

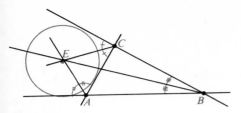

Diagram 353

Exercises

1 Assume that $C(O, r)$ is tangent to the two lines m and n
at points A and B respectively.

a Are lines OA and OB perpendicular to m and n
respectively?

b Is point O equidistant from m and n?

c Is $C(O, r)$ the only circle that is tangent to both m
and n? *Answer*

d If point Q is in the plane of m and n and is equidistant
from m and n, is there a circle $C(Q, k)$ that is tangent
to both m and n?

e If point Q is in the plane of m and n and is not
equidistant from m and n, is there a circle $C(Q, k)$
that is tangent to both m and n?

2 If $\angle A$ of $\triangle ABC$ is obtuse, how does Lemma 126a/4 imply that
the altitude from A has its foot between B and C?

3 If x and y are numbers such that $x + y > 12$ and $x < 3$,
we can determine a possible set of values for y
in the following way.

$$
\text{Add:} \quad \frac{\begin{array}{l} x + y > 12 \\ 3 > x \end{array}}{x + y + 3 > 12 + x} \qquad \text{Then add:} \quad \frac{\begin{array}{l} x + y + 3 > 12 + x \\ -x - 3 = -3 - x \end{array}}{y > 9}
$$

In each of the following cases, determine a possible set
of values for y.

a $x + y > 10$ and $x < 7$. *Answer*   c $x + y < 4$ and $x > 3$.

b $x + y > -5$ and $x < -3$.   d $x + y < 180$ and $x \geq 90$.

(Exercise 3d shows that, if x is not less than 90, then
y must be less than 90. This fact was used in the proof
of Lemma 126b/4.)

4 For the proof of Lemma 126b/4, explain each of the following.

a Why is B not equal to F?

b Why is $\overline{PB}$ longer than $\overline{PF}$? *Answer*

c Segment $\overline{PH}$ is how much shorter than $\overline{PG}$ if H is
between P and G?

d If $\overline{PH}$ is shorter than $\overline{PG}$, why is $H \neq F$?

223

e If $H \neq F$, why is $\overline{PF}$ shorter than $\overline{PH}$?

f What contradiction arises if you assume that $\overline{PF}$ is shorter than $\overline{PH}$ and that $\overline{PH}$ is shorter than $\overline{PG}$?

5 Prove Theorem 128/4. *Answer*

6 Prove Theorem 129/4. (Hint: Review Theorems 21/2 and 22/2.)

7 Prove Theorem 130/4.

8 Construct a triangle, together with its circumcircle, its incircle, and three excircles.

9 What is the locus of all points that are in the exterior of $\angle ABC$ and equidistant from the lines BA and BC? *Answer*

10 Criticize the following argument: Let $\triangle ABC$ denote any given triangle, and let O denote the point at which the bisector of $\angle A$ intersects the perpendicular bisector of side $\overline{BC}$ (D354). Let E and F be the feet of O in AC and AB respectively. Then, by the hypotenuse, angle congruence theorem for right triangles, $\triangle AOE \cong \triangle AOF$. Thus,

1 $d(A, E) = d(A, F)$,

and

2 $d(O, E) = d(O, F)$.

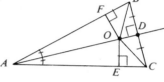

Diagram 354

Because O is in the perpendicular bisector of $\overline{BC}$,

3 $d(O, C) = d(O, B)$.

From statements 2 and 3, the hypotenuse, side congruence theorem for right triangles implies that $\triangle OEC \cong \triangle OFB$. Hence the theorem implies that

4 $d(E, C) = d(F, B)$.

Combining statements 1 and 4, it follows that

5 $d(A, E) + d(E, C) = d(A, F) + d(F, B)$,

or

6 $d(A, C) = d(A, B)$.

Hence it follows that $\triangle ABC$ is isosceles. Therefore, every triangle is isosceles.

♦ **11** Prove that the incenter I of any $\triangle ABC$ is the orthocenter of the triangle whose vertices are the three excenters of $\triangle ABC$.

12 a Under what conditions are the orthocenter, the incenter, and the circumcenter of a triangle a single point?

b Can two of the three centers be the same point and yet be a different point from the third center? *Answer*

♦ **13** An *incircle of a polygon* is a circle that is tangent to all of the sides of the polygon. That is, an incircle of a polygon is tangent to every line that contains a side of the polygon. Show that a polygon may have a circumcircle and not have an incircle. Can a polygon have an incircle and not have a circumcircle?

We now have, as sets of concurrent lines, the three altitude lines of a triangle, the three angle bisectors, and the perpendicular bisectors of the sides of a triangle. Still another set of concurrent lines is the set of *median lines* of a triangle. These lines are concurrent at a point called the *centroid* of a triangle.

Definition 71/4 *Median of a triangle*

The segment that joins a vertex of a triangle to the midpoint of the opposite side is a median of the triangle.

Theorem 131/4

The three medians of a triangle are concurrent at a point whose distance from each vertex is two thirds the length of the median from that vertex.

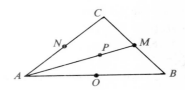

Diagram 355

Proof

Let $\overline{AM}$, $\overline{BN}$, and $\overline{CO}$ denote the three medians of $\triangle ABC$. (D355) In $\overline{AM}$, there is one point P such that

1 $d(A, P) = \frac{2}{3}d(A, M)$.

Let Q denote the point in which the median $\overline{CO}$ intersects $\overline{AM}$, and let r and s denote the respective lines through A and B that are parallel to CO. (D356a) Let u denote the line

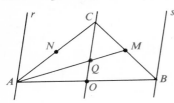

Diagram 356a

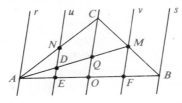

356b

that is the midparallel of r and CO and that intersects $\overline{AQ}$ at D and $\overline{AO}$ at E. Also let v denote the line that is the midparallel of CO and s and that intersects $\overline{OB}$ at F. Then, by Theorem 99/4, u bisects $\overline{AQ}$ and $\overline{AO}$. So

2 $d(A, D) = d(D, Q)$,

and

3 $d(A, E) = d(E, O)$.

Since the midparallel v bisects $\overline{CB}$ and $\overline{OB}$, it passes through M and

4 $d(O, F) = d(F, B)$.

Let x denote $d(A, B)$. Since O is the midpoint of $\overline{AB}$, $d(A, O) = d(O, B) = \frac{1}{2}x$. Also, since E is the midpoint of $\overline{AO}$ and F is the midpoint of $\overline{OB}$,

5 $d(A, E) = d(E, O) = d(O, F) = d(F, B) = \frac{1}{4}x$.

225

Since O is between E and F and $d(O, E) = d(O, F)$, point O is the midpoint of $\overline{EF}$. Then, because CO is parallel to u and v and bisects $\overline{EF}$, it is the midparallel of u and v. Therefore, CO bisects $\overline{DM}$, so

6 $d(D, Q) = d(Q, M)$.

From statements 2 and 6, the segments $\overline{AD}$, $\overline{DQ}$, and $\overline{QM}$ have a common length, say y, so

7 $d(A, D) = d(D, Q) = d(Q, M) = y$.

Since D is between A and Q,

8 $d(A, Q) = d(A, D) + d(D, Q) = 2y$.

Since Q is between A and M,

9 $d(A, M) = d(A, Q) + d(Q, M) = 2y + y = 3y$.

From statements 8 and 9, it follows that

10 $d(A, Q) = \frac{2}{3}d(A, M)$.

Therefore, from statements 1 and 10,

11 $Q = P$.

Thus, the median $\overline{CO}$ passes through P, and, by a similar argument, the median $\overline{BN}$ passes through P. Hence the three medians are concurrent.

If R is the point in $\overline{CO}$ such that

12 $d(C, R) = \frac{2}{3}d(C, O)$,

then the same argument shows that $\overline{AM}$ and $\overline{BN}$ pass through R. But $\overline{AM}$ and $\overline{BN}$ intersect at only one point, and they intersect at P. So $R = P$, and statement 12 becomes

13 $d(C, P) = \frac{2}{3}d(C, O)$.

By the same reasoning,

14 $d(B, P) = \frac{2}{3}d(B, N)$.

Definition 72/4 *Centroid of a triangle*

The centroid of a triangle is the intersection point of the medians of the triangle.

Exercises

1 Assume that points G and H are the midpoints of the sides $\overline{EF}$ and $\overline{FD}$ respectively of $\triangle DEF$ (D357).

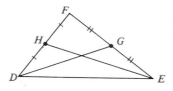

Diagram 357

a Which of the segments $\overline{DE}$, $\overline{HE}$, $\overline{FG}$, $\overline{HG}$, and $\overline{DG}$ are medians of $\triangle DEF$?

b Is $\overline{HG}$ parallel to $\overline{DE}$?

c Must $\overline{FJ}$ be a median of $\triangle DEF$ if $\overline{FJ}$ bisects side $\overline{DE}$?

d If $\overline{FX}$ is a median of $\triangle DEF$, must line FX bisect segment $\overline{DE}$?

e Is $\overline{GH}$ a median of $\triangle FDG$? Of $\triangle FHE$? *Answer*

2 Prove that $\triangle ABC$ is isosceles if median $\overline{CD}$ is perpendicular to side $\overline{AB}$ (D358).

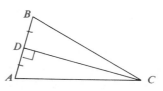

Diagram 358

3 Exercise 2 shows that, if a median of a triangle is an altitude, then the triangle is isosceles. State the converse of this theorem. Is the converse also a theorem? *Answer*

4 Give a definition of *corresponding medians in a correspondence of triangles*. Prove that, in a congruence of triangles, corresponding medians are congruent.

5 Assume that $\overline{AM}$ is a median of triangle $\triangle ABC$.
  a Prove that $\overline{AM}$ is shorter than one of the sides $\overline{AB}$ and $\overline{AC}$.
  b If median $\overline{AM}$ is shorter than both sides $\overline{AB}$ and $\overline{AC}$, then A must belong to a certain parallel strip. Try to identify and define this strip.

6 Prove that the centroid of a triangle is in the interior of the triangle.

7 Assume that medians $\overline{BF}$, $\overline{AE}$, and $\overline{CD}$ of $\triangle ABC$ are concurrent at point P.
  a What is $d(A, P)$ if $d(A, E) = 12$? *Answer*
  b What is $d(C, D)$ if $d(C, P) = 5$?
  c What is $d(B, F)$ if $d(P, F) = 2x$?
  d Find an upper bound for the length of $\overline{BP}$ if $d(A, F) = 5$ and $d(A, B) = 7$. *Answer*
  e Find $d(P, F)$ if $FA \perp AB$, $d(A, C) = 6$, and $\angle AFB^\circ = 60$.

8 A proof of Theorem 131/4 is given below. Give the reasons for each of statements 1 through 13 of the proof. Let $\overline{AM}$, $\overline{BN}$, and $\overline{CO}$ denote the medians of $\triangle ABC$ (D359a);

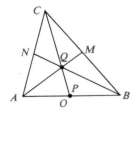
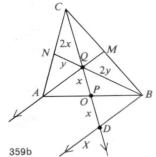

Diagram 359a   359b

let Q denote the intersection point of $\overline{AM}$ and $\overline{BN}$;
let P denote the intersection of $\overrightarrow{CQ}$ and $\overline{AB}$. Finally,
let D denote the intersection of open rays $\overrightarrow{CQ}$ and $\overrightarrow{BX}$,
where $\overrightarrow{BX}$ is the open ray from B that is parallel
and like directed to the open ray $\overrightarrow{MA}$.

  1 Q is the midpoint of $\overline{CD}$.
  2 NQ is parallel to AD.
  3 $ADBQ$ is a parallelogram.
  4 P is the midpoint of $\overline{AB}$.
  5 $P = O$, and $\overline{CP} \cong \overline{CO}$.
  6 The medians of the triangle are concurrent at Q.

227

Let x denote $d(P, Q)$, and let y denote $d(N, Q)$.

7 $d(C, Q) = d(Q, D) = 2x$.

8 $d(C, O) = 3x$.

9 $d(C, Q) = \frac{2}{3}d(C, O)$.

10 $d(A, D) = 2y$.

11 $d(Q, B) = 2y$.

12 $d(B, N) = 3y$.

13 $d(Q, B) = \frac{2}{3}d(B, N)$.

By a similar argument, $d(A, Q) = \frac{2}{3}d(A, M)$.

9 If $\overline{AB}$ is a segment in plane α, what is the locus of the centroids of right triangles in α that have $\overline{AB}$ as their hypotenuse?

The remaining exercises are construction problems. The following example shows the kind of detail and the mathematics expected in solutions of such problems.

Problem

Construct a right triangle, given the length of the hypotenuse and the length of the altitude to the hypotenuse.

Solution

Let $\overline{AB}$ and $\overline{CD}$ denote given segments such that the hypotenuse of the right triangle is to be congruent to $\overline{AB}$ and the altitude to the hypotenuse is to be congruent to $\overline{CD}$ (D360a).

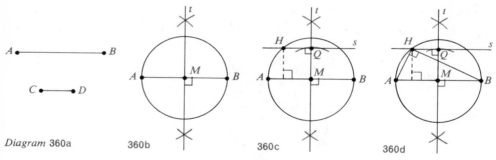

| Diagram 360a | 360b | 360c | 360d |

Use basic constructions to construct line t perpendicular to $\overline{AB}$ at its midpoint M, and construct circle $C(M, r)$ with $\overline{AB}$ as diameter so $r = \dfrac{d(A, B)}{2}$. In t, mark point Q so that $d(M, Q) = d(C, D)$. At Q, construct line s perpendicular to t. If s intersects $C(M, r)$ at H, then $\triangle AHB$ is the desired right triangle.

Discussion

The circle $C(M, r)$, except for points A and B, is the locus of all points P (that these points are in the plane of the construction is understood) such that $\measuredangle APB$ is a right angle. The line s is the locus of all points P in one side of AB at the distance $d(C, D)$ from line AB. Therefore, if s and

$C(M, r)$ intersect at H, $\angle AHB$ is a right angle. So $\overline{AB}$ is the hypotenuse of $\triangle AHB$. Also, because H is in s, the altitude to $\overline{AB}$ from H has the length $d(C, D)$. Line s will intersect $C(M, r)$ if Q is in $C(M, r)$ or interior to $C(M, r)$. (This has not yet been proved in the system.) Therefore, there will be a solution if the given altitude length $d(C, D)$ is equal to, or less than, one half the length of the given hypotenuse. Otherwise, there is no solution.

10 **a** Construct an isosceles triangle, given its base and the radius of its incircle. *Answer*
   b Construct an isosceles triangle, given its base and the radius of its circumcircle.

11 **a** Construct a triangle, given one side and the altitude and the median to that side.
   b Construct a triangle, given two of its sides and the median to one of these given sides.

12 **a** Construct a right triangle, given one of its legs and the altitude to the hypotenuse.
   b Given three noncollinear points D, E, and F, construct the triangle $\triangle ABC$ such that the midpoints of its three sides are points D, E, and F.

◆ **13** **a** Construct a triangle, given two sides and the median to the third side.
   b Construct a triangle, given its three medians.

◆ **14** **a** Given a segment $\overline{XY}$ and two angles $\angle A$ and $\angle B$ such that $\angle A° + \angle B° < 180$, construct a $\triangle DEF$ whose perimeter is $d(X, Y)$ and whose angles at D and F are congruent to $\angle A$ and $\angle B$ respectively. (Hint: Use D361.)

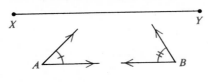

Diagram 361a

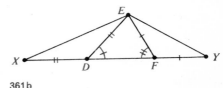

361b

   b Construct a triangle, given one side, an adjacent angle to that side, and a segment whose length equals the sum of the lengths of the other two sides.

Parallel planes 18/4

We previously noticed a pattern in the way that a point separates a line into opposite rays, a line separates a plane into opposite half-planes, and a plane separates space into opposite half-spaces.

When a relation in a set of a particular dimension is similar, or analogous, to a relation in a set of a different dimension, the two relations often are said to be *analogues* of each other. For example, in a plane, three noncollinear points form the vertices of a triangle. A space analogue of this is that four noncoplanar points form the vertices of a triangular pyramid.

In this section, we want to put into the system the basic relations of parallel planes and of parallel lines and planes, as well as the notion of an angle between planes. Nearly all of the definitions and theorems will just be natural analogues in space of definitions and relations that we already have in the plane. The relations themselves are ones you already know, and their proofs are quite straightforward. Therefore, we will follow our practice of saving time with foundation theorems by giving a few sample proofs and starring the other theorems.

Definition 73/4 *Parallel planes, parallel line and plane*

Two planes are parallel if they do not intersect. A line and a plane are parallel if they do not intersect.

Convention

The parallelism of planes α and β will be denoted by the sentence $\alpha \parallel \beta$. The parallelism of plane α and line t will be denoted by the sentence $\alpha \parallel t$. (D362)

$\alpha \parallel \beta$. $\qquad\qquad$ $\alpha \parallel t$.

Diagram 362

Theorem 132/4

A line that is in one of two parallel planes is parallel to the other plane. (D363)

Diagram 363

Proof idea

Line *t* in plane β cannot intersect plane α. Why?

Theorem 133/4

If a plane intersects two parallel planes, the intersections are two parallel lines. (D364)

Proof idea

1 Why is $\alpha \cap \gamma$ a line? Why is $\beta \cap \gamma$ a line?
2 Lines *s* and *t* cannot intersect. Why?

Theorem 134/4

Two planes that are each perpendicular to a line are parallel to each other. (D365)

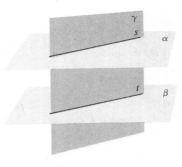

Diagram 364

Proof

Let α and β denote two planes that are each perpendicular to a line *t*.

    If there were a point *P* common to α and β, then α and β would be two planes through *P* that are each perpendicular to *t*. This would contradict Theorem 76/3. Therefore, α and β have no point in common, and so they are parallel.

Diagram 365

* Theorem 135/4

A line that intersects one of two parallel planes and is not contained in that plane also intersects the other plane.

* Corollary 135/4

If two planes are parallel, a third plane that intersects one of them also intersects the other. (D366)

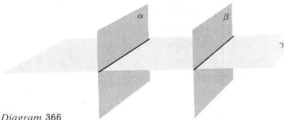

Diagram 366

Theorem 136/4

A line that is perpendicular to one of two parallel planes is perpendicular to the other. (D367)

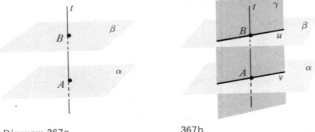

Diagram 367a   367b

Proof

Let α and β denote two parallel planes, and let t denote a line
that is perpendicular to α at A. Then t is not contained in α
and so intersects β at some point B. Let u denote any line
in β through B. Lines t and u determine a plane γ that
intersects plane α in a line v through A, and u is parallel
to v. But because t is perpendicular to α, t is perpendicular
to v. Since, in plane γ, t is perpendicular to one of two
parallel lines, namely v, it is perpendicular to the other,
that is, to u. Thus t is perpendicular to every line of β
through B and so is perpendicular to β.

Theorem 137/4

If P is a point not in plane α, then there is just one plane
through P that is parallel to α. (D368)

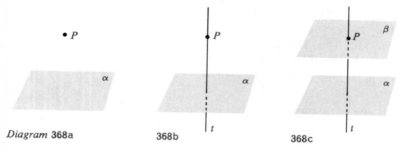

Diagram 368a   368b   368c

Proof

There is a line t through P that is perpendicular to α
(Theorem 79/3). There also is a plane β that is perpendicular
to t at P (Theorem 76/3). Since β and α are two planes that
are each perpendicular to t, then α is parallel to β (Theorem 134/4).

If β' is a plane through P that is parallel to α, then β' is
perpendicular to t at P (Theorem 136/4). But there is just one
plane that is perpendicular to t at P. Therefore, $\beta' = \beta$.

Corollary 137/4

Two planes that are each parallel to a third plane are parallel
to each other. (Weak transitivity property for parallelism of planes)

Proof

These two planes cannot intersect, or they would be two planes
through a point such that each would be parallel to a third
plane. This would contradict Theorem 137/4.

Exercises

1 Comment on the following argument: Two intersecting lines
  determine a plane, and two parallel lines determine a plane.
  Therefore, any two lines determine a plane.

2 Assume that line s is perpendicular to plane α at A and that
  line t is perpendicular to α at B. For each of the following

statements, indicate whether it is necessarily true (T),
possibly true (P), or necessarily false (F).

a If $A \neq B$, then s is parallel to t. *Answer*

b Point $A =$ point B if and only if $s = t$.

c If $s \neq t$, then s is perpendicular to AB.

d The lines s and t determine a plane.

e Any plane perpendicular to s is parallel to α.

3 Let α and β denote two parallel planes, and let t denote a
line that intersects α at point A only. Let P denote any
point of β. Supply the reasons in the following proof
of Theorem 135/4, which states that line t must intersect β.

Case I P is in t. Then t intersects β.

Case II P is not in t. Then P and t determine a plane γ
that intersects α in a line u and intersects β in a
line v (Why?). Line u is not t (Why?), and u is parallel
to v (Why?). Therefore, t is not parallel to v (Why?), and,
since t is coplanar with v, line t intersects line v (Why?).
Therefore, t intersects β (Why?).

4 Supply the reasons for the following proof of Corollary 135/4.
Planes α and β are parallel, and plane γ is a third plane
that intersects α at some point A. Then γ intersects α in a
line u through A. Let v denote any other line that is in γ
and that passes through A. Then v intersects α at A
only (Why?). Therefore, v intersects β (Why?), and so γ
intersects β (Why?).

5 Assume that planes α and β are parallel; the two points A
and C are in α; the two points B and D are in β. If $\overline{AB} \parallel \overline{CD}$,
prove that $\overline{AB} \cong \overline{CD}$. *Answer*

6 *Theorem*
A plane that contains one of two parallel lines either
contains the other line or is parallel to it.

7 If point P is not in plane α, explain why there are infinitely
many lines that pass through P and are parallel to α.

8 *Theorem*
If line t is parallel to plane α, then any plane that contains t is
either parallel to α or intersects α in a line parallel to t. *Answer*

♦ **9** *Theorem*
If line t is parallel to plane α, then any line that is
parallel to t and that intersects α is contained in α.

♦ **10** *Theorem*
If a line is parallel to each of two intersecting planes,
it is parallel to their line of intersection.

♦ **11** *Theorem*
If lines s and t are noncoplanar, then there is exactly
one plane that contains s and is parallel to t.

233

◆ **12** *Theorem*

If two intersecting lines *s* and *t* are parallel to a plane α, then the plane of *s* and *t* is parallel to α.

◆ **13** *Theorem*

The locus of points that are equidistant from the three noncollinear points *A*, *B*, and *C* is a line *t* that is perpendicular to the plane of the points at the circumcenter of △*ABC*.

Just as two intersecting lines form four angles, so two intersecting planes form four angles. However, the angles formed by planes are a type of angle that is new in our system. If *t* is the line of intersection of planes α and β, there are two sides of *t*, sides α′ and α″, in α. There also are two sides of *t*, sides β′ and β″, in β. The union of *t* with a side in α and a side in β is then called a *dihedral angle*. The four dihedral angles formed by planes α and β (D369) are α′ ∪ *t* ∪ β′, α′ ∪ *t* ∪ β″, α″ ∪ *t* ∪ β′, and α″ ∪ *t* ∪ β″.

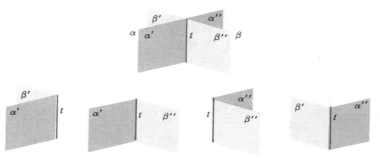

Diagram **369**

Definition 74/4 *Dihedral angle*

A dihedral angle is the union of a line with two noncoplanar open half-planes that have the line as a common edge. If *t* is the edge of the noncoplanar open half-planes α′ and β′, then α′ ∪ *t* ∪ β′ is a dihedral angle. The closed half-planes α′ ∪ *t* and β′ ∪ *t* are the faces of the dihedral angle. The half-planes α′ and β′ are the open faces of the angle.

Convention

The dihedral angle α′ ∪ *t* ∪ β′ will be denoted by the symbol ⊀α′ *t* β′. In other words, the symbol ⊀α′ *t* β′ will represent a set that consists of line *t* and two noncoplanar open half-planes α′ and β′ that have *t* as a common edge. The dihedral angle ⊀α′ *t* β′ also can be denoted by the symbol ⊀*A-BC-D* if *t* = *BC*, if *A* is in α and α′ is the *A*-side of *BC*, and if *D* is in β and β′ is the *D*-side of *BC*. By the properties of the union of sets, ⊀α′ *t* β′ = ⊀β′ *t* α′.

The intersection of a dihedral angle with a plane perpendicular
to its edge is a plane angle of the dihedral angle.

Because t is perpendicular to γ (D370), $\sphericalangle ABC$ is a plane
angle of dihedral angle $\sphericalangle \alpha'\, t\, \beta'$.

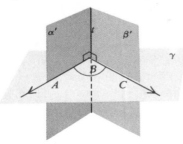

Diagram 370

The theorem that gives us a natural way of assigning a size to
a dihedral angle is the following.

Theorem 138/4
Two plane angles of a dihedral angle are congruent. (D371)

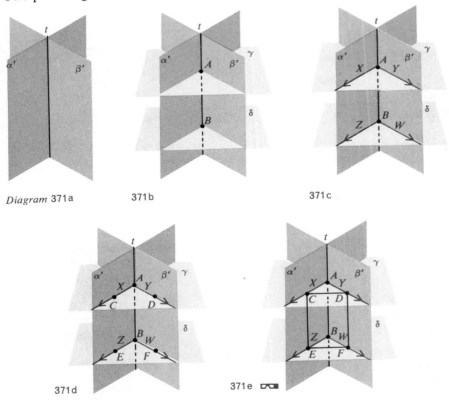

Diagram 371a   371b   371c

371d   371e

Proof

Let $\sphericalangle \alpha'\ t\ \beta'$ denote a dihedral angle, and let γ and δ denote two planes perpendicular to t at points A and B respectively. Let $\sphericalangle XAY$ and $\sphericalangle ZBW$ denote the plane angles of $\sphericalangle \alpha'\ t\ \beta'$ that are in γ and δ respectively such that $\overrightarrow{AX}$ and $\overrightarrow{BZ}$ are in α' and $\overrightarrow{AY}$ and $\overrightarrow{BW}$ are in β'. Because γ and δ are perpendicular to t, they are parallel planes. Therefore,
$$\overrightarrow{AX} \parallel \overrightarrow{BZ} \text{ and } \overrightarrow{AY} \parallel \overrightarrow{BW}.$$

Let k denote a positive number. Then there exist points C and D in $\overrightarrow{AX}$ and $\overrightarrow{AY}$ respectively at distance k from A. There also exist points E and F in $\overrightarrow{BZ}$ and $\overrightarrow{BW}$ respectively at distance k from B. Since $\overline{AC}$ and $\overline{BE}$ are parallel congruent segments, $ABEC$ is a parallelogram. Thus, as opposite sides of a parallelogram,
1 $\overline{AB} \cong \overline{CE}.$

Similarly, $\overline{AD}$ and $\overline{BF}$ are congruent parallel segments. Therefore, $ABFD$ is a parallelogram, and
2 $\overline{AB} \cong \overline{DF}.$

From statements 1 and 2,
3 $\overline{CE} \cong \overline{DF}.$

Because lines CE and DF are parallel to AB, they also are parallel to each other (Theorem 85/4). Thus, $\overline{CE}$ and $\overline{DF}$ are congruent parallel segments, and $CEFD$ is a parallelogram. As opposite sides of this parallelogram,
4 $\overline{CD} \cong \overline{EF}.$

Since
5 $\overline{AC} \cong \overline{AD} \cong \overline{BE} \cong \overline{BF},$

because each of these segments has length k, then, by the side, side, side congruence theorem,
6 $\triangle ACD \cong \triangle BEF.$

Therefore,
7 $\sphericalangle CAD \cong \sphericalangle EBF.$

This also can be stated as
8 $\sphericalangle XAY \cong \sphericalangle ZBW.$

Definition 76/4 *Measure of a dihedral angle*

The measure of a dihedral angle is the common measure of all of its plane angles.

Convention

The measure of a dihedral angle $\sphericalangle \alpha'\ t\ \beta'$ will be denoted by the symbol $(\sphericalangle \alpha'\ t\ \beta')°$. (D372)

Definition 77/4 *Congruent dihedral angles*

Two dihedral angles are congruent if they have the same measure.

Definition 78/4 *Right dihedral angle*

A dihedral angle that has a measure of 90 is a right dihedral angle.

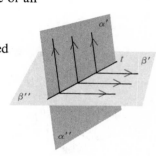

Diagram 372

Definition 79/4 *Perpendicular planes*
Two planes are perpendicular if they intersect and if their
four dihedral angles are right dihedral angles.

* **Theorem 139/4**
If one of the four dihedral angles of two intersecting
planes is a right dihedral angle, then all four
dihedral angles are right dihedral angles. (D373)

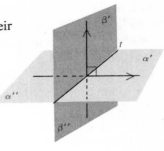

Diagram 373

Exercises

1 Assume that two planes ω and θ intersect in
line m. Make a drawing that represents these
intersecting planes. Label the sides of m in ω
and θ as ω', ω'', θ', and θ'', and denote the
four dihedral angles formed by the planes.

2 The two planes α and β intersect in the line t
(D374). Points B, P, and A are in β', t, and α'
respectively, and these points are such that
$BP \perp t$ and $AP \perp t$ at P.

  a Is PA in α?
  b Is BP in β?
  c Is t perpendicular to the plane of PA and PB?
  d If θ is the plane determined by PA and PB,
  what is the intersection of θ and β'? Of θ and t?
  Of θ and α'? *Answer*
  e If θ is the plane determined by PA and PB,
  what is the intersection of θ and $\angle \beta' t \alpha'$?

3 Use D374 to explain why $\angle BPA$ is a plane angle
of $\angle \beta' t \alpha'$.

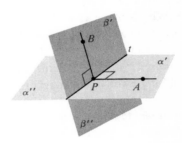

Diagram 374

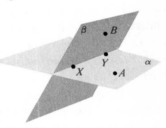

Diagram 375

4 From the convention concerning a dihedral angle,
the notation $\angle A\text{-}XY\text{-}B$ gives the following
information about the figure represented in D375.
Point A is not in line XY, so A and XY determine
a plane $\alpha(A, X, Y)$. Point B is not in the plane α,
so B and XY determine a second plane $\beta(B, X, Y)$.
The dihedral angle represented by $\angle A\text{-}XY\text{-}B$
has for its open faces the A-side of XY in α and
the B-side of XY in β. Use this alternative
symbolism for a dihedral angle (the names of two
points and a line) to name six different
dihedral angles of the triangular pyramid
$ABCD$ represented in D376.

5 For each of the following dihedral angles of the cube
represented in D377, name two plane angles. *Answer*

  a $\angle C\text{-}BF\text{-}E$ c $\angle C\text{-}FG\text{-}D$
  b $\angle A\text{-}DC\text{-}H$ d $\angle A\text{-}BC\text{-}E$

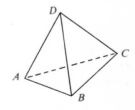

Diagram 376

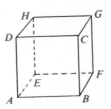

Diagram 377

237

6 Which of the following statements are implied
by the information that $\angle APB$ is a plane angle
of $\angle \alpha' t \beta'$, and A is in α' (D378)?

a $\overrightarrow{PB}$ is contained in β'.

b $t \perp PA$.

c PA is perpendicular to PB.

d $\angle APB° = (\angle \alpha' t \beta')°$.

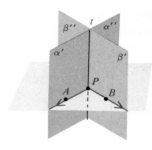

Diagram 378

7 Line AP intersects plane α only at point A, but
AP is not perpendicular to α. Point F is the foot
in α of P, and line FX in α is perpendicular to AF.

a Why is AF perpendicular to plane $\beta(P, F, X)$? *Answer*

b Why is plane $\gamma(A, P, F)$ perpendicular to α?

c If Q in AP has foot G in α and $G \neq F$, why must
A, F, and G be collinear?

8 If line AP intersects plane α only at point A
and if F, which is distinct from A, is the
foot in α of P, then AP is said to intersect α
at an acute angle of measure $\angle PAF°$ (D379). Let
r denote a number such that $0 < r < 90$.

a If A is a point of plane α, describe the
locus of all lines that intersect α at A
and at an angle with measure r. *Answer*

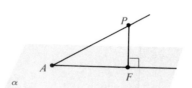

Diagram 379

b Can three of these lines be coplanar?

c If A and B are two points of α and if lines AP and BQ
intersect α at an angle with measure r, can the lines be
coplanar but not parallel?

d If the two lines described in exercise 8c are each
perpendicular to AB, must they be parallel?

The properties of perpendicular planes that are used, for
example, in planning the walls of a building can now be stated.

---

* Theorem 140/4

If a line t is perpendicular to a plane α, then every plane
containing t is perpendicular to α. (D380)

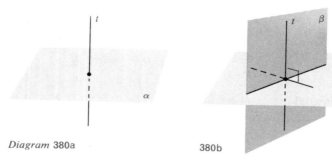

Diagram 380a   380b

*Theorem 141/4

A plane that is perpendicular to one of two parallel planes is perpendicular to the other. (D381)

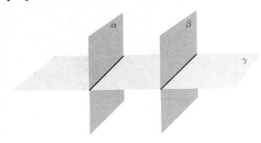

Diagram 381

*Theorem 142/4

If t is a line in plane α, there is just one plane that contains t and is perpendicular to α. (D382)

Diagram 382a   382b

Exercises

The following exercises are a sequence of theorems typical of those used to develop basic properties.

1 *Theorem*

If two planes α and β intersect in line AB and if AX in α and AY in β are each perpendicular to AB, then $\sphericalangle XAY$ is a plane angle of a dihedral angle formed by α and β. (D383) Complete the following proof.

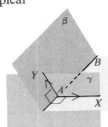

Diagram 383

Plane α is the only plane containing X, A, and B (Why?). Plane β is the only plane containing Y, A, and B (Why?). Since $\alpha \neq \beta$, it follows that X, A, and Y are noncollinear (Why?) and so determine a plane γ. The open ray $\overrightarrow{AX}$ is the intersection of γ and the X-side of AB in α, while the open ray $\overrightarrow{AY}$ is the intersection of γ and the Y-side of AB in β. The plane γ is perpendicular to AB (Why?), so, by definition, $\sphericalangle XAY$ is a plane angle of the dihedral angle $\sphericalangle X$-AB-Y.

239

2 *Theorem*

If line AY is perpendicular to plane α at A
and plane β contains AY, then β is
perpendicular to α. (D384)
Complete the following proof.
Plane β intersects α in some line AB (Why?).
There exists a line AX in α that is perpendicular
to AB (Why?). Then $\measuredangle XAY° = 90$
(Why?). Also, $\measuredangle XAY$ is a plane angle of the
dihedral angle $\measuredangle X\text{-}AB\text{-}Y$ (Why?). Therefore,
β is perpendicular to α. *Answer*

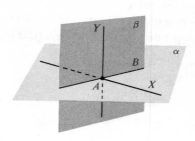

Diagram 384

3 *Theorem*

A line in one of two perpendicular planes is
perpendicular to the other plane if and
only if it is perpendicular to the line
of intersection of the two planes. (D385)
Complete the following proof.
Let α and β denote perpendicular planes that
intersect in line m, and let n denote a
line in α.

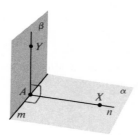

Diagram 385

If n is perpendicular to m at point A, let AY denote the
line in β that is perpendicular to m at A. Then, if X is
any point of n other than A, $\measuredangle XAY$ is a plane angle
of the dihedral angle $\measuredangle X\text{-}m\text{-}Y$ (Why?). Therefore,
$\measuredangle XAY° = 90$ (Why?). Thus AX is perpendicular to AY.
Therefore, AX is perpendicular to β (Why?).

If it is given that n is perpendicular to β, then n is
perpendicular to β at some point A that is in both α and β
(Why?). So A is a point of m. Then, since n has been defined
as a line perpendicular to β, line n is perpendicular
to m at A (Why?).

4 *Theorem*

If line AY is perpendicular to plane α at A, then any
plane β that is perpendicular to α and that contains A also
contains line AY.
Complete the following proof.
Let AB denote the intersection of α and β,
and let AX denote the line of α that is
perpendicular to AB. Then AX is perpendicular
to β (Why?). Therefore, AY is in β (Why?).

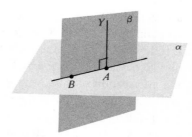

5 *Theorem*

If AB is a line of plane α, there is exactly
one plane that contains AB and is
perpendicular to α. (D386)
Complete the following proof.

Diagram 386

Let AY denote the line perpendicular to α at A. The plane
$\beta(A, B, Y)$ is perpendicular to α (Why?) and contains AB.

Let γ denote a plane that contains AB and is perpendicular
to α. Then γ contains AY (Why?) and $\gamma = \beta$ (Why?).

◆ **6** *Theorem*

If a line s is not perpendicular to a plane α,
then there is exactly one plane that contains
s and is perpendicular to α. (D387)
Complete the following proof.
There is a point P in s, and there is a line t
through P that is perpendicular to α
(Why?). Since $s \neq t$ (Why?), lines s and t
determine a plane β. The plane β contains
s and is perpendicular to α (Why?).

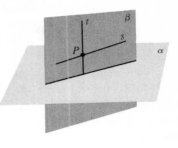

Diagram 387

Let γ denote a plane that contains s and is
perpendicular to α, and let r denote the intersection
of α and γ. In γ, there is a line t' through P that
is perpendicular to r (Why?). Then t' is perpendicular
to α (Why?). Therefore, $t' = t$ (Why?), and $\gamma = \beta$ (Why?).

◆ **7** *Theorem*

If two intersecting planes α and β are each
perpendicular to a plane γ, then their line
of intersection is perpendicular to γ.
(Hint: Use the theorem in exercise 6.)

◆ **8** *Theorem*

If two intersecting lines are respectively
perpendicular to two intersecting planes,
then the plane of the lines is perpendicular
to the intersection of the planes. (D388)
(Hint: Use the theorem in exercise 7.)

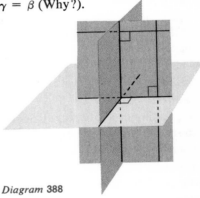

Diagram 388

◆ **9** *Theorem*

There is exactly one line that is perpendicular to two
noncoplanar, or skew, lines.

Notice that Theorem 142/4 implies the existence of dihedral
angles of all sizes between 0 and 180. Let $\sphericalangle ABC$ denote an angle
in plane α (D389a) that has measure r. Then there exist planes

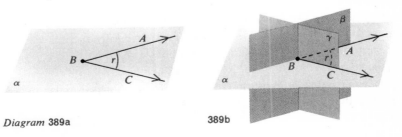

Diagram 389a   389b

β and γ that are perpendicular to α and such that β intersects α in line BA, and γ intersects α in line BC. Plane α is perpendicular to the intersection line of β and γ. Therefore, $\sphericalangle ABC$ is a plane angle of a dihedral angle between β and γ, and this dihedral angle has r as its measure.

The next few definitions and theorems follow a pattern that has become a familiar one in our system.

Definition 80/4 *Interior of a dihedral angle*

The interior of a dihedral angle $\sphericalangle \alpha' t \beta'$ is the intersection of the α'-side of the plane of β and the β'-side of the plane of α.

Definition 81/4 *Opposite dihedral angles*

Two dihedral angles are opposite dihedral angles if the faces of one are the closed half-planes opposite the faces of the other. (Opposite dihedral angles also are called vertical dihedral angles.)

* Theorem 143/4

Opposite dihedral angles are congruent.

Definition 82/4 *Bisector of a dihedral angle*

The open half-plane γ' with edge t is a bisector of the dihedral angle $\sphericalangle \alpha' t \beta'$ if γ' is in the interior of the angle and the measure of $\sphericalangle \alpha' t \gamma'$ equals the measure of $\sphericalangle \gamma' t \beta'$. A plane γ is a bisector of a dihedral angle if an open half-plane in γ is a bisector of the angle.

* Theorem 144/4

Corresponding to a dihedral angle, there is exactly one plane that bisects the dihedral angle, and this plane also bisects the opposite dihedral angle.

* Theorem 145/4

The locus of points that are equidistant from two intersecting planes is the union of the four open half-planes that are the bisectors of the four dihedral angles formed by the planes.

Definition 83/4 *Solid strip between parallel planes*

The solid strip between two parallel planes α and β is the intersection of the α-side of β and the β-side of α. A point, or a set of points, is between α and β if it is contained in the solid strip between α and β.

* Theorem 146/4

If α and β are two parallel planes, there exists a positive number k such that every point of α is at distance k from β and every point of β is at distance k from α.

* Theorem 147/4

The locus of points equidistant from two parallel planes α and β is a plane that is between α and β and is parallel to both α and β.

The plane that is equidistant from two parallel planes α and β
will be called the midparallel of α and β.

No doubt you have thought of several analogue theorems that
we have not stated. We will call attention to some more analogues
in the next set of exercises. Before we conclude this section, however, we want to put into our system two theorems for the plane
and their analogues for space. The plane theorems concern facts
that we have already established, but we now restate them in a
form that will be useful in our later work. The space theorems
are natural extensions of these plane theorems.

* Theorem 148/4

If two lines s and t intersect at A and if line u bisects an
angle formed by s and t, then, for each point X in s, other than
A, there is exactly one point Y in t such that X and Y have
the same foot in u. Corresponding points X and Y are at the
same distance from u and the correspondence $X \leftrightarrow Y$,
together with $A \leftrightarrow A$, is a one-to-one correspondence
between the points of s and t. (D390)

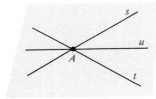

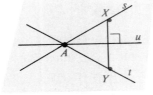

Diagram 390a   390b

* Theorem 149/4

If s and t are parallel lines and if u is their midparallel,
then, for each point X in s, there is exactly one point Y in t
such that X and Y have the same foot in u. Corresponding
points X and Y are at the same distance from u, and the
correspondence $X \leftrightarrow Y$ is a one-to-one correspondence between
the points of s and t. (D391)

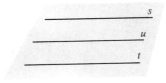

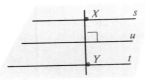

Diagram 391a   391b

If two planes α and β intersect in line t and if plane γ is a
bisector of a dihedral angle formed by α and β, then, for each
point X of α that is not in t, there is exactly one point Y
in β such that X and Y have the same foot in γ. Corresponding
points X and Y are at the same distance from γ. The
correspondence of each point of t with itself, together
with the correspondence $X \leftrightarrow Y$, is a one-to-one correspondence
between the points of α and β. (D392)

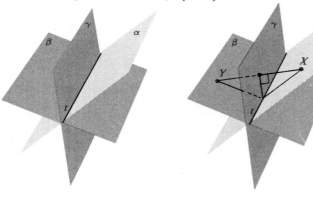

Diagram 392a   392b ⌒▪

* Theorem 151/4

If α and β are two parallel planes and plane γ is the midparallel
of α and β, then, for each point X in α, there is exactly one
point Y in β such that X and Y have the same foot in γ.
Corresponding points X and Y are at the same distance from γ,
and the correspondence $X \leftrightarrow Y$ is a one-to-one correspondence
between the points of α and β. (D393)

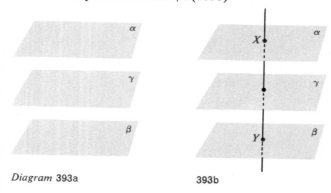

Diagram 393a   393b

Exercises

1 Assume that the two planes α and β intersect in the
line t. Line t separates α and β into the open
half-planes α', α'', β', and β'' respectively (D394).

244

a The interior of the dihedral angle $\angle\alpha''\ t\ \beta''$ is the intersection of which two open half-spaces?

b Name the dihedral angle whose interior is the intersection of the β''-side of plane α and the α'-side of plane β. *Answer*

c Name the dihedral angle that is opposite $\angle\alpha''\ t\ \beta'$. Name the dihedral angle that is opposite $\angle\alpha''\ t\ \beta''$.

d Must $\angle\alpha'\ t\ \beta'$ have measure r if $\angle\alpha''\ t\ \beta''$ has measure r? Why?

e Name a dihedral angle that is congruent to $\angle\beta'\ t\ \alpha''$.

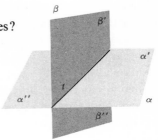

Diagram **394**

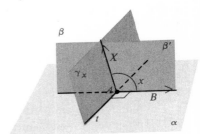

Diagram **395**

2 Here is one way of coordinatizing the planes through a line t. Let α denote a plane containing t (D395). In α, there is a closed ray $\overrightarrow{AB}$, with A in t, that is perpendicular to t. Let β denote the plane that passes through line AB and is perpendicular to α. Then $\overrightarrow{AB}$ can be taken as the initial ray for a ray coordinate system in an open half-plane of β, say β'. Corresponding to each number x such that $0 < x < 180$, there is an open ray $\overrightarrow{AX}$ in β' such that $\angle BAX° = x$. The number x can be assigned as a coordinate for the plane of AX and t, denoted, say, by the symbol γ_x. Every plane through t, except α, has a unique positive coordinate. We can denote α by the symbol γ_0.

a Does γ_{18} bisect a dihedral angle between γ_9 and γ_{27}?

b What is the coordinate of the plane through t that is perpendicular to α? *Answer*

c Does γ_0 bisect a dihedral angle between γ_{10} and γ_{170}? What is the coordinate of the other plane that bisects an angle between γ_{10} and γ_{170}? Are the two bisector planes perpendicular?

d What are the measures of the two dihedral angles between γ_{12} and γ_{168}?

3 We can coordinatize a family of parallel planes by using a coordinate system in any line t that is perpendicular to all the planes of the family. If point X in t has coordinate x, then x can be used as a coordinate for the plane that contains x and is perpendicular to t. We can denote this plane by the symbol γ_x.

a Is $|x - y|$ the distance between γ_x and γ_y if $x \neq y$?

b What is the midparallel of γ_{-7} and γ_{35}? *Answer*

c If γ_{-40} is the midparallel of γ_{-50} and γ_x, what is the value of x?

245

4 Give a definition for supplementary dihedral angles and for adjacent dihedral angles.

5 Assume that plane γ is contained in the solid strip between the two parallel planes α and β. Explain why γ is parallel to both α and β.

6 If the two points A and B in plane α have feet E and F respectively in a parallel plane β, explain why each of the following statements is true.

a $E \neq F$.   **d** $d(A, B) = d(E, F)$.

b $AE \parallel BF$.   **e** E and F have feet A and B

c $d(A, E) = d(B, F)$.   respectively in α. *Answer*

7 Let α, β, and γ denote three planes. For each of the following cases, describe in words and make a sketch of the set of points equidistant from all three of these planes.

a The planes α, β, and γ are parallel planes.

b The planes α, β, and γ intersect in a line t.

c The planes α and β intersect, and α and γ are parallel.

d The planes α, β, and γ intersect in a point.

e The planes α, β, and γ intersect by pairs in three parallel lines.

8 Assume that the open half-plane θ' (D396) is the bisector of the dihedral angle $\sphericalangle\alpha'\ t\ \beta'$. Let point F in θ' have foot T in t. If line s is perpendicular to θ' at F, explain why each of the following statements is true.

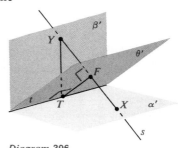

a Line s must intersect α' in a point X, and must intersect β' in a point Y.

b The plane $\gamma(X, Y, T)$ is perpendicular to line t.

c $\sphericalangle FTX \cong \sphericalangle FTY$.

Diagram 396

d $d(X, F) = d(Y, F)$.

(Hint: In Theorem 150/4, the points X and Y are corresponding points and have F as a common foot in θ.)

◆ **9** Let $F_\omega(X)$ denote the foot in plane ω of point X. [So if $F_\omega(X)$ exists, then X is not in ω.] If point A is in plane α and point B is in plane β, which of the following statements are necessarily correct?

a The statement "$F_\alpha(B) = F_\beta(A)$" implies that α is parallel to β.

b If plane α is parallel to plane β, then $F_\alpha(B) = F_\beta(A)$.

c If $F_\beta(A)$ is in α, then α is perpendicular to β.

d If $F_\alpha[F_\beta(A)] = A$, then $\alpha \parallel \beta$. *Answer*

e If $X = F_\beta(A)$ and $Y = F_\alpha(X)$ exist, then $d(A, X) \geqq d(X, Y)$.

◆ **10 a** What planes are equidistant from three collinear points?

b Show that there are infinitely many planes equidistant from three coplanar points.

c How many planes are equidistant from four noncoplanar points? *Answer*

Chapter review

1 Which of the following statements are necessarily true if the coplanar open rays $\overrightarrow{BC}$ and $\overrightarrow{AD}$ are in opposite sides of AB and $\sphericalangle BAD \cong \sphericalangle ABC$?

a $AB \parallel CD$.

b $\triangle CBA \cong \triangle DAB$.

c $CB \parallel DA$.

d If $CX \parallel AD$, then $CX = CB$.

e If CB is perpendicular to a plane α, then $DA \perp \alpha$.

f If $CB \parallel HJ$, then $AD \parallel HJ$.

2 Use the information given in D397 to determine the values of x, y, and z.

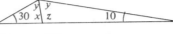

Diagram **397**

3 Assume that lines AB and CD in a plane α are parallel.

a Must point P be in the strip between AB and CD if P is in the B-side of CD?

b If P is in the strip between AB and CD, must P be in the B-side of CD?

c Must $d(A, C)$ and $d(B, D)$ be equal?

d If $\overline{AC} \cong \overline{BD}$, must AC be perpendicular to CD?

e What is the locus of all points in α that are equidistant from AB and CD?

4 If a, b, c, and x denote measures of angles as indicated in D398, which of the following statements are correct?

a $a + b + c = 180$.

b $\sphericalangle ACB° = b + c - a$.

c $a + b + c + x = 360$.

d $x = a + b - c$.

e $\sphericalangle BAC° = 180 - 2x + 2a - 2c$.

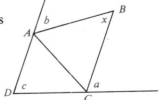

Diagram **398**

5 Five numbers are named below. For each of the following statements, select *all* of the given numbers that correctly complete the statement.

$$0, 1, 2, 3, 4$$

a In a trapezoid, the number of different sides that have the same length can be ⌇⌇⌇.

b In a trapezoid, there must be at least ⌇⌇⌇ obtuse angles.

c The number of right angles in a trapezoid can be ⌇⌇⌇.

247

6 Five geometric figures are listed below. For each of the following statements, select all of the figures in the list that correctly complete the statement.

square, parallelogram, trapezoid, rhombus, rectangle

a A quadrilateral with four sides of the same length must be a ~~~.
b A parallelogram cannot be a ~~~.
c A quadrilateral whose diagonals are not congruent can be a ~~~.
d A quadrilateral whose diagonals bisect each other cannot be a ~~~.

7 Each set of lines named in column 1 is related to a triangle. Each point named in column 2 is a point of intersection of a set of lines. Match each of the sets of lines with the point in which that set of lines intersect.

column 1	*column* 2
a Median lines	A Orthocenter
b Bisectors of the angles	B Centroid
c Perpendicular bisectors of the sides	C Incenter
d Altitude lines	D Circumcenter

8 Circle $C(O, 7)$ is contained in a plane β, and $\overline{AB}$ is a diameter of the circle. If point P denotes a point distinct from A and B, which of the following statements are necessarily true?

a If $\measuredangle APB° = 90$, then P is in $C(O, 7)$.
b If P is in $C(O, 7)$, then $\measuredangle APB° = 90$.
c If $\triangle ABP$ is a right triangle, then point O is its circumcenter.
d If $d(O, P) > 7$ and P is not in AB, then $\measuredangle APB° < 90$.
e If $d(O, P) = 7$, then $\measuredangle APB° = 90$.

9 Indicate which of the following statements are correct.

a If two planes are both perpendicular to a third plane, then the two planes are parallel.
b If two planes are both parallel to a common line, then the two planes are parallel.
c If two planes are both perpendicular to a common line, then the two planes are parallel.
d If each of two planes contains one of two parallel lines, then the two planes are parallel.

10 Assume that each triangle named below has one angle with a measure of 60. For each kind of triangle, are the measures of the other two angles then completely determined?

a Acute
b Isosceles
c Equilateral
d Obtuse
e Right

248

11 Is the interior of a dihedral angle a convex set? Are the faces of a dihedral angle convex? Is a dihedral angle convex? Is the union of the interior and one face of a dihedral angle convex?

12 Indicate whether each of the following statements is necessarily true (T), possibly true (P), or necessarily false (F).

a If α and β are parallel planes and $d(P, \alpha) > d(P, \beta)$, then P is not between α and β.

b If P is not in a plane α, then there is exactly one line through P parallel to α.

c If lines r and s are noncoplanar, then they are two nonintersecting lines.

d If line t intersects plane α and is not perpendicular to α nor contained in α, then there is exactly one line of α that is perpendicular to t.

e If P, Q, and R are three points of $\triangle ABC$ and belong to sides $\overline{AB}$, $\overline{BC}$, and $\overline{CA}$ respectively, then the perimeter of $\triangle ABC$ is equal to or greater than $d(P, Q) + d(Q, R) + d(R, P)$.

f If a circumcircle to a quadrilateral exists, then there also exists an incircle to the quadrilateral.

g If $\triangle PQR$ is the midpoint triangle of $\triangle ABC$, then the altitude lines of $\triangle ABC$ are the perpendicular bisectors of the sides of $\triangle PQR$.

h A line contained in the strip between two parallel planes is parallel to both planes.

i If the two planes α and β are perpendicular and line t is perpendicular to β, then $t \parallel \alpha$.

j If dihedral angle $\measuredangle A\text{-}BC\text{-}D$ is congruent to dihedral angle $\measuredangle A\text{-}BC\text{-}E$ and $E \neq D$, then the two dihedral angles are opposite angles.

k If two planes α and β intersect in line t and plane θ is a bisector of a dihedral angle between α and β, then, for every point P in θ not in t, $d(P, \alpha) = d(P, \beta)$.

Cumulative review

1 If the coordinates of points A and B in line AB are a and b respectively, determine $d(A, B)$ for the following values of a and b.

a $a = \frac{5}{12}$, $b = \frac{3}{7}$.   **c** $a = -0.0987$, $b = -0.0897$.

b $a = -\frac{4}{11}$, $b = \frac{7}{10}$.   **d** $a = \frac{23}{32}$, $b = -\frac{15}{17}$.

2 For each of the following, describe the set (open ray, segment, and so on) consisting of those points X in a line

249

such that the coordinate x of these points satisfies the given condition.

a $|x| \leq (0.001)^{1000}$.   d $|x| < 0$.

b $x \geq -10000000$.   e $|x| \geq 0$.

c $|x| > 0$.   f $x^2 - 2x = 63$.

3 For each of the following statements, decide whether the statement is necessarily true (T), possibly true (P), or necessarily false (F).

a If ray $\mathcal{S}$ is between rays $\mathcal{R}$ and $\mathcal{T}$, then $\mathcal{R} \cup \mathcal{T}$ is an angle.

b If $\overline{AB}$ and t denote respectively a segment and a line in space, then $AB \cup t$ is not a convex set.

c If the three closed rays $\overrightarrow{OA}$, $\overrightarrow{OB}$, and $\overrightarrow{OC}$ are coplanar, then one of them is between the other two.

d If the closed rays $\overrightarrow{AX}$, $\overrightarrow{BY}$, and $\overrightarrow{CZ}$ are like directed but not coplanar, then A, B, and C are noncollinear.

e If the closed rays $\overrightarrow{AX}$, $\overrightarrow{BY}$, and $\overrightarrow{CZ}$ are coplanar and like directed, then A, B, and C are collinear.

4 Which of the following cannot denote the measure of an angle?

a $|-72|$

b $400 \, (\measuredangle A°)$

c 58π

d $\measuredangle A_1° + \measuredangle A_2° + \measuredangle A_3° + \ldots + \measuredangle A_{181}°$

5 Assume that $\triangle ABC$ is in plane α, and set $\mathcal{S}$ is the union of the three lines AB, AC, and BC.

a Can there be a point of α with four feet in $\triangle ABC$?

b How many points in α have three feet in $\mathcal{S}$?

c What is the locus of points in α that have exactly two feet in $\mathcal{S}$?

d If $\measuredangle A$ and $\measuredangle B$ are acute, describe the set of points in α whose feet in $\triangle ABC$ all belong to $\overline{AB}$.

e Describe the set of points interior to $\triangle ABC$ that have exactly one foot in the triangle.

6 If 100, 8, and x are the lengths of the sides of a triangle, then which of the following must necessarily be true?

a $x \geq 90$.   d $x < 115$.

b $x < 100$.   e $x > 120$.

c $x > 92$.

7 Assume that the plane α separates space into two open half-spaces $\mathcal{R}'$ and $\mathcal{R}''$. If A and B are two points in space, which of the following statements are necessarily true?

a If A and B are in $\mathcal{R}'$ and $\mathcal{R}''$ respectively, then $\overline{AB} \cap \alpha$ is some point P in α.

b Space is the union of $\mathcal{R}'$ and $\mathcal{R}''$.

c If A and B are in $\mathcal{R}'$, then the intersection of $\overline{AB}$ and α is the empty set.

d If A is in α and B is not in α, then the open ray $\overrightarrow{AB}$ is contained in the B-side of α and the open ray $\overrightarrow{BA}$ is contained in the opposite side of α.

e If B is the foot of A in α, then A is in $\mathcal{R}'$ or in $\mathcal{R}''$.

8 For each of the following statements, indicate whether the statement is necessarily true (T), possibly true (P), or necessarily false (F).

a Corresponding to a line t and a point P not in t, there is exactly one line through P that does not intersect t.

b Two coplanar nonintersecting lines are parallel.

c Oppositely directed rays are opposite rays.

d If two like-directed rays are collinear, then one contains the other.

e If two oppositely directed rays are collinear, then one contains the other.

f If line a intersects line b and $a \neq b$, then each of the lines is a transversal of the other.

g If $\measuredangle A$ and $\measuredangle B$ are complements and $\measuredangle C$ and $\measuredangle D$ are complements, then $\measuredangle A$ and $\measuredangle C$ are congruent.

9 From the list of terms "centroid, circumcircle, orthocenter, incenter," select terms that will correctly complete the following statement. "A triangle and its midpoint triangle must have the same $\sim\!\sim$ and cannot have the same $\sim\!\sim$."

10 Points A, B, C, and D are collinear; $d(A, C) = 5$; $d(A, B) = 7$; $d(D, B) = 9$; $d(A, D) = 2$. Give the values of $d(B, C)$ and $d(C, D)$.

11 Lines s and t are parallel, and a point A is in the strip between s and t. How many circles that pass through A are tangent to s and t?

12 If three of the perpendicular bisectors of the sides of quadrilateral $ABCD$ are concurrent at a point O, must the perpendicular bisector of the fourth side pass through O? Why?

13 Assume that $\overline{DC}$ is the shorter base of trapezoid $ABCD$. If $\measuredangle D° = 100$, which of the following statements are correct?

a $\measuredangle C° > 60$.   **c** $\measuredangle A° < 100$.

b $\measuredangle B° < 100$.   **d** $\measuredangle C° > 100$.

14 In the plane of three noncollinear points A, B, and C, can a line t exist such that t is equidistant from A, B, and C but no point of t is equidistant from A, B, and C? Explain your answer.

The parallel- **19/5**
proportion You probably have noticed that, so far, we have very few nu-
problem merical relations. That is, we have very few formulas that allow us
to calculate the size of one part of a figure by using information
about the size of other parts. Without such formulas, our geometry would have little value for application to engineering, physics,
and other sciences. We can get such numerical relations, in a
natural way, from the proportion property of figures that have the
same shape but do not necessarily have the same size (D399).
Two such figures are said to be *similar*.

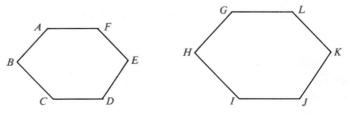

Diagram 399

The proportion property of two similar figures is the fact that
a correspondence exists between the figures such that if a segment

in one figure has a length k times that of the corresponding segment in the other, then every segment in the first has a length that is k times that of its corresponding segment in the other. Thus, in terms of lengths, one figure is k times the size of the other, and the lengths of the corresponding segments are proportional. This is a familiar property that we use in connection with reading maps and making models. We now want to establish this property in the formal system. We will establish it first for triangles and then for polygons. Later we will see how to extend the property to figures in general.

It is our parallel axiom that implies the existence of similar figures. Such figures do not exist in Lobachevsky's geometry. Consequently, it is not surprising that we begin our study of similarity with the properties of parallels. The following parallel-proportion problem is, in fact, a key to the whole theory of similarity. Suppose that a transversal s intersects parallel lines a, b, c, and d at points A, B, C, and D respectively (D400a). Also,

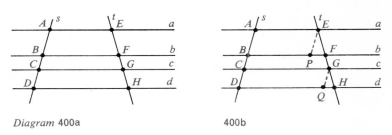

Diagram 400a   400b

suppose that a transversal t intersects a, b, c, and d at points E, F, G, and H respectively. The problem is to prove the following proportion.

1) $$\frac{d(A,\ B)}{d(C,\ D)} = \frac{d(E,\ F)}{d(G,\ H)}.$$

The relation of proportion 1 to similar triangles is indicated in D400b by the dotted segments $\overline{EP}$ and $\overline{GQ}$. From the parallelograms $BPEA$ and $DQGC$, we get the congruences $\overline{EP} \cong \overline{AB}$ and $\overline{GQ} \cong \overline{CD}$. Therefore, if proportion 1 can be proved, it will imply the following proportion.

2) $$\frac{d(E,\ P)}{d(G,\ Q)} = \frac{d(E,\ F)}{d(G,\ H)}.$$

Proportion 2 is a proportion between the sides of the similar triangles $\triangle EFP$ and $\triangle GHQ$.

As we will see, the parallel-proportion problem is extremely deceptive. The problem looks simple and, in one sense, its solution is easy. But in another sense, the problem involves some of the

253

most important and difficult ideas in mathematics. The best way to understand this situation is to study the problem in a straightforward manner. What is easy and what is difficult about the proof will turn up in a natural way as we go along.

We begin our work with some definitions and with a convention that will simplify the language without causing any confusion of ideas.

Convention

The phrase "ratio of segments" will always mean the ratio of the lengths of the segments.

Definition 84/5 *Corresponding points and segments in transversals of parallels*

If s and t are transversals of two parallel lines a and b in a plane α, then s and t are transversals of the set of lines $\mathbb{S}$ consisting of a, b, and all lines of α that are parallel to a and b. A point in s and a point in t are called corresponding points if both belong to the same parallel line in $\mathbb{S}$. A segment in s and a segment in t are corresponding segments if the endpoints of one are corresponding points to the endpoints of the other.

From Definition 84/5, points A, B, C, and D correspond respectively to E, B, G, and H (D401). Segment $\overline{CD}$ corresponds to $\overline{GH}$, and $\overline{DB}$ corresponds to $\overline{HB}$.

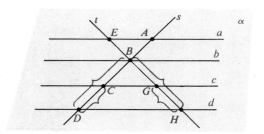

Diagram 401

Definition 85/5 *Segment intercepted by parallels*

If a transversal intersects two parallel lines a and b at points A and B respectively, $\overline{AB}$ is said to be cut off, or intercepted, by the parallels.

Suppose that a straight road, say Oak Avenue, cuts across a series of parallel streets, say A Street, B Street, and so on. The successive parallel streets may or may not be the same distance apart. Oak Avenue may or may not be perpendicular to the streets.

254

In any case, the following property seems intuitively obvious. If A Street and B Street are a mile apart but their intersections with Oak Avenue are one and one-half miles apart, then any two of the streets that are a mile apart will intersect Oak Avenue at points that are one and one-half miles apart. Moreover, if two intersections are one and one-half miles apart, then the corresponding parallel streets will be a mile apart. In other words, if line t is a transversal of parallels and if two of the parallels at distance d apart intercept a segment of length k in line t, then each two of the parallels at distance d will intercept a segment of length k in t. Conversely, every segment in t of length k will be intercepted by two parallels at distance d from each other.

The preceding example actually involves three ideas. The distance d depends upon k. The length k depends upon d. The way in which d and k determine each other is the same for all positions along the transversal. The proof of the next theorem shows how, with a little care, we can establish all three of these ideas at the same time.

_____

Theorem 152/5

If a transversal t intersects parallel lines a, b, c, and d
(some of which may be identical) at points A, B, C, and D
respectively and if segments $\overline{AB}$ and $\overline{CD}$ exist, then $\overline{AB}$ and $\overline{CD}$
are congruent if and only if the distance between a and b
equals the distance between c and d.

Proof
The existence of $\overline{AB}$ and $\overline{CD}$ implies that $A \neq B$, $a \neq b$, $C \neq D$, and $c \neq d$. It is to be shown that each of statements
$d(A, B) = d(C, D)$ and $d(a, b) = d(c, d)$ implies the other.

If t is perpendicular to the parallel lines, then
$d(A, B) = d(a, b)$ and $d(C, D) = d(c, d)$. Hence,
$d(A, B) = d(C, D)$ clearly implies $d(a, b) = d(c, d)$ and
conversely.

Consider the case in which t is not perpendicular
to the parallel lines. (D402a)

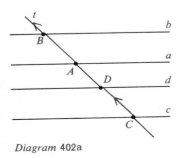

Diagram 402a

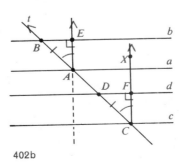

402b

255

Because segments $\overline{AB}$ and $\overline{CD}$ are in t, one of the closed rays $\overrightarrow{DC}$ or $\overrightarrow{CD}$ has the direction of $\overrightarrow{AB}$, and there is no loss of generality in supposing that

1 $\overrightarrow{AB}$ and $\overrightarrow{CD}$ are like directed.

Let E denote the foot in b of A. Because t is not perpendicular to b, $E \neq B$. So $\triangle BAE$ is a right triangle and

2 $\sphericalangle BAE$ is acute.

By Theorem 86/4, there is a closed ray $\overrightarrow{CX}$ such that

3 $\overrightarrow{AE}$ and $\overrightarrow{CX}$ are like directed.

If $C = A$, then $\overrightarrow{AE}$ and $\overrightarrow{CX}$ are the same ray and $\overrightarrow{AB}$ and $\overrightarrow{CD}$ are the same ray. Thus,

4 $\sphericalangle BAE \cong \sphericalangle DCX$.

If $C \neq A$, then $\overrightarrow{AE}$ and $\overrightarrow{CX}$ cannot be collinear since t then would intersect their line twice. Therefore, from statement 3, $\overrightarrow{AE}$ and $\overrightarrow{CX}$ are parallel. From statements 1 and 3, it follows that, for the transversal t of the parallel lines AE and CX, angles $\sphericalangle BAE$ and $\sphericalangle DCX$ are corresponding angles at A and C. These angles, therefore, are congruent, so statement 4 is correct in all cases. From statements 2 and 4, it follows that

5 $\sphericalangle DCX$ is acute.

Let F denote the foot in line CX of D. Then from statement 5 and Lemma 126a/4, F is in the open ray $\overrightarrow{CX}$, so $\overrightarrow{CX} = \overrightarrow{CF}$. Thus, statement 4 can be restated as

6 $\sphericalangle BAE \cong \sphericalangle DCF$.

The line DF is perpendicular to CF because F is the foot in CX of D. The line d is perpendicular to CF because d is perpendicular to AE, and line CF either is AE or is parallel to it. But through D, there is only one line that is perpendicular to CF. Therefore, $d = DF$, and F is in line d. Now because E is the foot in b of A and because F is the foot in d of C,

7 $d(A, E) = d(a, b)$

and

8 $d(C, F) = d(c, d)$.

Consider $\triangle BAE$ and $\triangle DCF$, which are right triangles. By statement 6, the angles at A and C are congruent. Also, the right angles at E and F are congruent. If $d(A, B) = d(C, D)$ is true, then $\triangle BAE \cong \triangle DCF$ by the hypotenuse, angle theorem. As corresponding segments of the congruence, $\overline{AE} \cong \overline{CF}$ and $d(A, E) = d(C, F)$. Therefore, from statements 7 and 8, $d(a, b) = d(c, d)$. Thus, $d(A, B) = d(C, D)$ implies $d(a, b) = d(c, d)$. If $d(a, b) = d(c, d)$ is true, then from statements 7 and 8, $\overline{AE} \cong \overline{CF}$. Thus, by the angle, side, angle congruence theorem, $\triangle BAE \cong \triangle DCF$. As corresponding parts of the congruence, $\overline{AB} \cong \overline{CD}$, so $d(A, B) = d(C, D)$. Thus $d(a, b) = d(c, d)$ implies $d(A, B) = d(C, D)$.

Notice that, from the way we constructed the statement and the proof of Theorem 152/5, we now have the property in a very general form. Segments $\overline{AB}$ and $\overline{CD}$ can have any positions in t. The segments may be the same (the theorem is then trivially correct), they may have an endpoint in common, they may overlap, or they may have positions like those pictured in D402b.

Exercises

1 A transversal line t intersects four parallel lines a, b, c, and d at A, B, C, and D respectively. A second transversal r intersects the parallel lines in the set of points E, F, G, and H.

a If C and H are corresponding points in t and r respectively, to which of the parallel lines does H belong? *Answer*

b If G is in d, which point of t corresponds to G?

c If B and E are corresponding points and $\overline{AB}$ and $\overline{FE}$ are corresponding segments, to which line does F belong?

d Illustrate by a diagram the relations given in exercises 1a, 1b, and 1c in which $<A, D, B>$ and $<D, B, C>$.

e Which segment in r is intercepted by b and d? Name the corresponding segment intercepted in t. *Answer*

f The parallel-proportion property, discussed on page 253, asserts that the ratio of $\overline{AB}$ to $\overline{DC}$ is the same as that of $\overline{FE}$ to $\sim\!\sim\!$.

2 Following step 5 in the proof of Theorem 152/5, we wanted to show that the foot F in d of point C was such that $\angle BAE \cong \angle DCF$. To do this, we first defined F to be the foot in $\overrightarrow{CX}$ of D. Then we showed that $CF = CX$ implied the angle congruence and that $DF = d$ implied that F was also the foot in d of C. Supply the reasons for the following alternate proof.

Let F denote the foot in d of C. Then F is not D (Why?), so $\angle DFC° = 90$ (Why?). Therefore, $\angle DCF$ is acute (Why?). Because AE and CF are both perpendicular to b (Why?), either $AE = CF$ or $AE \parallel CF$. Thus, $\overrightarrow{AE}$ and $\overrightarrow{CF}$ are either like directed or oppositely directed causing $\overrightarrow{CX}$ and $\overrightarrow{CF}$ to be either like directed or oppositely directed (Why?). Consequently, $\overrightarrow{CX}$ and $\overrightarrow{CF}$ are either the same ray or opposite rays (Why?). But because $\angle DCF$ and $\angle DCX$ are acute, $\overrightarrow{CF}$ cannot be opposite $\overrightarrow{CX}$ (Why?) and so $\overrightarrow{CF} = \overrightarrow{CX}$. Therefore, statement 4 of the proof on page 256 can be restated as $\angle BAE \cong \angle DCF$.

3 In the proof of Theorem 152/5, it is stated that there is no loss of generality in supposing that $\overrightarrow{AB}$ and $\overrightarrow{CD}$ are

like directed. To demonstrate this generality, consider the case in which $\overrightarrow{AB}$ and $\overrightarrow{CD}$ are oppositely directed. Then $\overrightarrow{AB}$ and $\overrightarrow{DC}$ are like directed. Interchange the letters C and D and the letters c and d throughout the proof (and in D402), and check that the conclusion of the theorem is just the same.

Corollary 152/5

If lines s and t are transversals of a set of parallel lines, two segments in s are congruent if and only if the corresponding segments in t are congruent. (D403)

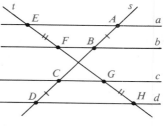

Diagram 403

Proof

Let $\overline{AB}$ and $\overline{CD}$ denote two segments in s that are intercepted respectively by the parallel lines a and b and by the parallel lines c and d. Let $\overline{EF}$ and $\overline{GH}$ denote the segments in t corresponding to $\overline{AB}$ and $\overline{CD}$. By Theorem 152/5, $\overline{AB} \cong \overline{CD}$ implies $d(a, b) = d(c, d)$. This in turn, by Theorem 152/5, implies $\overline{EF} \cong \overline{GH}$. By the same argument, the second congruence implies the first.

Exercises

1 Assume that a transversal t intersects three parallel lines $e, f,$ and g at points $E, F,$ and G respectively.
   a Does $t \perp f$ imply $d(e, g) = d(E, G)$?
   b Does $d(e, g) = d(E, G)$ imply $t \perp f$?
   c Does $d(E, F) = d(F, G)$ imply $d(e, f) = d(f, g)$? *Answer*
   d Does $d(E, F) = d(F, G)$ imply f is between e and g?

2 The transversal t intersects n coplanar parallel lines in n points, and the transversal r intersects these n coplanar parallel lines in n points as shown in D404.
   a Does $\overline{R_1 R_{10}} \cong \overline{T_3 T_5}$ imply $d(a_1, a_{10}) = d(a_3, a_5)$? *Answer*
   b Does $d(a_1, a_{10}) = d(a_3, a_5)$ imply $\overline{R_1 R_{10}} \cong \overline{T_3 T_5}$?
   c Does $\overline{R_7 R_{13}} \cong \overline{T_9 T_{10}}$ imply $\overline{R_9 R_{10}} \cong \overline{T_7 T_{13}}$?
   d Does $\overline{R_1 R_8} \cong \overline{R_2 R_5}$ imply $\overline{T_1 T_8} \cong \overline{T_2 T_5}$? *Answer*
   e If $d(R_1, R_2) = d(R_5, R_6) = 7$ and $d(T_1, T_2) = d(T_5, T_6) = x$, must $x = 7$?
   f In exercise 2e, can x equal 7? Can x be greater than 7? Can x be less than 7?
   g If $\overline{R_1 R_2}, \overline{R_5 R_9},$ and $\overline{T_1 T_2}$ have lengths 3, 3, and 8 respectively, what is the length of $\overline{T_5 T_9}$? *Answer*

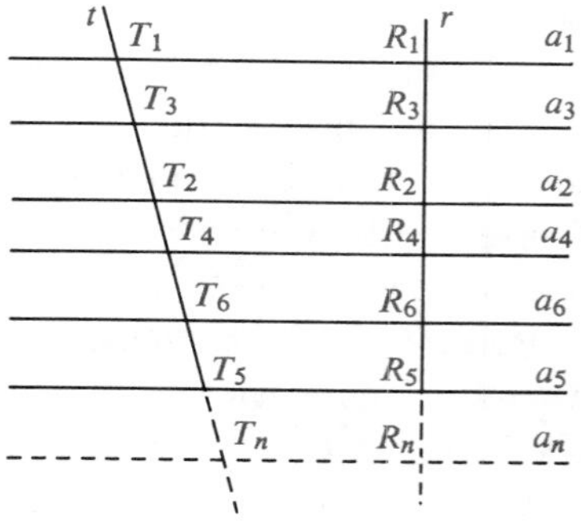

t		r	
T_1		R_1	a_1
T_3		R_3	a_3
T_2		R_2	a_2
T_4		R_4	a_4
T_6		R_6	a_6
T_5		R_5	a_5
T_n		R_n	a_n

Diagram 404

258

Corollary 152/5 tells us that, if a segment in s of length x corresponds to a segment in t of length y, then every segment in s of length x corresponds to one in t of length y. So if x is regarded as a kind of unit in s, then y, in general different from x, is a corresponding unit in t. Here is the basic idea of a difference in scale that we associate with proportion.

A natural thing to do next is to show that, corresponding to an addition of units in s, there is an addition of units in t. More exactly, we expect that, to a segment of length $2x$ in s, there should correspond a segment of length $2y$ in t. Likewise, a segment of length $3x$ should correspond to a segment of length $3y$, and so on.

To "add" segments in either s or t, we need the rather simple property that, if A, B, C, and D are four successive points in a line, then the length of $\overline{AD}$ is the sum of the lengths of the successive segments $\overline{AB}$, $\overline{BC}$, and $\overline{CD}$ (D405). This property is easy

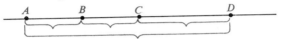

Diagram 405

to prove for four points or for five points, but the proof for n points requires a principle of logic called *mathematical induction*, which is discussed briefly in Appendix 2. Because it takes considerable time and practice to become thoroughly familiar with induction, we will star the few theorems whose proofs require this principle.

Definition 86/5 *Successive points and segments in a line*
The n collinear points P_1, P_2, P_3, $\ldots$, P_n, where $n > 2$, are successive points in a line in the order $(P_1, P_2, P_3, \ldots, P_n)$ if all the points belong to the closed ray $\overrightarrow{P_1 P_2}$ and if
$d(P_1, P_2) < d(P_1, P_3) < d(P_1, P_4) < \ldots < d(P_1, P_n)$.
The ordered set of segments $(\overline{P_1 P_2}, \overline{P_2 P_3}, \overline{P_3 P_4}, \ldots, \overline{P_{n-1} P_n})$ are the $n - 1$ successive segments in the line corresponding to the order $(P_1, P_2, P_3, \ldots, P_n)$ in which the points are successive in the line.

* Theorem 153/5
If the n collinear points P_1, P_2, P_3, $\ldots$, P_n are successive in a line in the order $(P_1, P_2, P_3, \ldots, P_n)$, then the length of $\overline{P_1 P_n}$ is the sum of the lengths of the successive segments $\overline{P_1 P_2}$, $\overline{P_2 P_3}$, $\overline{P_3 P_4}$, $\ldots$, $\overline{P_{n-1} P_n}$.

Theorem 153/5 will give us a way of adding distances along a transversal. But to relate the addition to corresponding segments in two transversals s and t, we need the fact that, if A, B, C, and D are successive points in s, then the corresponding points E, F, G, and H are successive in t (D406). Again, if we use the

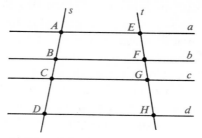

Diagram 406

betweenness properties of parallel lines, this fact is not difficult to show for four points or for five; however, the proof of this fact for n points requires induction.

---

* Theorem 154/5

If s and t are transversals of a set of parallel lines and the points P_1, P_2, P_3, ..., P_n are successive in s in the order $(P_1, P_2, P_3, ..., P_n)$, then the corresponding points Q_1, Q_2, Q_3, ..., Q_n are successive in t in the order $(Q_1, Q_2, Q_3, ..., Q_n)$.

Exercises

These three exercises verify each of Theorems 153/5 and 154/5 for the case of four points.

1 Four points A, B, C, and D are successive in that order in a line t. There exists a coordinate system for t in which a, b, c, and d are the respective coordinates of A, B, C, and D and in which $a = 0$. The open ray $\overrightarrow{AB}$ is the set of points with positive coordinates (D407).

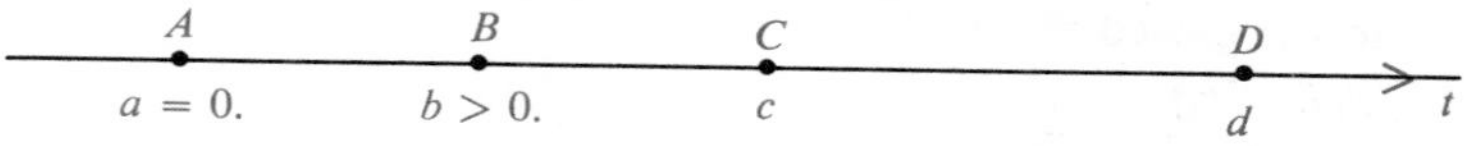

Diagram 407

a Why must C and D belong to $\overrightarrow{AB}$? *Answer*
b Why do $d(A, B)$, $d(A, C)$, and $d(A, D)$ have the values b, c, and d?
c Why is $a < b < c < d$?
d How does it follow from exercise 1c that $<A, B, C>$ and $<B, C, D>$?
e Why are the equalities $d(B, C) = c - b$ and $d(C, D) = d - c$ correct?
f Use exercises 1b and 1e to show that the following is true: $d(A, B) + d(B, C) + d(C, D) = d(A, D)$.

260

2 Assume that A, B, C, and D denote four collinear points such that $\langle A, B, C\rangle$ and $\langle B, C, D\rangle$. Let a, b, c, and d denote the respective coordinates for these points, with $a = 0$ and $b > 0$.

   a Show that $a < b < c < d$. *Answer*

   b Show that C and D belong to $\overrightarrow{AB}$.

   c Show that $d(A, B) < d(A, C) < d(A, D)$.

(Thus, from exercises 2a, 2b, and 2c, $\langle A, B, C\rangle$ and $\langle B, C, D\rangle$ imply that A, B, C, and D are successive in that order.)

3 Four parallel lines a, b, c, and d are intersected by transversal t at A, B, C, and D respectively and by transversal s at E, F, G, and H respectively (D408). Assume that in t the points A, B, C, and D are successive in that order. Then from exercise 1, it follows that $\langle A, B, C\rangle$ and $\langle B, C, D\rangle$.

   a Why do the relations $\langle A, B, C\rangle$ and $\langle B, C, D\rangle$ imply that b is between a and c and that c is between b and d?

   b How does exercise 3a imply that $\langle E, F, G\rangle$ and $\langle F, G, H\rangle$?

(Notice that from exercise 3b and exercise 2, it follows that E, F, G, and H are successive in s in that order.)

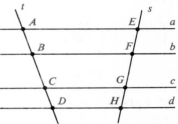

Diagram **408**

We can now establish a correspondence between the addition of segments on different transversals.

Theorem 155/5

If m is any positive integer and if s and t are transversals of a set of parallel lines such that a segment in s of length x corresponds to a segment in t of length y, then a segment in s of length mx corresponds to a segment in t of length my. (D409)

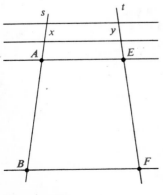

Diagram **409a**

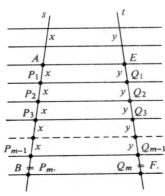

409b

261

Let $\overline{AB}$ denote a segment in s of length mx, and let E and F denote the points of t corresponding to A and B respectively. Then $\overline{EF}$ corresponds to $\overline{AB}$. There is a coordinate system for s in which A is the origin and the coordinate of B is positive. Let $P_1, P_2, P_3, \ldots, P_m$ denote the points of s that have the respective coordinates $x, 2x, 3x, \ldots, mx$. Let $Q_1, Q_2, Q_3, \ldots, Q_m$ denote the points of t corresponding to $P_1, P_2, P_3, \ldots, P_m$ respectively.

Because $d(A, P_m) = mx$ and $d(A, B) = mx$, point $P_m = B$. Likewise, the corresponding point Q_m is F.

From the nature of their coordinates, it is clear that $A, P_1, P_2, \ldots, P_m = B$ are successive in s in the order $(A, P_1, P_2, \ldots, P_m)$. Hence the corresponding points $E, Q_1, Q_2, \ldots, Q_m$ are successive in t in the order $(E, Q_1, Q_2, \ldots, Q_m)$.

The successive segments $\overline{AP_1}, \overline{P_1P_2}, \overline{P_2P_3}, \ldots, \overline{P_{m-1}B}$ in s each have length x. Since it is given that a segment of length x in s corresponds with one of length y in t, each of the successive segments $\overline{EQ_1}, \overline{Q_1Q_2}, \overline{Q_2Q_3}, \ldots, \overline{Q_{m-1}F}$ has length y. There are m of these successive segments. Therefore, by Theorem 153/5, $\overline{EF}$ has length my.

Exercises

1 Assume that the collinear points A, B, C, D, and E are successive in that order.

   a If the lengths of $\overline{AB}$, $\overline{AC}$, $\overline{DE}$, and $\overline{BE}$ are 2, 3, 4, and 8 respectively, what are the lengths of $\overline{BC}$ and $\overline{CD}$?

   b If the coordinates of A and B are -3 and -5 respectively, use the information given in exercise 1a to find the coordinates of C, D, and E. *Answer*

2 Lines s and t are transversals of a set of parallel lines. Assume that a segment in s of length 2 corresponds to a segment in t of length 7 and that a segment in s of length x corresponds to one in t of length y. Use this information, along with Theorem 155/5, to complete each of the following.

   a $x = 8 \Rightarrow y = $ ~~~~. *Answer*

   b $x = 12 \Rightarrow y = $ ~~~~.

   c $y = 21 \Rightarrow x = $ ~~~~.

   d $y = 35 \Rightarrow x = $ ~~~~.

3 The statement "The numbers a and b are proportional to the numbers c and d" is defined to mean $\dfrac{a}{b} = \dfrac{c}{d}$, where a, b, c, and d are nonzero. Thus, a and b, in that order, are proportional to c and d, in that order.

a If a and b are proportional to c and d, are c and d proportional to a and b? Why? *Answer*

b If a and b are nonzero numbers, are a and b proportional to a and b? Why?

c If a and b are proportional to c and d and if c and d are proportional to e and f, are a and b proportional to e and f? Why?

d Is the proportionality of ordered pairs of nonzero numbers an equivalence relation? Why?

4 For each of the following cases, determine the value of x.

a x and 7 are proportional to 3 and 5. *Answer*

b 1 and x are proportional to 4 and 9.

c -2 and 5 are proportional to x and 7.

d 2 and -4 are proportional to 3 and $-x$.

5 If a and b are proportional to c and d, where a, b, c, and d are nonzero, show that the following statements are true.

a a and c are proportional to b and d.

b b and a are proportional to d and c.

c d and b are proportional to c and a.

6 Using $a = 1$, $b = 2$, $c = 5$, and $d = 10$, verify each statement in exercise 5.

7 An ordered triple (a, b, c) is proportional to the ordered triple (d, e, f) if and only if $\dfrac{a}{d} = \dfrac{b}{e} = \dfrac{c}{f}$.

a Is the ordered triple $(2, -1, 6)$ proportional to the ordered triple $(-10, 5, -30)$?

b If the ordered triple $(2, 1, x)$ is proportional to $(3, y, 7)$, what are the values of x and y? *Answer*

c If the ordered triple $(x, 2, 5)$ is proportional to $(3, kx, 25)$, what are the values of x and k?

It might seem that we now have everything we need to establish the parallel-proportion property. For suppose that $\overline{AB}$ and $\overline{CD}$ are two segments in one transversal of parallel lines and that $\overline{EF}$ and $\overline{GH}$ are corresponding segments in another transversal. Pick some segment of length x that "divides" into $\overline{AB}$, say m times, and "divides" into $\overline{CD}$, say n times, where m and n are positive integers. Then the lengths of $\overline{AB}$ and $\overline{CD}$ are mx and nx. In the second transversal, some segment of length y corresponds to a segment of length x. So by Theorem 153/5, the lengths of $\overline{EF}$ and $\overline{GH}$ are my and ny. Therefore, $\dfrac{d(A, B)}{d(C, D)} = \dfrac{mx}{ny} = \dfrac{m}{n} = \dfrac{my}{ny} = \dfrac{d(E, F)}{d(G, H)}$. This argument corresponds to what we said was the easy part of the parallel-proportion problem. We now state the easy case as a theorem.

263

If s and t are transversals of a set of parallel lines with segments $\overline{AB}$ and $\overline{CD}$ in s corresponding respectively to $\overline{EF}$ and $\overline{GH}$ in t, and if the ratio of the length of $\overline{AB}$ to that of $\overline{CD}$ is $\frac{m}{n}$, where m and n are positive integers, then the ratio of the length of $\overline{EF}$ to that of $\overline{GH}$ is also $\frac{m}{n}$. (D410)

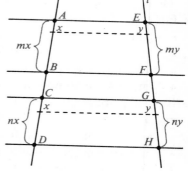

Proof

It is given that

$$1 \quad \frac{d(A, B)}{d(C, D)} = \frac{m}{n}.$$

So

$$2 \quad \frac{d(A, B)}{m} = \frac{d(C, D)}{n}.$$

Let x denote $\dfrac{d(A, B)}{m}$. Then from statement 2 it also follows that $x = \dfrac{d(C, D)}{n}$. Therefore,

$$3 \quad d(A, B) = mx \text{ and } d(C, D) = nx.$$

Diagram 410

Let y denote the length of any segment in t that corresponds to one in s of length x. Then, by Theorem 155/5, the segments $\overline{AB}$ and $\overline{CD}$ in s of lengths mx and nx must correspond to segments in t of lengths my and ny respectively. Thus,

$$4 \quad d(E, F) = my \text{ and } d(G, H) = ny.$$

Then

$$5 \quad \frac{d(E, F)}{d(G, H)} = \frac{my}{ny} = \frac{m}{n}.$$

Statements 1 and 5 together imply the parallel-proportion

$$\frac{d(A, B)}{d(C, D)} = \frac{d(E, F)}{d(G, H)}.$$

Although we have proved Theorem 156/5, we still have not solved the parallel-proportion problem. In the proof of Theorem 156/5, we defined x as $\dfrac{d(A, B)}{m}$ and then obtained $x = \dfrac{d(C, D)}{n}$. These equalities imply $m = \dfrac{d(A, B)}{x}$ and $n = \dfrac{d(C, D)}{x}$. The ancient Greeks discovered, when studying this solution of the parallel-proportion problem, that there exist pairs of numbers a and b such that, *for every real number* x, at least one of the numbers $\dfrac{a}{x}$ and $\dfrac{b}{x}$ is not an integer. Such a pair of numbers are said to be *in-*

commensurable. If there is a number x such that both $\dfrac{a}{x}$ and $\dfrac{b}{x}$ are integers, then a and b are called *commensurable*. Therefore, the method of proof in Theorem 156/5 succeeded because, in assuming that the ratio of $\overline{AB}$ to $\overline{CD}$ was the quotient of two integers $\dfrac{m}{n}$, we assumed that lengths of the segments were commensurable.

A real number that can be expressed as the quotient of two integers is called a *rational number,* and one that cannot be expressed in this form is called an *irrational number.* Theorem 156/5 shows that the parallel-proportion property is true when the ratio involved is a rational number. For the irrational case, one needs either a theory of limits for sets of numbers or properties of irrational numbers. Because of these difficulties, most introductory books take the general case of the parallel-proportion problem without proof. However, because this problem played such an important part in the history of mathematics and because the numerical relations of geometry and trigonometry depend upon it, we want to show how the general case, Theorem 157/5, can be proved. Nevertheless, to proceed more quickly with the geometry, your teacher may prefer to handle this theorem as a starred theorem and to have you simply read its proof and the description of its ideas.

First, for two integers m and n, since the sum $m + n$, the difference $m - n$, and the product $m \cdot n$ is again an integer (positive, negative, or zero), it follows by arithmetic that, for two rational numbers, the sum $\dfrac{m}{n} + \dfrac{m'}{n'}$, the product $\dfrac{m}{n} \cdot \dfrac{m'}{n'}$, and the quotient $\dfrac{m}{n} \div \dfrac{m'}{n'}$, is again a rational number (division by zero being excluded). Therefore, if I is one irrational number, then, for every rational number x, the product xI is an irrational number. For suppose that x is rational and that $xI = y$. Then $I = \dfrac{y}{x}$. Therefore, if y were rational, then $\dfrac{y}{x}$ would be rational. Then I would be rational, and this would be a contradiction. Since xI is irrational for all rational x, one can use a single irrational number to define as many other irrational numbers as there are rational numbers.

That there *is* an irrational number, and hence infinitely many, was proved in a very simple way. Any quotient of integers $\dfrac{m}{n}$ can be reduced to lowest terms. Therefore, if $\sqrt{2}$ is rational, it can be expressed in the form

1) $\sqrt{2} = \dfrac{m}{n}$,

where $\frac{m}{n}$ is in lowest terms. Then both m and n cannot be even integers or the fraction could be still further reduced. This eliminates one possibility for $\frac{m}{n}$ (D411).

Next suppose that m is odd. Then m^2 is odd. But from statement 1, $m^2 = 2n^2$ and $2n^2$ is even. An odd number and an even number cannot be equal, so m is not odd. This removes two more possibilities (D411). The only remaining case is when m is even and n is odd. But if m is even, it is twice some integer m'. Substituting $m = 2m'$ in assumption 1 gives $2n^2 = (2m')^2 = 4m'^2$, or $n^2 = 2m'^2$. But since n is odd, n^2 is odd, while $2m'^2$ is clearly even. So again there is a contradiction. Since all possibilities have been eliminated, $\sqrt{2}$ cannot be a rational number. Thus $\sqrt{2}$ is irrational, and so $x\sqrt{2}$ is irrational for every nonzero rational number x.

Now consider two points A and B in a coordinatized line, where the number a is the coordinate of A, the number b is the coordinate of B, and $a < b$ (D412). Since every negative integer is a rational number, there certainly is a rational number x that is less than a. (Remember that $-10 < -2$.) And since every positive integer also is a rational number, there is a rational number y that is greater than b. Suppose we call a point whose coordinate is a rational number a *rational point*. Then A and B are between the rational points X and Y that have coordinates x and y respectively (D413).

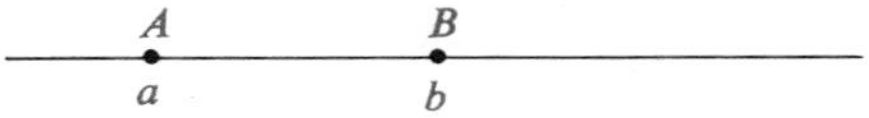

m	∉	O	O	E
n	∉	E	O	O

m	∉	Ø	Ø	E
n	∉	∉	Ø	O

Diagram 411

Diagram 412

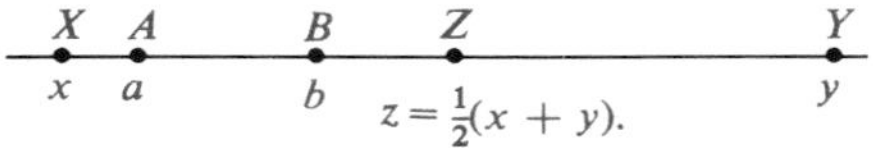

Diagram 413

$z = \frac{1}{2}(x + y).$

Next it is not difficult to show that the midpoint Z of $\overline{XY}$ has the coordinate $z = \frac{1}{2}(x + y)$. Since x and y are rational, $x + y$ is rational. And since $\frac{1}{2}$ is rational, $\frac{1}{2}(x + y)$ is rational. So z is rational. Thus the midpoint of two rational points X and Y is rational. By the same argument, the midpoint of X and Z and the midpoint of Z and Y are rational. Continuing in this way, by taking midpoints of midpoints, it seems clear that there is an infinite number of rational points between X and Y. Each stage in our "midpoint process" doubles the number of successive segments from X to Y, but it divides by 2 the distance between the adjacent rational endpoints of the segments. That is, if k is $d(X, Y)$, then, at the first stage, $\frac{k}{2}$ is the distance $d(X, Z)$ and $d(Z, Y)$. At the next stage, the rational points selected are at distance $\frac{k}{4}$ apart. Since, at each stage, they are evenly spaced between

266

X and Y, it follows that, when the distance between adjacent points becomes less than $d(A, B)$, then there has to be one of our rational points between A and B, and, therefore, a rational number between the numbers a and b.* Thus, the following properties seem reasonable.

Properties of real numbers

1) If a and b are two real numbers, then there is a rational number between a and b.

2) For any positive real numbers a and b, if every positive rational number greater than a is greater than b and if every positive rational number less than a is less than b, then $a = b$.

If a were not b in property 2, then, by property 1, there would be a positive rational number between a and b that would be a positive rational number that is greater than one of the numbers a or b and less than the other. This would contradict the information given in property 2.

Property 2 of real numbers gives us a way of getting at the equality of two irrationals by using inequalities with rationals. We will apply this method in the proof of Theorem 157/5. In doing so, we will use some simple properties of inequalities that first are reviewed in the following set of exercises.

Exercises

1 By definition, two numbers a and b are commensurable if there is a number x such that $\dfrac{a}{x} = m$ and $\dfrac{b}{x} = n$, where m and n are integers. To decide if a and b are commensurable, we try to express the ratio $\dfrac{a}{b}$ in the form $\dfrac{m}{n}$, where m and n are integers. If such integers m and n exist, then x can be defined by $x = \dfrac{a}{m} = \dfrac{b}{n}$. Find integers m and n and the corresponding number x for the following commensurable pairs a and b.

a $a = 3$; $b = 5$. *Answer*   d $a = 3.4$; $b = .07$.

b $a = \frac{1}{3}$; $b = \frac{5}{8}$.   e $a = \frac{2}{3}$; $b = .5$.

c $a = \frac{2\sqrt{7}}{3}$; $b = \frac{\sqrt{7}}{8}$. *Answer*   f $a = .875$; $b = \frac{1}{6}$.

2 Two segments $\overline{AB}$ and $\overline{CD}$ are said to be commensurable if their lengths $d(A, B)$ and $d(C, D)$ are a pair of commensurable numbers. A geometric way of expressing this

---

* The fact that dividing the number $k = d(X, Y)$ successively by 2, that is, dividing it by 2, 4, 8, 16, . . . , will finally produce a number less than $d(A, B)$ is also a definite property of real numbers.

property is to say that the two segments $\overline{AB}$ and $\overline{CD}$ are commensurable if there exists a segment $\overline{XY}$ of length x such that each of the segments $\overline{AB}$ and $\overline{CD}$ is the union of an integral number of successive segments that are congruent to $\overline{XY}$ (D414).

Diagram 414

If A, B, C, and D in line t have coordinates a, b, c, and d, show that, for each of the following sets of values, $\overline{AB}$ and $\overline{CD}$ are commensurable and give a value for x.

a $a = \frac{2}{3}$; $b = 10$; $c = \frac{1}{7}$; $d = \frac{3}{2}$. *Answer*

b $a = \sqrt{2}$; $b = 3\sqrt{2}$; $c = 5\sqrt{2}$; $d = 0$.

3 Prove that $\sqrt{3}$ is an irrational number. (Hint: Assume that $\sqrt{3} = \frac{m}{n}$, where m and n are integers. Use the fact that every integer can be expressed in one of the forms $3x$, $3x + 1$, or $3x + 2$, where x is an integer.)

4 Let the statement "$a \otimes b$" be defined to mean that the numbers a and b are commensurable. Show that $\otimes$ is an equivalence relation by establishing each of the following.

a $a \otimes a$.

b $a \otimes b \Rightarrow b \otimes a$.

c $a \otimes b$ and $b \otimes c \Rightarrow a \otimes c$.

5 Two basic properties of inequalities are given below. Use these properties to show that statements 5a and 5b are true.

$$x > y \text{ and } z > 0 \text{ imply } xz > yz.$$

$$z > 0 \text{ implies } \frac{1}{z} > 0.$$

a If $\frac{a}{b} > \frac{c}{b}$ and $b > 0$, then $a > c$. *Answer*

b If $a > c$ and $b > 0$, then $\frac{a}{b} > \frac{c}{b}$.

6 Give a numerical example that illustrates each of statements 5a and 5b.

7 Another basic property of inequalities is the transitive property, that is, $a > b$ and $b > c$ implies $a > c$. If x and y are *positive* numbers, show that each of the following statements is true.

a $x > y$ implies $x^2 > y^2$. (Hint: Show that $x^2 > xy$ and $xy > y^2$.)

268

b $x^2 > y^2$ implies $x > y$. (Hint: Show that $x = y$ and $y > x$ are incorrect.)

c Show that $\sqrt{2} < \frac{3}{2} < \sqrt{3}$, which shows the existence of a rational number between $\sqrt{2}$ and $\sqrt{3}$.

◆ **8** Find a rational number between $\sqrt{5}$ and $\sqrt{7}$.

By using property 2 of real numbers (page 267), we can now modify the proof of Theorem 156/5 for the parallel-proportion problem so that the proof holds in all cases. That is, we can modify the proof so that it holds even if the ratio of the segments is not a rational number.

Theorem 157/5 *Parallel-proportion theorem*

If s and t are transversals of a set of parallel lines, with points A, B, C, and D in s corresponding to points E, F, G, and H in t so that segments $\overline{AB}$ and $\overline{CD}$ exist, then

$$\frac{d(A, B)}{d(C, D)} = \frac{d(E, F)}{d(G, H)}. \quad \text{(D415)}$$

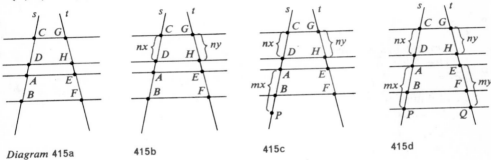

Diagram 415a   415b   415c   415d

Proof

Let the positive numbers a and b be defined by

$$1 \quad a = \frac{d(A, B)}{d(C, D)}, \quad b = \frac{d(E, F)}{d(G, H)}.$$

Let $\frac{m}{n}$ denote any positive rational number, where m and n denote positive integers. We propose to show that $\frac{m}{n} > a$ implies $\frac{m}{n} > b$

and that $\frac{m}{n} < a$ implies $\frac{m}{n} < b$. Hence we propose to show, by property 2 of real numbers, that $a = b$.

Let the number x be defined by

$$2 \quad x = \frac{d(C, D)}{n}, \quad \text{so } d(C, D) = nx.$$

Let y be defined to be the length of a segment in t that corresponds to one in s of length x. Then, by Theorem 155/5,

269

since $\overline{CD}$ in s has length nx, the corresponding segment in t has length ny. So

3 $d(G, H) = ny$.

In the closed ray $\overrightarrow{AB}$, there exists a point P such that

4 $d(A, P) = mx$.

If Q denotes the point of t corresponding to P, the segment $\overline{EQ}$ corresponds to $\overline{AP}$. So, by Theorem 155/5, the length of $\overline{EQ}$ is my, that is,

5 $d(E, Q) = my$.

From statements 4 and 2, we have

6 $\dfrac{d(A, P)}{d(C, D)} = \dfrac{mx}{nx} = \dfrac{m}{n}$.

From statements 5 and 3, we have

7 $\dfrac{d(E, Q)}{d(G, H)} = \dfrac{my}{ny} = \dfrac{m}{n}$.

We now carry through separate arguments for $\dfrac{m}{n} > a$ and $\dfrac{m}{n} < a$. Suppose that

8 $\dfrac{m}{n} > a$.

Then, from statements 6 and 1,

9 $\dfrac{d(A, P)}{d(C, D)} > \dfrac{d(A, B)}{d(C, D)}$.

Statement 9 implies

10 $d(A, P) > d(A, B)$.

Accordingly,

11 B is between A and P, so A, B, and P are successive in s. By Theorem 154/5, it follows that, for the points E, F, and Q corresponding to A, B, and P, we then have

12 E, F, and Q are successive in t, so F is between E and Q. This betweenness relation implies that

13 $d(E, Q) > d(E, F)$

and, therefore, that

14 $\dfrac{d(E, Q)}{d(G, H)} > \dfrac{d(E, F)}{d(G, H)}$.

Substituting from statements 7 and 1 in statement 14 gives

15 $\dfrac{m}{n} > b$.

Next suppose that

16 $\dfrac{m}{n} < a$.

Then, from statements 6 and 1,

17 $\dfrac{d(A, P)}{d(C, D)} < \dfrac{d(A, B)}{d(C, D)}$.

Statement 17 implies that

18 $d(A, P) < d(A, B)$.

Accordingly,

19 P is between A and B, so A, P, and B are successive in s.
By Theorem 154/5, it follows that, for the points E, F, and Q
corresponding to A, B, and P, we then have

20 E, Q, and F are successive in t, so Q is between E and F.
This betweenness relation implies that

21 $d(E, Q) < d(E, F)$

and, therefore, that

22 $\dfrac{d(E, Q)}{d(G, H)} < \dfrac{d(E, F)}{d(G, H)}$.

By substituting from statements 7 and 1 in statement 22, we get

23 $\dfrac{m}{n} < b$.

From statements 8 and 15,

24 $\dfrac{m}{n} > a$ implies $\dfrac{m}{n} > b$;

while from statements 16 and 23,

25 $\dfrac{m}{n} < a$ implies $\dfrac{m}{n} < b$.

Therefore, $a = b$, so $\dfrac{d(A, B)}{d(C, D)} = \dfrac{d(E, F)}{d(G, H)}$.

We conclude this section with a kind of converse to the
parallel-proportion problem. Although the theorem is somewhat
clumsy to put into words, it is not hard to prove and is a theorem
that we will find useful.

Theorem 158/5

Let s and t denote transversals of a set of parallel lines, and
let A, B, C, and D denote points in s for which $\overline{AB}$ and $\overline{CD}$ exist.
(D416)

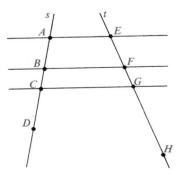

Diagram 416a

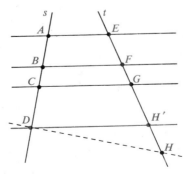

416b

271

If points E, F, and G in t correspond to A, B, and C respectively and if point H in t is in the D-side of the parallel through C, then $\dfrac{d(A, B)}{d(C, D)} = \dfrac{d(E, F)}{d(G, H)}$ implies that H is the point in t corresponding to D. If $H \neq D$, then line HD is parallel to the lines of the parallel set.

Proof

Let H' denote the point in t corresponding to D. By the parallel-proportion theorem, Theorem 157/5,

1 $\dfrac{d(A, B)}{d(C, D)} = \dfrac{d(E, F)}{d(G, H')}.$

It is given that

2 $\dfrac{d(A, B)}{d(C, D)} = \dfrac{d(E, F)}{d(G, H)}.$

From algebra, statements 1 and 2 imply that

3 $d(G, H) = d(G, H').$

Because H and H' are both in the D-side of the parallel line through C, point H' belongs to the closed ray $\overrightarrow{GH}$. Since there cannot be two points in a ray at the same distance from its origin, statement 3 implies that $H' = H$. Therefore, H is the point in t corresponding to D.

Notice that the proof of Theorem 158/5 is valid for all positions of $\overline{AB}$ and $\overline{CD}$ in s. The following special case will be particularly useful when we work with triangles.

Corollary 158/5

If a line w intersects $\sphericalangle BAD$ at P in the open ray $\overrightarrow{AB}$ and at Q in the open ray $\overrightarrow{AD}$, then the lines BD and PQ are identical or parallel if and only if $\dfrac{d(A, P)}{d(A, B)} = \dfrac{d(A, Q)}{d(A, D)}.$ (D417)

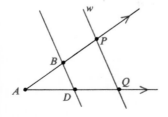
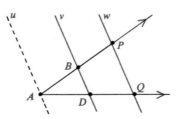

Diagram 417a   417b

Proof

Let v denote BD, and let u denote the line through $\dot{A}$ that is parallel to v. If the line $w = PQ$ is either identical with v or parallel to it, then, in the transversal AB, the points A, B, and P correspond to A, D, and Q respectively in transversal AD. Therefore, the proportion follows from the parallel-proportion theorem, Theorem 157/5. On the other hand, if the proportion is correct, then Q corresponds to P, by Theorem 158/5, and since B and P correspond respectively to D and Q, the lines BD and PQ are either identical or parallel.

Exercises

1 Lines s and t are transversals of a set of parallel lines and points A, B, C, and D in s correspond to E, F, G, and H respectively in t (D418). The lengths of $\overline{AB}$, $\overline{CD}$, and $\overline{EF}$ are 2, 5, and 3 respectively.

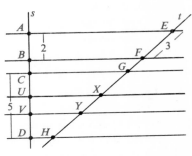

Diagram 418

  a What is the length of $\overline{GH}$? *Answer*
  b If $d(E, G) = 4$, what is the length of $\overline{AC}$?
  c What is the ratio of $\overline{AB}$ to $\overline{EF}$?
  d What is the ratio of $\overline{CD}$ to $\overline{GH}$?
  e What is the ratio of $\overline{AC}$ to $\overline{EG}$?
  f If $\overline{UV}$ in s corresponds to $\overline{XY}$ in t, what is the ratio of $\overline{UV}$ to $\overline{XY}$? *Answer*

2 If s and t are transversals of a set of parallel lines and if $\overline{AB}$ and $\overline{CD}$ in s correspond respectively to $\overline{EF}$ and $\overline{GH}$ in t, show that the ratio of $\overline{AB}$ to $\overline{EF}$ is the same as that of $\overline{CD}$ to $\overline{GH}$. (Hence prove that the ratio of corresponding segments is constant.)

3 Assume that points D and E are respectively in $\overline{AB}$ and $\overline{AC}$ of $\triangle ABC$ and are such that $DE \parallel BC$ (D419).

Diagram 419

  a The ratio of $\overline{AD}$ to $\overline{DB}$ equals the ratio of $\sim\!\sim$ to $\sim\!\sim$.
  b The ratio of $\overline{AB}$ to $\overline{AC}$ equals the ratio of $\sim\!\sim$ to $\sim\!\sim$.
  c If $d(D, E) = \frac{1}{2} d(B, C)$, what is the ratio of $\overline{AD}$ to $\overline{DB}$?
  d What is the length of $\overline{EC}$ if the lengths of $\overline{AB}$, $\overline{AC}$, and $\overline{DB}$ are 18, 24, and 6 respectively? If the lengths are 7, 3, and $\sqrt{2}$ respectively? *Answer*
  e What is the length of $\overline{AC}$ if the lengths of $\overline{AD}$, $\overline{DB}$, and $\overline{AE}$ are $\frac{1}{2}$, $\frac{2}{3}$, and $\frac{3}{4}$ respectively? If the lengths are 5, $\sqrt{11}$, and $\sqrt{2}$ respectively?

4 The lengths of sides $\overline{AB}$ and $\overline{AC}$ of $\triangle ABC$ are 9 and 6 respectively. Assume that point X is in the open ray $\overrightarrow{AB}$ and point Y is in the open ray $\overrightarrow{AC}$.
  a Is $CB \parallel YX$ if $d(A, X)$ and $d(A, Y)$ are 6 and 9 respectively? If the lengths are 9 and 6 respectively?

b If $CB \parallel YX$ and Y is in the A-side of CB, is $d(A, X) > 9$?

c What are the possible values of $d(A, X)$ if $CB \parallel YX$ and $d(C, Y) = 3$? *Answer*

d What is the length of $\overline{AY}$ if $CB \parallel YX$ and $d(B, X) = 5\pi$?

e Is $YX \parallel CB$ if $d(A, X) = 9 + \sqrt{5}$ and

$$d(A, Y) = \frac{18 + 2\sqrt{5}}{3}?$$

5 Line t passes through the centroid Q of $\triangle ABC$ (the intersection point of the medians) and is parallel to side $\overline{AB}$ (D420). Show that t divides each of the other sides into two segments whose lengths have the ratio $\frac{1}{2}$.

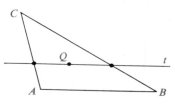

Diagram 420

◆ **6** Given segments $\overline{AB}$, $\overline{CD}$, and $\overline{EF}$, explain a construction (see section 16/4) of segment $\overline{GH}$ such that the lengths of $\overline{AB}$ and $\overline{CD}$ are proportional to those of $\overline{EF}$ and $\overline{GH}$.

7 Let $\overrightarrow{AB}$ denote a given segment (D421), and choose a closed ray $\overrightarrow{AX}$ that is noncollinear with $\overline{AB}$. In $\overrightarrow{AX}$, let $\overline{AP_1}$, $\overline{P_1P_2}$, and $\overline{P_2P_3}$ be successive congruent segments. Assume that the lines through P_1 and P_2 that are parallel to P_3B intersect $\overline{AB}$ at points Q_1 and Q_2 respectively.

a Explain why $\overline{AQ_1}$, $\overline{Q_1Q_2}$, and $\overline{Q_2B}$ are successive congruent segments.

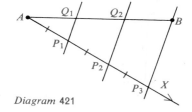

Diagram 421

b What is the ratio of $\overline{AQ_1}$ to $\overline{Q_1B}$? *Answer*

c Explain how the method in this exercise could be used to construct a point Q_7 between A and B such that $\dfrac{d(A, Q_7)}{d(Q_7, B)} = \dfrac{7}{10}$.

◆ **8** Given three segments $\overline{AB}$, $\overline{CD}$, and $\overline{EF}$, explain a construction to determine a point X in $\overline{EF}$ such that $\dfrac{d(A, B)}{d(C, D)} = \dfrac{d(E, X)}{d(X, F)}$.

9 Assume that point P is not in line t. What is the locus of all the midpoints of segments joining P and points in t?

10 The open ray $\overrightarrow{OQ}$ is between the open rays $\overrightarrow{OP}$ and $\overrightarrow{OR}$ (D422). Points A, B, and C are in $\overrightarrow{OP}$, $\overrightarrow{OQ}$, and $\overrightarrow{OR}$ respectively, and $PQ \parallel AB$ and $QR \parallel BC$. Prove that $PR \parallel AC$.

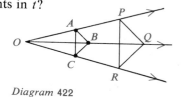

Diagram 422

◆ **11** Let $\overline{AB}$ denote a segment, and let r denote any positive number.

a Prove that there is exactly one point P between A and B such that $\dfrac{d(A, P)}{d(P, B)} = r$. *Answer*

b Prove that, if $r \neq 1$, then there is exactly one other point Q of line AB such that $\dfrac{d(A, Q)}{d(Q, B)} = r$.

Similar 20/5
triangles We now define a similarity of two triangles in much the same way that we defined a congruence of triangles.

Definition 87/5 *Similarity of triangles*
A correspondence of $\triangle ABC$ and $\triangle DEF$ is a similarity if corresponding angles are congruent and if the three sides of $\triangle ABC$ are proportional to the corresponding sides of $\triangle DEF$. If there is a similarity of $\triangle ABC$ and $\triangle DEF$, then the triangles are similar triangles. (D423)

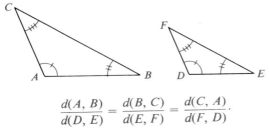

$$\frac{d(A, B)}{d(D, E)} = \frac{d(B, C)}{d(E, F)} = \frac{d(C, A)}{d(F, D)}.$$

Diagram 423

Convention
The fact that $ABC \leftrightarrow DEF$ is a similarity of $\triangle ABC$ and $\triangle DEF$ will be denoted by the sentence $\triangle ABC \sim \triangle DEF$.

Comment
$\triangle ABC \sim \triangle DEF$ implies $\triangle DEF \sim \triangle ABC$.

Comment
Every congruence of triangles is a similarity (the ratio of each side to its corresponding side is 1), so every triangle is similar to itself.

Similarity between triangles has the identity property and is a symmetric relation. Theorem 159/5 shows that similarity also is transitive.

Theorem 159/5
The existence of a similarity between triangles is a transitive relation, that is, $\triangle ABC \sim \triangle DEF$ and $\triangle DEF \sim \triangle GHI$ imply $\triangle ABC \sim \triangle GHI$.

Proof
From the transitivity of the congruence of angles, the given congruences
1   $\angle A \cong \angle D, \ \angle B \cong \angle E, \ \angle C \cong \angle F$
and
2   $\angle D \cong \angle G, \ \angle E \cong \angle H, \ \angle F \cong \angle I$

275

imply

3 $\angle A \cong \angle G, \ \angle B \cong \angle H, \ \angle C \cong \angle I.$

From $\triangle ABC \sim \triangle DEF$, it follows that there is a number a
such that

$$4 \quad \frac{d(A, B)}{d(D, E)} = \frac{d(B, C)}{d(E, F)} = \frac{d(C, A)}{d(F, D)} = a.*$$

From $\triangle DEF \sim \triangle GHI$, there is a number b such that

$$5 \quad \frac{d(D, E)}{d(G, H)} = \frac{d(E, F)}{d(H, I)} = \frac{d(F, D)}{d(I, G)} = b.$$

From statements 4 and 5, we obtain

6 $d(A, B) = a\, d(D, E)$

and

7 $d(D, E) = b\, d(G, H).$

Substituting from statement 7 in statement 6 yields
$d(A, B) = ab\, d(G, H)$. Therefore,

$$8 \quad \frac{d(A, B)}{d(G, H)} = ab.$$

By the same argument, from statements 4 and 5,

$$9 \quad \frac{d(B, C)}{d(H, I)} = ab \text{ and } \frac{d(C, A)}{d(I, G)} = ab.$$

Hence,

$$10 \quad \frac{d(A, B)}{d(G, H)} = \frac{d(B, C)}{d(H, I)} = \frac{d(C, A)}{d(I, G)}.$$

By statements 3 and 10,

11 $\triangle ABC \sim \triangle GHI.$

After we defined congruence of triangles, we established a
number of congruence conditions such as the angle, side, angle
theorem and the side, side, side theorem. We now want to establish various conditions that determine two similar triangles. We
will find a pattern of theorems much like those that we have for
congruence. The proofs of these theorems will be simplified by
Lemma 160/5.

Lemma 160/5

If Y' belongs to the open ray $\overrightarrow{XY}$ and if $\angle XYZ$ and $\angle XY'Z'$
are congruent coplanar angles with $\overrightarrow{YZ}$ and $\overrightarrow{Y'Z'}$ in the same side
of line XY, then the lines YZ and $Y'Z'$ are either identical
or parallel.

Proof

If $Y' = Y$, then, by Axiom 10/2, $\angle XYZ^\circ = \angle XY'Z'^\circ$ implies
$\overrightarrow{YZ} = \overrightarrow{Y'Z'}.$

---

* Since a is the common value of the three ratios, it is sometimes called the *ratio of proportionality.*

If $Y' \neq Y$, then $\sphericalangle XYZ$ and $\sphericalangle XY'Z'$ are congruent, corresponding angles. (D424) Hence, by Corollary 88a/4, YZ and $Y'Z'$ are parallel.

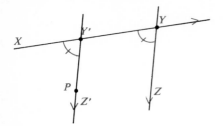

Diagram 424

The essential property of similar figures is that they have the same shape. The shape of triangles is determined by the size of the angles. However, the size of the angles does not determine the shape of quadrilaterals, since two differently shaped rectangles have angles of the same size. For triangles, in fact, two angles are sufficient to determine the triangle's shape, and this gives us a remarkably simple similarity condition.

Theorem 160/5 *Angle, angle similarity theorem*
If a correspondence of triangles is such that two angles of one triangle are congruent to their corresponding angles, then the third pair of corresponding angles are congruent and the correspondence is a similarity. (D425)

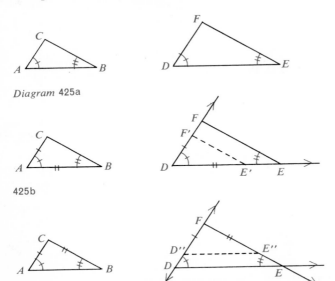

Diagram 425a

425b

425c

277

Proof*

Let $ABC \leftrightarrow DEF$ denote a correspondence of $\triangle ABC$
and $\triangle DEF$ in which $\measuredangle A \cong \measuredangle D$ and $\measuredangle B \cong \measuredangle E$.
Then $\measuredangle A° + \measuredangle B° = \measuredangle D° + \measuredangle E°$.
Since $\measuredangle C° = 180 - (\measuredangle A° + \measuredangle B°)$ and
$\measuredangle F° = 180 - (\measuredangle D° + \measuredangle E°)$, it follows that $\measuredangle C \cong \measuredangle F$; so

1 $\measuredangle A \cong \measuredangle D, \measuredangle B \cong \measuredangle E, \measuredangle C \cong \measuredangle F$.

In $\overrightarrow{DF}$ there is a point F' and in $\overrightarrow{DE}$ there is a point E'
such that

2 $d(A, C) = d(D, F')$ and $d(A, B) = d(D, E')$.

By the side, angle, side axiom,

3 $\triangle ABC \cong \triangle DE'F'$.

So as corresponding angles of a congruence,

4 $\measuredangle C \cong \measuredangle F'$.

From statements 1 and 4, $\measuredangle F' \cong \measuredangle F$, that is,

5 $\measuredangle DF'E' \cong \measuredangle DFE$.

Because of statement 5 and Lemma 160/5, the lines FE and $F'E'$
are either identical (if $F' = F$) or parallel (if $F' \neq F$).
So by Corollary 158/5,

6 $\dfrac{d(D, F')}{d(D, F)} = \dfrac{d(D, E')}{d(D, E)}.$

Substituting from statement 2 in statement 6 yields

7 $\dfrac{d(A, C)}{d(D, F)} = \dfrac{d(A, B)}{d(D, E)}.$

In $\overrightarrow{FD}$ there is a point D'' and in $\overrightarrow{FE}$ there is a point E''
such that

8 $d(A, C) = d(F, D'')$ and $d(C, B) = d(F, E'')$.

Then, by the side, angle, side axiom,

9 $\triangle ABC \cong \triangle D''E''F$.

Therefore, as corresponding angles,

10 $\measuredangle A \cong \measuredangle D''$.

From statements 10 and 1, $\measuredangle D'' \cong \measuredangle D$, that is,

11 $\measuredangle FD''E'' \cong \measuredangle FDE$.

Because of statement 11 and Lemma 160/5, the lines
DE and $D''E''$ are either identical (if $D'' = D$) or parallel
(if $D'' \neq D$). So by Corollary 158/5,

12 $\dfrac{d(F, D'')}{d(F, D)} = \dfrac{d(F, E'')}{d(F, E)}.$

Substituting from statement 8 in statement 12 yields

13 $\dfrac{d(A, C)}{d(D, F)} = \dfrac{d(C, B)}{d(F, E)}.$

---

* Notice how closely the proofs of this theorem and of the following similarity theorems resemble the proofs of the triangle congruence theorems.

Combining statements 7 and 13, we have

14 $\dfrac{d(A,\,B)}{d(D,\,E)} = \dfrac{d(B,\,C)}{d(E,\,F)} = \dfrac{d(C,\,A)}{d(F,\,D)}.$

Statement 14, together with statement 1, establishes

15 $\triangle ABC \sim \triangle DEF.$

Exercises

1 Assume that the correspondence $RST \leftrightarrow YXZ$ is a similarity
of $\triangle RST$ and $\triangle YXZ$.

   a Must $\measuredangle R$ and $\measuredangle Y$ be congruent? Must $\measuredangle S$ and $\measuredangle Z$ be
congruent?

   b Must $\overline{RS}$ be congruent to $\overline{YX}$? Could $\overline{RS}$ be congruent to $\overline{YX}$?

   c If $\triangle RST$ is obtuse, must $\triangle YXZ$ be obtuse?

   d Could $\triangle RST$ and $\triangle YXZ$ be congruent? Must these
triangles be congruent? *Answer*

   e Is $\triangle YXZ \sim \triangle RST$? Is $\triangle YXZ \sim \triangle YXZ$?

   f The ratio of $\overline{RS}$ to $\overline{YX}$ equals the ratio of $\overline{RT}$ to $\sim\!\sim\!\sim$.
This ratio is also the ratio of $\sim\!\sim\!\sim$ to $\overline{XZ}$.

   g If $\triangle YXZ$ is similar to $\triangle ABC$, is $\triangle RST \sim \triangle ABC$?

2 Three pairs of similar triangles are shown in D426.

  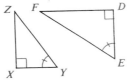 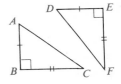

Diagram 426a   426b   426c

   For each pair of triangles, give a correspondence
of the triangles that is a similarity, and express
the proportion of the corresponding sides.

3 Assume that two triangles are similar and that the lengths
of the sides of the first triangle are 9, 8, and 10.
If the shortest side of the second triangle has length 10,
what are the lengths of the other two sides of this
triangle? What is the ratio of proportionality? *Answer*

4 Sides $\overline{AB}$, $\overline{BC}$, and $\overline{CA}$ of $\triangle ABC$ have lengths 6, 8, and 10
respectively. What are the lengths of the sides of $\triangle XYZ$
if $\triangle XYZ \sim \triangle ABC$ and the perimeter of $\triangle XYZ$ is 12?
If the perimeter of $\triangle XYZ$ is 40?

5 *Theorem*

   Corresponding altitudes of two similar triangles have
the same ratio as any two corresponding sides. (In a
correspondence of triangles, altitudes from corresponding
vertices to corresponding sides are corresponding altitudes.) *Answer*

6 Given $\triangle ABC$ and segment $\overline{EF}$, construct $\triangle EFG$ such that $\triangle ABC \sim \triangle FEG$.

7 In polygon $ABCD$, angle $\angle A$ is a right angle, the open ray $\overrightarrow{BD}$ bisects $\angle B$, and $BD \perp DC$ (D427). Prove that $\triangle ABD$ and $\triangle BDC$ are similar. Which sides of the triangles are proportional?

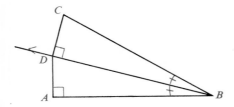

Diagram 427

8 Assume that $\triangle ABC$ is acute and that point D is between C and A. How many points X are there in line CB such that $\triangle CDX$ and $\triangle ABC$ are similar? Make a sketch for each possible X and indicate the correspondence that is a similarity.

9 Prove that two isosceles triangles are similar if each of the following is true.

a A base angle of one is congruent to a base angle of the other.

b Their vertex angles are congruent. *Answer*

c Each triangle is equilateral.

10 Assume that in $\triangle ABC$, point D is the midpoint of $\overline{BC}$ and that $\angle BAC$, $\angle BCA$, and $\angle ADC$ are congruent. If $d(B, C) = 2\sqrt{2}$, what are the lengths of the following segments?

a $\overline{DC}$ **b** $\overline{AB}$ **c** $\overline{AC}$ *Answer*   **d** $\overline{AD}$

11 In $\triangle ABC$, angle $\angle B$ has a measure of 90, and D is the foot of B in $\overline{AC}$. First show that $\triangle ABC$, $\triangle ABD$, and $\triangle BDC$ are similar. Then denote the correspondences that are similarities. Finally, indicate those segments of $\triangle ABD$ and $\triangle BDC$ whose ratios equal the ratio of $\overline{AB}$ to $\overline{AC}$.

♦ 12 Prove that, if line AB intersects line t at point R distinct from A and B, then the lengths of $\overline{AR}$ and $\overline{BR}$ are proportional to the distances of A and B from t, that is,

$$\frac{d(A, R)}{d(B, R)} = \frac{d(A, t)}{d(B, t)} \text{ (D428).}$$

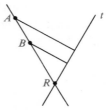
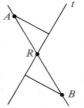

Diagram 428

Theorem of Menelaus＊

If A, B, and C are the vertices of a triangle and P, Q,
and R are three other points such that point P is in BC,
point Q is in CA, and point R is in AB, then P, Q, and
R are collinear if and only if the following is true:
(1) Either none or exactly two of the three points P, Q,
and R belong to $\triangle ABC$, and
(2) $\dfrac{d(A, R)}{d(R, B)} \cdot \dfrac{d(B, P)}{d(P, C)} \cdot \dfrac{d(C, Q)}{d(Q, A)} = 1.$
Prove that, if P, Q, and R are collinear in a line t, then
conditions 1 and 2 hold. (Hint: Obtain condition 1
from Pasch properties. To establish condition 2, let a,
b, and c denote the distances of A, B, and C from t
and use the property in exercise 12.)

◆ **14** *Theorem of Ceva*†

If A, B, and C are the vertices of a triangle and P, Q,
and R are three other points such that point P is
in BC, point Q is in CA, and point R is in AB, then
the three lines AP, BQ, and CR are concurrent at a point
if and only if the following is true:
(1) All three or else exactly one of the three points
P, Q, and R belong to $\triangle ABC$, and
(2) $\dfrac{d(A, R)}{d(R, B)} \cdot \dfrac{d(B, P)}{d(P, C)} \cdot \dfrac{d(C, Q)}{d(Q, A)} = 1.$
Prove that, if the three lines are concurrent at a point O, then
conditions 1 and 2 hold. (Hint: To establish condition 2,
apply Menelaus' theorem to $\triangle CAR$ and points Q, O,
and B and also to $\triangle CBR$ and points A,
O, and P.)

◆ **15** Prove that the concurrence of the medians of a triangle
is a corollary of Ceva's theorem.

Two other similarity conditions for triangles now can be
obtained in much the same way as the angle, angle similarity
condition was obtained.

Theorem 161/5 *Side, angle, side similarity theorem*
If, in a correspondence of triangles, two sides are proportional
to their corresponding sides and the corresponding angles

＊ Menelaus was a Greek mathematician and astronomer who lived in Alexandria in the first
century A.D.
† Though this theorem follows directly from that of Menelaus, it was not discovered until the
seventeenth century. It was proved by the Italian mathematician Ceva (pronounced "Cheva").

between these sides are congruent, then the correspondence
is a similarity. (D429)

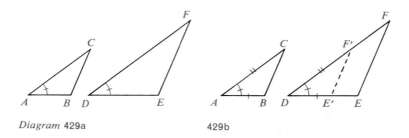

Diagram 429a   429b

Proof

Let $ABC \leftrightarrow DEF$ denote a correspondence of $\triangle ABC$ and $\triangle DEF$
such that

1 $\dfrac{d(A, B)}{d(D, E)} = \dfrac{d(A, C)}{d(D, F)}$

and

2 $\angle A \cong \angle D$.

There exists a point E' in $\overrightarrow{DE}$ and a point F' in $\overrightarrow{DF}$ such that

3 $d(A, B) = d(D, E')$ and $d(A, C) = d(D, F')$.

Substituting from statements 3 and 1 yields

4 $\dfrac{d(D, E')}{d(D, E)} = \dfrac{d(D, F')}{d(D, F)}$.

Then, by Corollary 158/5, lines EF and $E'F'$ are identical
or parallel, and, in either case (either as identical or
as corresponding angles),

5 $\angle DEF \cong \angle DE'F'$ and $\angle DFE \cong \angle DF'E'$.

By the angle, angle similarity theorem, statements 2 and 5
imply

6 $\triangle DEF \sim \triangle DE'F'$.

But from statements 2 and 3,

7 $\triangle ABC \cong \triangle DE'F'$

by the side, angle, side congruence theorem.
From statements 6 and 7 and the transitivity of similarity
(Theorem 159/5), we have

8 $\triangle ABC \sim \triangle DEF$,

which was to be shown.*

---

* In Latin geometries, the phrase "which was to be shown" was added to the end of proofs in
the form "quod erat demonstrandum." In time, this Latin phrase was shortened to the initials
"Q.E.D.," and these initials were used for many years in American textbooks.

Theorem 162/5 *Side, side, side similarity theorem*

If, in a correspondence of triangles, the three sides of one triangle are proportional to the corresponding sides in the other triangle, then the correspondence is a similarity. (D430)

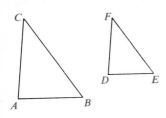

Diagram 430a

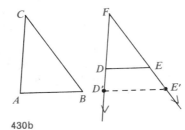

430b

Proof

Let $ABC \leftrightarrow DEF$ denote a correspondence of $\triangle ABC$ and $\triangle DEF$ in which

$$1 \quad \frac{d(A, B)}{d(D, E)} = \frac{d(B, C)}{d(E, F)} = \frac{d(C, A)}{d(F, D)} = r,$$

where r is defined as the common ratio.

In $\overrightarrow{FD}$ there is a point D' and in $\overrightarrow{FE}$ there is a point E' such that

$$2 \quad d(C, A) = d(F, D') \text{ and } d(C, B) = d(F, E').$$

Substituting from statement 2 in statement 1 gives

$$3 \quad \frac{d(F, D')}{d(F, D)} = r \text{ and } \frac{d(F, E')}{d(F, E)} = r.$$

Therefore,

$$4 \quad \frac{d(F, D')}{d(F, D)} = \frac{d(F, E')}{d(F, E)}.$$

Since statement 4 shows that the sides of $\angle F$ in $\triangle D'E'F$ and $\triangle DEF$ are proportional and since $\angle F \cong \angle F$, it follows, from Theorem 161/5, that

$$5 \quad \triangle D'E'F \sim \triangle DEF.$$

Statement 5, together with statement 3, gives

$$6 \quad \frac{d(F, D')}{d(F, D)} = \frac{d(F, E')}{d(F, E)} = \frac{d(D', E')}{d(D, E)} = r.$$

The last equality in statement 6 implies that

$$7 \quad d(D', E') = r d(D, E).$$

But from statement 1,

$$8 \quad d(A, B) = r d(D, E).$$

Therefore,

$$9 \quad d(A, B) = d(D', E').$$

The equalities in statements 2 and 9 show that

$$10 \quad \triangle ABC \cong \triangle D'E'F$$

by the side, side, side congruence theorem. From statements 10

283

and 5 and the transitivity of similarity, we then have

11 △ABC ∼ △DEF.

By using these last few theorems, it is possible to establish the similarity of triangles in a variety of situations and to obtain a great many numerical relations from the proportions. We state a typical example and leave its proof to you.

Theorem 163/5

A bisector of an angle of a triangle divides the opposite side into segments that are proportional to the other two sides. (D431)

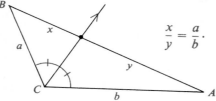

$$\frac{x}{y} = \frac{a}{b}.$$

Diagram 431

For our purposes, it will not be necessary to derive very many numerical relations. The important fact is that we now could do so if we wished. For example, formulas that relate the measures of angles in a triangle to the measures of sides of the triangle can be obtained from the proportionality of similar triangles. Such relations are part of the subject of trigonometry. In the next section, however, we will derive one of the most basic of all the numerical relations in geometry, the so-called *theorem of Pythagoras.*

Exercises

1 Six pairs of triangles are shown in D432. Decide if the information given in the diagram about each pair of triangles is sufficient to imply that the two triangles are similar. If the information is sufficient, state a correspondence that is a similarity and state a similarity condition that is satisfied by the given facts.

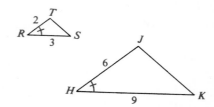

Diagram 432a

432b

284

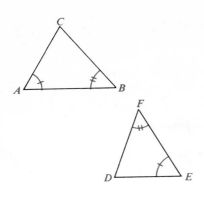

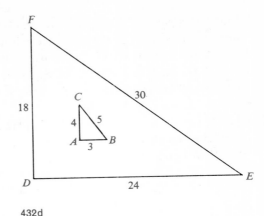

432c

432d

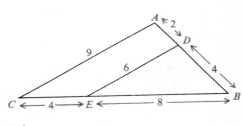

432e

432f

2 For each of the following cases, indicate whether or not the given information implies that the correspondence $ABC \leftrightarrow DEF$ is necessarily a similarity of $\triangle ABC$ and $\triangle DEF$.

a $\angle A \cong \angle D$; $\angle B \cong \angle E$.

b $\angle A \cong \angle B$; $\angle D \cong \angle E$. *Answer*

c $\dfrac{d(A, C)}{d(D, F)} = \dfrac{d(A, B)}{d(D, E)}$.

d Both triangles are equilateral.

e Both triangles are isosceles, and $\angle C \cong \angle F$.

f $\overline{AC} \cong \overline{AB}$; $\overline{DF} \cong \overline{DE}$; $\angle A \cong \angle D$.

g The perimeter of each triangle is 24.

h Corresponding sides are proportional.

3 The two segments $\overline{AB}$ and $\overline{CD}$ intersect at a point X that is between the endpoints of both segments (D433). If the lengths of $\overline{AX}$, $\overline{BX}$, and $\overline{CX}$ are a, b, and c respectively, what lengths of $\overline{DX}$ would guarantee that $\triangle ACX$ and $\triangle BDX$ are similar? *Answer*

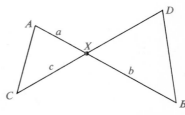

Diagram 433

4 Line AB is parallel to CD, and $\overline{AD}$ and $\overline{BC}$ intersect at point X in the strip determined by AB and CD (D434). If $<A, R, B>$ and $<C, S, D>$ such that X is in $\overline{RS}$, explain why $\overline{CS}$ and $\overline{SD}$ are proportional to $\overline{BR}$ and $\overline{RA}$.

5 Prove Theorem 163/5.

◆ **6** Let M denote the midpoint of $\overline{AB}$ in plane α, and let r denote a positive number less than 1 (D435).

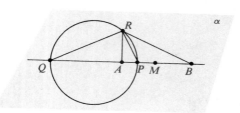

Diagram **434**

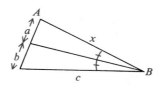

Diagram **435**

a Show that there are two points P and Q in AB such that
$$\frac{d(P, A)}{d(P, B)} = \frac{d(Q, A)}{d(Q, B)} = r,$$ and that $<A, P, M>$ and $<P, A, Q>$.
(Hint: See exercise 11, page 274.)

b Show that, in plane α, all points R such that $\dfrac{d(R, A)}{d(R, B)} = r$
are in the circle with diameter $\overline{PQ}$. (This is called the *circle of Appolonius*.) (Hint: Show that RP and RQ must be the bisectors of the angles formed by AR and RB with vertex R and, hence, that $\measuredangle PRQ$ is a right angle.)

7 For each triangle shown in D436, find the length x of the segment $\overline{AB}$. *Answer*

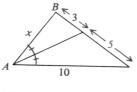

Diagram **436a**

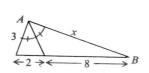

436b

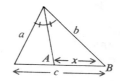

436c

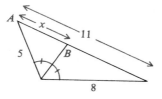

436d

436e

286

8 Prove that a similarity exists between $\triangle ABC$ and its midpoint triangle.

◆ **9** In the isosceles triangle $\triangle ABC$, segments $\overline{AB}$ and $\overline{BC}$ are congruent and D is between A and B such that $\measuredangle DCA \cong \measuredangle ABC$ (D437).

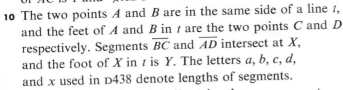
Diagram **437**

a Show that, for such a point D to exist, the measure of $\measuredangle ABC$ must be less than 60.

b Prove that $\triangle ACD \sim \triangle ABC$.

c In exercise 9b, what other similarity exists between $\triangle ACD$ and $\triangle ABC$? *Answer*

d If $\measuredangle ABC° = 36$, compute the measures of the other angles shown in D437.

e What is the length of $\overline{BC}$ if the length of $\overline{AC}$ is 1 and $\measuredangle ABC° = 36$?

10 The two points A and B are in the same side of a line t, and the feet of A and B in t are the two points C and D respectively. Segments $\overline{BC}$ and $\overline{AD}$ intersect at X, and the foot of X in t is Y. The letters a, b, c, d, and x used in D438 denote lengths of segments.

a Name three pairs of similar triangles shown in the diagram.

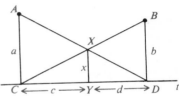

b Is $\dfrac{x}{b} = \dfrac{c}{d}$? Is $\dfrac{x}{b} = \dfrac{c}{c+d}$?

c Is $\dfrac{x}{a} = \dfrac{d}{c}$? Is $\dfrac{x}{a} = \dfrac{d}{c+d}$?

d Show that $\dfrac{1}{a} + \dfrac{1}{b} = \dfrac{1}{x}$ *Answer*

Diagram **438**

11 *Theorem*

Corresponding medians of two similar triangles have the same ratio as any two corresponding sides of the triangles.

12 Polygon $RSTQ$ is a trapezoid whose diagonals $\overline{RT}$ and $\overline{SQ}$ intersect at X. Prove that $RSTQ$ is isosceles if the parallel sides are $\overline{RS}$ and $\overline{QT}$ and $\triangle RXQ \sim \triangle SXT$.

13 *Theorem*

If $\measuredangle C$ of $\triangle ABC$ is a right angle, and the foot of C in $\overline{AB}$ is D, then each of the following is true. (D439)

(1) $\overline{AD}$ and $\overline{CD}$ are proportional to $\overline{CD}$ and $\overline{DB}$.

(2) $\overline{AD}$ and $\overline{AC}$ are proportional to $\overline{AC}$ and $\overline{AB}$.

(3) $\overline{BD}$ and $\overline{BC}$ are proportional to $\overline{BC}$ and $\overline{BA}$.

(The number $b = \dfrac{a+c}{2}$ is called the *arithmetic mean* to a and c. The number b such that $\dfrac{a}{b} = \dfrac{b}{c}$, or $b^2 = ac$, is called the *geometric mean*, or the *mean proportional*, to a and c.

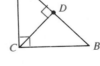
Diagram **439**

Thus, part 1 of the theorem states that the altitude to the hypotenuse is the geometric mean, or mean proportional, to the segments into which it divides the hypotenuse.)

14 In $\triangle ABC$, angle $\sphericalangle C$ is a right angle and the foot of C in $\overline{AB}$ is D (D439). What are the lengths of $\overline{CA}$, $\overline{CD}$, $\overline{CB}$, $\overline{AD}$, and $\overline{DB}$ for each of the following cases?
   a $d(A, D) = 4$, and $d(D, B) = 5$. Answer
   b $d(A, D) = 4$, and $d(C, D) = 8$.
   c $d(A, C) = 6$, and $d(A, D) = 4$.

15 If the lengths of the hypotenuse and the altitude to the hypotenuse of a right triangle are 13 and 6 respectively, find the length of each leg of the triangle and the lengths of the segments in the hypotenuse that are cut off by the altitude.

16 Assume that point X is in the circle $C(O, r)$, and the foot of X in the diameter $\overline{AB}$ is the point Y. For each of the following cases, what is the length of $\overline{XY}$ in terms of r?
   a $d(Y, O) = 2$.   b $d(B, X) = r$.

17 If the diagonals $\overline{AC}$ and $\overline{BD}$ of quadrilateral $ABCD$ intersect at E and if $\overline{AE}$ and $\overline{EC}$ have lengths proportional to those of $\overline{BE}$ and $\overline{ED}$, prove that $ABCD$ is either a trapezoid or a parallelogram.

18 A triangular pyramid $ABCD$ has its base, $\triangle ABC$, in plane α, and $d(D, A) = 42$. A plane β that is parallel to α intersects $\overline{DA}$ at A', $\overline{DB}$ at B', $\overline{DC}$ at C', and $d(D, A') = 14$. If the sides of $\triangle ABC$ opposite A, B, and C have lengths 20, 10, and 15 respectively, find the lengths of the sides of $\triangle A'B'C'$. Is the distance between α and β determined? If not, how short could this distance be? How long could this distance be? Answer

19 Let $\triangle ABC$ denote a triangle; let D denote a point in line CB; let E denote a point in line CA. Prove that $\triangle ABC$ is isosceles with congruent sides $\overline{CA}$ and $\overline{CB}$ if each of the following statements is true.
   a $\overline{AD}$ and $\overline{BE}$ are congruent altitudes.
   b $\overline{AD}$ and $\overline{BE}$ are congruent medians.
   c $\overline{AD}$ and $\overline{BE}$ are congruent and are contained in the bisectors of $\sphericalangle A$ and $\sphericalangle B$ respectively.

The Pythagorean theorem 21/5

The theorem of Pythagoras is that, in every right triangle, the square of the length of the hypotenuse is the sum of the squares of the lengths of the legs. Historically, this is probably the most famous of all geometric theorems. It was known in very ancient times, and, among mathematical relations that are important and not obvious, that of Pythagoras may well be the first ever discovered.

Theorem 164/5 *Pythagorean theorem*

The square of the length of the hypotenuse of a right triangle is the sum of the squares of the lengths of the sides. (D440)

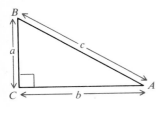

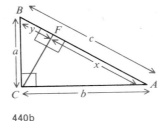

Diagram 440a   440b

Proof

Let $\triangle ABC$ denote a right triangle with hypotenuse $\overline{AB}$, and define c as $d(A, B)$, b as $d(A, C)$, and a as $d(B, C)$.

Since $\angle A$ and $\angle B$ are acute, the foot F in AB of C is between A and B. Consequently, if $x = d(A, F)$ and $y = d(B, F)$, then

1   $x + y = c$.

The right triangles $\triangle ABC$ and $\triangle ACF$ have congruent right angles at C and F respectively, and $\angle A$ is in both triangles and congruent to itself. Therefore, by the angle, angle similarity theorem,

2   $\triangle ABC \sim \triangle ACF$.

So

3   $\dfrac{d(A, C)}{d(A, F)} = \dfrac{d(A, B)}{d(A, C)}$ or $\dfrac{b}{x} = \dfrac{c}{b}$,

which implies

4   $b^2 = cx$.

The right triangles $\triangle BAC$ and $\triangle BCF$ have congruent right angles at C and F respectively, and $\angle B$ is in both triangles and congruent to itself. Therefore, by the angle, angle similarity theorem,

5   $\triangle BAC \sim \triangle BCF$.

So,

6   $\dfrac{d(B, C)}{d(B, F)} = \dfrac{d(B, A)}{d(B, C)}$ or $\dfrac{a}{y} = \dfrac{c}{a}$,

which implies

7   $a^2 = cy$.

From statements 7 and 4, we obtain

8   $a^2 + b^2 = cx + cy = c(x + y)$.

Statement 8, together with statement 1 that $x + y = c$, implies

9   $a^2 + b^2 = c^2$.

289

The next result is a converse of the Pythagorean theorem.

In $\triangle ABC$, if the sides opposite A, B, and C have lengths a, b, and c respectively such that $c^2 = a^2 + b^2$, then $\triangle ABC$ is a right triangle and $\angle C$ is a right angle. (D441)

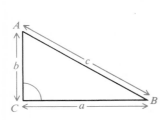 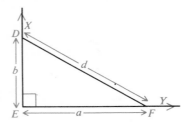

Diagram 441

Proof

Let $\overrightarrow{EX}$ and $\overrightarrow{EY}$ denote two perpendicular closed rays. In $\overrightarrow{EX}$ there is a point D such that $d(E, D) = b$, and in $\overrightarrow{EY}$ there is a point F such that $d(E, F) = a$. Let d denote the length of the hypotenuse $\overline{DF}$ in the right triangle $\triangle DEF$.
By the Pythagorean theorem,
1 $d^2 = a^2 + b^2$.
It is given that
2 $c^2 = a^2 + b^2$.
Therefore,
3 $d^2 = c^2$.
Since c and d are positive numbers, statement 3 implies
4 $d = c$.
The congruence $\triangle ABC \cong \triangle DEF$ now follows from the side, side, side congruence theorem. Since $\angle C$ is congruent to the corresponding right angle, $\angle E$, $\triangle ACB$ is a right triangle.

In the proof of Theorem 165/5, we used the fact that $d^2 = c^2$ implies $d = c$ if d and c are positive. It may be well to review a few ideas about square roots.

A number x is a square root of a number b if $x^2 = b$. From the rules for multiplying positive and negative real numbers, it follows that there is no real number that is the square root of a negative real number. A positive real number b has two square roots, one positive and the other negative. These square roots have the same absolute value. Thus the square roots of 4 are 2 and -2, and $|2| = |-2|$. The positive square root of a number b is indicated by the symbol $\sqrt{b}$, and the negative square root of b is indicated by the symbol $-\sqrt{b}$. In common practice, the phrase "*the* square root" always refers to the positive square root. The number zero is its own square root, and $\sqrt{0} = -\sqrt{0} = 0$.

When we apply the Pythagorean theorem, we will want to use square roots in both equalities and inequalities. Probably the simplest general rule to remember is that you can correctly square both sides of an inequality or take square roots of both sides of an inequality *if neither side is a negative number.* When negative numbers are involved, we must be more cautious. For example, squaring both sides of $3 > -5$ would give the incorrect result $9 > 25$. However, if x and y are not negative numbers, then all the following implications are correct.

1) $x > y \Rightarrow x^2 > y^2$.
2) $x \geq y \Rightarrow x^2 \geq y^2$.
3) $x > y \Rightarrow \sqrt{x} > \sqrt{y}$.
4) $x \geq y \Rightarrow \sqrt{x} \geq \sqrt{y}$.

When you work with letters that represent numbers, caution is also sometimes needed with equalities. Unless you know that the numbers x and y have the same sign, you cannot say that $x^2 = y^2$ implies $x = y$. Because neither x^2 nor y^2 is negative, what is correct is that $x^2 = y^2$ implies $\sqrt{x^2} = \sqrt{y^2}$. (So of course, $-\sqrt{x^2} = -\sqrt{y^2}$.) But $\sqrt{x^2} = |x|$, and $\sqrt{y^2} = |y|$. Therefore, $x^2 = y^2$ implies $|x| = |y|$. And if x and y have the same sign, then $|x| = |y|$ implies $x = y$. Very seldom is there any trouble with particular numbers, since you can see that $(-2)^2 = (2)^2$ does not imply $-2 = 2$. But with numbers represented by letters, one must be careful.

Exercises

1 Assume that segment $\overline{AB}$ is the hypotenuse of a right triangle $\triangle ABC$; $d(A, B) = c$; $d(A, C) = b$; $d(B, C) = a$.
  a What is c if $a = 1$ and $b = 11$?
  b What is c if $a = 3\pi$ and $b = 5\pi$?
  c Find a if $c = 10$ and $b = 4$.
  d Find b and c if the perimeter of $\triangle ABC$ is 24 and $a = 6$.
  e What is b if $a = \frac{1}{3}$ and $c = \frac{1}{2}$? *Answer*
2 In each of the following, the lengths of the sides of $\triangle ABC$ are given. For each case, decide if $\triangle ABC$ is a right triangle.
  a 3, 4, and 5
  b 1, $\sqrt{2}$, and $\sqrt{3}$
  c 10, 15, and 11 *Answer*
  d 246, 328, and 410
  e $\frac{\sqrt{17}}{6}$, $\frac{2}{12}$, and $\frac{2}{3}$

3 Assume that each of the following numbers is the perimeter of an equilateral triangle. Find the length of an altitude of each of these equilateral triangles.

   a 30   **b** 6   **c** $3x$

4 Each of the following numbers is the length of an altitude of an equilateral triangle. What is the perimeter of each of these equilateral triangles?

   a 8 *Answer*   **b** $11\sqrt{3}$ **c** $\left(\dfrac{x}{2}\right)\sqrt{3}$ **d** x

5 Show that, if the sides of a triangle have the lengths x, $\dfrac{x}{2}$, and $\left(\dfrac{x}{2}\right)\sqrt{3}$ respectively, then the angles have the measures 90, 30, and 60 respectively.

6 If the length, width, and depth of a rectangular box are 12, 4, and 3 respectively, what is the length of the longest stick that will fit into the box? *Answer*

7 Segments $\overline{AB}$ and $\overline{CD}$ are two chords of the circle $C(O, r)$ such that $d(A, B) > d(C, D)$. Prove that $\overline{AB}$ is closer to the center O of the circle than $\overline{CD}$.

8 If chord $\overline{AB}$ of $C(O, r)$ is closer to the center O than chord $\overline{CD}$, prove that $\overline{AB}$ is longer than $\overline{CD}$.

9 If the measures of the sides of a right triangle are integers such as 3, 4, and 5, then the triple of numbers 3, 4, 5 is called a *Pythagorean triple*. Prove that a triple of integers that is proportional to a Pythagorean triple is itself a Pythagorean triple.

10 a How long are the legs of a right triangle if the bisector of the right angle divides the hypotenuse into segments of lengths 15 and 20 (D442)? (Hint: Use Theorems 163/5 and 164/5.)

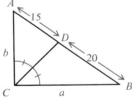

Diagram 442

   b Find the lengths of the legs if the hypotenuse is divided by the angle bisector into segments of lengths p and q. *Answer*

11 a Show, by using Theorem 165/5, that Pythagorean triples (mentioned in exercise 9) can be found by the following procedure.
Let m and n be integers such that $m > n > 0$. Select $m^2 - n^2$ and $2mn$ as the lengths of the legs of a right triangle. Then $m^2 + n^2$ will be the length of its hypotenuse.

   b Find six right triangles whose sides have lengths that are Pythagorean triples such that the greatest number of the triple is less than or equal to 25. Use the process described in exercise 11a to find these numbers.

12 Segment $\overline{AC_1}$ is the hypotenuse of $\triangle ABC_1$
(D443), and $\overline{C_2C_1} \perp \overline{AC_1}$, $\overline{C_3C_2} \perp \overline{AC_2}$,
$\overline{C_4C_3} \perp \overline{AC_3}$, $\ldots$, $\overline{C_{n+1}C_n} \perp \overline{AC_n}$, where
n is a positive integer. Find the
lengths of the following segments
if each of segments $\overline{AB}$, $\overline{BC_1}$, $\overline{C_1C_2}$,
$\overline{C_2C_3}$, $\ldots$, $\overline{C_nC_{n+1}}$, $\ldots$ have unit length.

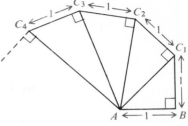

a $\overline{AC_1}$ **d** $\overline{AC_4}$

Diagram 443

b $\overline{AC_2}$ **e** $\overline{AC_{43}}$

c $\overline{AC_3}$ *Answer*   **f** $\overline{AC_n}$, where n is a positive integer

13 Given two segments $\overline{AB}$ and $\overline{CD}$, construct the segment $\overline{XY}$
such that $\overline{XY}$ is the geometric mean (exercise 13, page 287)
of $\overline{AB}$ and $\overline{CD}$. In other words, construct $\overline{XY}$ so that
$$\frac{d(A, B)}{d(X, Y)} = \frac{d(X, Y)}{d(C, D)}.$$

14 Assuming that the length of a given segment $\overline{AB}$ is one unit,
construct segments whose lengths are respectively $\sqrt{2}$, $\sqrt{3}$,
$\sqrt{5}$, and $\sqrt{7}$.

15 a What is the length of the hypotenuse of an isosceles
right triangle if each leg has the length 3? The length $\frac{1}{2}$?
The length $\sqrt{2}$? The length $\sqrt{512}$? The length x?
b What is the length of each leg of an isosceles right
triangle if the hypotenuse has the length $7\sqrt{2}$? The length
$\pi\sqrt{2}$? The length 5? The length x?

16 Two straight metal beams (represented in D444
as $\overline{AB}$ and $\overline{BC}$), each 1 mi. long, are positioned
end to end in a straight line. During the heat
of the day, each beam expands and increases
its length by 1 ft. Assume that the beams are
firmly fastened at A and C and remain straight
during expansion. Therefore, the beam ends
at B will rise into the air into a position B'.
First, guess which of the following is the closest
approximation of the length of $\overline{BB'}$. Then check
your approximation by calculating the length
of $\overline{BB'}$.

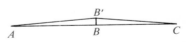

Diagram 444

a $\frac{1}{2}$ ft.   **d** 10 ft.

b 1 ft.   **e** 50 ft.

c 5 ft.   **f** 100 ft.

♦17 Given a line segment $\overline{XY}$, construct the square $ABCD$ such
that $d(X, Y) = d(A, C) + d(C, B)$, that is, such that the
sum of the lengths of a diagonal and a side of the square
must equal the length of the given segment.

18 Draw a segment $\overline{AB}$ and denote its length as m. Construct a
segment $\overline{CD}$ whose length is $m\sqrt{3}$.

19 In △ABC, segments $\overline{AB}$, $\overline{BC}$, and $\overline{AC}$ have the lengths 6, 14, and 18 respectively. Prove that ∡B is obtuse, and find the length of the altitude from C to line AB.

20 The base of a triangular pyramid is an equilateral triangle △ACD, each side of which has the length 2 (D445). The vertex B of the pyramid is at the distance 2 from A, C, and D. Find the length of $\overline{XY}$, where X is the midpoint of $\overline{DC}$ and where Y is the midpoint of $\overline{AB}$. *Answer*

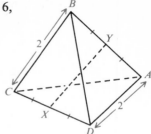

Diagram 445

It is interesting to observe that, in building a system, the relations that seem simplest do not always come first. We have proved some complicated relations among circles and lines, but we still have not established the circumstances under which a line and a circle intersect, except for the case of a line through the center of a circle. We now use the Pythagorean theorem to prove some seemingly obvious facts.

Theorem 166/5

In a plane α, if the point P is at distance a from line t, then the circle $C(P, r)$ in α does not intersect t if $r < a$. If $r = a$, the circle is tangent to t. If $r > a$, the circle intersects t at exactly two points equidistant from the foot in t of P.

Proof

Let F denote the foot in t of P. Then it is given that $a = d(P, F)$. If $r < a$, the existence of a point Q that is common to t and $C(P, r)$ would imply that $d(P, Q) < d(P, F)$. (D446) This would contradict the fact that F is the foot in t of P. Therefore, there is no such point Q, and the line does not intersect the circle. If $r = a$, the circle and line t are tangent at F, by Theorem 123/4. (D447)

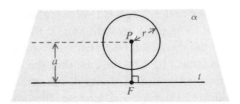

Diagram 446

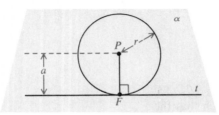

Diagram 447

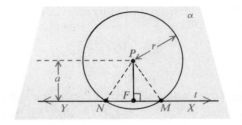

Diagram 448

If $r > a$, then, because r and a are both positive numbers, $r^2 > a^2$ and $r^2 - a^2 > 0$. (D448)

294

Thus, $\sqrt{r^2 - a^2}$ is a positive number. In the closed ray $\overrightarrow{FX}$ of line t there is a point M, and in the opposite closed ray $\overrightarrow{FY}$ there is a point N, such that

1 $d(F, M) = d(F, N) = \sqrt{r^2 - a^2}$

To show that M and N are also in $C(P, r)$, first it follows, from statement 1, that

2 $d(F, M)^2 = d(F, N)^2 = r^2 - a^2$.

By applying the Pythagorean theorem to right triangle $\triangle PFM$, we get

3 $d(P, M)^2 = d(P, F)^2 + d(F, M)^2$.

Using statement 2 and $a = d(P, F)$ in statement 3 yields

4 $d(P, M)^2 = a^2 + (r^2 - a^2) = r^2$.

Since both r and $d(P, M)$ are positive, statement 4 implies that

5 $d(P, M) = r$.

By a similar argument

6 $d(P, N) = r$.

Thus M and N are in $C(P, r)$. That F is the midpoint of $\overline{NM}$ follows from the way in which N and M were defined.

Now let Q denote any point in t and in $C(P, r)$. Then Q is a point of t such that $d(P, Q) = r$, and $r > a$ implies $d(P, Q) > d(P, F)$. So $Q \neq F$, and, therefore, the right triangle $\triangle PFQ$ exists with hypotenuse $\overline{PQ}$. By the Pythagorean theorem,

7 $d(P, F)^2 + d(F, Q)^2 = d(P, Q)^2$,

or

8 $a^2 + d(F, Q)^2 = r^2$.

Hence

9 $d(F, Q)^2 = r^2 - a^2$,

and

10 $d(F, Q) = \sqrt{r^2 - a^2}$.

From statement 10, it follows that Q must be either M or N, depending on whether Q is in closed ray $\overrightarrow{FX}$ or in closed ray $\overrightarrow{FY}$. Therefore, M and N are the only two points of intersection of $C(P, r)$ and t.

Exercises

1 Line t and point P not in t determine the plane α, and $d(P, t) = 6$. Which of the following circles in α intersect t in one and only one point? Which intersect t in exactly two points? Which do not intersect t?

a $C(P, 6)$

b $C(P, 999)$

c $C(P, \sqrt{35.99})$

d $C(P, \frac{1}{3}\sqrt{324})$

e $C(P, \pi)$

2 Let $ABCD$ denote a rectangle contained in a plane β. Assume that its diagonals intersect at M and that the lengths

of $\overline{AB}$ and $\overline{BC}$ are 4 and 3 respectively (D449).
In each of the following cases, a circle
and a line in β are named. Indicate if
the circle and the line intersect, and,
if they do, tell in how many points
they intersect.

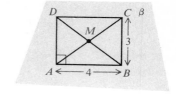

Diagram 449

a $C(D, 4)$; AB *Answer*   **d** $C(A, 8000)$; DB

b $C(M, 2)$; BC **e** $C(D, \frac{12}{5})$; AC

c $C(B, \pi)$; AD

3 If chord $\overline{MN}$ is at a distance x from the center O of the
circle $C(O, r)$, prove that $x < r$. *Answer*

◆ **4** Prove that no chord of a circle $C(O, r)$ is longer than a
diameter of the circle.

5 Assume that points P and X are in the line AB and that P
is between A and B.

a Must X be in $\overrightarrow{PA}$ or $\overrightarrow{PB}$?

b If $P \neq X$, must X be in $\overrightarrow{PA}$ or in $\overrightarrow{PB}$?

c Must P be the midpoint of $\overline{AB}$ if $\overline{AP} \cong \overline{PB}$?

d If P is the midpoint of $\overline{AB}$ and $<A, X, B>$, must
$d(P, X) < d(P, B)$? Must $d(P, X) < d(P, A)$? *Answer*

e Does $<F, P, A>$ and $<P, A, E>$ imply $<F, A, E>$?

f Does $<F, A, P>$ and $<F, P, E>$ imply $<F, A, E>$?

◆ **6** A light is 10 ft. above the ground (regard the ground as
a plane α). A man 6 ft. tall walking in a straight line
(line t in α) passes exactly 8 ft. from a point directly
beneath the light.

a What is the length of his shadow when he is nearest
the light?

b What is the length of his shadow when he has walked
9 ft. beyond the point nearest the light? *Answer*

c Prove that the tip of his shadow always is the same
distance from t.

In the next two theorems, we clear up a question we considered
at the end of Chapter 2. We show that a segment that joins an interior point and an exterior point of a circle must intersect the
circle.

Theorem 167/5

If A and B are points of a line t that does not pass through P
and if F is the foot in t of P, then $d(P, B) > d(P, A)$ if and
only if $d(F, B) > d(F, A)$. (D450)

Proof

The equality

1 $d(P, B) = \sqrt{d(P, F)^2 + d(F, B)^2}$

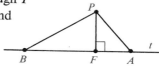

Diagram 450

follows from the identity property if $B = F$,
in which case $d(F, B) = 0$. It follows from
the Pythagorean theorem for right triangle
$\triangle PBF$ when $F \neq B$. In the same way, the equality

2 $d(P, A) = \sqrt{d(P, F)^2 + d(F, A)^2}$

is correct, whether or not A is F. If it is assumed that

3 $d(P, B) > d(P, A)$,

then, from statements 1 and 2, this inequality can be expressed as

4 $\sqrt{d(P, F)^2 + d(F, B)^2} > \sqrt{d(P, F)^2 + d(F, A)^2}$.

Squaring the inequality of statement 4 yields

5 $d(P, F)^2 + d(F, B)^2 > d(P, F)^2 + d(F, A)^2$

or

6 $d(F, B)^2 > d(F, A)^2$.

Therefore, since distances are not negative,

7 $d(F, B) > d(F, A)$.

So $d(P, B) > d(P, A)$ implies $d(F, B) > d(F, A)$.
But statements 3 through 7 are reversible since, at no stage,
are any of the quantities negative. That is, statement $7 \Rightarrow$
statement $6 \Rightarrow$ statement $5 \Rightarrow$ statement $4 \Rightarrow$ statement 3.
Therefore, $d(F, B) > d(F, A)$ implies $d(P, B) > d(P, A)$.
This last result can also be obtained by starting with
$d(F, B) > d(F, A)$ in the form
$\sqrt{d(P, B)^2 - d(P, F)^2} > \sqrt{d(P, A)^2 - d(P, F)^2}$.
Then $d(P, B)^2 - d(P, F)^2 > d(P, A)^2 - d(P, F)^2$.
So $d(P, B)^2 > d(P, A)^2$. Therefore, $d(P, B) > d(P, A)$.

Theorem 168/5
If point A is interior to the circle $C(P, r)$ and point B is
exterior to the circle, then line AB intersects the circle in exactly
two points and point A is between these two intersection points.

Proof
If P is in line AB, then the two points E and F of AB at
distance r from P (Theorem 9/2) belong to the circle. Point P
is the midpoint of $\overline{EF}$. Hence, if $A = P$, then $\langle E, A, F \rangle$.
If $A \neq P$, then A is in $\overrightarrow{PE}$ or in $\overrightarrow{PF}$, and $d(A, P) < r$ implies
either $\langle P, A, E \rangle$ or $\langle P, A, F \rangle$. (D451)
In either case, A is between E and F.

   If P is not in AB, let F denote the foot in AB of P. (D452)

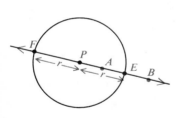

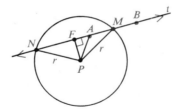

Diagram 451

Diagram 452

297

By the definition of a foot,

1 $d(P, A) \geqq d(P, F)$.

Because A is interior to $C(P, r)$, $r > d(P, A)$.

2 So $r > d(P, F)$.

Then, by Theorem 166/5, there are exactly two points M and N in $t = AB$ at distance r from P, and F is the midpoint of $\overline{MN}$. Any point in t and $C(P, r)$ is a point of t at distance r from P and so must be either M or N.

If $A = F$, point A is between M and N. If $A \neq F$, point A belongs to either $\overrightarrow{FM}$ or $\overrightarrow{FN}$. Because $d(P, A) < d(P, M)$ and $d(P, A) < d(P, N)$, then $d(F, A) < d(F, M)$ and $d(F, A) < d(F, N)$. Therefore, by Corollary 10/2, point A is between M and N.

Exercises

1 In each of the following four examples of Theorem 167/5, the lengths of three segments are given. For each case, verify the theorem by calculating the lengths of the other two segments and then comparing appropriate lengths (D453).

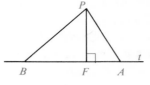

Diagram 453

	$d(P, F)$	$d(P, A)$	$d(P, B)$	$d(F, A)$	$d(F, B)$
a	10	11	12		
b	1			1.1	1.2
c	7		8	$\sqrt{14}$	
d	$h, h < \sqrt{443}$	$\sqrt{443}$			$\sqrt{444 - h^2}$

2 Use Theorem 167/5 to prove the following generalization of the theorem: If A and B are points of a plane α that does not pass through P, and if F is the foot in α of P, then $d(P, B) > d(P, A)$ if and only if $d(F, B) > d(F, A)$ (D454).

3 Let β denote a plane that contains A but does not contain P. Let F denote the foot in β of P, where $F \neq A$. What is the set $\mathcal{S}$ of all points X in β that satisfy $d(P, X) = d(P, A)$? That satisfy $d(P, X) < d(P, A)$? That satisfy $d(P, X) > d(P, A)$?

Diagram 454

4 If point A is interior to the circle $C(P, r)$ and point B is exterior to the circle, which of the following statements are true (T) and which are false (F)?

a Segment $\overline{AB}$ intersects $C(P, r)$ in exactly two points.

b The open ray $\overrightarrow{AB}$ intersects $C(P, r)$ in exactly one point.

c The open ray $\overrightarrow{BA}$ intersects $C(P, r)$ in exactly one point.

d Line AB intersects the circle in exactly two points and A is between these two points.

5 Assume that point A is interior to the circle $C(P, r)$ and that B is exterior to the circle. Let point F denote the foot of P in line AB if P is not in AB. If P is in AB, let $P = F$. In each of the following, the numbers given are the respective values of $d(P, F)$, $d(P, A)$, and $d(P, B)$. For each of these cases, find the possible values of $d(A, B)$.

a 3, 5, 20 *Answer*   **c** 0, 4, 16

b 1, $\sqrt{2}$, $\sqrt{3}$ **d** 0, 0, 13

6 The lengths of segments $\overline{AB}$, $\overline{BP}$, and $\overline{PA}$ of $\triangle ABP$ are 6, 9, and 4 respectively (D455). Assume that the circle $C(P, r)$ and $\triangle ABP$ are coplanar.

a What is the set of possible values of r if A is in the interior of $C(P, r)$ and B is in the exterior of the circle? *Answer*

b What is the set of possible values of r if both A and B are in the interior of $C(P, r)$? If both are in the exterior of $C(P, r)$?

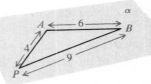

Diagram 455

c For what value of r is AB tangent to $C(P, r)$?

[Hint: First find $d(F, A)$ where F is the foot in AB of P. Then calculate $d(F, P)$.]

7 Prove that the interior of a circle is convex and that its exterior is not convex.

8 The *projection* of a segment $\overline{AB}$ on a coplanar line t is the segment $\overline{CD}$ cut off in t by parallel lines through A and B that are perpendicular to t. (D456)

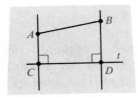 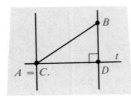 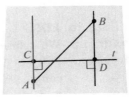

Diagram 456

By using the notion of a projection of a segment, along with the *product of segments*, meaning the product of their lengths, one can state a generalization of the Pythagorean theorem as follows:

299

The square of one side of a triangle is the sum of the squares of the other two sides plus or minus twice the product of either of those sides by the projection on its line of the other side. The product is added or subtracted to yield a correct result depending upon whether or not the angle opposite the initial side is obtuse or acute.* (D457)

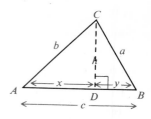

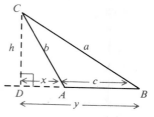

a From the information given in D457, prove that $a^2 = b^2 + c^2 - 2cx$.

b From the information given in D457, prove that $a^2 = b^2 + c^2 + 2cx$.

Diagram 457

◆ **9 a** Assume that, in $\triangle ABC$, the sides opposite A, B, and C have lengths a, b, and c respectively and the median to $\overline{AB}$ has length m (D458). Prove that $2(a^2 + b^2) = c^2 + 4m^2$. (Hint: Apply the theorem in exercise 8.)

b Prove that, for any triangle, the sum of the squares of the lengths of the medians is $\frac{3}{4}$ of the sum of the squares of the lengths of the sides.

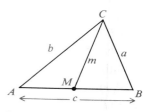

Diagram 458

10 Point B is between A and C, $d(B, A) = 1$, and $d(B, C) = 2$. Line PB is perpendicular to AB at B. For any point H in PB, let $h = d(B, H)$, and let $r_h = \dfrac{d(H, A)}{d(H, C)}$. Thus, for $H = B$, $h = 0$ and $r_0 = \dfrac{d(B, A)}{d(B, C)} = \frac{1}{2}$ (D459).

a Show that $r_0 < r_1 < r_2 < r_3$.

b Prove that $r_h \geqq r_0$.

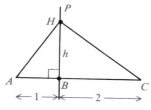

Diagram 459

Similar and 22/5
congruent We defined a congruence of triangles before we defined a simi-
polygons larity of triangles. However, we then observed that a triangle congruence is just a special triangle similarity. This suggests that, in dealing with polygons, we should first define a similarity of polygons, and then specialize the conditions to define a congruence of polygons.

---

* If the initial side is the hypotenuse of a right triangle, then the product of one leg by the projection on its line of the other leg must be taken as zero, and the Pythagorean theorem results as a special case.

A correspondence of a polygon $P_1P_2P_3 \ldots P_n$ and a polygon
$Q_1Q_2Q_3 \ldots Q_n$ is a correspondence of P_1 with Q_1, P_2 with Q_2,
P_3 with Q_3, $\ldots$, P_n with Q_n respectively; a correspondence
of the angles at P_1, P_2, P_3, $\ldots$, P_n with those at
Q_1, Q_2, Q_3, $\ldots$, Q_n respectively; and a correspondence
of the sides $\overline{P_1P_2}$, $\overline{P_2P_3}$, $\ldots$, $\overline{P_{n-1}P_n}$, $\overline{P_nP_1}$ with the sides
$\overline{Q_1Q_2}$, $\overline{Q_2Q_3}$, $\ldots$, $\overline{Q_{n-1}Q_n}$, $\overline{Q_nQ_1}$ respectively.

Convention

A correspondence of a polygon $P_1P_2P_3 \ldots P_n$ and a polygon
$Q_1Q_2Q_3 \ldots Q_n$ will be indicated by the notation
$P_1P_2P_3 \ldots P_n \leftrightarrow Q_1Q_2Q_3 \ldots Q_n$.

Definition 89/5 *Similarity of polygons*

A correspondence of polygons is a similarity of the polygons
if corresponding angles are congruent and if the sides of one polygon
are proportional to the corresponding sides of the other. If there is a
similarity of two polygons, the polygons are said to be similar polygons.

Convention

That the correspondence $P_1P_2P_3 \ldots P_n \leftrightarrow Q_1Q_2Q_3 \ldots Q_n$ is a
similarity of the polygons will be indicated by the notation
$P_1P_2P_3 \ldots P_n \sim Q_1Q_2Q_3 \ldots Q_n$. (D460)

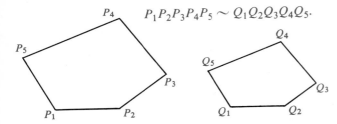

$$P_1P_2P_3P_4P_5 \sim Q_1Q_2Q_3Q_4Q_5.$$

Diagram 460

Definition 90/5 *Congruence of polygons*

A correspondence of polygons in which
corresponding angles are congruent
and corresponding sides are congruent
is a congruence of the polygons.
If there is a congruence of the
polygons, then the polygons are
said to be congruent polygons.

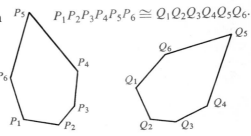

$$P_1P_2P_3P_4P_5P_6 \cong Q_1Q_2Q_3Q_4Q_5Q_6.$$

Diagram 461

Convention

That the correspondence
$P_1P_2P_3 \ldots P_n \leftrightarrow Q_1Q_2Q_3 \ldots Q_n$ is a congruence
of polygons will be indicated by the notation
$P_1P_2P_3 \ldots P_n \cong Q_1Q_2Q_3 \ldots Q_n$. (D461)

A congruence of two polygons is a similarity of the polygons
in which the ratio of corresponding sides is 1. From the
definition of a similarity of polygons, the similarity
of two polygons is a symmetric relation that also has the
identity property in the sense that every polygon is similar to itself.

The proof of the transitive property of similar polygons pro-
ceeds in the same way as the proof of this property for similar
triangles (Theorem 159/5).

* Theorem 169/5

Similarity between polygons is a transitive relation, that is,
$P_1P_2P_3 \ldots P_n \sim Q_1Q_2Q_3 \ldots Q_n$ and
$Q_1Q_2Q_3 \ldots Q_n \sim R_1R_2R_3 \ldots R_n$ imply
$P_1P_2P_3 \ldots P_n \sim R_1R_2R_3 \ldots R_n$.

Exercises

1 Consider the correspondence $ABCD \leftrightarrow KLHJ$ of
trapezoid $ABCD$ and square $HJKL$ (D462).

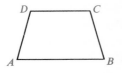

a Points A and D of $ABCD$ correspond respectively with
points ⌇⌇ and ⌇⌇ of $KLHJ$.
b The angles at C and B correspond respectively with
the angles at ⌇⌇ and ⌇⌇.
c Sides $\overline{DA}$ and $\overline{AB}$ correspond respectively with sides
⌇⌇ and ⌇⌇.
d Must $\sphericalangle A$ be congruent to $\sphericalangle K$? Could these angles be
congruent? *Answer*

e Must $d(A, B) = d(K, L)$? Could $d(A, B) = d(K, L)$?

Diagram 462

f Indicate the correspondence between $ABCD$ and $LHJK$ if
A corresponds to L, B to K, C to J, and D to H.
2 Assume that polygons $ABCDEF$ and $PQRSTU$ are similar
under the correspondence $ABCDEF \leftrightarrow RQPUTS$.
a Which angle of $RQPUTS$ must be congruent to $\sphericalangle B$?
To $\sphericalangle D$? To $\sphericalangle EFA$? *Answer*
b Must $\overline{AB}$ and $\overline{RQ}$ be congruent? Could they be congruent?
c Must $ABCDEF$ and $RQPUTS$ be coplanar? Could
$ABCDEF = RQPUTS$?
d Under the given correspondence, which side of $ABCDEF$
corresponds to $\overline{RQ}$? To $\overline{TU}$? To $\overline{SR}$?
e If $\dfrac{d(B, C)}{d(Q, P)} = 6$, must $\dfrac{d(D, E)}{d(P, U)} = 6$?
f If $\dfrac{d(A, B)}{d(R, Q)} = 3$, then ⌇⌇ $= 3d(U, T)$, and
⌇⌇ $= \frac{1}{3}d(E, F)$. *Answer*

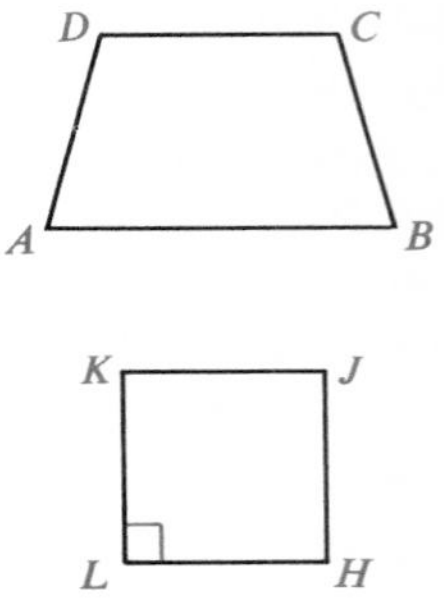

g Under the correspondence $ABCDEF \leftrightarrow RQPUTS$, must the two polygons be congruent? If they are congruent, then $\dfrac{d(A, B)}{d(R, Q)}$ is what number?

3 The following statements concern polygons $P_1P_2P_3 \ldots P_{20}$ and $Q_1Q_2Q_3 \ldots Q_{20}$. If the correspondence $P_{20}P_{19}P_{18} \ldots P_1 \leftrightarrow Q_1Q_2Q_3 \ldots Q_{20}$ is a congruence of the polygons, indicate which of the following statements are true (T) and which are false (F).

a $P_{20}P_{19}P_{18} \ldots P_1 \sim Q_1Q_2Q_3 \ldots Q_{20}$.

b $P_1P_2P_3 \ldots P_{20}$ and $Q_1Q_2Q_3 \ldots Q_{20}$ are congruent polygons. *Answer*

c The correspondence $P_1P_2P_3 \ldots P_{20} \leftrightarrow Q_1Q_2Q_3 \ldots Q_{20}$ must also be a congruence.

d $d(P_1, P_2) = d(P_2, P_3)$.

e Two corresponding points are P_{13} and Q_{18}.

f Two corresponding segments are $\overline{P_{19}P_{18}}$ and $\overline{Q_2Q_3}$.

g $\dfrac{d(P_6, P_5)}{d(Q_{15}, Q_{16})} = 1$.

4 Indicate which of the following statements are true (T) and which are false (F).

a Two squares are always similar.

b Two rectangles are always similar.

c Two isosceles triangles are always similar.

d Two similar equilateral triangles are always congruent.

e Any two regular polygons are similar.

f Two regular similar polygons are congruent.

g Any two congruent polygons are similar.

h The ratio of the measures of corresponding angles in similar polygons is 1.

i The ratio of corresponding sides of similar polygons must be 1.

j Two rhombuses are similar if an angle of one is congruent to any angle of the other.

k If a side of one rectangle is congruent to a side of a second rectangle, then the two rectangles must be similar.

l All polygons are similar to themselves.

m All right triangles are similar.

n All right triangles with a given segment for a hypotenuse are similar.

5 Which of the following statements are necessarily true if $ABCDE \sim FGHJK$, $FGHJK \sim RSTWV$, and $RSTWV \cong MNXYZ$?

a $FGHJK \sim ABCDE$.

b $ABCDE \sim RSTWV$.

c $MNXYZ \cong FGHJK$.

d $ABCDE \sim MNXYZ$.

e $FGHJK \cong FGHJK$.

f $RSTWV \cong VWTSR$.

6 a If $P_1P_2P_3 \ldots P_7 \sim Q_1Q_2Q_3 \ldots Q_7$ and $\dfrac{d(P_1, P_2)}{d(Q_1, Q_2)} = 3,$

show that

$$\frac{d(P_1, P_2) + d(P_2, P_3) + \ldots + d(P_6, P_7) + d(P_7, P_1)}{d(Q_1, Q_2) + d(Q_2, Q_3) + \ldots + d(Q_6, Q_7) + d(Q_7, Q_1)} = 3.$$

b What general theorem concerning the perimeter of similar polygons is suggested by exercise 6a?

7 Assume that sides $\overline{AB}, \overline{BC}, \overline{CD}, \overline{DE},$ and $\overline{EA}$ of polygon $ABCDE$ have lengths 2, 3, 5, 3, and 6 respectively, and $ABCDE \sim FGHJK.$

a Find the lengths of $\overline{GH}, \overline{KJ},$ and $\overline{FK}$ if $d(F, G) = 3.$

b Find the lengths of $\overline{FG}$ and $\overline{KJ}$ if $d(F, K) = \pi\sqrt{2}.$ *Answer*

c Find the lengths of the sides of $FGHJK$ if its perimeter is 57.

d Find the lengths of the sides of $FGHJK$ if its perimeter is 20.

e Must $\overline{GH}$ and $\overline{KJ}$ be congruent for all perimeters of $FGHJK$?

f What is the ratio of $\overline{FG}$ to $\overline{HJ}$?

g Is the ratio of the perimeter of $ABCDE$ to the perimeter of $FGHJK$ a constant?

8 The correspondence $P_1P_2P_3 \ldots P_n \leftrightarrow P_1P_2P_3 \ldots P_n$ is the *identity correspondence* of the polygon with itself. A correspondence of a polygon with itself is called a *symmetry* of the polygon if it is a congruence and is not an identity correspondence. List the symmetries of the quadrilateral $ABCD$ for each of the following cases.

a Quadrilateral $ABCD$ is a nonsquare rectangle. *Answer*

b Quadrilateral $ABCD$ is a nonsquare rhombus.

c Quadrilateral $ABCD$ is a parallelogram that is neither a rectangle nor a rhombus.

d Quadrilateral $ABCD$ is an isosceles trapezoid with bases $\overline{AB}$ and $\overline{CD}.$

9 a If $ABCD \leftrightarrow EFGH$ is a similarity of quadrilaterals and $ABCD \leftrightarrow BADC$ is a symmetry of the first quadrilateral, must $EFGH \leftrightarrow FEHG$ be a symmetry of the second quadrilateral? (See exercise 8.)

b What does exercise 9a suggest about the number of symmetries of two similar polygons?

We have talked informally about the shape of a figure, but we have never defined "shape." We can regard the definition of simi- lar polygons as being a definition not of "shape" but of "sameness of shape." In the case of triangles, such a definition seems need- lessly complicated because the congruence of corresponding angles is sufficient to give all the properties we expect from two triangles that have the same shape. However, for similar quadrilaterals, it is clear that we need both the condition of congruence for the angles and also the proportionality of the sides. A square and a nonsquare rectangle both satisfy the congruent angle condition, but, clearly, these two figures do not have the same shape. A square whose sides each have length 1 and a nonsquare rhombus whose sides each have length 2 have proportional sides, but, clearly, they do not have the same shape.

Neither the congruence of angles nor the proportionality of sides is enough, by itself, to force "sameness of shape" for two polygons (other than triangles). The question is "Are the two conditions sufficient?" To put the question in a more definite form, suppose that $P_1P_2P_3 \ldots P_n \sim Q_1Q_2Q_3 \ldots Q_n$. If any three vertices, say P_i, P_j, P_k, are selected, then is the triangle $\triangle P_iP_jP_k$ similar to the triangle with corresponding vertices, $\triangle Q_iQ_jQ_k$? And if these triangles are similar, is the ratio of their corresponding sides the same as that of the corresponding sides of the polygons? The answer to both of these questions is yes. A complete proof, in the general case, requires the use of mathematical induction; therefore, we will star this theorem.

___

* Theorem 170/5

If $P_1P_2P_3 \ldots P_n \sim Q_1Q_2Q_3 \ldots Q_n$ is a similarity of polygons and if P_i, P_j, and P_k are three vertices of one polygon with corresponding vertices Q_i, Q_j, Q_k in the other polygon, then $\triangle P_iP_jP_k \sim \triangle Q_iQ_jQ_k$ and the ratio of corresponding sides of the triangles is the same as that of the corresponding sides of the polygons. (D463)

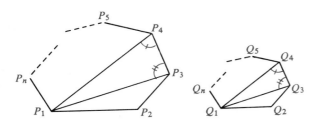

Diagram 463

___

In studying a polygon $P_1P_2P_3 \ldots P_n$, it is sometimes useful to consider all of the triangles that have P_1 as one vertex, that have the other two vertices in the set $\{P_2, P_3, \ldots, P_n\}$, and are such that no two of their interiors intersect. For this reason, we make a convention to name these triangles.

In the polygon $P_1P_2P_3 \ldots P_n$, the triangles $\triangle P_1P_2P_3$, $\triangle P_1P_3P_4$, $\triangle P_1P_4P_5$, $\ldots$, $\triangle P_1P_{n-2}P_{n-1}$, $\triangle P_1P_{n-1}P_n$ will be called the set of successive triangles of the polygon at P_1.

* Corollary 170a/5

In a similarity of polygons, each triangle in the set of successive triangles at a vertex is similar to the corresponding triangle in the set of successive triangles

As a special case of Theorem 170/5, we also have the following corollary.

* Corollary 170b/5

If two polygons are congruent, then any three vertices of one polygon determine a triangle that is congruent to the triangle determined by the three corresponding vertices of the other polygon.

The preceding theorems show that our definition of similar polygons does imply properties that we would expect if similar polygons really do have the same shape. Later we will see how we can make this idea still more precise.

Using the set of successive triangles at a vertex P_1 of a polygon, we can easily see what the sum of the measures of all the angles of the polygon must be. If the polygon has n sides, that is, if it is the n-gon $P_1P_2P_3 \ldots P_n$, then the sum of the measures of all the vertex angles at P_1 of the different triangles will be the measure of $\sphericalangle P_1$ (D464). The measure of the angle P_k of the poly-

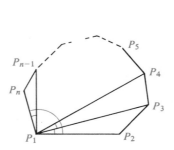

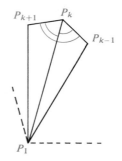

Diagram 464a   464b

gon is the measure of $\sphericalangle P_{k-1}P_kP_1$ plus the measure of $\sphericalangle P_1P_kP_{k+1}$. The measure of the angle P_k of the polygon is, therefore, the measure of an angle of $\triangle P_1P_{k-1}P_k$ and an angle of $\triangle P_1P_kP_{k+1}$. When the measures of all the angles of the triangles in the set of successive triangles at P_1 are added, the sum is the measure of all the angles of the polygon. However, there are $n - 2$ triangles in the set, and the sum of the measures of the angles in each triangle is 180. Therefore, the sum of the measures of the angles of the polygon must be $(n - 2)180$. We thus have an informal proof of Theorem 171/5.*

★ Theorem 171/5

The sum of the measures of the angles of an n-gon is $(n - 2)180$.

Corollary 171/5

If one exterior angle of a polygon is selected at each vertex, then the sum of the measures of these angles is 360. (D465)

Diagram 465

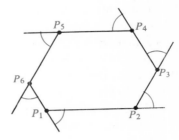

Proof

Let $\measuredangle P_1$, $\measuredangle P_2$, $\measuredangle P_3$, . . . , $\measuredangle P_n$ denote the angles of polygon $P_1P_2P_3 \ldots P_n$ and let $\measuredangle P_1'$, $\measuredangle P_2'$, $\measuredangle P_3'$, . . . , $\measuredangle P_n'$ denote exterior angles at P_1, P_2, P_3, . . . , P_n respectively. Then each of the pairs $\measuredangle P_i$ and $\measuredangle P_i'$ are supplements. So

1 $(\measuredangle P_1^\circ + \measuredangle P_1'^\circ) + (\measuredangle P_2^\circ + \measuredangle P_2'^\circ) + \ldots + (\measuredangle P_n^\circ + \measuredangle P_n'^\circ) = (n)180.$

By Theorem 171/5,

2 $\measuredangle P_1^\circ + \measuredangle P_2^\circ + \ldots + \measuredangle P_n^\circ = (n - 2)180.$

Therefore, using statements 1 and 2, we have

$\measuredangle P_1'^\circ + \measuredangle P_2'^\circ + \ldots + \measuredangle P_n'^\circ = (n)180 - (n - 2)180 = 360.$

Exercises

Diagram 466

1 Assume that polygons $ABCD$ and $EFGH$ are a rectangle and a square respectively and that the lengths of their sides are as indicated in D466.

a Are corresponding angles of the two polygons congruent under the correspondence $ABCD \leftrightarrow EFGH$?

b What is the ratio of $\overline{DA}$ to $\overline{HE}$? Of $\overline{AB}$ to $\overline{EF}$? *Answer*

c Is $ABCD \sim EFGH$?

d If a correspondence between two polygons exists such that corresponding angles are congruent, is the correspondence always a similarity?

2 Polygons $ABCD$ and $EFGH$ are a square and a rhombus respectively such that $\measuredangle E^\circ = 60$. Assume that the lengths

---

* Again one needs induction to make the proof of this theorem completely precise.

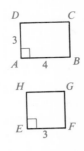

of the sides of the two figures are as indicated in D467 and
consider the correspondence $ABCD \leftrightarrow EFGH$ of the polygons.

a Are corresponding sides of the two polygons congruent?
b Are $\angle D$ and $\angle H$ congruent? Are any corresponding
angles congruent? *Answer*

c Is $ABCD \sim EFGH$?
d If a correspondence between two polygons exists such
that corresponding sides are congruent, is the
correspondence always a similarity?

Diagram 467

e Is a correspondence like the one described in exercise 2d
a similarity if the polygons are triangles? Is such a
correspondence between triangles always a congruence?

3 Assume that the correspondence $ABCDEFGH \leftrightarrow P_1P_2P_3 \ldots P_8$
is a similarity of the polygons.
   a What point corresponds to F? To P_4? *Answer*
   b Denote the set of successive triangles of $ABCDEFGH$ at B.
   c Denote the set of successive triangles of $P_1P_2P_3 \ldots P_8$ at P_2.
   d Which triangle from the set denoted in exercise 3b is
   similar to $\triangle P_2P_1P_8$? To $\triangle P_2P_5P_7$?
   e If the ratio of $\overline{AB}$ to $\overline{P_1P_2}$ is r, is the ratio of $\overline{AC}$ to $\overline{P_1P_3}$
   equal to r? Is the ratio of $\overline{GD}$ to $\overline{P_4P_8}$ necessarily equal to r?

4 Prove that the two polygons of exercise 3 are congruent
if $\triangle P_1P_2P_3 \cong \triangle ABC$.

5 Given polygon $ABCDE$ and a segment $\overline{XY}$ (D468), explain
a construction for a polygon $FGHJK$ such that
$FGHJK \sim ABCDE$ and $d(F, G) = d(X, Y)$.

Diagram 468

6 a Given $\triangle ABC$ and a segment $\overline{XY}$, construct $\triangle A'B'C'$ such
that $\triangle A'B'C' \sim \triangle ABC$ and the perimeter of $\triangle A'B'C'$
equals $d(X, Y)$.
   b Given polygon $ABCD$ and a segment $\overline{RS}$, construct polygon
   $EFGH$ such that $EFGH \sim ABCD$ and the perimeter of
   $EFGH$ equals $d(R, S)$.

7 Assume that rectangle R_1 has sides of lengths x and $x - 3$
and that rectangle R_2 has sides of lengths $x - 1$ and $x + 4$.
What are the dimensions of R_1 and R_2 if they are similar? *Answer*

8 From the similarity $ABCDE \sim A'B'C'D'E'$ and the relations
$\angle A° = 90$, $d(A, B) = 5$, $d(A, E) = 4$, and $d(A', B') = 2$,
determine the value of $d(B', E')$. *Answer*

9 Let $ABCD$ denote a rectangle that is not a square (D469).
Point O is the foot of D in diagonal $\overline{AC}$.
Point E is the intersection of DO
and BC, and point F is the foot in AD of E.

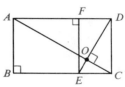

   a Prove that $\triangle AOD \sim \triangle ADC$.

Diagram 469

   b Prove that $\overline{AD}$ and $\overline{DC}$ are proportional to $\overline{DC}$ and $\overline{CE}$.

308

c Prove that $ABCD \sim ECDF$.

10 Find the sum of the measures of the angles of polygons that have the following number of sides.

a 6   **b** 10   **c** 1002   **d** $x - 3$

11 A polygon has how many sides if the sum of the measures of its angles is 1800? 540? 32,400? *Answer*

12 a What is the measure of each angle of a regular polygon of 8 sides? Of 180 sides?

b A regular polygon has how many sides if the measure of each angle is 174? If the measure of each angle is x?

13 The number of sides of each of six regular polygons are given below. What is the measure of each exterior angle of each polygon?

a 6   **c** 50   **e** 720

b 20 *Answer*   **d** 100   **f** n

◆ **14** Assume that point P is interior to $\sphericalangle ABC$. It is desired to find point J in $\overrightarrow{BA}$ and point R in $\overrightarrow{BC}$ such that P is in $\overline{JR}$ and $\dfrac{d(P, J)}{d(P, R)} = \frac{1}{2}$. Show that there is exactly one such segment, and explain how its position can be determined.

◆ **15** A rectangle $ABCD$ is given and also a figure $\mathbb{S}$ that consists of a diameter $\overline{EF}$ of a circle, together with the points of the circle in one side of $\overline{EF}$ (that is, a semicircle and its diameter). Show that there exists a rectangle $GHIJ$ whose vertices belong to $\mathbb{S}$, with $\overline{GH}$ contained in $\overline{EF}$, and such that $GHIJ \sim ABCD$.

◆ **16** A triangle $\triangle ABC$ and a rectangle $DEFG$ are given (D470).

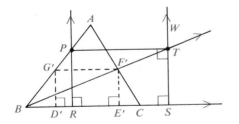

Diagram 470

It is desired to find a rectangle $\mathbb{R}$ that is similar to $DEFG$ and is inscribed in the triangle in the sense that its vertices are in the triangle and one of its sides is contained in a side of the triangle. Justify the following explanation of why such a rectangle must exist: At least two of the angles of $\triangle ABC$ are acute, so it may be supposed that $\sphericalangle B$ and $\sphericalangle C$ are acute. Let P be such that $<A, P, B>$, and let R denote the foot in $\overline{BC}$

of P. Then $<B, R, C>$ (Why?). In $\overrightarrow{RC}$, there is a point S
such that $\overline{PR}$ and $\overline{RS}$ are proportional to $\overline{GD}$ and $\overline{DE}$.
Let the open ray $\overrightarrow{SW}$ be like directed to $\overrightarrow{RP}$, and let T
be the foot in SW of P. Then $PRST \sim GDEF$ (Why?).
The open ray $\overrightarrow{BT}$ intersects AC at F' and $<A, F', C>$ (Why?).
The line through F' that is parallel to BC intersects AB
at G' and $<A, G', B>$ (Why?). Let E' and D' denote the
feet in BC of F' and G' respectively. Then $<B, E', C>$
(Why?), $<B, D', C>$ (Why?), and $D'E'F'G' \sim DEFG$ (Why?).

A midway **23/5**
summary In this section, we pause to look from a new perspective at the
things we have accomplished. We do this so that we may look
ahead and see our future work more clearly as part of a logical
plan. To accomplish these objectives, it will be helpful first to talk
briefly about something that we have hardly mentioned so far.
This is the practical value of geometry.

We can regard the formal system that we are developing as an
attempt to represent, in a mathematical way, the geometric nature
of the physical world and of the objects in it. The formal system
does this by means of its definitions and the relations stated in its
theorems. The practical purpose of such a system is to devise
methods of attacking geometric problems and of obtaining information that is useful for science and for the needs of society.

To serve such a practical end, a system need not actually say
anything about its usefulness or its applications. For example,
suppose that a manufacturer of life preservers wants to know the
amount of material needed to fill a circular life buoy of a given size
and the amount of canvas needed for the cover. In a geometric
system, he should be able to find a figure that corresponds to a
life preserver. The mathematical name of such a figure is a torus.
He also should be able to find theorems that give the numerical
relation of the volume and the surface area of a torus to both its
inner and outer radius. With these formulas, he can then compute
the answers he wants. The system, of course, need not say anything about life preservers. In fact, it would be inefficient for the
system to make such statements. Instead, the system concentrates
on developing general relations that then can be applied to any
number of particular physical objects as special cases of the
relations.

Let us consider our system in terms of the practical goals implied above. We now have established the general structure of a
three-dimensional Euclidean space so that it does correspond with

our ideas of physical space. We have developed a language of geometric relations that enables us to describe figures and properties accurately, without depending on diagrams, and that allows us to investigate geometric problems by means of logic. With the congruence conditions and, now, the similarity conditions, we can establish geometric properties that are neither obvious to see nor obvious to prove. For example, we can now establish that the centroid, the orthocenter, and the circumcenter of a triangle are either collinear or the same point.

On the other hand, our model space is clearly incomplete in a number of ways. We have not yet introduced either the notion of area or that of volume. These are, as we will see, notions that involve all of the difficulties of the parallel-proportion problem but in a more complicated form. By means of some very special axioms, we will be able to obtain area and volume formulas for a few familiar, standard figures. However, a general treatment of area and volume belongs to more advanced mathematics.

Looked at in a practical way, however, our system has a much more serious weakness than the absence of area and volume relations. In terms of representing the world of physical objects, our system is nearly empty. We have not defined any figure that corresponds to a three-dimensional object. Moreover, in the plane, the only curved figure we have is a circle.

Our situation, at this point, is natural enough; you have to build a house before you furnish it. But if our space is to be at all practical in representing the world of objects, we need to define a great many figures for both the plane and space. To do this will be the object of the next chapter. There we will turn our attention to an important side of mathematics that differs from that of proving theorems.

To solve any physical problem by means of mathematics, whether it is to find the area of a field or to compute the intersection paths for two rockets, the problem first has to be stated in a purely mathematical form. To find such a way of stating the problem is often the hardest part. Similarly, it is sometimes harder to define a geometric figure in a satisfactory mathematical way than it is to obtain its properties once the figure has been properly defined.

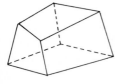

Diagram 471

To give an example of the difficulty of defining a geometric figure, consider the figure pictured in D471. This figure might be described as a space analogue of a polygon. It has faces as well as edges and vertices. But there is no natural circuit order for either the vertices or the faces to use in defining the figure. Some new idea is needed. In the process of defining new plane figures, we will find such an idea by looking at polygons in a new way.

It is typical of all scientific systems that, as they grow, the points of view and definitions that were first used are later replaced by more general ones. It is this important process that we want to emphasize in the next chapter. We will need to show, of course, that new definitions make sense and do not contradict old ones, and it takes theorems to do this. But our interest will be in the kind of theorems that are necessary rather than in the proofs of these theorems. We will describe the kind of arguments that could be given, but we will take most of the facts as starred theorems.

Following this chapter of definitions, Chapter 6, we want to show how the new figures (or in fact, any figure) can be moved freely in space and how they can be expanded or contracted to a similar figure of a different size. These again are very natural properties of physical space, and we can establish them quite simply in the system by using our congruence and similarity conditions.

After we have made our space more practical in these ways, we will return to the investigation of particular figures. However, we will have improved the tools we use, and we will have a much better understanding of the wide range of objects to which geometry applies.

Another feature of our plan is perhaps the most important of all. In this plan, we will encounter a number of ideas that are of great importance in more advanced mathematics and also in other sciences. Many of these ideas arose in geometry and still can be seen in geometry in their simplest form. If you continue with mathematics, a knowledge of these ideas will be of great help to you.

Chapter review

1 The three parallel lines q, r, and s are intersected by a transversal t in points Q, R, and S respectively. Indicate whether each of the following statements is necessarily true (T), possibly true (P), or necessarily false (F).
   a The lines q, r, and s are coplanar.
   b If $\overline{QR} \cong \overline{RS}$, then $d(q, r) = d(r, s)$.
   c If $d(q, s) = d(q, r)$, then $\overline{QS} \cong \overline{QR}$.
   d Point R is in the strip determined by q and s.
   e If s is the midparallel of r and q, then $d(r, q) = 2\,d(R, S)$.
   f Segments $\overline{RQ}$ and $\overline{RS}$ are the same segment.
2 The coordinates of the five points A, B, C, D, and E in a line t are respectively -3, 18, 1, -5, and 0.
   a The five points are successive in t in what order? Is there more than one such order?

b Do all points belong to the open ray $\overset{\longrightarrow}{DA}$? To the closed ray $\overset{\cdots\longrightarrow}{BC}$?

c Is $d(D, A) < d(A, E) < d(E, C) < d(C, B)$?

d Is $d(B, C) < d(B, E) < d(B, A) < d(B, D)$?

e The ruler placement axiom (Axiom 7/2) permits a selection of a different coordinate system for t in which the coordinate of D is zero. What are the new coordinates of E, C, and B if the new coordinate of A is 4?

3 By definition, two numbers a and b are commensurable if there exists a number x such that $a = mx$ and $b = nx$, where m and n are integers. Find the greatest possible x and the corresponding integers m and n for the following commensurable pairs a and b.

a $a = 6$; $b = 40$.   **c** $a = 0.010$; $b = 0.004$.

b $a = 7$; $b = 13$.   **d** $a = \sqrt{8}$; $b = \sqrt{50}$.

4 A straight, flat cement highway has parallel lines painted across it. These lines are perpendicular to the edges of the road. Each two of these successive parallel lines are x ft. apart. A wheel of circumference 3π ft. rolls down the middle of the road, and a tiny tar spot on the wheel happens to roll onto the middle of one of the lines. If mathematical accuracy were possible in this situation, explain why the following statements would be true.

a If x is rational, the tar spot would never hit the middle of any of the other parallel lines.

b If the spot *did* hit a second parallel line but missed five other lines between the two lines touched, x would have to be an irrational number of the form $\dfrac{m\pi}{2}$, where m is a positive integer.

5 A trapezoid $ABCD$ is such that $AB \parallel CD$, $d(A, D) = 10$, and $d(B, C) = 12$. A line parallel to the bases intersects $\overline{AD}$, $\overline{AC}$, and $\overline{BC}$ at points E, P, and F respectively such that $\dfrac{d(A, P)}{d(A, C)} = \dfrac{4}{9}$.

a Find $\dfrac{d(A, E)}{d(E, D)}$ and $\dfrac{d(C, F)}{d(F, B)}$.

b What are the lengths of $\overline{ED}$ and $\overline{BF}$?

6 From the information given in D472, decide which of the following statements are necessarily correct.

a $a^2 = b^2 + c^2$.

b If $c > a$, then $x > y$.

c $yc = xa$.

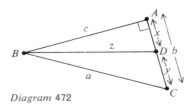

Diagram 472

313

d $a^2 = c^2 + x^2 + y^2$.

e $\triangle ABD \sim \triangle ACB$.

f $z^2 - c^2 = x^2$.

7 Line BD is tangent to $C(O, r)$ at B, segment $\overline{AB}$ is a diameter of the circle, and secant DA intersects $C(O, r)$ in points C and A (D473). Let x, y, a, and b denote the lengths of segments $\overline{AC}$, $\overline{CD}$, $\overline{DB}$, and $\overline{CB}$ respectively.

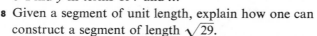

a Is $\triangle ABC \sim \triangle ADB$? Is $\triangle DCB \sim \triangle DAB$?

b Find b if $x = 12$ and $y = 4$.

c What is the value of x if $r = 5$ and $b = 3$?

d Find y if $x = 9$ and $a = 12$.

Diagram 473

e Find y in terms of r and x.

8 Given a segment of unit length, explain how one can construct a segment of length $\sqrt{29}$.

9 If x and y are real numbers, indicate whether each of the following is necessarily true (T), possibly true (P), or necessarily false (F).

a If $x \neq y$, then $x^2 \neq y^2$.　　**d** $\sqrt{x^2 + y^2} = |x + y|$.

b If $x^2 > y^2$, then $x > y$.　　**e** $\sqrt{x^2 y^2} = |x| \cdot |y|$.

c $\sqrt{x^2} = -x$.　　**f** If $x > y > 0$, then $\sqrt{x} > \sqrt{y}$.

10 Assume that point F is the foot in line AB of point P. For each of the following conditions, indicate, if possible, which of the two segments $\overline{PA}$ or $\overline{PB}$ must be the longer. If the condition is insufficient to determine which segment is longer, indicate this by the word "insufficient."

a $F = A$.　　**d** $\sphericalangle PAF° = 60$; $\sphericalangle PBF° = 40$.

b $d(F, B) > d(F, A)$.　　**e** $\sphericalangle BPF° > \sphericalangle FPA°$; $<B, F, A>$.

c $\overline{FA} \cong \overline{AB}$.　　**f** A is in the B-side of PF.

11 Points A and B in a line t have coordinates $a = 3$ and $b = 8$ respectively. What values are possible for the coordinates of a point X in t if $\dfrac{d(X, A)}{d(X, B)}$ equals each of the following numbers?

a $\frac{2}{3}$　　**b** $\frac{4}{1}$　　**c** $\frac{3}{7}$

12 Consider the correspondence $ABCDE \leftrightarrow MNOPQ$ of polygons $ABCDE$ and $MNOPQ$.

a Must this correspondence be a congruence? A similarity?

b If the correspondence is a similarity, must $\sphericalangle D$ and $\sphericalangle P$ be congruent? Must $\overline{AB}$ and $\overline{MN}$ be congruent?

c If $ABCDE \sim MNOPQ$, then what side must have length $\dfrac{d(A, E)\, d(P, O)}{d(M, Q)}$?

d If the ratio of corresponding sides is 1, must the correspondence be a congruence?

e If $ABCDE = MNOPQ$, must the correspondence be a congruence?

Cumulative review

1 The coordinates of three points X, Y, and Z in a line t are x, y, and z respectively. Which of the following statements are implied by $\langle y, x, z \rangle$?

a $\langle Z, X, Y \rangle$.

b $d(Y, X) + d(Z, X) = d(Z, Y)$.

c $y < z$.

d $|x - y| < |y - z|$.

e Y is contained in $\overrightarrow{ZX}$.

f Z is contained in $\overline{XY}$.

g If $y = 0$, then $z > x > 0$ or $z < x < 0$.

h $x \neq y \neq z$.

2 Seven possible relationships between the measures of $\sphericalangle ABC$ and $\sphericalangle XYZ$ are given below. Indicate by number those relationships implied by each of statements a through k.

(1) $\sphericalangle ABC° = \sphericalangle XYZ°$.

(2) $\sphericalangle ABC° + \sphericalangle XYZ° = 90$.

(3) $\sphericalangle ABC° + \sphericalangle XYZ° = 180$.

(4) $\sphericalangle ABC° + \sphericalangle XYZ° < 360$.

(5) $\sphericalangle ABC° > \sphericalangle XYZ°$.

(6) $\sphericalangle ABC° < \sphericalangle XYZ°$.

(7) $\sphericalangle ABC° \neq \sphericalangle XYZ°$.

a The angles are complementary.

b The angles are opposite angles.

c The angles are supplementary.

d $\sphericalangle ABC$ and $\sphericalangle XYZ$ are base angles of an isosceles triangle.

e $\sphericalangle XYZ$ is an exterior angle at B of $\triangle ABC$.

f $\sphericalangle XYZ$ is an exterior angle at C of $\triangle ABC$.

g $\overrightarrow{YX} = \overrightarrow{BC}$ and $\langle C, Z, A \rangle$.

h The angles are adjacent angles.

i $\triangle ABC \sim \triangle XYZ$.

j $AB \perp BC$ and $XZ \perp ZY$.

k $ABCXYZ$ is a regular 6-gon.

3 a How many different one-to-one correspondences exist between the vertices of $\triangle ABC$ and $\triangle PQR$?

b In $\triangle ABC$ and $\triangle PQR$, if $\overline{AB} \cong \overline{BC} \cong \overline{PQ} \cong \overline{QR}$ and if $\overline{AC}$ is not congruent to $\overline{PR}$, how many of the one-to-one correspondences between their vertices will match two pairs of congruent sides?

c How many of the one-to-one correspondences between $\triangle ABC$ and $\triangle PQR$ will match $\sphericalangle A$ and $\sphericalangle P$? Will match $\overline{AB}$ and $\overline{PQ}$?

4 Side $\overline{AB}$ is the base of isosceles triangle $\triangle ABC$, and points D and E of the triangle are such that AD bisects $\measuredangle A$ and BE bisects $\measuredangle B$. Which of the following relations are implied by these given conditions?

a $<B, D, C>$ and $<A, E, C>$.

b $\triangle ADC \cong \triangle BEC$.

c $ED \parallel AB$.

d $\overline{CD} \cong \overline{DB}$.

e $AD \perp BC$.

f $\measuredangle ADC° > \measuredangle ADB°$.

5 Certain angles and exterior angles of $\triangle ABC$ are labeled in D474. Use the diagram to decide which of the following statements are necessarily correct.

a If $\measuredangle 2° \geq 90$, then $\measuredangle 3° < 90$.

b $\measuredangle 1° + \measuredangle 4° > 180$.

c $\measuredangle 6° = 180 - \measuredangle 4° - \measuredangle 1°$.

d If $\measuredangle 4° = 135$ and $\measuredangle 2° = 91$, then $d(A, C) > d(A, B)$.

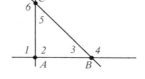

Diagram 474

e If $\measuredangle 6° = \measuredangle 4°$, then $\triangle ABC$ is isosceles.

6 Indicate whether each of the following statements is necessarily true (T), possibly true (P), or necessarily false (F).

a If the three points B, C, and E are collinear and $\measuredangle ACE° > \measuredangle ABC°$, then $\measuredangle ACE$ is an exterior angle of $\triangle ABC$.

b If $\measuredangle ACD$ and $\measuredangle BCE$ are exterior angles of $\triangle ABC$, then $\measuredangle ACD \cong \measuredangle BCE$.

c If $\measuredangle A$ of $\triangle ABC$ is acute, then either $\measuredangle B$ or $\measuredangle C$ is acute.

d The perpendicular bisector of the base of an isosceles triangle also is the bisector of the vertex angle of the triangle.

e If $\measuredangle A \cong \measuredangle B$ in right triangle $\triangle ABC$, then $d(A, C) > d(A, B)$.

f If two sides and an angle of $\triangle ABC$ are congruent respectively to two sides and an angle of $\triangle DEF$, then the triangles are congruent.

g If the two planes α and β have a point in common, then the two planes have a line in common.

h If planes α and β are perpendicular to the line AB at A, then the intersection of α and β is a line t that passes through A.

i If line t is the perpendicular bisector of $\overline{PQ}$, then there is exactly one plane α that contains t and the midpoint of $\overline{PQ}$.

7 Which one of the following statements is necessarily true if lines r, s, and t are such that $r \parallel s$ and $s \parallel t$?

a $r \parallel t$.

b $r = t$.

c $s = t$.

d s is in the r-side of t.

e $r \neq s$.

f r, s, and t are coplanar.

8 Which *one* of the following statements is necessarily false
if $\sphericalangle ABC$ and $\sphericalangle BAD$ are a pair of alternate
interior angles formed by a transversal that intersects
the parallel lines s and t?

  a Line AB is a transversal of lines s and t.

  b The open rays $\overrightarrow{DA}$ and $\overrightarrow{BC}$ are like directed.

  c $\overline{DB} \cong \overline{AC}$.

  d $d(A, D) > d(B, C)$.

  e $d(D, B) < d(s, t)$.

  f $AB \perp t$.

9 Which *one* of the following statements is necessarily true
if points M and N are in $\overline{AC}$ and $\overline{BC}$ respectively
of $\triangle ABC$ and t is a line through C?

  a If t does not intersect AB and if MN bisects $\overline{AC}$ and $\overline{BC}$,
then MN is the midparallel of t and AB.

  b If $MN \parallel AB$, then $d(M, N) = \frac{1}{2} d(A, B)$.

  c $\sphericalangle A° + \sphericalangle AMN° + \sphericalangle B° > 180$.

  d If $\overline{AM} \cong \overline{MC}$ and $\overline{BN} \cong \overline{NC}$, then $2\,d(M, N) = d(A, B)$.

  e $d(A, B) > d(M, N)$.

10 For a point A in a plane α and a given positive real
number r, which of the following is the locus of all
points P in α such that circle $C(P, r)$ contains A?

  a A circle $C(P, r)$ **d** Line AP

  b Plane α **e** Circle $C(A, r)$

  c Point A

11 Let S and $\overline{AB}$ denote a point and a segment in a given
plane α. What is the locus of all points in α that are
equidistant from A and B and at a given distance r from S?

12 Which of the following numbers are rational and which are
irrational?

  a 4   **d** $\left(\frac{\sqrt{4}}{9}\right)^3$

  b $\sqrt[3]{334}$ **e** $\frac{1}{2}(\sqrt{5} + \sqrt{5})$

  c 0   **f** $-\frac{4}{3}$

13 Which of the following statements are necessarily true
if $\triangle ABC \sim \triangle DEF$ and the lengths of $\overline{AB}$ and $\overline{DE}$
are 7 and 9 respectively?

  a $\overline{AB}$ and $\overline{DE}$ are incommensurable segments.

  b $d(B, C) = \frac{9}{7} d(F, E)$.

  c $\sphericalangle B \cong \sphericalangle E$.

  d $d(D, F) = \frac{9}{7} d(A, C)$.

  e If $d(B, C)$ is irrational, then $d(F, E)$ is irrational.

  f The perimeter of $\triangle ABC$ equals $\frac{7}{9}$ the perimeter
of $\triangle DEF$.

  g If $d(B, C) = 8$, then $\sphericalangle D° > \sphericalangle F°$.

  h If $\sphericalangle F° = 90$, then $d(A, C) \leq \sqrt{7}$.

Plane convex **24/6**
figures To see how we are led to a study of convexity at this point, consider the following problem. Suppose that, in the system, we want
to define a reasonable number and variety of plane figures to
correspond with physical objects in the world around us. One of
the most common ways in which we encounter physical plane
figures is in the plane surfaces of objects, for example, the top of
an oval coffee table or the side of a box. In a physical way, these
objects could be represented by the class of figures that could be
cut, each in one piece, from flat sheets of paper (D475). Call this

Diagram 475

class of figures F. Let us try to define these flat paper figures in a
mathematical way. That is, let us try to define, in the formal
system, a class of sets 𝔉 in such a way that these mathematical sets
have the kind of properties we associate with the physical paper
figures in F.

Clearly, we want the sets in $\mathcal{F}$ to be nonempty and nonlinear, as well as planar. Next we might notice that each figure of F, being a physical object, has an actual size and does not stretch away indefinitely in the way that a half-plane does, for example. This limitation to the extent of a figure is called *boundedness*. We can define this notion for our planar sets in the following way.

A planar set is bounded if it is contained in the interior of a circle. (D476)

Diagram 476

Next we must require that each set in $\mathcal{F}$ be, in some sense, "all in one piece" like its corresponding paper figure. It is possible to define a kind of "connectedness" that would serve for all the shapes in set F, but "connectedness" cannot be defined in any simple way without first developing a number of ideas and methods that belong to more advanced mathematics. However, we easily can get around this difficulty if we are less ambitious.

Suppose that F′ denotes the subclass of set F that consists of convex paper figures. Then, if we simply require the corresponding sets of $\mathcal{F}'$ to be convex, we automatically will require these sets of $\mathcal{F}'$ to have the "one piece" property that we want. For if a set $\mathcal{S}$ is convex, the fact that each two of its points are joined by a segment that is also in $\mathcal{S}$ means that all parts of $\mathcal{S}$ are connected to each other in a very special way. This is one reason why convex figures are so natural for geometric study. Also, we actually do not give up a great deal in restricting ourselves to convex figures, since most other figures of geometric interest can be represented as the union of convex sets.

We now have almost all that we need to define the mathematical sets that correspond to convex paper figures. The sets must be planar, nonlinear, bounded, and convex. But consider the interior of a mathematical triangle. This triangle has all of the properties listed. But it cannot be the set that corresponds to a paper triangle, since the edges of the paper triangle are part of the figure. What we need is quite clear. If a set is bounded, and "all in one piece," then our natural feeling is that there has to be a boundary of the set consisting of points that are in the edge of the set. Definition 92/6 puts this notion into our system.

Definition 92/6 *Boundary point of a planar set*

A point P is a boundary point of a planar set S if, in the plane of S, every circle with center P has in its interior at least one point that belongs to S and at least one point that does not belong to S. The set of all boundary points of S is the boundary of S.

Comment

A boundary point of a set may or may not belong to the set.*

Though we have defined the boundary notion for any planar set, we can easily check that, in all the figures with which we have worked, the definition selects the set that we think of as the boundary. A line in a plane is the boundary of each of its half-planes, and a triangle and a circle are the boundaries of their respective interiors and exteriors (D477).

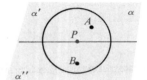 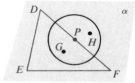 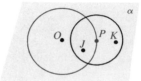

Diagram 477

We now define the class of sets that seem to correspond to convex paper figures and, hence, correspond to a wide range of planar objects.

Definition 93/6 *Plane convex figure*

A nonempty set S is a plane convex figure if it is planar, nonlinear, bounded, and convex, and if it contains its boundary.† (D478)

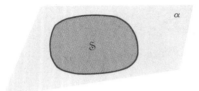

Diagram 478

---

* A set that contains all of its boundary points is commonly called a *closed* set. A closed ray and a closed half-plane, for example, are closed sets.
† We also could study unbounded plane convex figures, but we will not do so. A closed half-plane is an example of such a figure.

Exercises

1 Points A, M, and B are in a plane α (D479) such that M is the midpoint of the segment $\overline{AB}$ and $d(A, B) = 8$. Which of the following circles in α contain $\overline{AB}$ in their interiors? *Answer*

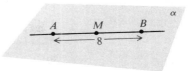

Diagram 479

  a $C(M, 5)$ **d** $C(A, 10)$

  b $C(M, 4)$ **e** $C(B, 8.01)$

  c $C(A, 7)$ **f** $C(B, 83456)$

2 The square $ABCD$ is in the plane α and its diagonals intersect at point O (D480). If $d(A, B) = 1$, which of the following circles in α contain $ABCD$ in their interiors?

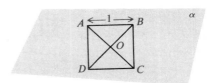

Diagram 480

  a $C(O, \sqrt{2})$ **d** $C(B, 1)$

  b $C(A, \sqrt{2})$ **e** $C(O, .71)$

  c $C(D, \sqrt{3})$ **f** $C(A, 7000)$

3 Which of the following are not bounded planar sets?

  a The plane α

  b The union of polygon $P_1P_2P_3 \ldots P_n$ and its interior

  c The strip between the parallel lines r and s

  d The three noncollinear points A, B, and C

  e The four noncoplanar points A, B, C, and D

  f The interior of $\angle BAC$

4 Assume that line t is in plane α (D481) and that the coordinates of points A, D, B, and F in line t are 0, 1, 4, and 6 respectively. Which of the following circles in α contain in their interiors at least one point of the segment $\overline{AB}$ and at least one point of α not in $\overline{AB}$?

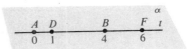

Diagram 481

  a $C(D, 3)$ **d** $C(A, .0000000000000000001)$

  b $C(A, .01)$ **e** $C(F, 1)$

  c $C(A, .0000001)$ **f** $C(D, .00000001)$

5 a In exercise 4, which of the points A, D, B, and F are boundary points of the segment $\overline{AB}$?

  b What is the set of *all* boundary points of $\overline{AB}$? *Answer*

  c If $\mathcal{S}$ is the set of all points between A and B, does the interior of the circle $C(A, .000001)$ contain at least one point of $\mathcal{S}$? If r is a positive real number, does the interior of the circle $C(A, r)$ contain at least one point of $\mathcal{S}$?

  d What is the set of all boundary points of the set $\mathcal{S}$ described in exercise 5c? *Answer*

  e Must all boundary points of a planar set belong to the set?

321

6 Which of the following sets are not bounded plane convex figures? Explain in each case why the given set does not qualify under the definition.

a The polygon $ABCD$ <small>Answer</small>

b The union of the polygon $ABCD$ and its interior

c The interior of the polygon $ABCD$

d The segment $\overline{AB}$

e The plane α

The fact that the mixed inequality $d(A, C) \leq d(A, B) + d(B, C)$ is correct for points A, B, and C *without any restriction* is sometimes called the *triangle inequality*. Some or all of the points can be the same, or they can be either collinear or noncollinear.* Assume this fact in the following exercises.

7 If A and C denote points interior to the circle $C(B, r)$, show that $d(A, C) < 2r$. <small>Answer</small>

8 Assume that circles $C(A, 1)$ and $C(B, 3)$ are in plane α and that the coordinates of A and B in line t are 2 and 7 respectively (D482). Let $\mathcal{R}$ denote the union of both circles and their interiors, and let P denote a point of $\mathcal{R}$.

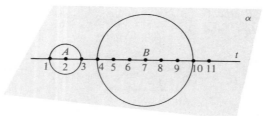

Diagram 482

a Where is P in α if $d(A, P) = 1$? If $d(A, P) > 1$? If $d(B, P) \leq 3$?

b Must $d(A, P) \leq 1$? Must $d(B, P) \leq 3$? Must at least one of these relations be true?

c Point P must be interior to which of the following circles in α?

(1) $C(A, 5)$ (3) $C(A, 8.1)$

(2) $C(A, 8)$ (4) $C(B, 72)$

d If m and n are positive real numbers, will there always be a circle $C(A, r)$ in α whose interior will contain the coplanar circles $C(A, m)$ and $C(B, n)$ and their interiors?

---

* If A, B, and C are noncollinear, then the *strict triangle inequality* holds, that is, $d(A, C) < d(A, B) + d(B, C)$.

9 Let $C(A, x)$ and $C(B, y)$ denote coplanar circles. Let $\mathcal{R}$ denote the union of both circles and their interiors, and let P denote a point of $\mathcal{R}$. Then at least one of the relations $d(A, P) \leqq x$ and $d(B, P) \leqq y$ is correct. Prove that, if $z = d(A, B) + x + y$, then $d(A, P) < z$. That is, show that both the given circles and their interiors are inside $C(A, z)$. (Hint: If $a < b$ and $x > 0$, then $a < b + x$.)

10 Prove that, if $\mathcal{Q}$ and $\mathcal{B}$ are bounded sets in the same plane, then their union, $\mathcal{Q} \cup \mathcal{B}$, is also a bounded set in the plane.

♦ 11 In a plane α, let P denote a point at a positive distance r from a line t. If Q denotes any point in α such that $d(P, Q) < r$, prove that Q is in the P-side of t. That is, prove that the interior of $C(P, r)$ is contained in the P-side of t.

♦ 12 In a plane α, if P does not belong to a set $\mathcal{S}$ but has a foot F in $\mathcal{S}$, show that no point interior to $C(P, r)$ can belong to $\mathcal{S}$ if $r < d(P, F)$. That is, show that, if a point not in a set has a foot in the set, it cannot be a boundary point of the set.

♦ 13 For the case where $\mathcal{S}$ consists of four points A, B, C, and D, prove the following: If a set $\mathcal{S}$ consists of a finite number of points and if P is a boundary point of $\mathcal{S}$, then P must belong to $\mathcal{S}$.

By working from a few properties suggested by certain physical objects, we have defined a class of plane convex figures. But do the sets that we have defined really exist, and do they have other basic properties like those of the physical objects with which we started? We now describe how these questions about the existence and properties of plane convex figures can be answered.

Let $\mathcal{S}$ denote a plane convex figure. Because $\mathcal{S}$ is nonempty and nonlinear, it must possess at least three noncollinear points, A, B, and C. These points determine a plane α, and, since $\mathcal{S}$ is planar, $\mathcal{S}$ is contained in α (D483a). Next, because $\mathcal{S}$ is convex, not only A, B, and C but also $\overline{AB}$, $\overline{BC}$, and $\overline{CA}$ are in $\mathcal{S}$. Then, by the convexity of $\mathcal{S}$, all points between C and points of $\overline{AB}$ are in $\mathcal{S}$. Hence, the interior of $\triangle ABC$ is contained in $\mathcal{S}$. Consider any point P interior to $\triangle ABC$. If x, y, and z denote the distances from P to the lines AB, BC, and CA respectively, then $C(P, r)$ is contained in the interior of $\triangle ABC$ if r is positive and less than x, y, and z. Because all points in the interior of $C(P, r)$ are contained in $\mathcal{S}$, point P is a point of $\mathcal{S}$ but is not a boundary point.

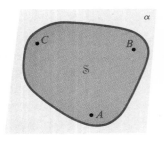
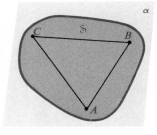
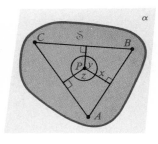

Diagram 483a	483b	483c

Thus, all of the points interior to $\triangle ABC$ belong to $\mathcal{S}$, but these points are not boundary points. We will call this type of point an inner point.

Definition 94/6 *Inner point of a planar set*
A point of a planar set $\mathcal{S}$ is an inner point of $\mathcal{S}$ if it is not a boundary point of $\mathcal{S}$.*

We have seen that an inner point of a plane convex figure must exist. But consider what an inner point Q of any planar set $\mathcal{S}$ must be like. Because Q belongs to $\mathcal{S}$, every circle with center Q automatically has a point of $\mathcal{S}$ in its interior. If every such circle in the plane of $\mathcal{S}$ also had in its interior some point not in $\mathcal{S}$, then Q would be a boundary point. Since Q is not a boundary point, there must exist at least one circle $C(Q, r)$ that has all of its interior points contained in $\mathcal{S}$. On the other hand, if all points interior to some circle with center Q belong to $\mathcal{S}$, then the center Q also belongs to $\mathcal{S}$, and Q clearly cannot be a boundary point. *Thus Q is an inner point of a planar set $\mathcal{S}$ if and only if there exists a circle with center Q whose interior consists entirely of points in $\mathcal{S}$.*

From this last property, we at once get the fact that, *if Q is an inner point of $\mathcal{S}$, then Q is an inner point of any set $\mathcal{R}$ that contains $\mathcal{S}$.* This fact follows because a circle whose interior is contained in $\mathcal{S}$ automatically is a circle whose interior is contained in $\mathcal{R}$.

Suppose now that Q is an inner point of a plane convex figure $\mathcal{S}$ in plane α and that D is any other point of $\mathcal{S}$ (D484a). Let t denote the line in α that is perpendicular to QD at Q. Because Q is an inner point of $\mathcal{S}$, there is some circle $C(Q, a)$ whose interior is contained in $\mathcal{S}$. So in t, there are two points E and F of $\mathcal{S}$ that are interior to $C(Q, a)$ and such that Q is between them.

---

* Notice that we do not need convexity in this definition.

324

Then, from the convexity of $\mathcal{S}$, it follows that $\overline{DE}$, $\overline{EF}$, $\overline{FD}$, and all interior points of $\triangle DEF$ are contained in $\mathcal{S}$. But, by our previous argument, all interior points of $\triangle DEF$ are inner points of $\mathcal{S}$. Thus, all points between Q and D are inner points. Therefore, *all points between an inner point* Q *of* $\mathcal{S}$ *and any other point* D *of* $\mathcal{S}$ *are inner points of* $\mathcal{S}$.

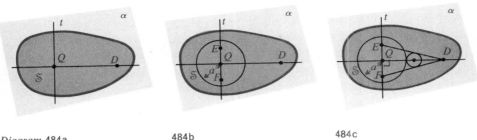

Diagram 484a   484b   484c

From the above property, it follows that an open ray $\overrightarrow{QZ}$ from an inner point Q cannot intersect the boundary of $\mathcal{S}$ in two points A and B. For if the ray did intersect the boundary twice, one of the pair A and B would be between D and the other point. Hence, one of the points A and B would be an inner point instead of a boundary point. Thus, *a ray from an inner point of* $\mathcal{S}$ *intersects the boundary of* $\mathcal{S}$ *in at most one point.* Also, if D, as well as Q, is an inner point of $\mathcal{S}$, then, because all points between Q and D are inner points, it follows that *the set of inner points of* $\mathcal{S}$ *is a convex set.*

Now, returning to the inner point Q, consider any closed ray $\overrightarrow{QZ}$ in α (D485a). Because $\mathcal{S}$ is bounded, it is interior to some circle

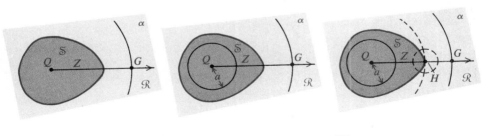

Diagram 485a   485b   485c

$\mathcal{R}$. The closed ray $\overrightarrow{QZ}$ intersects $\mathcal{R}$ at some point G that is not in $\mathcal{S}$. Starting from Q along $\overrightarrow{QZ}$, you first pass through points of $\mathcal{S}$ in the ray that are inside $C(Q, a)$. From G on in the ray, there are only points that are not in $\mathcal{S}$. And because $\mathcal{S}$ is convex, there cannot be any switching from points in $\mathcal{S}$ to points not in $\mathcal{S}$ and back again. For if Z belongs to $\mathcal{S}$, the whole segment $\overline{QZ}$ is contained in $\mathcal{S}$. Thus, no point of $\mathcal{S}$ can be preceded by a point not in $\mathcal{S}$. There then must be a point H at which a separation occurs so that H is preceded by points in S and followed by points not in S. Thus, any circle with center H will have inside it points of S and points not in S. Therefore, H must be a boundary point, and the last point of S in the ray.

The above description can be made a proof by using coordinates in line QZ and a property of real numbers called the *Dedekind property*. If all the real numbers are separated into two nonempty sets $\mathcal{A}$ and $\mathcal{B}$, and if every number in $\mathcal{A}$ is less than every number in $\mathcal{B}$, then, by the Dedekind property, there is a number h that is either the greatest number in $\mathcal{A}$ or the least number in $\mathcal{B}$. If a set $\mathcal{B}$ is defined as the coordinates of all points not in S that belong to the closed ray $\overrightarrow{QZ}$ (regarded as the positive direction) and if $\mathcal{A}$ is the set of coordinates of all other points of line QZ, one can show that the *Dedekind* number h separating $\mathcal{A}$ and $\mathcal{B}$ exists and is just the coordinate of our boundary point H.* (In this case, h is the greatest number in $\mathcal{A}$.)

We now have seen, in an informal way, that plane convex figures have the following properties.

* Theorem 172/6

The set of inner points of a plane convex figure is a nonempty, nonlinear, convex set.

** Theorem 173/6

If P is an inner point of a plane convex figure S, then, in the plane of S, each ray with origin P intersects the boundary of S at exactly one point.

* Corollary 173a/6

A line that is in the plane of a plane convex figure S and that passes through an inner point of S intersects the boundary at exactly two points.

* Corollary 173b/6

The boundary of a plane convex figure is not a convex set.

Exercises

1 Which of the following planar sets contain inner points?
 a Point P
 b The three points A, B, and C
 c The thirty-eight points $P_1, P_2, P_3, \ldots, P_{38}$
 d Segment $\overline{AB}$

---

* Though such a proof borrows a limit property from the real numbers, it is more like collecting a debt than borrowing. Establishing the real-number system and its basic properties was one of the greatest achievements in mathematics. Ideas suggested by geometry, both here and in the parallel-proportion problem, played an important part in that achievement.

e Polygon $P_1P_2P_3 \ldots P_n$

f Circle $C(O, r)$ and its interior

g The interior of $\triangle ABC$

h Plane α

i The plane convex figure $\mathcal{S}$

j The interior of $\sphericalangle ABC$

2 Which of the sets described in exercise 1 contain only inner points? Which contain only boundary points? *Answer*

3 Assume that point M is an inner point of a plane convex figure $\mathcal{S}$ in the plane α and that D is a boundary point of $\mathcal{S}$. Which of the following points in α must be inner points of $\mathcal{S}$?

a All points in the open ray $\overrightarrow{MD}$

b All points between M and D

c All points X such that $d(M, X) < d(M, D)$

d All points in $\overline{MD}$

e All points of the planar set $\mathcal{R}$ where $\mathcal{R}$ contains $\mathcal{S}$

4 Let $\mathcal{S}$ denote the set of points in plane α that are in circle $C(Q, 8)$ or in its interior. Let D denote a point in $\mathcal{S}$ other than point Q, and let the coordinates of Q and D in the line QD be 0 and d respectively, where $d > 0$.

a Is the point X in QD an inner point of $\mathcal{S}$ if the coordinate of X is 7.99999? If the coordinate of X is 8.00001? *Answer*

b Is there a last point in $\mathcal{S}$ that is in the closed ray $\overrightarrow{QD}$?

c In the closed ray $\overrightarrow{QD}$, is point P the first point not in $\mathcal{S}$ if its coordinate is 8? If its coordinate is 8.001? If its coordinate is 8.000000000001?

d In the open ray $\overrightarrow{QD}$, is there a first point not in $\mathcal{S}$ whose coordinate is greater than 8?

e Answer the questions in parts a through d for the set $\mathcal{S}$ that contains *only* the points interior to the circle $C(Q, 8)$.

5 When P is an inner point of a plane convex figure $\mathcal{S}$ and Q is any other point of $\mathcal{S}$, we showed that any point between P and Q is an inner point of $\mathcal{S}$. Explain how this fact implies that there cannot be two boundary points A and B in the closed ray $\overrightarrow{PQ}$. *Answer*

6 If $\mathcal{S}$ is a plane convex figure, then there exists a point P that is an inner point of $\mathcal{S}$. There is a line t through P that intersects the boundary of $\mathcal{S}$ at two points A and B. From these facts, prove that the boundary of $\mathcal{S}$ cannot be a convex set.

7 If $C(Q, a)$ denotes a given circle, explain, in terms of properties of our system, why there must exist two points E and F that are in the interior of $C(Q, a)$ and such that Q is between these two points. (Hint: Consider the opposite rays at Q in a line t through Q.)

8 Show that, if B is in the circle $C(A, r)$ and $C(B, x)$ is any circle coplanar with $C(A, r)$, then there is a point E that is interior to both circles (D486). Show also that there is a point F interior to $C(B, x)$ that is not interior to $C(A, r)$. [The two facts show that any point of $C(A, r)$ is a boundary point of the interior of $C(A, r)$.]

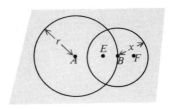

Diagram 486

9 If B is interior to a given circle $C(A, r)$ and P is interior to a coplanar circle $C(B, x)$, then, by definition, $d(A, B) < r$ and $d(B, P) < x$. From the triangle inequality (see the note before exercise 7, page 322), we know that $d(A, P) \leq d(A, B) + d(B, P)$. Using these facts, show that, if $x < r - d(A, B)$, then $d(A, P) < r$ (D487). [This shows that there is a circle at B whose interior is contained in the interior of $C(A, r)$.]

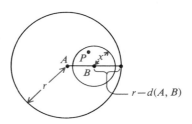

Diagram 487

10 How does exercise 9 show that, if B is interior to a circle $C(A, r)$, then B is not a boundary point of the interior points of $C(A, r)$?

11 Prove that a triangle $\triangle ABC$ is a bounded set of points. *Answer*

The boundaries of plane convex figures now provide a natural class of curves in our system, and this class clearly includes circles and polygons as special cases. If the boundary of a plane convex figure is the union of noncollinear segments, then the boundary is a polygon. Here we have a way of considering polygons that does not depend upon a circuit order of the vertices. Extending this point of view to space will give us a way of defining the figure called a polyhedron.

Because the boundaries of plane convex figures occur in so many important problems, there is a standard language about them. These boundaries are called *simple, closed, convex curves.* The term "simple" means that these boundaries do not cross themselves as, for example, a figure eight does. The term "closed" is used to indicate that these boundaries rejoin themselves like a loop. Finally, though the boundaries are not convex sets, they are called *convex curves* because they are the boundaries of convex sets. We now add the notion of a simple, closed, convex curve to the system.

Definition 95/6 *Simple, closed, convex curve*

The boundary of a plane convex figure is a simple, closed, convex curve.

Convention

Unless otherwise stated, the term "closed convex curve" always will mean a "simple, closed, convex curve."*

We now will state some definitions and theorems that establish a connection between our earlier point of view concerning planar figures and our present point of view about these figures.

---

*Theorem 174/6

The union of a polygon and its set of interior points is a plane convex figure S. The polygon is the boundary of S, and the interior of the polygon is the set of inner points of S.

Definition 96/6 *Full polygon*

The union of a polygon and its interior is a full polygon.

Convention

A full triangle whose boundary is $\triangle ABC$ will be denoted by the symbol $+\triangle ABC$. A full polygon whose boundary is polygon $P_1P_2P_3 \ldots P_n$ will be denoted by the symbol $+P_1P_2P_3 \ldots P_n$.

*Theorem 175/6

The union of a circle and its interior is a plane convex figure S. The circle is the boundary of S, and the interior of the circle is the set of inner points of S.

Definition 97/6 *Full circle*

The union of a circle and its interior is a full circle.

Convention

The full circle with boundary $C(P, r)$ will be denoted by the symbol $+C(P, r)$.

Definition 98/6 *Interior of a plane convex figure*

The set of inner points of a plane convex figure S also is called the interior of S. An inner point of S also is said to be interior to the boundary of S. A point in the plane of S that does not belong to S or to its boundary is said to be exterior to S and exterior to the boundary curve of S.

---

* The term "convex curve" often is used for the boundary of a convex set, whether or not the set is bounded. The boundary of a half-plane, for example, would then be a convex curve.

We have now opened the way to a great number of ideas and problems that form one of the many separate subjects of Euclidean geometry, that is, the study of convex figures. In this course, we do not have time to develop the subject, and we can only indicate a few of its basic notions. One of these notions, however, we want to define formally.

Definition 99/6 *Supporting line*

A line in the plane of a convex figure $\mathfrak{S}$ is a supporting line of $\mathfrak{S}$ if the line intersects $\mathfrak{S}$ and $\mathfrak{S}$ is contained in a closed half-plane of the line. The line also is said to be a supporting line of the boundary curve of $\mathfrak{S}$. (D488)

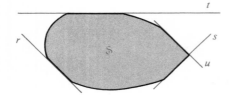

Diagram 488

Because plane convex figures are defined in such a general way, the whole spirit of the subject is to work with more general forms of the notions that we have studied. For example, it can be shown that, through each boundary point of a convex figure, there is at least one supporting line.* If there is more than one supporting line through a boundary point, the point is called a *corner point.* Thus, the vertices of a polygon are just its corner points. A convex curve that contains no segments is said to be a *strictly convex* curve. The "smooth" and everywhere "curved" ovals, then, are the strictly convex curves without corner points. The circle, of course, is an example of this kind of convex curve.

Consider now a plane convex figure $\mathfrak{S}$ in a plane α and a line r in α (D489a). Corresponding to r, there is a family of lines in α consisting of r and all lines of α that are parallel to r. Some lines of the family will intersect $\mathfrak{S}$, but because $\mathfrak{S}$ is bounded, an unlimited number of pairs of lines in the parallel set are such that $\mathfrak{S}$ is in the strip between them. In particular, two of the lines, say, s and t, will form a strip such that $\mathfrak{S}$ is contained in the closed strip between s and t but is not contained in the open strip. In descriptive language, as the parallels that do not intersect $\mathfrak{S}$ move toward $\mathfrak{S}$, they reach the positions of s and t as "first contact" lines in either side. The lines s and t are supporting lines of $\mathfrak{S}$ and

---

* This can be proved with the Dedekind property, but the proof is quite complicated.

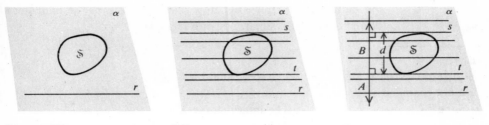

Diagram 489a   489b   489c

are said to be the *two supporting lines of* S *in the direction of* r. This means that each of the supporting lines s and t is either parallel or identical to r.

The distance d between the two parallel supporting lines s and t is called a *width* of S (D489c). Because you measure the width of a hallway, for example, in a direction perpendicular to the walls, the number d is said to be the width of S *in the direction* $\overrightarrow{AB}$ (*or* $\overrightarrow{BA}$) where AB is any line perpendicular to s and t. Thus, to find the width for a given direction, one locates the two parallel supporting lines that are perpendicular to rays in the given direction. The distance between the two parallel lines is the desired width.

The widths of a closed convex curve $\mathcal{B}$ are just the widths of the plane convex figure S of which $\mathcal{B}$ is the boundary. In these terms, the lengths of the sides of a rectangle are just particular widths. The length of a diagonal is the greatest width of the figure, and the length of the shortest side of the figure is the least width.

As further examples, we list a few generalizations that are suggested by the circle. If a point P that is interior to a closed convex curve bisects every chord that passes through it, point P is called a *center of the curve*. In this general sense, a parallelogram, as well as a circle, has a center. If point P is interior to a closed convex curve and if all the chords through P have the same length, then P is called an *equichord point*. Whether or not there exists a closed convex curve with two equichord points is still an unsolved problem.

Another extremely useful idea is that of the diameter of a set. If the set of all distances corresponding to pairs of points in a set S has a maximum,* this maximum is the *diameter of the set*. It can be shown that, if S is bounded and contains its boundary points (that is, if S is closed and bounded), then the diameter exists. So all plane convex figures and closed convex curves have a diameter. In these terms, the diameter of a circle is still twice

---

* The maximum of a set of numbers $\{a, b, c, \ldots\}$ is a number x such that the following is true: The number x is in the set, and no number in the set is greater than x. For any finite set of numbers a maximum always exists. See *Some conventions about sets of numbers*, Appendix 1.

the radius of the circle. But now one can speak of the diameter of a segment, of a square, or of a triangle.

Exercises

1 Which of the following planar sets have boundaries but are not bounded sets? *Answer*

  a Line t
  b The open half-plane α'
  c The interior of $\triangle ABC$
  d The interior of $\measuredangle HJK$
  e Polygon $P_1P_2P_3 \ldots P_n$
  f Plane α

2 Which of the following sets are closed convex curves?

  a The triangle $\triangle ABC$
  b The circle $C(P, r)$
  c The plane convex figure $^+P_1P_2P_3 \ldots P_n$
  d The boundary of the plane convex figure S
  e The angle $\measuredangle BAC$

3 Which of the following statements are true (T) and which are false (F)? *Answer*

  a If B is in $^+P_1P_2P_3 \ldots P_{18}$, then B must be an inner point of the full polygon.
  b The union of all boundary points and inner points of $\triangle ABC$ is $^+\triangle ABC$.
  c The set $^+C(Q, m)$ is a plane convex figure.
  d The intersection of $^+C(Q, m)$ and the coplanar open ray $\overrightarrow{QD}$ is a point X such that $d(Q, X) = m$.
  e The intersection of $\triangle ABC$ and $^+\triangle ABC$ is the empty set.

4 Which of the following statements are true (T) and which are false (F)?

  a The line AB is a supporting line of $\triangle ABC$.
  b The line AB is a supporting line of $^+\triangle ABC$.
  c Any two supporting lines of a convex figure S are parallel.
  d Any line perpendicular at Q to the radial segment $\overline{PQ}$ of $C(P, r)$ is a supporting line of $C(P, r)$.
  e A supporting line of a convex figure S contains boundary points of S but no inner points of S. *Answer*

5 Assume that polygon $ABCD$ is a rectangle such that $d(A, B) = 4$ and $d(B, C) = 3$ (D490).

  a What is the width of $ABCD$ in the direction $\overrightarrow{AD}$? In the direction $\overrightarrow{DC}$? In the direction $\overrightarrow{AC}$? *Answer*
  b Does a diameter exist for $ABCD$? If so, what is it?
  c Is there a center of the curve $ABCD$? If so, what is its location?
  d If H is the midpoint of $\overline{DC}$, what is the width of $ABCD$ in the direction $\overrightarrow{BH}$? (Hint: Use similar triangles.) *Answer*

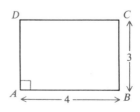

Diagram 490

6 What is the width of $C(P, r)$ in all directions?

7 What is the width of $\triangle ABC$ in the direction $\overrightarrow{AB}$? (Hint: Consider the possibilities for $\sphericalangle A$ and $\sphericalangle B$.) What is the width of $\triangle ABC$ in a direction perpendicular to $\overrightarrow{AB}$? *Answer*

8 Consider an equilateral triangle $\triangle DEF$ with sides of length r (D491). Let each two vertices of the triangle be joined by a circular arc with radius r and with its center at the third vertex. Such a curve is called a *Reuleaux triangle*. Call this particular curve the curve $\mathcal{C}$.

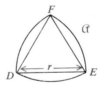

Diagram 491

a Does a Reuleaux triangle have any corner points?

b If s and t are two parallel supporting lines of $\mathcal{C}$ and if s passes through D, then t must intersect what part of $\mathcal{C}$?

c What is the greatest and the least width of $\mathcal{C}$?

d If a Reuleaux triangle of constant width h were to be rotated freely within a square of length and width h, then this triangle would touch how many sides of the square at all times?

◆ 9 Let the term "*b*-arc" be used for an arc in a circle with radius b. Let $\triangle ABC$ denote an equilateral triangle whose sides each have length $2b$ (D492). Using this information, consider a closed convex curve that is constructed in the following way. With A as a center, a $3b$-arc is drawn from one arm of $\sphericalangle A$ to the other arm, and a b-arc is constructed from arm to arm of the angle opposite $\sphericalangle A$. With B as a center, a $3b$-arc is constructed from arm to arm of $\sphericalangle B$, and a b-arc

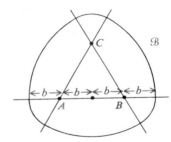

Diagram 492

is constructed from arm to arm of the opposite angle. With center C, another such pair of arcs are drawn. The union of the six arcs is a closed convex curve $\mathcal{B}$ without corner points or segments. The supporting line at any point P in $\mathcal{B}$ is the line perpendicular at P to the radial segment to P. Find the greatest and the least width of $\mathcal{B}$.

◆ 10 Assume that points A and B are two points of a plane convex figure $\mathbb{S}$ (D493). Explain why there must be a width of $\mathbb{S}$ that is at least as great as $d(A, B)$. (Consider the width in the direction $\overrightarrow{AB}$.) How does this show that the greatest width of $\mathbb{S}$ is equal to or greater than the diameter of $\mathbb{S}$?

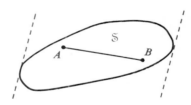

Diagram 493

♦ 11 Any point that is in a plane convex figure S
and is also in a supporting line t is
called a *contact point* of t. If A and
B are contact points respectively in the
parallel supporting lines s and t (D494),
explain why $d(A, B)$ must be at least as
great as $d(s, t)$. How does this show
that the diameter of S is equal to
or greater than the greatest width of S?

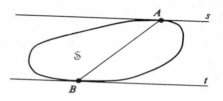

Diagram **494**

♦ 12 How do exercises 10 and 11 imply that the greatest width
of a plane convex figure S is the diameter of S (assuming
that both exist)?

♦ 13 Suppose that s and t are parallel supporting lines of a
plane convex figure S and that $d(s, t)$ is the greatest
width of S. Show that there is exactly one contact
point in s and exactly one in t. Show also that the
chord joining these contact points is perpendicular
to both s and t.

♦ 14 A curve (like the circle and the curves in exercises 8
and 9) for which all the widths are the same is called
a *curve of constant width*. Using exercise 13, show
that a curve of constant width must be strictly convex,
that is, show that it cannot contain a segment.

♦ 15 Show that a triangle has no center.

16 Let $\mathcal{R}$ denote a closed convex curve in plane α. Show that,
corresponding to any line t in α, the following exist.
a A rectangle $ABCD$ such that the lines of its sides are
supporting lines of $\mathcal{R}$ and such that AB is either parallel
to or identical with t
b An equilateral triangle $\triangle EFG$ such that the lines
of its sides are supporting lines of $\mathcal{R}$ and such that EF
is either parallel to or identical with t

♦ 17 **a** Under what circumstances are all of the circumscribed
rectangles described in exercise 16a squares of the same
size?
b Can the curve $\mathcal{R}$ described in exercise 16 ever be such
that all of the rectangles are squares but not
necessarily squares of the same size?

Before we leave the subject of convex curves, we want to put
into the formal system some information about curve intersections. With the Pythagorean theorem, we could establish the
conditions for two circles to intersect. But among closed convex
curves, this is a very special case. We therefore make the following axiom.

If $\mathcal{C}$ and $\mathcal{B}$ are two simple, closed,
convex curves in the same plane
and if $\mathcal{B}$ contains a point
interior to $\mathcal{C}$ and a point
exterior to $\mathcal{C}$, then $\mathcal{B}$ intersects
$\mathcal{C}$ in at least two points.
(D495)

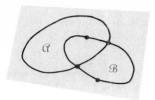

Diagram 495

We now establish some special intersection relations for circles. Theorem 176/6 is a theorem that concerns coplanar circles as well as noncoplanar circles.

Theorem 176/6

Two circles with different centers intersect in at most
two points.

Proof

Assume that two circles $\mathcal{C}$ and $\mathcal{B}$ intersect at three points A,
B, and C. If A, B, and C are noncollinear, then both
$\mathcal{C}$ and $\mathcal{B}$ are circumcircles of $\triangle ABC$. This contradicts
the fact that a triangle has only one circumcircle
(Corollary 116b/4).

If A, B, and C are collinear in a line t, then, since t
contains two points of $\mathcal{C}$, line t is in the plane of $\mathcal{C}$
(and also in the plane of $\mathcal{B}$). Line t either passes
through the center of $\mathcal{C}$ or it does not. If t contains the
center of $\mathcal{C}$, then A, B, and C are three points in t
at the same distance from a point of t (the center of $\mathcal{C}$).
This contradicts Theorem 9/2. If t does not contain the
center of $\mathcal{C}$, then the existence of three points common
to t and $\mathcal{C}$ contradicts Theorem 166/5.

Since all possibilities lead to contradictions, $\mathcal{C}$ and $\mathcal{B}$
cannot have three points in common.

Definition 100/6 *Concentric circles*

Circles that are coplanar and have the same center are
concentric circles.

Theorem 177/6

If $C(A, x)$ and $C(B, y)$ are two coplanar, nonconcentric circles
and if $z = d(A, B)$ is the distance between the centers,
then the circles intersect in exactly two points if and only
if $x + y > z$, $z + x > y$, and $y + z > x$. If the
circles intersect in two points, then the line of centers
AB is the perpendicular bisector of the segment joining the
two intersection points.

Proof

Part I   If the circles intersect at two points P and Q,
then, by Theorem 176/6, they intersect only at P and Q.
Because A and B are each equidistant from P and Q, line AB
is the perpendicular bisector of $\overline{PQ}$ (Corollary 75b/3).
Hence, neither P nor Q is in line AB. Then A, B, and P
are the vertices of a triangle whose sides have the
lengths x, y, and z. Therefore, by Theorem 59/3, $x + y > z$,
$z + x > y$, and $y + z > x$.

Part II   Assume that
1 $x + y > z$, $z + x > y$, and $y + z > x$.
Let D and E denote the intersections of $C(A, x)$ with line AB,
with E denoting the intersection in $\overrightarrow{AB}$ and D denoting
the intersection in the opposite ray $\overrightarrow{AX}$. Then A is
between D and B, so
2 $d(B, D) = d(B, A) + d(A, D) = z + x$.
And since, by statement 1, $z + x > y$, the point D is exterior
to the circle $C(B, y)$.

   For Case 1 (D496), point E in $\overrightarrow{AB}$ is between A and B.

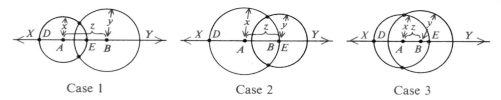

Case 1   Case 2   Case 3

Diagram **496**

For Case 2, E is B. For Case 3, E is in $\overrightarrow{BY}$ opposite $\overrightarrow{BA}$.
   For Case 1 $d(A, E) + d(B, E) = d(A, B)$. So
3 $d(B, E) = d(A, B) - d(A, E) = z - x$.
But from statement 1, $z < x + y$. Hence, $z - x < y$. Using
$z - x < y$ and statement 3, we have
4 $d(B, E) < y$.
Corresponding to Case 2, $E = B$, and so $d(B, E) = 0$. Therefore,
5 $d(B, E) < y$.
Corresponding to Case 3, B is between A and E, and so
$d(A, B) + d(B, E) = d(A, E)$, and
6 $d(B, E) = d(A, E) - d(A, B) = x - z$.
But from statement 1, $x < y + z$. Hence, $x - z < y$. Using
$x - z < y$ and statement 6, we have
7 $d(B, E) < y$.
In all three possible cases, statements 4, 5, and 7 show
that E is interior to $C(B, y)$.

336

Since the circle $C(A, x)$ passes through D exterior to $C(B, y)$ and through E interior to $C(B, y)$, then, by Axiom 15/6, the two closed convex curves $C(A, x)$ and $C(B, y)$ intersect in at least two points. By Theorem 176/6, they cannot intersect at more than two points, so they intersect at exactly two points.

Exercises

1 Assume that circles $\mathcal{C}$ and $\mathcal{B}$ are coplanar and that point X in $\mathcal{B}$ is interior to $\mathcal{C}$. Illustrate each of the following cases with a diagram.

  a $\mathcal{C} \cap \mathcal{B}$ is the empty set. In this case, can $\mathcal{B}$ contain a point exterior to $\mathcal{C}$?

  b $\mathcal{C} \cap \mathcal{B}$ is a set containing exactly one point. Can $\mathcal{C}$ and $\mathcal{B}$ have different supporting lines at this point?

  c $\mathcal{B}$ passes through a point exterior to $\mathcal{C}$. How many intersection points are there?

2 Sets $\mathcal{R} = ABCD$ and $\mathcal{S} = EFGH$ are two coplanar squares. Illustrate each of the following cases with a diagram.

  a $\mathcal{R} \cap \mathcal{S}$ is a point, and $\mathcal{S}$ contains a point exterior to $\mathcal{R}$.

  b $\mathcal{R} \cap \mathcal{S}$ is a set containing exactly two points, and $\mathcal{R}$ contains no points exterior to $\mathcal{S}$.

  c $\mathcal{R} \cap \mathcal{S}$ is a set containing exactly three points. *Answer*

  d $\mathcal{R} \cap \mathcal{S}$ is a set containing exactly four points.

  e $\mathcal{R} \cap \mathcal{S}$ is an infinite set.

3 Under what conditions can a closed convex curve $\mathcal{R}$ contain a point that is interior to a closed convex curve $\mathcal{S}$ and a point that is exterior to $\mathcal{S}$ without intersecting $\mathcal{S}$? Illustrate your answer. *Answer*

♦ 4 Assume that the closed convex curves $\mathcal{R}$ and $\mathcal{S}$ are coplanar, and $\mathcal{S}$ intersects the interior and exterior of $\mathcal{R}$. Show that $\mathcal{R}$ intersects the exterior of $\mathcal{S}$.

5 If n is any positive integer, show that there exist two closed convex curves whose intersection set contains exactly n points.

6 Points A and B in line t have coordinates 3 and 10 respectively. In each of the following exercises, two coplanar circles are named. Draw the two circles to scale and indicate whether their intersection set contains two points, one point, or no points at all.

  a $C(A, 2)$ and $C(B, 4)$　　　 d $C(A, 8)$ and $C(B, 3)$ *Answer*

  b $C(A, 6)$ and $C(B, 14)$　　　 e $C(A, 2)$ and $C(B, 9)$

  c $C(A, 1)$ and $C(B, 6)$　　　 f $C(A, 1)$ and $C(B, 1)$

7 *Theorem*

If $C(A, x)$ and $C(B, y)$ are two coplanar circles and if $x + y = d(A, B)$, then the circles intersect in exactly one point P, and this point is between A and B.*

Proof idea

Show that the point P in $\overrightarrow{AB}$, such that $d(A, P) = x$, belongs to both circles. Use Theorem 177/6 to show that P is the only point contained in both circles. *Answer*

8 *Theorem*

If $A \neq B$ and if $C(A, x)$ and $C(B, y)$ are two coplanar circles such that $x = y + d(A, B)$, then the circles intersect at exactly one point P, and B is between A and P.

Proof idea

Use the same plan as you used for exercise 7.

9 Show that, if $C(A, x)$ and $C(B, y)$ are two coplanar circles and if $d(A, B) > x + y$, then the circles do not intersect. *Answer*

10 a Show that, if $C(A, x)$ and $C(B, y)$ are two coplanar circles and if $d(A, B) + y < x$, then the two circles do not intersect.

b State another condition under which the coplanar circles $C(A, x)$ and $C(B, y)$ do not intersect.

11 Line t and circles $C(A, x)$ and $C(B, y)$ are coplanar (D497). Each of the lines a_1 and a_2 is tangent to $C(A, x)$ and is parallel to or identical with t. Each of the lines b_1 and b_2 is tangent to $C(B, y)$ and is parallel to or identical with t. Let the greatest distance between any two of the lines a_1, a_2, b_1, and b_2 be defined as a width of the set $\mathcal{R} = C(A, x) \cup C(B, y)$. Corresponding to different positions of A, B, and t but for fixed x and y, answer each of the following.

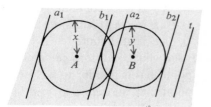

Diagram 497

a What is the least possible width of $\mathcal{R}$? What is the greatest possible width of $\mathcal{R}$? *Answer*

b What relation of the circles is implied if the greatest width is $2(x + y)$? Is $2x$?

c If the greatest and the least widths of $\mathcal{R}$ are equal, must the circles be the same circle?

---

* Two coplanar circles with exactly one point P in common have a common tangent line at P. The circles are said to be tangent *internally* at P or tangent *externally* at P depending on whether the circles (except for point P) are in the same side or in opposite sides of the tangent line.

◆ 12 Assume that the coplanar circles
$C(A, 13)$ and $C(B, 37)$ intersect at C
and D, that F is the foot of C in $\overline{AB}$,
and that $d(A, B) = 40$ (D498).

a Find the lengths of $\overline{AF}$, $\overline{CF}$,
and $\overline{FB}$.

b If s and t are each perpendicular to
BC and each tangent to one of the
circles, what is the greatest possible
value of $d(s, t)$?

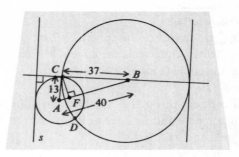

Diagram 498

Convex solids 25/6

The whole pattern of ideas that we have used for plane convex
figures—the definitions, the theorems, even the types of proof—
can now be extended to space and used to obtain a class of sets
called *convex solids*. In the plane, we used the circle in our definitions, and then we used properties of circles and triangles to show
the existence of the nonlinear, convex interiors of the figures. In
space, the *sphere* takes over the role of the circle, and the tetrahedron, which is a pyramid with triangular faces, replaces the
triangle.

Once again, we will simply describe the way in which a careful
mathematical treatment could be carried through.

Definition 101/6 *Sphere*
Corresponding to a point P and a positive number r, the set
of all points at a distance r from P is a sphere. Point P
is the center of the sphere, and r is the radius of the sphere.
Point P and all points at a distance less than r from P
form the interior of the sphere. The points whose
distance from P is greater than r form the exterior
of the sphere.
Convention
The sphere with center P and radius r will be denoted by
the symbol $S(P, r)$.

The following theorem will allow us to make our general
definitions in such a way that they will include our previous
definitions. The proof of Theorem 178/6 is left to you, and the
proof is an example of how the Pythagorean theorem enters into
space arguments.

339

Theorem 178/6

If Q is interior to the sphere $S(P, r)$, then any plane α that contains Q intersects the sphere in a circle, and the interior of the circle is interior to the sphere.

Proof idea

If α passes through P, the theorem follows from the definition of a sphere and its interior and from the definition of a circle and its interior.

If α does not contain P, then P has a foot F in α (D499). Also, $a = d(P, F)$ must be less than r because $d(P, F) \leqq d(P, Q)$ and $d(P, Q)$ is given as less than r. Define $b = \sqrt{r^2 - a^2}$, and let X denote any point common to the plane and the sphere. Then $X \neq F$, and $\triangle PFX$ is a right triangle. From the Pythagorean theorem, it follows that, if X is in the circle $C(F, b)$ in α, then X is in the sphere. And if X is in the sphere, it is in the circle.

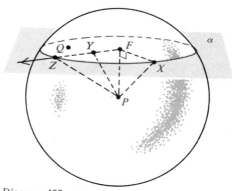

Diagram 499

If Y is a general point interior to $C(F, b)$, then $\overrightarrow{FY}$ intersects $C(F, b)$ at Z. Use Theorem 167/5 to show that $d(F, Y) < d(F, Z)$ implies $d(P, Y) < d(P, Z)$ and hence that Y is inside the sphere.

Now we use the sphere to replace the circle in our previous definitions.

Definition 102/6 *Bounded set*

A set is bounded if it is contained in the interior of a sphere.

Definition 103/6 *Boundary point of a set*

A point P is a boundary point of a set $\mathcal{S}$ if the interior of every sphere with center P contains a point of $\mathcal{S}$ and also contains a point not in $\mathcal{S}$.

From Theorem 178/6, we also have the following facts. If a set $\mathcal{S}$ is planar, then boundedness of $\mathcal{S}$ in the planar sense implies boundedness in the general sense, and conversely.

Exercises

1 Points A, B, C, and D are four successive points in a line t and these points have coordinates 0, 3, 12, and 20 respectively. For each sphere named below, decide if B is in the sphere, in its interior, or in its exterior.

a $S(A, 3)$ **c** $S(B, 1)$ *Answer*   **e** $S(A, 2000)$

b $S(D, 15)$ **d** $S(C, 9)$

2 Point Q is in a plane α and is interior to the sphere
$S(P, 6)$. If point Q is not P, which of the following
statements are true?

a The distance from P to Q is less than 6.

b Point P cannot be in α.

c The intersection of α and $S(P, 6)$ is a circle.

d If the intersection of α and $S(P, 6)$ is $C(X, 6)$, then
X must be P.

e If the intersection of α and $S(P, 6)$ is $C(Q, 3)$,
then $PQ \perp \alpha$.

f If the intersection of α and $S(P, 6)$ is $C(A, r)$, then
$d(P, A) = \sqrt{r^2 - 36}$.

g If F is the foot of P in α, then $d(P, F)$ must be less
than $d(F, Q)$.

h All points of $S(P, 6)$ are interior to $S(Q, 12)$.

i If the intersection of α and $S(P, 6)$ is $C(A, r)$, then Q
is interior to $C(A, r)$.

j The interior of $S(P, 6)$ is a bounded set.

3 Assume that the distance between A and B is x.

a Must $\overline{AB}$ be contained in the interior of the circle
$C(A, x + 1)$?

b Must $\overline{AB}$ be contained in the interior of the sphere
$S(A, x + 1)$?

c What points of $\overline{AB}$ are interior to $S(B, x)$?

d Is $\overline{AB}$ its own boundary? *Answer*

4 Let point M in the open ray $\overrightarrow{AB}$ be such that $<A, B, M>$,
$d(A, B) = x$, and $d(B, M) = a$. Which of the following
spheres contain a point of $\overline{AB}$ in their interior?

a $S(A, x)$ **d** $S\left(M, a + \dfrac{x}{2}\right)$ **g** $S\left(B, \dfrac{a}{100}\right)$

b $S(A, a)$ **e** $S\left(M, \dfrac{x + a}{2}\right)$ **h** $S\left(M, \dfrac{a}{2}\right)$

c $S(M, x + a)$ **f** $S(M, a)$ **i** $S\left(A, \dfrac{x}{10,000}\right)$

5 If $\mathcal{S}$ is a set in a plane α and if $\mathcal{S}$ is bounded in the
planar sense, then $\mathcal{S}$ is interior to some circle $C(A, r)$.
Prove that $\mathcal{S}$ is bounded in the general sense. *Answer*

6 If $\mathcal{S}$ is nonempty and is bounded in a general sense, then
$\mathcal{S}$ is interior to some sphere $S(A, r)$, where point A
is not necessarily in the plane of $\mathcal{S}$.* Prove that,
if $\mathcal{S}$ also is a planar set, then it is bounded in the
planar sense.

---

* Since an empty set is contained in every set, an empty set is regarded as a bounded set.

7 a Can a set have boundary points and not be bounded? Explain.

b Can a set be bounded but contain no boundary points? Explain. *Answer*

8 a Show that every sphere is a bounded set.

b Show that the union of two spheres is a bounded set.

9 Explain how exercise 8b implies that the union of two bounded sets is a bounded set. How does this fact, together with exercise 8b, imply that the union of three bounded sets is a bounded set?*

10 Prove that a set S is bounded if and only if there exists a positive number b such that no two points of S are farther apart than b. *Answer*

11 Let $\mathcal{R}'$ and $\mathcal{R}''$ denote the open half-spaces determined by a plane α. Let P denote any point in α, and let $S(P, r)$ denote any sphere with center P. Prove that the interior of $S(P, r)$ contains a point in α, a point in $\mathcal{R}'$, and a point in $\mathcal{R}''$. (This proof shows that α consists of boundary points of $\mathcal{R}'$ and $\mathcal{R}''$.)

12 For each of the following, give an example of a nonplanar set S that satisfies the given condition.

a No point of S is a boundary point.

b Every point of S is a boundary point.

c Some points of S are boundary points, and some points of S are not boundary points.

13 The *complement* of a set S is the set of all points that do not belong to S.

a What is the complement of space? What is the complement of the empty set?

b What is the complement of set $\mathcal{R}$ if $\mathcal{R}$ is the complement of set S?

c Must the complement of an unbounded set be a bounded set? *Answer*

d Explain why a set and its complement cannot both be bounded.

e If $\mathcal{R}$ is the complement of S, explain why a boundary point of $\mathcal{R}$ also is always a boundary point of S.

♦ 14 a Show that, if P is a boundary point of set S, then P does not have a foot in S.

b Show that, if point P has F as a foot in a set S, then F is a boundary point of S.

---

* By mathematical induction, one can show, in this way, that the union of any finite number of bounded sets always is a bounded set.

342

15 Give examples that illustrate each of the following
true statements.

  a The boundary of the union of two sets may or may not
  be the union of the boundaries.

  b The boundary of the intersection of two sets may or
  may not be the intersection of the boundaries.

◆ 16 Point P in $\mathcal{S}$ is *farthest* from A if $d(P, A) \geqq d(X, A)$
for every point X in $\mathcal{S}$. If $\mathcal{S}$ is a polygon, A is
any point of space, and P is the point of $\mathcal{S}$ farthest
from A; prove that P is a vertex of the polygon.

◆ 17 We defined an inner point of a set $\mathcal{S}$ for any set, not just
for convex figures. Correspondingly, we can define
the *interior of any set* $\mathcal{S}$ to be the set of inner points
of $\mathcal{S}$. Using this definition, prove each of the
following.

  a The interior of $\mathcal{R} \cup \mathcal{S}$ contains the union of the
  interiors of $\mathcal{R}$ and $\mathcal{S}$.

  b The interior of $\mathcal{R} \cap \mathcal{S}$ is the intersection of the
  interior of $\mathcal{R}$ and the interior of $\mathcal{S}$.

We next define the class of sets in which we are interested.

Definition 104/6 *Convex solid*

A set is a convex solid if it is nonempty and nonplanar,
bounded and convex, and contains its boundary.

Definition 105/6 *Inner point of a set*

A point that belongs to a set $\mathcal{S}$ is an inner point of $\mathcal{S}$ if it
is not a boundary point of $\mathcal{S}$.

By the same reasoning as we used in the case of a plane, we get
the following properties: P *is an inner point of* $\mathcal{S}$ *if and only if there
exists some sphere* S(P, r) *whose interior consists entirely of points
in* $\mathcal{S}$. *An inner point of a set* $\mathcal{S}$ *is an inner point of any set that
contains* $\mathcal{S}$.

Exercises

1 Explain why each of the following sets is not a
convex solid.

  a A closed half-space

  b The interior of a sphere

  c A full circle

  d The solid strip between parallel planes *Answer*

  e The union of spheres $S(P, x)$ and $S(Q, y)$ and their
  interiors if $d(P, Q) = x$ and $y < x$

2 Set S is the interior of the sphere $S(P, 10)$ and A is in the sphere. Point B is in $\overrightarrow{PA}$, and is such that $d(P, B) = 9$.

a Which of the following spheres are such that their interiors are contained in S?

(1) $S(B, 9)$ (4) $S(B, 1)$

(2) $S(B, 4)$ (5) $S(B, .001)$

(3) $S(B, 2)$ (6) $S(B, .00001)$

b Is B an inner point of S? *Answer*

c Is the interior of $S(A, 11)$ contained in S?

d Is A an inner point of S? Why?

e If $d(P, Q) = x$, if Q is in S, and if $y = \dfrac{10 - x}{2}$, is the interior of $S(Q, y)$ contained in S?

f Is every point of S an inner point of S?

3 If P is an inner point of set S in the space sense and if P is in plane α, must P be an inner point in the plane sense of the set $S \cap \alpha$? *Answer*

4 If S is a planar set, why is there no point of S that is an inner point in the space sense of inner point? Does this imply that an inner point of S in the plane sense is a boundary point of S in the space sense?

5 Give an example that shows that, if α is a plane through P, point P may be a boundary point in the space sense to a set S and an inner point in the planar sense to a set $S \cap \alpha$.

Because any convex solid S is nonempty and nonplanar, it contains at least four noncoplanar points A, B, C, and D. Then the convexity of S implies that the four full triangles that these points determine by threes must also be in S. The figure formed in this way is a tetrahedron, and we make a separate definition for it.

Definition 106/6 *Tetrahedron*

Four noncoplanar points A, B, C, and D and the union of the four full triangles that are each determined by three of the noncoplanar points is a tetrahedron. The four points are the vertices of the tetrahedron; the four full triangles are its faces; the sides of the triangles are the edges of the tetrahedron. (D500)

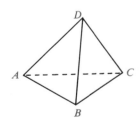

Diagram 500

Definition 107/6 *Interior and exterior of a tetrahedron*

The interior of a tetrahedron with vertices A, B, C, and D is the intersection of the following four half-spaces: the A-side of $\alpha(B, C, D)$; the B-side of $\beta(C, D, A)$; the C-side

of $\gamma(D, A, B)$; and the D-side of $\delta(A, B, C)$. Points that
are not in the tetrahedron or in its interior form the
exterior of the tetrahedron.

We saw that every convex solid S must contain a tetrahedron.
To follow the pattern we used for the plane, we want to show that
the interior of a tetrahedron also must be contained in S and
that this interior must consist of inner points of S. In the case of
the plane, we already had the properties of a triangle that we
needed. But in the case of space, the corresponding properties of
a tetrahedron now would have to be established. Let us look
briefly at how this job could be done.

You will recall that, if P is in a plane α and Q is not in α, then
the open ray $\overrightarrow{PQ}$ is contained in the Q-side of α (D501). This is
the relation we need.

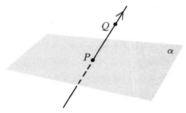

Diagram 501

Suppose that A, B, C, and D are the vertices of a tetrahedron
and that α, β, γ, and δ are the planes containing the faces opposite
A, B, C, and D respectively (D502). Call these the face-planes of

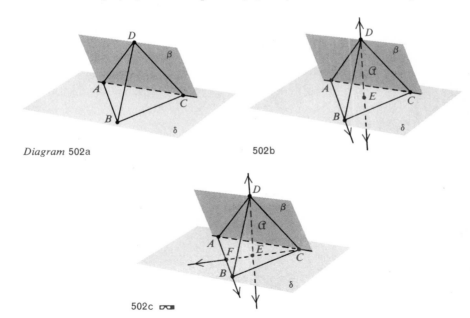

Diagram 502a   502b

502c

345

the tetrahedron. Let E denote any point interior to $\triangle ABC$ and call the set of points between D and E in segment $\overline{DE}$ the set $\mathcal{C}$. Because E is in face-plane δ and D is not, the open ray $\overrightarrow{ED}$ belongs to the D-side of δ. Hence, $\mathcal{C}$ is contained in the D-side of δ.

Next, consider, for example, the B-side of β. Because E is interior to $\triangle ABC$, the open ray $\overrightarrow{CE}$ intersects $\overline{AB}$ at some point F between A and B, and E is between C and F. The point A is in β (the face-plane of $\triangle ACD$), and B is not in β. Therefore, $\overrightarrow{AB}$ is in the B-side of β. Then F in $\overrightarrow{AB}$ also is in the B-side of β. Point C belongs to β, so the open ray $\overrightarrow{CF}$ is in the B-side of β. Therefore, point E, between C and F, is in the B-side of β. But D belongs to β; so the open ray $\overrightarrow{DE}$ is in the B-side of β. Therefore, set $\mathcal{C}$ is in the B-side of β.

By the same kind of argument, $\mathcal{C}$ is contained in the A-side of α and in the C-side of γ. So, by definition, $\mathcal{C}$ is contained in the interior of the tetrahedron. Thus, all the points that are between a vertex of a tetrahedron and an interior point of the opposite face belong to the interior of the tetrahedron.

What we want to show is that, because a convex solid $\mathcal{S}$ must contain a tetrahedron, it must also contain the interior of the tetrahedron. We then can show that the interior points of the tetrahedron must be inner points of $\mathcal{S}$. For this purpose, we need a converse property of the tetrahedron. That is, we need the idea that, if a point is interior to a tetrahedron, then the point is between a vertex and some point interior to the opposite face.

In the plane, we have the property that, if P is interior to $\measuredangle XDY$, then $\overrightarrow{DP}$ must intersect $\overline{XY}$ at a point between X and Y (D503). Now consider the closed rays $\overrightarrow{DA}$, $\overrightarrow{DB}$, and $\overrightarrow{DC}$ determined

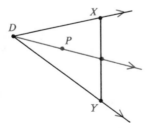

Diagram 503

by the vertices of a tetrahedron (D504a). Each two of these closed rays form an angle. The three angles with their interiors form three planar regions, and the union of these regions is the boundary to a three-dimensional set that contains the interior of the tetrahedron. The union of the three angles $\measuredangle ADB$, $\measuredangle BDC$, and $\measuredangle CDA$ and their interiors is called a *solid angle*, and can be

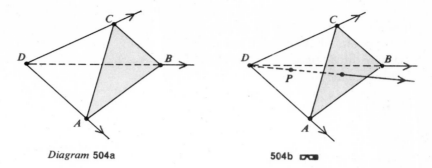

Diagram 504a   504b ▭▩

denoted by the symbol $\not\prec D\text{-}ABC$.* The three-dimensional region, for which the solid angle is a boundary, is the intersection of the A-, B-, and C-sides of $\alpha(B, C, D)$, $\beta(C, D, A)$, and $\gamma(A, B, D)$ respectively, and this three-dimensional region is called the *interior* of the solid angle. The analogue of the plane property is then the fact that, if P is interior to a solid angle $\not\prec D\text{-}ABC$, the closed ray $\overrightarrow{DP}$ must intersect the full triangle $^+\triangle ABC$ at a point interior to the triangle. Thus, the property we want for a tetrahedron is a special case of this space analogue.†

   If A, B, C, and D are the vertices of a tetrahedron and if P is an interior point, then P is between D and some point E interior to $\triangle ABC$ (D505). A proof of this property can be obtained from

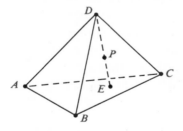

Diagram 505

the simple order relations we already have for points, rays, and planes. However, the proof is a surprisingly long argument, and we will not describe it. But this property, together with its converse, implies that the interior of the tetrahedron consists of all points that are between D and some points interior to $\triangle ABC$. So a convex set that contains A, B, C, and D must contain both the tetrahedron and its interior.

---

* Because of its three faces, the angle also is called a *trihedral angle*.
† Solid angles make more complete the analogy of a triangle and a tetrahedron. Since a triangle has three vertices, three sides, and three angles, while a tetrahedron has four vertices and four faces, the comparison suggests that a tetrahedron should have four angles. It does, of course, have four solid angles. These four solid angles, rather than the twelve plane angles in the faces, or the six dihedral angles of the tetrahedron, are the analogues of the angles of a triangle.
   Analogues are just patterns of relations that resemble each other, and an analogy is not, in any sense, a proof. But analogues obviously can give valuable suggestions.

347

Exercises

1 If the points *M, N, J,* and *K* are the vertices of a
tetrahedron $\mathbb{S}$ (D506), which of the following statements
are inaccurate?

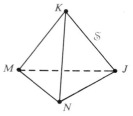

a $\triangle MNJ$ is a face of $\mathbb{S}$.

b JK is an edge of $\mathbb{S}$.

c $\mathbb{S}$ has six edges.

d $\mathbb{S}$ is convex.

e The faces of $\mathbb{S}$ are convex sets.

f The interior of $\mathbb{S}$ is in the *J*-side of $\alpha(M, N, J)$.

g $\mathbb{S}$ is the union of its six edges.

h $\mathbb{S}$ is a convex solid.

Diagram 506

2 a What is the nature of the set of points that are
interior to a dihedral angle $\sphericalangle C\text{-}AB\text{-}D$ and are
equidistant from the two faces of the angle? *Answer*

b What is the nature of the set of points that are
interior to a solid (trihedral) angle $\sphericalangle A\text{-}DBC$ and are
equidistant from the three faces of the angle?

3 Let *A, B, C,* and *D* denote the vertices of a tetrahedron,
and let *E* denote the center of the circumcircle
of $\triangle ABC$.

a Prove that, if *X* is in the line *t* perpendicular to
$\alpha(A, B, C)$ at *E*, then $d(A, X) = d(B, X) = d(C, X)$.

b If *Y* is a point equidistant from *A, B,* and *C,* prove
that *Y* is in line *t* described in exercise 3a.
(Hint: Show that *Y* must be in β or in γ, where β and γ
are the perpendicular bisectors of $\overline{AB}$ and $\overline{BC}$ respectively.) *Answer*

c If δ is the plane that is the perpendicular bisector
of $\overline{CD}$, must δ intersect *t* (see exercise 3a)
at exactly one point *O*? If so, why is point *O* equidistant from
A, B, C, and *D*?

d The previous parts of this exercise contain the
elements of a proof that there is exactly one sphere
that contains the vertices of a tetrahedron. Such a sphere
is called the *circumsphere.* You will recall that the
lines that are the perpendicular bisectors of the sides
of a triangle are concurrent at the circumcenter of the
triangle. What is an analogue theorem for
a tetrahedron?

◆ 4 We earlier gave an argument, illustrated in D502, to
show that a particular set $\mathfrak{C}$ is in the *D*-side of a plane δ
and in the *B*-side of a plane β. Using the same conditions,
give a similar argument to show that $\mathfrak{C}$ is in the *A*-side
of plane α.

348

5 If a tetrahedron is the space analogue of a triangle and a solid angle is the analogue of a plane angle, what type of solid angle $\not\subset D\text{-}ABC$ in a tetrahedron might be a reasonable analogue of a right angle in a right triangle? (This solid angle is called a *right trihedral angle.*)

6 If the area of a face of a tetrahedron is the analogue of the length of a side in a triangle, what kind of "Pythagorean theorem" for the right tetrahedron of exercise 5 might be a reasonable possibility? Assume the area formula for a triangle (one half the length of the base times the height). Then try either to prove or disprove your guess for at least one particular case.

7 A line that is in the plane of a triangle and that passes through an interior point of the triangle must intersect at least two sides of the triangle. What property related to an inner point of a tetrahedron might be an analogue?

♦ **8** A line through a vertex of a tetrahedron and perpendicular to the opposite face-plane is an altitude line of the tetrahedron. Analogy with the triangle suggests that the four altitude lines of a tetrahedron are concurrent. Either.prove or disprove this conjecture.

9 A set $\mathcal{S}$ is said to be *star-shaped from a point* A if, for every point Q in $\mathcal{S}$ that is distinct from A, the segment $\overline{AQ}$ is also in $\mathcal{S}$. Which of the following sets are star-shaped from A? *Answer*

   a $^+\triangle ABC$ **e** $\not\subset ABC$

   b $C(A, r)$ **f** Tetrahedron $ABCD$

   c $\overline{AJ}$ **g** $^+\triangle ABC \cup {}^+\triangle ADE$

   d AB

♦ **10** Prove that a set $\mathcal{S}$ is convex if and only if it is star-shaped from every one of its points.

♦ **11** **a** Prove that, if $\mathcal{S}_1$ and $\mathcal{S}_2$ are star-shaped from A, then $\mathcal{S}_1 \cup \mathcal{S}_2$ and $\mathcal{S}_1 \cap \mathcal{S}_2$ are star-shaped from A.
   b Prove that, if $\mathcal{S}_1$ and $\mathcal{S}_2$ are convex, then $\mathcal{S}_1 \cup \mathcal{S}_2$ is star-shaped from every point in $\mathcal{S}_1 \cap \mathcal{S}_2$.

♦ **12** One can define a set $\mathcal{S}$ to have *convexity of type* n if, for each two points A and B in $\mathcal{S}$, there is a segment path from A to B of n or fewer segments that are contained in $\mathcal{S}$. Thus, ordinary convexity is type 1.
   a Prove that, if $\mathcal{S}$ is star-shaped from any point, then it has type 2 convexity.
   b Define a set that has type 5 convexity but does not have type n convexity for $n < 5$.

We need one more property of a tetrahedron that we easily can obtain from the following fact. If P is at a positive distance b from a plane β and if r is a positive number less than b, then the interior of the sphere $S(P, r)$ is contained in the P-side of β (D507).

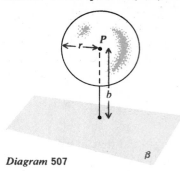

Diagram 507

Now let P denote a point interior to a given tetrahedron with vertices A, B, C, and D opposite face-planes α, β, γ, and δ respectively. By the definition of the interior of the tetrahedron, P does not belong to any of the face-planes. Let a, b, c, and d denote the respective distances of α, β, γ, and δ from P. There is a positive number r less than a, b, c, and d. And by the property mentioned above, the interior of $S(P, r)$ is contained in the A-, B-, C-, and D-sides respectively of α, β, γ, and δ. So the interior of $S(P, r)$ is contained in the interior of the tetrahedron. Therefore, *at each interior point* P *of a tetrahedron, there exists a sphere* S(P, r) *whose interior is contained in the interior of the tetrahedron.*

The facts that any convex solid has a nonplanar convex interior and that its boundary exists now can be obtained from the same pattern of argument that we used for the plane. Let P denote an inner point of a convex solid $\mathcal{S}$, and let D denote any second point of $\mathcal{S}$. Because P is an inner point of $\mathcal{S}$, there exists some sphere $S(P, r)$ whose interior contains only points of $\mathcal{S}$ (D508a).

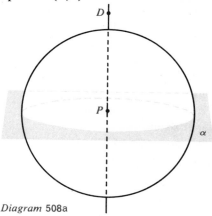

Diagram 508a

350

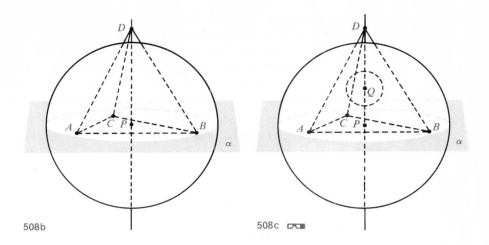

508b 508c

Let α denote the plane that is perpendicular at P to the line PD.

The intersection of α and $S(P, r)$ is a circle $C(P, r)$. Because the interior of $C(P, r)$ is contained in the interior of $S(P, r)$, all points interior to $C(P, r)$ are points of S. In particular, there exist three points, say, A, B, and C, interior to $C(P, r)$, such that P is interior to $\triangle ABC$. Because A, B, C, and D belong to S and S is convex, the segments determined by these points belong to S. Then, from convexity, the four full triangles determined by the segments also must be in S. Therefore, the tetrahedron $ABCD$ is contained in S. By the argument that we discussed earlier, every point interior to the tetrahedron is between a vertex and a point in the interior of the opposite triangular face. Since these two points are in S, the entire segment determined by them is in S. Thus, the interior of the tetrahedron also consists of points that are in S.

It also is true that, if a point is between a vertex of a tetrahedron and a point interior to the opposite triangular face, then the point is interior to the tetrahedron. Therefore, if Q is any point between D and P, then Q is interior to the tetrahedron. Because Q is interior to the tetrahedron, a sphere $S(Q, a)$ also is interior to the tetrahedron if the radius a is less than the distance of Q from any one of the four face-planes of the tetrahedron. Since such a sphere is contained in the interior of the tetrahedron and since the interior of the tetrahedron is contained in S, then the interior of $S(Q, a)$ is contained in S. So, by definition, Q is an inner point of S. Thus, every point between P and D is an inner point of S.

In the previous argument, D was simply any point of S, and P was any inner point of S. From the conclusion reached, it follows that *any point between a point of S and an inner point of S must be*

351

an inner point of S. Since inner points of S belong to S, it follows that *the set of inner points of* S *is a convex set.*

If P is an inner point of the convex solid and $\overrightarrow{PX}$ is any open ray from P, then, by definition, any boundary point of S in $\overrightarrow{PX}$ is a point of S, and it is not P. If there were two such boundary points in $\overrightarrow{PX}$, one would be between the other point and P and so would be an inner point of S. From this contradiction, it follows that there is at most one boundary point of S in any ray whose origin is an inner point of S. From these results, it follows, just as in the case of the plane, that *there is exactly one boundary point of* S *in a ray whose origin is an inner point of* S.

From the properties we have mentioned, it follows that a convex solid has the kind of interior and boundary that we associate with physical convex objects. A formal proof of these properties can be obtained from the arguments we have described together with more care about certain details.

The boundaries of convex solids now give us a natural class of surfaces, and we include a name for them in the following list of facts.

---

* Theorem 179/6

The set of inner points of a convex solid forms a nonplanar convex set.

* Theorem 180/6

If P is an inner point of a convex solid S, then each closed ray $\overrightarrow{PX}$ contains exactly one boundary point of S.

* Corollary 180a/6

Each line through an inner point of S contains exactly two boundary points of S.

Definition 108/6 *Simple, closed, convex surface*

The boundary of a convex solid is a simple, closed, convex surface.

* Corollary 180b/6

A simple, closed, convex surface is not a convex set.

We used special definitions for the sphere and the tetrahedron. To include these surfaces in our general classification, we now state the following theorems.

---

* Theorem 181/6

The set S that is the union of a sphere and its interior is a convex solid. The interior points of the sphere are the inner points of S, and the sphere is the boundary of S.

* Theorem 182/6

The set S that is the union of a tetrahedron and its interior is a convex solid. The interior points of the tetrahedron are the inner points of S, and the tetrahedron is the boundary of S.

Definition 109/6 *Solid sphere*

The union of a sphere $S(P, r)$ and its interior is a solid sphere. Point P is the center of the solid sphere, and r is the radius of the solid sphere.

Convention

We will indicate the solid sphere that is the union of the sphere $S(P, r)$ and its interior by the notation $^+S(P, r)$.

Definition 110/6 *Solid tetrahedron*

The union of a tetrahedron and its interior is a solid tetrahedron.

Definition 111/6 *Interior point of a convex solid*

An inner point of a convex solid also will be called an interior point of the solid. A point interior to the solid also will be said to be interior to the boundary surface of the solid.

Exercises

1 For this exercise, consider the following sets: a convex set; a proper convex polygon; a bounded, plane, convex figure; a simple, closed, convex curve; a convex solid; a simple, closed, convex surface.

  a Which of the sets are *not* convex sets?

  b Which of the sets must be planar sets?

  c Which of the sets must be bounded? *Answer*

  d Which of the sets consist entirely of boundary points?

  e Which of the sets are never planar sets?

2 Prove that, if Q is at a distance b from a plane β, then any point X in the solid sphere $^+S\left(Q, \dfrac{b}{2}\right)$ is in the Q-side of β.

3 a If P is an inner point of a set S, why must P belong to S?

  b If P and Q are inner points of a convex solid S, why must $\overline{PQ}$ be contained in S? *Answer*

♦ 4 If $\overrightarrow{PX}$ is an open ray from an inner point P of a convex solid S, prove that each of the following is true.

  a There are infinitely many inner points of S in $\overrightarrow{PX}$.

  b There are infinitely many points of $\overrightarrow{PX}$ that are not contained in S. (That is, there are infinitely many points of $\overrightarrow{PX}$ that are exterior points of S.)

5 Let $\mathcal{B}$ denote a simple, closed, convex surface that is the boundary of a convex solid S. Prove that $\mathcal{B}$ is not a convex set. (Hint: Let t denote a line through an inner point of S, and consider the points of $\mathcal{B}$ in t.)

6 Let S denote a convex solid, and let $\mathscr{E}$ denote its exterior (that is, points not in S).

   a Is $\mathscr{E}$ a bounded set? *Answer*

   b What is the boundary of $\mathscr{E}$?

   c Is $\mathscr{E}$ convex?

   d What is the set of inner points of $\mathscr{E}$? *Answer*

7 Let a denote the length of the longer of the two sides $\overline{PA}$ and $\overline{PB}$ in $\triangle PAB$. (Or let a denote their common length if $\overline{PA}$ and $\overline{PB}$ are congruent.)

   a If X is a point in $\overline{AB}$, prove that $d(P, X) \le a$. (Hint: If $<A, X, B>$, show that one of the triangles, $\triangle PXA$ or $\triangle PXB$, must be either a right triangle or an obtuse triangle.) *Answer*

   b If X is a point of $^{+}\triangle PAB$, prove that $d(P, X) \le a$.

8 In the tetrahedron $PABC$, let a denote the maximum of the lengths of $\overline{PA}$, $\overline{PB}$, and $\overline{PC}$.*

   a Prove that, if X is any point of the tetrahedron, then $d(P, X) \le a$.

   b Prove that, if X is any point of the solid tetrahedron $^{+}PABC$, then $d(P, X) \le a$.

   c Prove that a solid tetrahedron is a bounded set.

♦ **9** Show that a tetrahedron has type 2 convexity (see exercise 12, page 349) but is not star-shaped from any of its points.

10 The *convex hull* of a set S is defined as the intersection of all convex sets that contain S. Thus, if $\mathscr{H}$ is the convex hull of S, then $\mathscr{H}$ is convex, because it is the intersection of convex sets. Also, every convex set that contains S contains $\mathscr{H}$. Thus, in a sense $\mathscr{H}$ is the smallest convex set that contains S.

   a Explain why the statement "Every convex set that contains S also contains $\mathscr{H}$" is true.

   b If S itself is convex, why must $S = \mathscr{H}$?

11 One way to see the nature of the convex hull $\mathscr{H}$ of a set S is the following. If S is not convex, define S' as the union of S and all segments whose endpoints are in S. (That is, fill in all the points between points of S.) If S' is convex, then it is $\mathscr{H}$. If S' is not convex, then define S'' to be the union of S' and all segments whose endpoints are in S'. If S'' is convex, then it is $\mathscr{H}$. Assuming that this

---

* See Appendix 1.

process produces the convex hull, what is the convex hull of S if S is each of the following?

a $\overline{AB}$ *Answer*

b $C(P, r)$

c $\triangle RST$

d Two points A and B

e Noncollinear points A, B, and C

f Plane α

g Noncoplanar points A, B, C, and D

h $\measuredangle HJK$

i Line t

12 a Give an example of a set that is not a plane but whose convex hull is a plane.

b Give an example of a set that is not space but whose convex hull is space.

13 Why must the convex hull of a linear set be a linear set? Why is the convex hull of a planar nonlinear set also planar and nonlinear?

14 a Prove that, if S is a linear set, then the set S', defined in exercise 11, is a convex set.

b What seems to be the analogue theorem to the theorem in exercise 14a when S is planar? When S is nonplanar?

The analogue to a supporting line of a plane convex figure is a supporting plane of a convex solid.

Definition 112/6 *Supporting plane*

A plane α is a supporting plane of a convex solid S if it intersects S and if S is contained in a closed half-space whose face is α. Such a plane also is called a plane of support to the boundary surface of S. (D509)

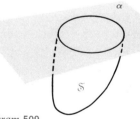

Diagram 509

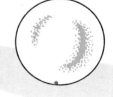

Diagram 510

Definition 113/6 *Tangent*

A plane is tangent to a sphere if it intersects the sphere in exactly one point. The plane and the sphere are said to be tangent to each other at their intersection point. (D510)

Just as the tangent lines of a circle are its supporting lines, so the tangent planes to a sphere are its supporting planes. If S is

355

a convex solid, then it can be proved that, through each boundary point of S, there is at least one supporting plane of S. Any plane α determines a family of planes that consists of α and all planes that are parallel to α. Exactly two of these planes are supporting planes of S, and the distance between these planes is the width of S in the direction of a ray that is perpendicular to α.

Convex surfaces can be classified in a variety of ways. For example, a surface may or may not contain segments, or plane convex figures, or points through which there pass more than one supporting plane. The smooth and curved "egg-shaped" surfaces have just one plane of support at each point and just one contact point in each supporting plane. The sphere, of course, is an example of such a surface.

Finally, there is a simple connection between convex solids and plane convex figures. If P is interior to a convex solid S and α is a plane through P, then the intersection of α and S is clearly a convex set $\mathcal{R}$. The fact that $\mathcal{R}$ is a nonempty and a nonlinear set follows from the properties of the inner point P. The intersection of α and S is bounded because S is bounded, and the intersection contains its boundary. The intersection, therefore, is a plane convex figure.

---

* Theorem 183/6

If P is an interior point of a convex solid S, then every plane through P intersects S in a plane convex figure.

Definition 114/6 *Plane section of a solid and of a surface*

The nonempty intersection of a plane and a convex solid is a plane section of the solid. (The plane section may be a point or a segment.) The intersection of such a plane section and the boundary surface of the solid is a plane section of the surface.

Exercises

1 If plane α is a supporting plane of the solid tetrahedron determined by points A, B, C, and D, which of the following statements are true?

a If α does not contain A, B, or C, then α must contain D.

b If α contains A and B, then α must contain either C or D.

c If α contains A, then B and C must be in the D-side of α.

d If $^+\triangle ABC$ is a subset of α, then D is not in α.

e If A, B, and D are not in α, then the plane determined by A, B, and D must be parallel to α.

2 *Theorem*

A plane α and a sphere $S(P, r)$ are tangent at point A if and only if they intersect at A and if the radial segment $\overline{PA}$ is perpendicular to α at A.

Proof idea

If $\overline{PA} \perp \alpha$, prove that $d(P, Q) > r$ for any second point Q in α and, hence, that $S(P, r) \cap \alpha$ is point A. If α is tangent to $S(P, r)$ at A, assume that $\overline{PA}$ is not perpendicular to α. Obtain a contradiction of this last statement from the fact that the foot of P in α would be interior to $S(P, r)$.

3 a Prove that, at each point A in a sphere $S(P, r)$, there is exactly one plane tangent to the sphere at A. *Answer*

b Prove that a plane tangent to a sphere is a supporting plane of the sphere.

c Prove that a supporting plane of a sphere is a plane tangent to the sphere.

4 a From Theorem 183/6, what is the nature of a plane section of a closed convex surface? *Answer*

b What is the nature of the plane sections of a sphere? Of a tetrahedron?

5 The *width* of a convex solid $+\mathcal{S}$ (and of its boundary $\mathcal{S}$) in the direction of $\overrightarrow{PX}$ is defined as the distance between the two parallel supporting planes that are perpendicular to line PX. The *diameter* of $+\mathcal{S}$ is the maximum value of $d(X, Y)$ for all pairs of points X and Y in $+\mathcal{S}$. As in the case for a plane convex figure, the diameter and the maximum width of the convex solid $+\mathcal{S}$ exist and are equal.

a What is the minimum width of a sphere?*

b Describe, in a geometric way, the maximum and the minimum widths of a tetrahedron. *Answer*

6 a If α and β are two supporting planes of a convex surface $\mathcal{S}$ at point P in $\mathcal{S}$, why must there be infinitely many supporting planes through P all of which have some line t in common?

b Show that the supporting planes through this line t may or may not be all the supporting planes through P. (Hint: Consider P in the edge of a tetrahedron.)

A great many familiar shapes with special names can now be introduced as particular convex solids. We define some of these, starting with those space figures that are the analogues of full polygons in the plane.

---

* There are infinitely many surfaces of constant width that are not spheres. But such surfaces cannot be constructed as simply in relation to a tetrahedron as the constant width curves can be constructed in relation to the triangle. However, if a Reuleaux triangle is rotated about a median line of its equilateral triangle, the union of all the points it contacts is a surface of constant width.

A convex solid whose boundary is the union of a finite number
of full polygons, no two of which are coplanar, is a solid
polyhedron and its boundary is a polyhedron. The full polygons
are the faces of the polyhedron; the sides of the polygons
are the edges of the polyhedron; and the vertices of the
polygons are the vertices of the polyhedron. A dihedral angle
between two face-planes and containing two of the
faces is a dihedral angle of the polyhedron. The angles
of the polygons in the faces are plane angles (or face angles)
of the polyhedron. A segment that joins two vertices and is
not in a face of the polyhedron is a diagonal of the polyhedron.

Definition 116/6 *Regular polyhedron*

A polyhedron is a regular polyhedron if each two of its
dihedral angles are congruent and if all the polygons in the
faces are regular polygons with the same number of sides.

A very famous theorem is the fact that there are only five
differently shaped regular polyhedra. These five polyhedra are
shown in D511.

tetrahedron   cube   octahedron   dodecahedron   icosahedron

Diagram 511

Polyhedra also are divided into other special classifications.
The next group of definitions puts some of these classifications
into our system.

Definition 117/6 *Prism*

A polyhedron of $n + 2$ faces is
a prism if two of its faces,
called the bases of the prism,
are full n-gons in parallel
planes and each of the remaining
n faces is a full parallelogram.†
(D512)

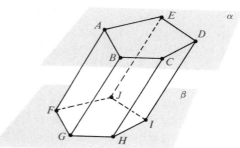

Diagram 512

* The plural of "polyhedron" is "polyhedra."
† Prisms sometimes are referred to in terms of their base faces. A *triangular prism*, for example,
is a prism whose bases are full triangles.

358

A prism in which the nonbase faces are full rectangles is a
right prism. (D513)

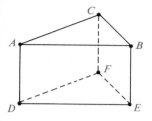
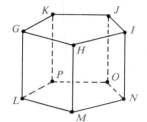

Diagram 513

A prism of six faces such that the bases are also full
parallelograms is a parallelepiped. If the bases are full
rectangles, the figure is a rectangular parallelepiped. If all
faces are rectangles, it is a right rectangular parallelepiped.
A parallelepiped whose faces are all full squares is a cube.
(D514)

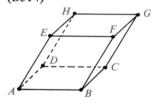
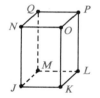
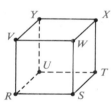

Diagram 514

A polyhedron that has *n* vertices and is
such that $n - 1$ of these vertices are
coplanar is a pyramid. The face of the
coplanar set is a base of the pyramid,
and the vertex not in this face sometimes
is called *the* vertex of the pyramid.
(D515)

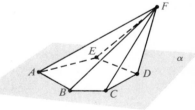

Diagram 515

We conclude this group of definitions with the definition of
two convex surfaces that are not polyhedra.

A solid circular cylinder is a set that consists
of two full circles that have equal
radii and are in parallel planes and all

segments that have an endpoint in each of
these full circles. The boundary of this
solid is a circular cylinder. The full
circles are the bases of the circular
cylinder, and the line joining the two
centers of the bases is the axis of the
circular cylinder. The circular
cylinder is a right circular cylinder
if the axis is perpendicular to the
base planes. (D516)

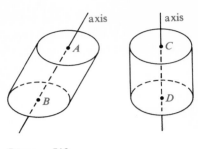

Diagram 516

Definition 122/6 *Solid circular cone*

A set that consists of all segments joining
points of a full circle $^+C(P, r)$ to a
point Q not in the plane of the circle is
a solid circular cone, and its boundary
is a circular cone. The point Q is
the vertex of the circular cone; the
circle $^+C(P, r)$ is the base of the
circular cone; and the line PQ is the
axis of the circular cone. If PQ is
perpendicular to the plane of the base,
then the circular cone is a right circular cone.
(D517)

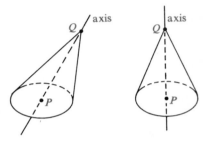

Diagram 517

We want to illustrate how planar properties are used in studying space figures. For the example we have chosen, we need the
following property of plane geometry that we will introduce as a
lemma. This lemma is a converse of exercise 11 on page 131.

Lemma 184/6

If, in a correspondence of triangles, two sides in one triangle
are congruent to their corresponding sides in the other, but
the third side of the first triangle is greater than its
corresponding side in the other, then the angle in the first
triangle that is opposite this third side is greater than
the corresponding angle of the second triangle that is
opposite the shorter side. (D518)

$d(A, B) > d(A', B').$

$\sphericalangle ACB° > \sphericalangle A'C'B'°.$

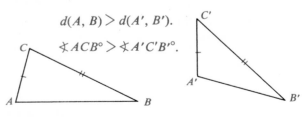

Diagram 518

360

If three points are noncollinear, then the three segments they determine have lengths that satisfy the strict triangle inequality. An analogue of this relation exists for three noncoplanar rays from a point. The three angles they determine have measures that satisfy an inequality relation like the strict triangle inequality.

Theorem 184/6

If $\overrightarrow{PA}$, $\overrightarrow{PB}$, and $\overrightarrow{PC}$ are three noncoplanar closed rays; then, in pairs, they determine three angles, and the sum of the measures of each two of these three angles is greater than the measure of the third. (D519)

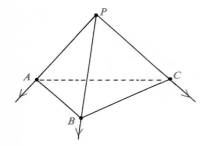 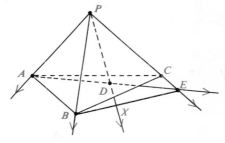

Diagram 519a   519b ▱▰■

Proof
Assume that $\angle APC$ is as great as or greater than either $\angle APB$ or $\angle BPC$. Then it will be sufficient to prove that $\angle APB° + \angle BPC° > \angle APC°$. In the plane of A, P, and C, let $\overrightarrow{PX}$ denote an open ray in the C-side of AP such that
  1 $\angle APX° = \angle APB°$.
In $\overrightarrow{PX}$, let D denote the point such that
  2 $\overline{PD} \cong \overline{PB}$.
Let E denote the intersection of $\overrightarrow{AD}$ and $\overrightarrow{PC}$. By the s.a.s. congruence axiom,
  3 $\triangle APD \cong \triangle APB$.
Hence,
  4 $\overline{AD} \cong \overline{AB}$.
If $\angle APB° = \angle APE°$, then $\angle APB° + \angle BPE°$ clearly is greater than $\angle APE°$, and the theorem is correct.
So assume that $\angle APB° < \angle APE°$. Then, from statement 1, it follows that $\angle APD° < \angle APE°$. Thus D is between A and E. Therefore,
  5 $d(A, E) = d(A, D) + d(D, E)$.
Since, in $\triangle ABE$,
  6 $d(A, B) + d(B, E) > d(A, E)$,

361

it follows that

7 $d(A, B) + d(B, E) > d(A, D) + d(D, E)$.

This last relation, together with $d(A, B) = d(A, D)$, implies that

8 $d(B, E) > d(D, E)$.

Consider the correspondence $BPE \leftrightarrow DPE$ for $\triangle BPE$ and $\triangle DPE$. Because $\overline{BP} \cong \overline{DP}, \overline{EP} \cong \overline{EP}$, and $d(B, E) > d(D, B)$, it follows, by Lemma 184/6, that

9 $\measuredangle BPE° > \measuredangle DPE°$.

This inequality and statement 3 imply that

10 $\measuredangle APB° + \measuredangle BPE° > \measuredangle APD° + \measuredangle DPE°$.

Because $\overrightarrow{PD}$ is between $\overrightarrow{PA}$ and $\overrightarrow{PE}$, $\measuredangle APD° + \measuredangle DPE° = \measuredangle APE°$. Therefore, statement 10 may be expressed as

11 $\measuredangle APB° + \measuredangle BPE° > \measuredangle APE°$,

which was to be proved.

Corollary 184/6

In a tetrahedron, the sum of the measures of each two of the three angles at a vertex is greater than the measure of the third angle.

Exercises

1 In a polyhedron, the Euler formula that relates the number of faces F, the number of vertices V, and the number of edges E is $F + V - E = 2$. First give the values of F, V, and E for each of the five regular polyhedra. Then check the Euler formula in each case.

2 Using D520, match each "part" of the polyhedron given in the list at the left with its correct name in the list at the right.

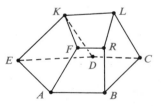

Diagram 520

a R A Face

b $\measuredangle ABC$ B Edge

c $\overline{AL}$ c Vertex

d $\overline{BR}$ D Dihedral angle

e $\measuredangle K$-EA-C E Face angle

f $+KFEA$ F Diagonal

3 a What is the least number of faces that a polyhedron may have?

  b What regular polyhedron has no diagonals?

  c What is the smallest type of convexity (see exercise 12, page 349) of a regular octahedron? Of a dodecahedron? *Answer*

4 Which of the following statements are true and which are false?

  a In a prism, at least two faces must be in parallel planes.

362

b The least number of faces a prism may have is six.

c The planar boundaries of the bases of a prism are congruent polygons.

d If $\overline{AJ}$ and $\overline{BK}$ are two edges of a prism, then $\overline{AJ} \parallel \overline{BK}$ and $d(A, J) = d(B, K)$.

e In a right prism, two edges with a common vertex must be perpendicular.

f Every prism is a polyhedron.

g All polyhedra are prisms.

h All parallelepipeds are prisms.

i All prisms are parallelepipeds.

5 a If a prism has ten faces, how many of these faces must be full parallelograms? *Answer*

b A prism has how many faces if every face of the prism is a full rhombus?

c Can a triangular prism be a right prism?

d Must a square prism be a right prism?

e Can a prism have seventy-three vertices? Explain.

f Can a polyhedron have seventy-three vertices? If so, how could such a polyhedron be formed?

g If a prism has more than one pair of bases, must the prism be a cube?

h What is the diameter of a rectangular parallelepiped whose dimensions are 3, 4, and 5?

i If the bases of a prism are full *n*-gons, what are the values of F, V, and E? (Remember that F represents the number of faces; V, the number of vertices; and E, the number of edges of a polyhedron.)

6 Which of the following can be a plane section of a cube? *Answer*

  a A point   **f** A trapezoid
  b A triangle   **g** A pentagon
  c A line   **h** A hexagon
  d A square   **i** An octagon
  e A rectangle

7 Show that, if a pyramid has two bases, then the pyramid is a tetrahedron. (Therefore, it has four bases.)

8 a What is the nature of a plane section of a circular cylinder in a plane parallel to the cylinder's axis? In a plane parallel to the bases?

b Is a circle the plane section of a circular cylinder in a plane that is perpendicular to the axis?

9 Assume that line *t* is the axis of a right circular cylinder S and that *t* intersects the bases of S at O and O' respectively. If *r* is the radius of the circular bases and $h = d(O, O')$, what is the greatest and the least width of S for each of the following values of r and h?

a $r = 2; h = 10.$ *Answer*

b $r = 1; h = 1.$

c $r = \sqrt{3}; h = \pi.$

10 A point P of a convex surface S sometimes is said to be a *regular point* of S if there is only one supporting plane of S at P. Give two examples of a surface in which there is a regular point such that the supporting plane at the point intersects the surface in a segment.

♦ 11 In this exercise, we have given the steps of a proof of the theorem that the angles at the vertex of a pyramid have measures whose sum is less than 360 (D521).* Supply the reasons for the final steps of the proof.

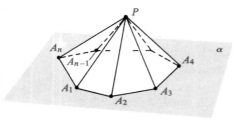

Diagram 521

Proof

Let P denote the vertex of a pyramid whose base is the full n-gon $^{+}A_1A_2A_3 \ldots A_n$ in plane α.

  1 Let x denote the sum of the measures of the angles in the base n-gon.

And let

  2 $y = \sphericalangle PA_1A_n{}^\circ + \sphericalangle PA_1A_2{}^\circ + \ldots + \sphericalangle PA_{n-1}A_n{}^\circ,$
  which is the sum of the measures of the angles of the pyramid that are not in α and do not have P as a vertex.

Let

  3 $z = \sphericalangle A_1PA_2{}^\circ + \sphericalangle A_2PA_3{}^\circ + \ldots + \sphericalangle A_{n-1}PA_n{}^\circ,$
  which is the sum of the measures of the angles at P.

Applying Corollary 184/6 to vertex A_1 of the tetrahedron $PA_nA_1A_2$, we obtain

  4 $\sphericalangle PA_1A_n{}^\circ + \sphericalangle PA_1A_2{}^\circ > \sphericalangle A_nA_1A_2{}^\circ.$

Similarly, Corollary 184/6, applied to vertex A_2 of $PA_1A_2A_3$, yields

  5 $\sphericalangle PA_2A_1{}^\circ + \sphericalangle PA_2A_3{}^\circ > \sphericalangle A_1A_2A_3{}^\circ.$

---

* The same argument shows that, at a vertex of a polyhedron, the angles have measures whose sum is less than 360. However, in this case, one must show the existence of a plane that intersects all the rays from the vertex that contain the edges of the polyhedron.

Continuing in succession, we finally arrive at

6 $\sphericalangle PA_nA_{n-1}° + \sphericalangle PA_nA_1° > \sphericalangle A_{n-1}A_nA_1°.$

The sum of the left-hand members of the inequalities in statements 4, 5, and 6 is y, while the sum of the right-hand members is x. Hence

7 $y > x.$

But

8 $y = n \cdot 180 - z$ (Why?),

and

9 $x = n \cdot 180 - 360$ (Why?).

Substituting from statements 8 and 9 in statement 7 yields

10 $n \cdot 180 - z > n \cdot 180 - 360,$

and, hence,

11 $z < 360.$

Chapter review

1 Points P and Q are in line t, and t separates plane α into the open half-planes α' and α''. Of which of the following sets is P a planar boundary point?

  a Line t **d** $\alpha' \cup \alpha''$

  b $\overline{PQ}$ **e** $C(P, x)$ in α

  c $\overrightarrow{PQ}$ **f** α

2 Some of the following statements are necessarily true, and some are possibly true. Which statement is necessarily false?

  a If point P is a boundary point of a set S, then P belongs to S.

  b If point A is an inner point of a set $\mathcal{R}$, then A is not a boundary point of $\mathcal{R}$.

  c If A and B are two inner points of a set S, then $\overline{AB}$ belongs to S.

  d If S is a plane convex figure, then a line passing through an inner point of S intersects the boundary of S at exactly two points.

  e If A and B are two inner points of a plane convex figure S, then line AB intersects S at exactly two points.

3 Segments $\overline{AB}$ and $\overline{BC}$ of rectangle $ABCD$ have lengths 10 and 3 respectively. Select all of the following statements that are correct.

  a AD is a supporting line of the full polygon ^+ABCD.

  b AB and CD are two parallel supporting lines of the rectangle.

c The maximum width of $ABCD$ is 10.

d The minimum width of $ABCD$ is 3.

e The width of $ABCD$ in the direction $\overrightarrow{AC}$ is $\sqrt{91}$.

4 If $\mathcal{C}$ and $\mathcal{B}$ are two coplanar, simple, closed, convex curves and if they intersect in at least two points, must one curve contain a point interior to and also another point exterior to the other curve? Explain.

5 If $\mathcal{C}$ and $\mathcal{B}$ are two coplanar, simple, closed, convex curves and if $\mathcal{C}$ contains a point interior to $\mathcal{B}$ and also a point exterior to $\mathcal{B}$, must $\mathcal{B}$ contain a point interior to $\mathcal{C}$ and a point exterior to $\mathcal{C}$?

6 a Give an example of a bounded planar set S that consists entirely of inner points.

b Give an example of a planar set S that consists entirely of plane boundary points.

c Give an example of a planar set S that consists entirely of inner points and is such that no planar boundary point of S exists.

7 If P and Q are boundary points of a plane convex figure S, must a point between P and Q be an inner point of S? Explain.

8 Assume that point F is the foot in plane α of point P. Describe the intersection of α and the sphere $S(P, 5)$ if each of the following is true.

a $d(P, \alpha) = 5$.   **c** $d(P, \alpha) = 5.001$.

b $d(P, F) = 3$.   **d** $d(P, F) = 1$.

9 By our definition, a convex solid must be nonplanar, bounded, and convex, and the solid must contain its boundary. Each of the following examples has all but one of these properties. For each case, state the one property that is lacking.

a A closed half-space   **c** A tetrahedron

b A full circle   **d** The interior of a sphere

10 Indicate which of the following statements are necessarily true (T), possibly true (P), or necessarily false (F).

a If P is an inner point of a set S, then there exists a sphere $S(P, r)$ whose interior consists entirely of points in S.

b The tetrahedron $ABCD$ is the union of the four triangles determined by the points A, B, C, and D.

c Every convex solid must contain a tetrahedron.

d If a point is interior to a tetrahedron, then it is between a vertex and some point interior to the opposite face.

366

e If $ABCD$ is a tetrahedron and if F is the foot in $\alpha(A, B, C)$ of D, then F belongs to the full triangle $+\triangle ABC$.

f If A and B are inner points of a convex solid, then $\overline{AB}$ is contained in the solid.

g If segment $\overline{CD}$ is contained in a convex solid, then C and D are inner points of the solid.

11 If β is a plane of support to the solid sphere $+S(P, r)$, are all points of the solid sphere in the P-side of β? Explain.

12 Which of the following sets are possible plane sections of a solid cube?

   a A full rectangle   **d** A full triangle

   b A point   **e** A full equilateral triangle

   c The empty set   **f** A full 5-gon

13 Which of the following statements are necessarily true?

   a All parallelepipeds have six faces.

   b A cube is a right prism.

   c At least two faces of a prism are in parallel planes.

   d All faces of a right prism are full rectangles.

   e The minimum width of a right circular cylinder is the diameter of its base.

   f If point P is the vertex of a cone and the full circle $+C(Q, r)$ is its base, then Q is the foot of P in the plane of the base circle.

   g The least number of faces that a prism may have is four.

   h At least two faces of a parallelepiped are squares.

   i A pyramid has at least four faces.

   j A plane section of a cone is a triangle.

Cumulative review

1 For each of the following, determine from the given information which one of the three collinear points A, B, and C is between the other two.

   a $d(A, B) - [d(B, C) + d(C, A)] = 0$.

   b A belongs to $\overline{BC}$.

   c A does not belong to $\overrightarrow{BC}$.

   d $\overrightarrow{AB}$ and $\overrightarrow{AC}$ are opposite rays.

   e $d(A, C) [d(C, B) - d(B, A)] = 0$.

   f A belongs to $\overrightarrow{BC}$ and $3d(A, B) = 4d(B, C)$.

   g $\dfrac{d(A, C)}{d(A, B)} < 1$ and $\dfrac{d(A, B)}{d(B, C)} > 1$.

   h $\overrightarrow{XB}$ is between $\overrightarrow{XA}$ and $\overrightarrow{XC}$.

   i $\angle BXC$ and $\angle AXC$ are adjacent angles.

   j $\angle CBD$ is an exterior angle of $\triangle ADB$.

2 In plane α, if $\angle ABC$ is bisected by the closed ray $\overrightarrow{BP}$, then P necessarily belongs to which of the following sets?

- **a** $\angle ABC$
- **b** α
- **c** $\overline{AC}$
- **d** $\overrightarrow{PB}$
- **e** Space
- **f** $\angle ABC \cap BP$
- **g** The C-side of AB
- **h** The A-side of BP
- **i** The interior of $\angle ABC$
- **j** The interior of $\triangle ABC$
- **k** $\triangle ABP$
- **l** The segment path determined by (A, B, C, P)

3 What is the measure of $\angle XYZ$ for each of the following cases?

- **a** $\angle XYZ$ and $\angle ABC$ are congruent supplementary angles.
- **b** $\triangle XYZ$ is a regular polygon.
- **c** $2(\angle XYZ^\circ) + 40 = 5(\angle XYZ^\circ) + 22$.
- **d** $5| -(\angle XYZ^\circ)| = 3| -\sqrt{100}|$.
- **e** $\triangle XYZ$ is a right triangle, and segments $\overline{XY}$ and $\overline{XZ}$ are congruent.
- **f** $\angle YXZ^\circ = 90$ and $d(X, Z) = \frac{1}{2} d(Y, Z)$.

4 In each of the following, a set of conditions concerning $\triangle ABC$ and $\triangle XYZ$ are given. For each case, state a congruence of the triangles, if one exists, and give an axiom or a theorem that implies the congruence.

- **a** $\overline{AB} \cong \overline{YZ}$; $\angle A \cong \angle Z$; $\overline{CB} \cong \overline{YX}$.
- **b** $\overline{AC} \cong \overline{BC}$; $\overline{ZX} \cong \overline{XY}$; $\angle C \cong \angle X$.
- **c** $A = Z$; $B = Y$; $\overline{AC} \cong \overline{ZX}$.
- **d** $\angle C^\circ = \angle Y^\circ = 90$; $\overline{AB} \cong \overline{ZX}$; $\overline{AC} \cong \overline{ZY}$.
- **e** $\angle B^\circ = \angle Z^\circ = 90$; $\overline{AC} \cong \overline{XY}$; $\angle C \cong \angle X$.
- **f** $\angle A \cong \angle Z$; $\angle B \cong \angle Y$; $\overline{CB} \cong \overline{XY}$.
- **g** $\angle A \cong \angle X$; $\angle B \cong \angle Y$; $\angle C \cong \angle Z$.
- **h** $\overline{AB} \cong \overline{XY}$; $\angle A \cong \angle X$; $\overline{BC} \cong \overline{YZ}$.

5 Assume that the measure of $\angle ABX$ is 30, that $d(A, B) = 14$, and that C is a point, other than B, in BX. Using this information, correctly complete each statement below by selecting a number or a set from the following list: 0, 7, 14, 60, 90, 150, $\angle ACB^\circ$, $\angle ABC^\circ$, $\overrightarrow{BX}$, $\overrightarrow{XB}$, and $\overline{XB}$.

- **a** If B is between C and X, then $d(A, C)$ is greater than ∿.
- **b** The least possible value of $d(A, C)$ is ∿.
- **c** If $14^2 = 7^2 + [d(B, C)]^2$, then $\angle BAC^\circ =$ ∿.
- **d** If $d(A, C) > d(A, B)$, then $\angle ABC^\circ >$ ∿.
- **e** If $\overline{AB} \cong \overline{AC}$, then C is contained in ∿.
- **f** The measure of $\angle ACB$ is always greater than ∿ and less than ∿.

6 Which of the following statements, each considered independently, imply that the two specified lines are parallel?

- **a** The two lines do not intersect.
- **b** The two lines are both perpendicular to a third line.

c The two lines are both perpendicular to a common plane.

d The two lines are intersected by a common transversal and are coplanar.

e The two lines are each parallel to a third line.

f There exists a ray in one line that is oppositely directed to a ray in the other line.

g The two lines are coplanar, and all points of one line are in the same side of the other line.

h The two lines are lines of the opposite sides of a trapezoid.

i Each of the lines is between two parallel lines.

7 Assume that the diagonals of rhombus $ABCD$ intersect at M. Find the measures of the following segments and angles if $\sphericalangle B^\circ = 120$ and $d(M, B) = \sqrt{7}$.

a $\sphericalangle BAC$ **d** $\overline{BD}$

b $\sphericalangle DMA$ **e** $\overline{AC}$

c $\overline{BC}$ **f** $\sphericalangle MDA$

8 In the plane of $\triangle ABC$, what is the locus of all points that are exterior to the triangle and are equidistant from lines BA and BC?

9 For each of the following cases, determine the value of x.

a x and 3 are proportional to 5 and 8.

b 1 and x are proportional to π and 7.

c -2 and -5 are proportional to 9 and x.

d x and 4 are proportional to 16 and 4.

10 For each of the following cases, determine the ratio of x to y.

a $5y = 3x$.

b $\dfrac{x + 1}{y + 1} = \dfrac{7}{3}$, and $y = 2$.

c $4(x + 1) = 3(y - 1)$, and $x = 11$.

d $\dfrac{x + y}{7} = \dfrac{x - y}{3}$.

11 If $\triangle ABC$ is a right triangle with hypotenuse $\overline{AB}$ and F is the foot in AB of C, which of the following statements are necessarily correct?

a $<B, F, A>$.

b $\triangle ABC \sim \triangle AFC$.

c $\triangle ACF \sim \triangle CBF$.

d $\dfrac{d(B, C)}{d(A, C)} = \dfrac{d(C, F)}{d(B, F)}$.

e $d(A, B)\,d(C, F) = d(A, C)\,d(B, C)$.

f $d(C, F) < d(A, B)$.

g If $\overline{BF} \cong \overline{FA}$, then $\sphericalangle ACF^\circ = 45$.

h $\triangle AFC \cong \triangle CFB$.

i $[d(C, F) - d(A, F)]\,[d(C, F) - d(B, F)] = 0$.

12 In each of the following, the measure of each angle of a regular n-gon is given. For each case, find the value of n.

a 60   **d** 108

b 144   **e** 179

c 170   **f** $179\frac{2}{3}$

13 Show that the measure of each angle of a regular polygon can never be an irrational number.

14 Indicate whether each of the following statements is necessarily true (T), possibly true (P), or necessarily false (F).

a Any set bounded in the planar sense is bounded in the general sense.

b If a planar set is bounded in the general sense, then it is bounded in the planar sense.

c If $\overline{AB}$ is a diameter of the sphere $S(P, r)$, then $\overline{AB}$ is a diameter of a circle $C(P, r)$.

d The intersection of the circle $C(O, k)$ and the interior of the sphere $S(O, k)$ is the empty set.

e If A and B are two boundary points of a set S, then the line AB must intersect the set S at least once.

f If *two* circles have the same center, then their intersection is the empty set.

g If s and t are two supporting lines of the circle $C(P, 8)$, then $d(s, t) = 16$.

h If A is contained in the circle $C(H, 6)$, then the circle $C(A, 2)$ intersects the circle $C(H, 6)$ in exactly two points.

i If A is contained in the sphere $S(H, 6)$, then the sphere $S(A, 2)$ intersects the sphere $S(H, 6)$ in exactly two points.

j If A is an interior point of the solid sphere $^+S(P, r)$, then $d(P, A) < r$.

k If A and B are two inner points of the solid sphere $^+S(P, r)$, then $d(A, B) \leq r$.

Mappings and **26/7**
invariants The ruler axiom (Axiom 6/2) gave us the statement of a correspondence between the points of a line and the real numbers in which the distance between two points is the positive difference of the corresponding numbers. We first used this axiom to show that the correspondence related betweenness for numbers to betweenness for points. With this fact, together with the order relations of numbers, we then obtained all of the order relations of points that we needed for rays and segments.

This way of regarding the ruler axiom provides two of the most important and most powerful ideas in all of mathematics, and these ideas have applications that extend far beyond geometry. The first of these notions is simply the nonsymmetrical way of regarding a correspondence as being *from* one set *to* a second set. Looked at in this way, the correspondence is called a *mapping*, or a *transformation*, of one set onto the other. The second important notion is the idea that such a transformation may carry over, from the first set to the second, some property or relation. Such a property or relation is said to be *preserved by the mapping*, or unchanged, or *invariant* in the mapping. Thus, the ruler axiom correspondence can be regarded as a mapping of real numbers

371

onto points so that betweenness of the numbers is carried over to betweenness of the corresponding points.

The power of these two notions, mappings and invariants, lies in their extreme generality. The notion of a correspondence can be applied to sets of any kind. In the ruler axiom, we have a correspondence of points and numbers; in the protractor axiom (Axiom 10/2), we have a correspondence of rays and numbers; in triangle correspondences, we have points, segments, and angles that correspond respectively with points, segments, and angles. Similarly, the kind of relation that might be unchanged, or invariant, in a mapping could be almost any relation one could think of. Finally, the generality of mappings and invariants has power as a mathematical tool because, once you know that a certain kind of transformation preserves some property, then that property automatically holds whenever you apply the mapping,* and it does not have to be proved. We will be particularly interested, for example, in certain mappings of space onto itself, such as a rotation of space, in which congruence is preserved. Such a mapping is called a *motion* of space. When you apply a motion to space, you automatically know that *every* figure maps onto a congruent figure. Such mappings will give us a way of defining congruence for general sets, and they will extend our method of congruent triangles by providing us with an infinite number of congruences simultaneously.

To establish a theory of mappings for geometry presents very little mathematical difficulty. We can do it with a succession of quite simple ideas and with theorems that are not hard to understand and whose proofs are straightforward. The principal difficulty is not in the mathematics but simply in becoming familiar with the language and the notation of mappings and in learning to use this language to express ideas that already are familiar. An example may help to explain the use of this new language.

Suppose that both the first- and the second-string quarterbacks of a football team are injured and that the coach suddenly has to use a third-string substitute who has never played with the first team. How can this quarterback direct players with whom he has not even practiced? The answer, of course, is that the training of a team is done in terms of correspondences, which could be regarded as mappings. The plays are defined in terms of the positions: what the halfbacks do, what the tackles and guards do, and so on. Selecting a team sets up a correspondence between

---

* Though "transformation" and "mapping" are both in common usage, we will use the term "mapping" from now on in this book.

each player and his position. The nature of a play is invariant under this correspondence. If the play calls for a halfback to pass to an end, then the player corresponding to the halfback passes to the player corresponding to the end. The new quarterback simply uses this invariance to transfer to the first team all the knowledge and experience gained from practice with a different team.

We need a language and notation to express such familiar ideas in a mathematical form. To start in the simplest way, suppose that $A \leftrightarrow B$ denotes a correspondence between two elements A and B. We can look at this as a mapping of A onto B if we regard A as the first element and B as the second element of the corresponding pair. But this notion of a first element and a second element is exactly what is meant by the ordered pair (A, B). This ordered pair often is indicated by the notation $A \rightarrow B$. Also, our point of view can be emphasized by calling B the *image* of A and by saying that A has the image B. (This language probably was suggested by the correspondence of an object with its reflection in a mirror.)

From a correspondence $A \leftrightarrow B$, then, we obtain a mapping of A onto B, denoted by the symbol (A, B) or $A \rightarrow B$, in which B is the image of A. Clearly, there also is a mapping of B onto A, denoted by the symbol (B, A) or $B \rightarrow A$. The two mappings are natural opposites of each other, and each is called the *inverse* of the other.

To extend these ideas, a mapping of a set $\mathcal{R}$ onto a set $\mathcal{S}$ is a correspondence between the elements in $\mathcal{R}$ and those in $\mathcal{S}$ such that each element of $\mathcal{R}$ has *exactly one* image in $\mathcal{S}$ and each element of $\mathcal{S}$ is the image of exactly one element in $\mathcal{R}$.* The mapping is defined by a set of ordered pairs whose first elements belong to $\mathcal{R}$ and whose second elements belong to $\mathcal{S}$. The set $\mathcal{R}$ is called the *domain set*, or just the *domain*, of the mapping. The set $\mathcal{S}$ is called the *range set*, or just the *range*, of the mapping. Any set $\mathcal{C}$ in $\mathcal{R}$ is mapped onto a set $\mathcal{B}$ in $\mathcal{S}$, and $\mathcal{B}$ is called the image of set $\mathcal{C}$. For this reason, $\mathcal{S}$ also is sometimes called the image of $\mathcal{R}$.

The inverse of a mapping of $\mathcal{R}$ onto $\mathcal{S}$ is the mapping of $\mathcal{S}$ onto $\mathcal{R}$ in which the role of an element and its image are interchanged. That is, (Y, X) belongs to the inverse mapping if and only if (X, Y) belongs to the original mapping. Thus, in the inverse mapping, the domain and the range are interchanged.

---

* More general mappings can be defined by many-to-one correspondences instead of by one-to-one correspondences, but we will not deal with these more general mappings.

Because a mapping is a set of ordered pairs, we have a natural definition for equal mappings. Two mappings are the same, or equal, if they are the same set of ordered pairs. Otherwise, the two mappings are different mappings.

We can illustrate all of these terms with an example. Let a mapping be given by $\{(A, B), (C, D), (E, F)\}$. Clearly, the members of this mapping could be denoted by the symbols $A \rightarrow B$, $C \rightarrow D$, and $E \rightarrow F$ respectively. The domain of the mapping is the set $\mathcal{R} = \{A, C, E\}$. The image of $\mathcal{R}$, or the range of the mapping, is the set $\mathcal{S} = \{B, D, F\}$. The image of A is B, and F is the image of E. The set $\{A, C\}$ in $\mathcal{R}$ has $\{B, D\}$ in $\mathcal{S}$ as its image.

The inverse of the mapping $\{(A, B), (C, D), (E, F)\}$ is the mapping $\{(B, A), (D, C), (F, E)\}$. We can also denote the members of this inverse mapping by the symbols $B \rightarrow A$, $D \rightarrow C$, and $F \rightarrow E$ respectively. This inverse mapping is a mapping of $\mathcal{S}$ onto $\mathcal{R}$.*

Exercises

1 A mapping maps A onto P, S onto D, E onto G, and H onto R. Express the mapping both as a set of ordered pairs and by correspondences using arrows.

2 What are the domain and the range of the mapping defined in exercise 1?

3 Use ordered pairs to express the inverse of the mapping defined in exercise 1.

4 Use ordered pairs to express the six mappings of the set $\{A, B, C\}$ onto the set $\{D, E, F\}$. *Answer*

5 One mapping of $\mathcal{R} = \{A, B, C\}$ onto itself is $\{(A, A), (B, C), (C, B)\}$. Express the other five mappings of $\mathcal{R}$ onto $\mathcal{R}$.

6 a Use ordered pairs to express the mapping of the first five positive integers onto their squares.

b What is the domain of the mapping defined in exercise 6a? What is the range?

c In the mapping for exercise 6a, what is the image of 3? What positive integer is mapped onto 25?

d Express the inverse of the mapping defined in exercise 6a. *Answer*

e In the inverse mapping of exercise 6d, what is the image of 4?

7 Why is $\{(1, 5), (10, 2), (3, -4), (-6, 8), (3, 2), (7, 4)\}$ not a mapping?

---

* It is important to use the term "onto" instead of "into." Later we will see that, in mappings, these two terms do not have the same meaning.

374

8 a Is $\{(A, B), (C, D), (E, F)\}$ the same mapping as $\{(C, D), (A, B), (E, F)\}$? Why?

b Is $A \to B, H \to K, L \to M, V \to P$ the same mapping as $\{(L, M), (V, P), (A, B), (H, K)\}$? Why?

9 Consider a mapping of the set of nonnegative integers, $I = \{0, 1, 2, 3, \ldots\}$, onto the set $S = \{0, 1, 4, 9, \ldots\}$, in which each member of I is mapped onto its square.* Then the mapping is the set of all ordered pairs (x, x^2) such that x is a member of I.

a Does this mapping preserve betweenness? (That is, if a, b, and c are members of I, does $\langle a, b, c\rangle$ imply $\langle a^2, b^2, c^2\rangle$?)

b A pair of integers a and b is said to have the *same parity* if $a + b$ is an even integer. Is sameness of parity an invariant of this mapping? (That is, if a and b are in I and $a + b$ is an even integer, must $a^2 + b^2$ be an even integer?) *Answer*

c Let "5-divisibility" of two numbers a and b be defined to mean that $\dfrac{a + b}{5}$ is an integer. Is the "5-divisibility" of number pairs preserved by this mapping?

10 Assume that the elements in the domain of a mapping are the circles in a plane α, and the image of $C(A, r)$ in α is the circle $C(A, 3r)$ in α.

a Does every pair of intersecting circles map onto a pair of intersecting circles?

b Let two circles be called a *nested pair* if one is contained in the interior of the other. Is this "nestedness" preserved by the mapping?

11 Why is the correspondence of each triangle with its circumcircle not a mapping in the sense in which we are considering mappings? *Answer*

Because a mapping is a set of ordered pairs and, hence, a set that differs from the range or the domain, we will use capital Greek letters, such as Γ, Φ, and Ψ, to denote mappings.

It also is useful to have a convenient way of referring to the image of a general element in a mapping. One method that is commonly used is to employ primes for images, so A' is the image of A and set $\mathcal{C}'$ is the image of set $\mathcal{C}$. But when more than one mapping is involved, an element may have different images, and then the use of primes is not efficient. A different scheme is to

---

* See remarks on *Cardinality of sets*, Appendix 1.

use the symbol for the mapping itself and to use the notation $A\Gamma$ for the image of A in the mapping Γ.* Then set $\mathcal{C}\Gamma$ is the image of the set $\mathcal{C}$. Thus, the fact that (A, B) belongs to a mapping Γ can be indicated by the notations $A \to B$, $A' = B$, and $A\Gamma = B$. Each of these notations has its own advantages.

Nothing in the definition of a mapping of a set $\mathcal{R}$ onto a set $\mathcal{S}$ requires that $\mathcal{R}$ and $\mathcal{S}$ be different sets. All or part of a set may be mapped onto itself, and any number of elements may be their own images. An element A that is its own image, so that $A \to A$, or (A, A), belongs to the mapping, is called a *fixed element* of the mapping. A set that maps onto itself is said to be *invariant* in the mapping. If this set maps onto itself by each of its points mapping onto itself, then it is said to be *pointwise invariant*.

Consider a full isosceles triangle $+\triangle ABC$ with base $\overline{AB}$. If you turned the triangle over about the line joining C to the midpoint M of $\overline{AB}$, you would map the full triangle onto itself. In this mapping, all points of $\overline{CM}$ would be fixed points, and $\overline{CM}$ would be pointwise invariant. The base $\overline{AB}$ would map onto itself and so would be an invariant set in the mapping, but not a pointwise invariant set (only point M of the segment maps onto itself). Neither is side $\overline{CA}$ invariant since it maps onto a different set, side $\overline{CB}$.

A mapping in which every element in the domain is a fixed element, so the mapping consists entirely of pairs (A, A), is called the *identity* mapping of the domain onto itself.

Exercises

1 If $\mathcal{R} = \{A, X, M, D\}$, $\mathcal{S} = \{B, X, D, M\}$, and Γ is the mapping $\{(A, B), (X, X), (M, D), (D, M)\}$; then which of the following statements are correct? *Answer*

a $A\Gamma = B$.

b $M\Gamma = M$.

c $\mathcal{R}\Gamma = \mathcal{S}$.

d $\mathcal{S}\Gamma = \mathcal{R}$.

e X is a fixed element of Γ.

f $\mathcal{R}$ is invariant in Γ.

g $\mathcal{R}$ maps onto $\mathcal{S}$.

h In the mapping Γ, the image of M is D.

i $\mathcal{R} = \mathcal{S}$.

2 If $\mathcal{C} = \{X, Y, Z\}$, $\mathcal{B} = \{Y, X, Z\}$, and Ψ is the mapping $\{(X, X), (Y, Y), (Z, Z)\}$, which of the following statements are correct?

a $X\Psi = X$.

b $\mathcal{C}\Psi = \mathcal{B}$.

c $\mathcal{C}\Psi = \mathcal{C}$.

d Y is a fixed element of Ψ.

e $\mathcal{C}$ is invariant in Ψ.

f $\mathcal{C}$ is pointwise invariant under Ψ.

g Ψ is an identity mapping.

h $\mathcal{C}$ is a fixed element of Ψ.

i $\mathcal{C} = \mathcal{B}$.

* Many books use $\Gamma(A)$ instead of $A\Gamma$.

3 Let the three mappings Γ, Φ, and Ψ be defined as follows.

$\Gamma = \{(1, 10), (2, 3), (3, 8), (6, 6)\}$.

$\Phi = \{(a, c), (b, a), (c, b)\}$.

$\Psi = \{(A, A), (B, B)\}$.

a Which of the above mappings have fixed elements?

b What sets are invariant under these mappings? *Answer*

c What sets are pointwise invariant under these mappings?

d Which of the mappings are identity mappings?

e If a domain set is pointwise invariant under a mapping, must that mapping be an identity mapping?

4 Let Γ be the mapping of a line t onto itself expressed in terms of coordinates by $x \rightarrow x + 3$, or by the set of all pairs $(x, x + 3)$. Thus a point with coordinate x is mapped onto a point with coordinate $x + 3$.

a What is 5Γ? $(-3)\Gamma$? $\sqrt{2}\Gamma$? $\pi\Gamma$?

b If $x\Gamma = -18$, what is x? *Answer*

c Are there any fixed elements in this mapping?

d Is the line t invariant in this mapping?

5 a If Γ_1 is a mapping of a line onto itself given in coordinates by $x \rightarrow -x$, show that Γ_1 has just one fixed element. (Hint: Find the x such that $x\Gamma_1 = -x = x$.)

b If Γ_2 is a mapping of a line onto itself given in coordinates by $x \rightarrow 3x - 4$, show that Γ_2 has just one fixed element. *Answer*

6 a Why can you not use the notation $x \rightarrow x^2$ for a one-to-one mapping, in terms of coordinates, of a line onto itself?

b Can the notation $x \rightarrow \dfrac{1}{x}$ be used for a one-to-one mapping, in terms of coordinates, of a line onto itself? Explain.

7 Let Γ denote the mapping onto itself of the set of all points in a line with nonnegative coordinates, and let Γ be defined in terms of coordinates by the set of all pairs (x, x^2). Show that Γ has two fixed points. Show that the set of all points P, with coordinate x such that $0 \leq x \leq 1$, is invariant but not pointwise invariant.

8 In terms of coordinates, express the identity mapping of a line onto itself.

9 Do the mappings in exercises 4, 5a, 5b, and 7 preserve betweenness? Do these mappings preserve distance? (That is, does $|x - y| = |x\Gamma - y\Gamma|$?)

10 There are six mappings of the set $\{A, B, C\}$ onto itself. How many of these mappings have no fixed points? *Answer*

We now will add to the formal system some of the notions
that have been discussed informally.

Definition 123/7 *One-to-one mapping*

A one-to-one mapping of a set $\Re$ onto a set $\mathfrak{S}$ is a collection
of ordered pairs that has the following properties. Each
element of $\Re$ is a first element in exactly one ordered pair.
Each element of $\mathfrak{S}$ is a second element in exactly one
ordered pair. Each ordered pair in the collection has its
first element in $\Re$ and its second element in $\mathfrak{S}$.

Convention

Unless otherwise stated, the term "mapping" will always mean
a one-to-one mapping.

Conventions

Mappings will be denoted by capital Greek letters, usually the
letters Γ, Φ, and Ψ. If Γ denotes a mapping of $\Re$ onto $\mathfrak{S}$,
then $\Re$ will be called the *domain* of the mapping and $\mathfrak{S}$ will be
called the *range* of the mapping. If (X, Y) is an ordered pair
in Γ, X is said to be mapped onto Y. The element Y will be
called the image of X and will be indicated by the notation
$X \rightarrow Y$ and also by the notation $Y = X\Gamma$. Occasionally,
the image of X also will be denoted by the symbol X'. If $\mathfrak{A}$
is a set contained in $\Re$, then the image of $\mathfrak{A}$ is the set
consisting of all the images of elements in $\mathfrak{A}$ and will be
indicated by the notation $\mathfrak{A}\Gamma$.

Definition 124/7 *Inverse of a mapping*

If Γ is a mapping, then the inverse of Γ is the mapping defined
by the set of ordered pairs (Y, X) such that (X, Y) belongs to Γ.

Convention

The inverse of a mapping Γ will sometimes be denoted by the
symbol Γ'.

Definition 125/7 *Fixed point, fixed set, identity mapping*

In a mapping, a point that maps onto itself is a fixed point
of the mapping. A set that maps onto itself is a fixed set,
or an invariant set, of the mapping. An invariant set is
a pointwise invariant set if each of its points is a fixed
point. A mapping in which every point is a fixed point is
an identity mapping.

It would seem natural, at this point, to introduce the second
basic idea about mappings, that of invariant properties. However,
we can do this more effectively if we first look at some natural ways
of combining different mappings. We will introduce these in the
next section.

Exercises

1 The mappings Γ and Ψ are defined below. Let their inverses be denoted by Γ' and Ψ' respectively.

$$\Gamma = \{(A, B), (C, D), (E, F)\}.$$
$$\Psi = \{(X, Y), (R, R), (S, T)\}.$$

a Give the ordered pairs in Γ' and Ψ'.

b What is the domain of Γ'? What is the range of Ψ'?

c Does Γ' have any fixed points? Does Ψ' have any fixed points? *Answer*

d Is the domain of Γ the range of Γ'?

e Is the domain of Ψ' the range of Ψ?

2 a Must a fixed element of a one-to-one mapping Γ also be a fixed element of the inverse mapping?

b If Γ' is the inverse of Γ, what is the inverse of Γ'?

3 If n is a positive integer, the product of all the different positive integers equal to or less than n often is denoted by the symbol $n!$, which is read "n factorial." Thus $1! = 1; 2! = 2 \cdot 1 = 2; 3! = 3 \cdot 2 \cdot 1 = 6$. The number of different mappings of a set of n different elements onto itself is $n!$. (See Appendix 1.) How many mappings of a set of five different elements onto itself have exactly one fixed point? How many have exactly four fixed points? *Answer*

4 If each of the sets $\mathcal{R}$ and $\mathcal{S}$ has n different elements, then there are $n!$ (see exercise 3) mappings of $\mathcal{R}$ onto $\mathcal{S}$. (And there are $n!$ inverse mappings of $\mathcal{S}$ onto $\mathcal{R}$.) If $\mathcal{R}$ is the set of the four vertices of quadrilateral $ABCD$ and $\mathcal{S}$ is the set of the four vertices of quadrilateral $EFGH$, show that, of the $4!$ mappings of $\mathcal{R}$ onto $\mathcal{S}$, only eight of these mappings are such that they preserve *sides* and *diagonals*. That is, only eight of these mappings are such that each two endpoints of a side in $\mathcal{R}$ map onto two points that are endpoints of a side in $\mathcal{S}$.

5 If $\mathcal{P} = P_1P_2P_3 \ldots P_n$ and $\mathcal{Q} = Q_1Q_2Q_3 \ldots Q_n$ are n-gons, how many different correspondences are there of $\mathcal{P}$ with $\mathcal{Q}$? (These correspondences correspond to the *side-preserving* mappings of the vertices of $\mathcal{P}$ onto the vertices of $\mathcal{Q}$.) *Answer*

6 Any mapping of a finite set $\mathcal{S}$ onto itself can be expressed in terms of *cycles* in the following sense. Point A in $\mathcal{S}$ maps onto some point $A\Gamma$. If $A\Gamma = A$, then A is a fixed point called a 1-cycle. If $A\Gamma \neq A$, then $A\Gamma$ is mapped onto some other point in $\mathcal{S}$, say B. Since B is in $\mathcal{S}$, B maps onto some point $B\Gamma$. If $B\Gamma = A$, then the

listing *A-B-A* is a 2-cycle. If $B\Gamma \neq A$, then $B\Gamma$ is some other
point, say *C*, in $\mathcal{S}$. Since *C* is in $\mathcal{S}$, *C* maps onto some
point $C\Gamma$. If $C\Gamma = A$, then *A-B-C-A* is a 3-cycle. If
$C\Gamma \neq A$, then $C\Gamma$ is some other point *D* in $\mathcal{S}$, and so on.
Because the set is finite, one must return to *A* in a cycle.
Any point not in the cycle starts a new cycle.

a Find the cycles for the mapping

$\{(A, D), (B, C), (C, F), (D, E), (E, G), (F, B), (G, A)\}$. *Answer*

b If Γ is a mapping of a finite set onto itself, what
is the relation of the cycles of Γ to those of the inverse mapping?

◆ **7** The domain of a mapping Γ is the set
$\mathcal{S} = \{1, 2, 3, 4, 5, 6, 7, 8, 9\}$. The image of *x*
in $\mathcal{S}$ is the number $13x - 10n$ where *n* is a positive
integer such that $0 < 13x - 10n < 10$. Determine
the cycles of Γ (see exercise 6) by finding the ordered
pairs in Γ, and show that Γ maps $\mathcal{S}$ onto itself.

Combining **27/7**

mappings If a mapping Γ sends *A* onto *B* and a mapping Ψ sends *B* onto *C*,
then it is natural to think of Γ followed by Ψ as sending *A* onto *C*.
To attach the second mapping onto the first, we need the property
that the range of the first mapping is the domain of the second. If
the range of Γ is the domain of Ψ, then, for each (X, Y) in Γ, there
is a pair (Y, Z) in Ψ. Thus, Γ followed by Ψ can be defined by the
set of all pairs (X, Z). This new mapping is expressed by the notation $\Gamma\Psi$, and $\Gamma\Psi$ maps the domain of Γ onto the range of Ψ.

A pictorial way of symbolizing the mapping $\Gamma\Psi$, that is,
Γ followed by Ψ, is given in D522. The mapping Γ takes $\mathcal{R}$ onto $\mathcal{S}$,
and the succeeding mapping Ψ takes $\mathcal{S}$ onto $\mathcal{T}$. Consequently,
Γ followed by Ψ, that is, $\Gamma\Psi$, maps $\mathcal{R}$ onto $\mathcal{T}$. If we wished to
consider the reverse order, that is, Ψ followed by Γ, we would have
to start with the domain of Ψ, namely with $\mathcal{S}$. Because Ψ maps $\mathcal{S}$
onto $\mathcal{T}$, Γ could follow Ψ only by mapping $\mathcal{T}$ somewhere. But if $\mathcal{T}$
is not $\mathcal{R}$, Γ isn't even defined on set $\mathcal{T}$; so the mapping $\Psi\Gamma$ does
not exist.

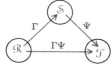

Diagram 522

In the case where $\mathcal{T}$ is $\mathcal{R}$, our original picture looks like the
one in D523. In the order $\Gamma\Psi$, the mapping takes $\mathcal{R}$ onto $\mathcal{S}$ and
then back onto $\mathcal{R}$. Hence, $\Gamma\Psi$ is a mapping of $\mathcal{R}$ onto itself. The
reverse order, that is, $\Psi\Gamma$, takes $\mathcal{S}$ onto $\mathcal{R}$ and then back onto $\mathcal{S}$;
and, therefore, it is a mapping of $\mathcal{S}$ onto itself. Now both $\Gamma\Psi$
and $\Psi\Gamma$ exist, but, if $\mathcal{R} \neq \mathcal{S}$, they are clearly different mappings.

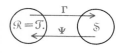

Diagram 523

Even when $\mathcal{R} = \mathcal{S} = \mathcal{T}$ so that both $\Gamma\Psi$ and $\Psi\Gamma$ are mappings
of $\mathcal{R}$ onto itself, they need not be the same mapping of $\mathcal{R}$ onto

itself. Consider the example in which $\mathcal{R} = \{A, B, C\}$ and Γ and Ψ are the following mappings:

$$\Gamma: A \rightarrow A,\ B \rightarrow C,\ C \rightarrow B.$$
$$\Psi: A \rightarrow B,\ B \rightarrow C,\ C \rightarrow A.$$

Then Γ followed by Ψ is

$$\Gamma\Psi: A \rightarrow B,\ B \rightarrow A,\ C \rightarrow C,$$

while Ψ followed by Γ is

$$\Psi\Gamma: A \rightarrow C,\ B \rightarrow B,\ C \rightarrow A;$$

so $\Gamma\Psi \neq \Psi\Gamma$.

The combination of Γ followed by Ψ, if it exists, is called the *product of Γ and Ψ*. There is no obvious reason why the term "product" should be used. However, in later courses, you will find that there are advantages to the name. Meanwhile, we will use "product of $\Gamma\Psi$" in the simple sense of something produced by Γ and Ψ. Again, we want to stress the importance of the order of the symbols Γ and Ψ in the product $\Gamma\Psi$, since $\Gamma\Psi$ and $\Psi\Gamma$ have different meanings.

Exercises

1 Let Γ denote the mapping $\{(1, B), (2, A), (3, C), (4, D)\}$, and let Ψ denote the mapping $\{(B, 3), (A, 4), (C, 1), (D, 2)\}$.
   a Find $\Gamma\Psi$ if it exists. *Answer*
   b Find $\Psi\Gamma$ if it exists.
   c Is $\Gamma\Psi$ the same as $\Psi\Gamma$?

2 Let Γ denote the mapping $\{(4, 8), (7, -1), (-5, 6)\}$, and let Φ denote the mapping $\{(1, 7), (3, -5), (-2, 4)\}$.
   Find $\Gamma\Phi$ and $\Phi\Gamma$ if they exist. *Answer*

3 Let Γ denote the mapping of $\mathcal{R} = \{A, B, C\}$ onto $\mathcal{S} = \{D, E, F\}$ given by $\{(A, E), (B, D), (C, F)\}$.
   Let Ψ denote the mapping of $\mathcal{S}$ onto $\mathcal{R}$ given by $\{(E, C), (D, A), (F, B)\}$. Show that $\Gamma\Psi$ is a mapping of $\mathcal{R}$ onto itself and that $\Psi\Gamma$ is a mapping of $\mathcal{S}$ onto itself.

4 Let Γ and Ψ denote the following mappings.
   $$\Gamma = \{(1, 4), (2, 3), (3, 2), (4, 1)\}.$$
   $$\Psi = \{(1, 1), (2, 4), (3, 2), (4, 3)\}.$$
   The notation $3\Gamma\Psi$ denotes the image of 3 under the product mapping $\Gamma\Psi$. Because $3\Gamma = 2$ and $2\Psi = 4$, then $3(\Gamma\Psi) = (3\Gamma)\Psi = 2\Psi = 4$.
   Calculate the following.
   a $4\Gamma\Psi$ *Answer*   d $2\Gamma\Psi\Gamma$
   b $1\Gamma\Psi$ e $4\Psi\Gamma\Gamma\Psi$ *Answer*
   c $3\Psi\Gamma$ f $1\Gamma\Psi\Gamma\Psi$

5 If Γ' and Ψ' denote the inverses of Γ and Ψ given in
exercise 4, find the following.

a $4\Psi'$ f $4\Gamma'\Psi'$

b $1\Gamma\Psi'$ g $4(\Psi\Gamma)'$

c $2\Gamma'\Psi$ h $3\Psi'\Gamma'$

d $2\Psi'\Gamma$ i $3(\Gamma\Psi)'$

e $2\Gamma'\Gamma'$ *Answer*   j $1\Gamma'\Psi'(\Psi\Gamma)'$

6 If Γ and Ψ are mappings such that $\Gamma\Psi$ exists, then,
for $\Gamma\Psi$, its inverse $(\Gamma\Psi)'$ is $\Psi'\Gamma'$, that is,
the inverse is the product of the inverses but
in the reverse order. Verify that this is true
for each of the following mappings.

$\Gamma = \{(A, B), (C, D), (E, F)\}.$

$\Psi = \{(D, G), (B, H), (F, I)\}.$

7 If Γ is a mapping of set $\mathcal{R}$ onto $\mathcal{S}$ and Γ' is the inverse
of Γ, why must both $\Gamma\Gamma'$ and $\Gamma'\Gamma$ exist? What
mapping of $\mathcal{R}$ onto itself is $\Gamma\Gamma'$? What mapping of $\mathcal{S}$
onto itself is $\Gamma'\Gamma$? Why does $\mathcal{R} = \mathcal{S}$ imply that
$\Gamma\Gamma' = \Gamma'\Gamma$?

Now we will define formally the products that we have been
discussing informally.

Definition 126/7 *Product of two mappings*

If Γ is a mapping of $\mathcal{R}$ onto $\mathcal{S}$ and Ψ is a mapping of $\mathcal{S}$ onto $\mathcal{T}$;
then, for each element Y in $\mathcal{S}$, there is exactly one element X
in $\mathcal{R}$ such that (X, Y) belongs to Γ and there is exactly
one element Z in $\mathcal{T}$ such that (Y, Z) belongs to Ψ. The set
of ordered pairs (X, Z) is the mapping of $\mathcal{R}$ onto $\mathcal{T}$ that is
the product of Γ and Ψ.

Convention

The product of a mapping Γ and a mapping Ψ will be denoted
by the symbol $\Gamma\Psi$. If (X, Y) belongs to Γ and (Y, Z)
belongs to Ψ, then Z is the image of X in the mapping $\Gamma\Psi$
and $Z = X(\Gamma\Psi)$. Because $X\Gamma = Y$ and $Y\Psi = Z$, it is
correct that $X(\Gamma\Psi) = (X\Gamma)\Psi = Y\Psi = Z$. Hence,
there is no confusion in the meaning of $Z = X\Gamma\Psi$.

Convention

The inverse of a mapping Γ also will be denoted by the
exponent notation Γ^{-1}.

The reason for the exponential notation in denoting an inverse
is that different mappings of a set $\mathcal{R}$ onto itself combine to form
products by very much the same kind of rules as those we use
for exponents in numerical products. Suppose that Γ and Ψ are

mappings of $\mathcal{R}$ onto itself and that I is the identity mapping of $\mathcal{R}$ onto itself. Then the product $\Gamma\Gamma$ exists and is denoted by the symbol Γ^2. Similarly, $\Psi\Psi\Psi$ is defined as either of the (equal) mappings $\Psi\Psi^2$ or $\Psi^2\Psi$ and is denoted by the symbol Ψ^3. If Γ' is the inverse of Γ, then $\Gamma\Gamma' = \Gamma'\Gamma = I$. This suggests that Γ' be denoted by the symbol Γ^{-1} and that Γ^0 be considered I.

We will not need these various exponent rules for the product of two mappings, but they are useful in other parts of mathematics.

Some properties of distance-preserving mappings

28/7

We now take up the idea that gives mappings so much of their usefulness—the idea that a mapping can carry properties from the domain to the range. First we will concentrate on those mappings that preserve distance and then on those that preserve shape and the ratio of distances, as was true of similarities. Before we consider either type of mapping, we want to express generally the notion of something being unchanged by a mapping.

With two points A and B, we associate the distance $d(A, B)$. This number also is associated with the segment $\overline{AB}$ as its length. With an angle $\sphericalangle ABC$, we associate the number $\sphericalangle ABC^\circ$. In the last chapter, we defined the diameter of a set. Later we will be assigning an area to a plane convex figure and a volume to a convex solid. All of these examples can be thought of as particular cases of a *measure on a set*.

Definition 127/7 *Measure on a set*
A real number that is defined to correspond to a set will be called a measure on the set.

Convention
A particular measure on a set $\mathcal{C}$ will be denoted by $m(\mathcal{C})$.

Definition 128/7 *Invariant measure*
A particular measure on sets will be said to be invariant in a mapping Γ if, when the measure exists for a set in the domain of Γ, the measure also exists and is the same number for the image of that set in the range of Γ.

We also have had many examples of a relation existing between sets—congruence or similarity of two sets that are polygons, perpendicularity of two sets that are lines, parallelism of two sets that are planes. Such relations may or may not be preserved by a mapping. When a relation is preserved, it is called an *invariant relation* of the mapping.

A relation of sets will be said to be invariant in a
mapping Γ if this relation for sets in the domain of Γ
always implies the same relation for the image sets
in the range of Γ.

Exercises

1 A particular measure of any polygon is its perimeter.
Denote this measure of a polygon $\mathcal{P}$ by $m(\mathcal{P})$, and
find $m(\mathcal{P})$ for each of the following polygons.
  a An equilateral triangle $\triangle ABC$ in which $d(A, B) = 5$
  b The square $ABCD$ in which $d(A, C) = 2$ *Answer*
  c The rhombus $EFGH$ in which $\angle HEF° = 60$ and
  $d(E, H) = 2\sqrt{3}$
  d The regular hexagon $ABCDEF$ in which $d(A, D) = 12$
2 Let Γ denote a mapping of a line t onto itself given in
coordinates by $x \rightarrow x + 3$. Each two points A and B of
line t form a set $\mathcal{A} = \{A, B\}$, and, with each such set $\mathcal{A}$,
one associated measure $m(\mathcal{A})$ is $d(A, B)$.
  a What is $m(\mathcal{A})$ if the coordinates of A and B are
  respectively 6 and -13? If they are -3 and -10? *Answer*
  b What is $x\Gamma$ if $x = 50$? If $x = -10$? If $x = -3$?
  c If $\mathcal{A}'$ is the image of $\mathcal{A}$ under Γ, what are $m(\mathcal{A})$ and
  $m(\mathcal{A}')$ if the coordinates of A and B are respectively 8
  and 20? If they are -5 and 10?
  d Is $m(\mathcal{A})$ an invariant measure in Γ?
3 Show that, in exercise 2, $m(\mathcal{A})$ is invariant under Γ^{-1}.
4 Let Γ and Ψ denote mappings of a line t onto itself given
in coordinates by $x \rightarrow x + 10$ and $x \rightarrow x - 8$
respectively. Associate with each two points A and B
the measure $m(\mathcal{A})$ where $\mathcal{A} = \{A, B\}$ and $m(\mathcal{A}) = d(A, B)$.
Show that $m(\mathcal{A}) = m(\mathcal{A}\Gamma) = m(\mathcal{A}\Psi) = m(\mathcal{A}\Gamma\Psi)$.
[In other words, show that
$d(A, B) = d(A\Gamma, B\Gamma) = d(A\Psi, B\Psi) = d(A\Gamma\Psi, B\Gamma\Psi)$.]

Though we will work with definite properties and measures,
one can see the spirit of the general approach that we have been
discussing in the following theorem.

Theorem 185/7

If a particular measure on sets is invariant under the
mappings Γ and Ψ, then the measure is invariant under
their product $\Gamma\Psi$ if this product exists.

Proof

Let $\mathcal{C}$ denote a set in the domain of $\Gamma\Psi$ for which the number $m(\mathcal{C})$ exists as the measure of $\mathcal{C}$. It is to be proved that $m(\mathcal{C}\Gamma\Psi)$ exists and that $m(\mathcal{C}) = m(\mathcal{C}\Gamma\Psi)$.

Because the domain of $\Gamma\Psi$ also is the domain of Γ, the set $\mathcal{C}$ exists in the domain of Γ. And because the measure on $\mathcal{C}$ is invariant under Γ, $m(\mathcal{C}) = m(\mathcal{C}\Gamma)$.

Since the product $\Gamma\Psi$ exists, the set $\mathcal{C}\Gamma$ in the range of Γ also is in the domain of Ψ. And because the measure on $\mathcal{C}\Gamma$ is invariant under Ψ, $m(\mathcal{C}\Gamma) = m[(\mathcal{C}\Gamma)\Psi]$. This equality, together with $m(\mathcal{C}) = m(\mathcal{C}\Gamma)$, implies that $m(\mathcal{C}) = m(\mathcal{C}\Gamma\Psi)$, as we wished to show.

Theorem 185/7 did not depend, in any way, on the nature of the measure on a set but only on the way mappings and invariance are defined. By almost identical reasoning, one can show the following.

* Theorem 186/7

A relation that is invariant under the mappings Γ and Ψ also is invariant under their product $\Gamma\Psi$ if this product exists.

One obvious invariant relation of one-to-one mappings is that of sets intersecting or not intersecting.

Theorem 187/7

The intersection and the nonintersection of sets are preserved by all one-to-one mappings.

Proof

Let $\mathcal{C}$ and $\mathcal{B}$ denote sets in the domain of a mapping Γ and let $\mathcal{C}'$ and $\mathcal{B}'$ denote their image sets. If $\mathcal{C}$ and $\mathcal{B}$ intersect, they have a point P in common. Since $\mathcal{C}'$ consists of the images of points in $\mathcal{C}$, then P' is in $\mathcal{C}'$. Similarly, because P is in $\mathcal{B}$, then P' is in $\mathcal{B}'$. Therefore, P' is in $\mathcal{C}' \cap \mathcal{B}'$, so the intersection of $\mathcal{C}$ and $\mathcal{B}$ implies the intersection of $\mathcal{C}'$ and $\mathcal{B}'$.

Next consider the case in which $\mathcal{C}$ and $\mathcal{B}$ do not intersect. Assume that $\mathcal{C}'$ and $\mathcal{B}'$ do intersect. Then there is a point P' in $\mathcal{C}' \cap \mathcal{B}'$. Because P' is in $\mathcal{C}'$ and $\mathcal{C}'$ consists *only* of the images of points in $\mathcal{C}$, P' is the image of a point P in $\mathcal{C}$. Similarly, because P' is in $\mathcal{B}'$, point P is in $\mathcal{B}$. Therefore, P is in $\mathcal{C} \cap \mathcal{B}$, and this contradicts the case being considered. From this contradiction, it follows that the nonintersection of $\mathcal{C}$ and $\mathcal{B}$ implies the nonintersection of $\mathcal{C}'$ and $\mathcal{B}'$.

We now turn to a class of mappings that are particularly important for geometry, those in which distance is invariant. When we develop the properties of these mappings, we will see that they give us a way of moving figures in space that corresponds to the way we move physical objects in physical space without changing the shape or the size of the objects.

Definition 130/7 *Distance-preserving mapping*

A mapping in which the measure of distance between pairs of points is invariant is called a distance-preserving mapping. Thus Γ is distance preserving if for each pair of points P and Q in the domain of Γ, $d(P, Q) = d(P\Gamma, Q\Gamma)$.

Theorem 188/7

If Γ and Ψ are distance-preserving mappings and the product $\Gamma\Psi$ exists, then the product is also a distance-preserving mapping.

Proof

This theorem is just a special case of Theorem 185/7.

Theorem 189/7

If Γ is a distance-preserving mapping, then its inverse is a distance-preserving mapping.

Proof

Let $\mathcal{R}$ denote the domain of Γ, let $\mathcal{S}$ denote the range, and let A and B denote two points of $\mathcal{S}$. Under Γ^{-1}, A and B have image points A' and B' in $\mathcal{R}$. Because Γ preserves distance, $d(A', B') = d(A'\Gamma, B'\Gamma)$. But by the definition of an inverse mapping, $A'\Gamma = A$ and $B'\Gamma = B$, so $d(A', B') = d(A, B)$ and, therefore, Γ^{-1} preserves distance.

Exercises

1 Let Γ denote a mapping of a line onto itself given in coordinates by $x \rightarrow x + 2$. If a and b are any two coordinates, show that $|a - b| = |a\Gamma - b\Gamma|$ and, hence, that Γ is a distance-preserving mapping.

2 Let Γ denote a mapping of a line onto itself given in coordinates by $x \rightarrow 3x - 4$. Show that Γ is not a distance-preserving mapping. *Answer*

3 Let Γ denote the mapping of a line onto itself given in coordinates by $x \rightarrow -x - 6$. Show that Γ is a distance-preserving mapping with just one fixed point. If the coordinate of this point is $\bar{x}$, find the value of $\bar{x}$, and show that the fixed point is the midpoint of every segment determined by X and $X\Gamma$. (Hint: Show that $|x - \bar{x}| = |x\Gamma - \bar{x}|$.) *Answer*

4 The mapping $\Psi: x \rightarrow -3x + 2$ (that is, the mapping Ψ given in coordinates by $x \rightarrow -3x + 2$) is not a

distance-preserving mapping. However, it does preserve betweenness. Hence Ψ maps segments onto segments and rays onto rays. Show, with examples, that Ψ reverses directions of rays and maps any segment onto a segment three times as long.

5 The mapping $\Gamma: x \rightarrow -3x + 2$ also can be expressed by $w = -3x + 2$ if w is understood to denote the image of x under Γ. Show that Γ is the product of the three mappings $\Gamma_1, \Gamma_2, \Gamma_3$ given by $\Gamma_1: y = -x$, $\Gamma_2: z = 3y$, and $\Gamma_3: w = z + 2$, where Γ_1 is the set of ordered pairs (x, y), Γ_2 is the set of ordered pairs (y, z), and Γ_3 is the set of ordered pairs (z, w). Describe how each of the mappings $\Gamma_1, \Gamma_2, \Gamma_3$ moves points in the line. Check how the point with coordinate $\frac{1}{2}$ moves away from itself under the first two mappings and then back onto itself under the third mapping.

6 If $A, B, C, \ldots$ are points in space and Φ is a distance-preserving mapping of space onto itself, which of the following statements are necessarily true?

a The mapping Φ^{-1} is distance preserving.

b $d(A, A\Phi) = d(B, B\Phi)$.

c $d(A, B) = d(A\Phi, B\Phi)$.

d If $C = A\Phi$ and $D = B\Phi$, then $d(A, B) = d(C, D)$.

e If $A = C\Phi$ and $B = D\Phi$, then $d(B, D) = d(A, C)$.

f If $d(A, B) + d(B, C) > d(A, C)$,
then $d(A\Phi, B\Phi) + d(B\Phi, C\Phi) > d(A, C)$.

7 If Γ is a distance-preserving mapping of space onto itself, then the image of a sphere $S(P, r)$ under Γ is the sphere $S(P\Gamma, r)$. Supply reasons for the statements in the following proof of this fact.

Proof

Let A denote a point of $S(P, r)$.

  1 Then $d(P, A) = r$.

  2 $d(P\Gamma, A\Gamma) = r$.

  3 $A\Gamma$ is in the sphere $S(P\Gamma, r)$.

  4 $\therefore$ $S(P, r)\Gamma$ is contained in $S(P\Gamma, r)$.

Let B denote a point of $S(P\Gamma, r)$.

  5 $d(B, P\Gamma) = r$.

  6 $d(B\Gamma^{-1}, P) = r$.

  7 $B\Gamma^{-1}$ is in the sphere $S(P, r)$.

  8 Γ maps $B\Gamma^{-1}$ onto B.

  9 $\therefore$ $S(P\Gamma, r)$ is contained in $S(P, r)\Gamma$.

From statements 4 and 9, it follows that

  10 $S(P, r)\Gamma = S(P\Gamma, r)$.

The distance-preserving mappings correspond to our idea of moving an object without bending, stretching, or compressing it so that the shape and the size of the object are unchanged. To show this idea in a mathematical way, we need to prove that, if distance is preserved, then a great many other properties and relations also must be preserved. We start with the relation of betweenness.

Theorem 190/7

If Γ is a distance-preserving mapping of $\mathcal{R}$ onto $\mathcal{S}$, then point C is between points A and B in $\mathcal{R}$ if and only if its image point $C\Gamma$ is between the image points $A\Gamma$ and $B\Gamma$ in $\mathcal{S}$.

Proof

Let A' denote $A\Gamma$, let B' denote $B\Gamma$, and let C' denote $C\Gamma$. Then
1 $d(A, B) = d(A', B')$, $d(B, C) = d(B', C')$, and
$\quad d(C, A) = d(C', A')$.
By Corollary 59/3, point C is between A and B if and only if
2 $d(A, C) + d(C, B) = d(A, B)$.
From statements 1 and 2, it follows that C is between A and B if and only if
3 $d(A', C') + d(C', B') = d(A', B')$,
and, thus, if and only if C' is between A' and B'.

From Theorem 190/7, it follows that, if Γ is distance preserving, then any point P in a line AB maps onto a point P' in the line $A'B'$ determined by the images of A and B. But it does not yet follow that line $A'B'$ is the image of line AB. For line AB might map into rather than onto line $A'B'$. (From an earlier footnote, you will recall that "into" and "onto" have different meanings.) That is, $(AB)\Gamma$ might be contained in $A'B'$, but might not be the whole line $A'B'$. To prove that the image of AB must be a whole line and not just part of a line, we will use the following lemma.

Lemma 191/7

If P, Q, and R are three collinear points and if A and B are two points such that $d(A, B) = d(P, Q)$, then there is exactly one point C in line AB such that $d(A, C) = d(P, R)$ and $d(B, C) = d(Q, R)$. (D524)

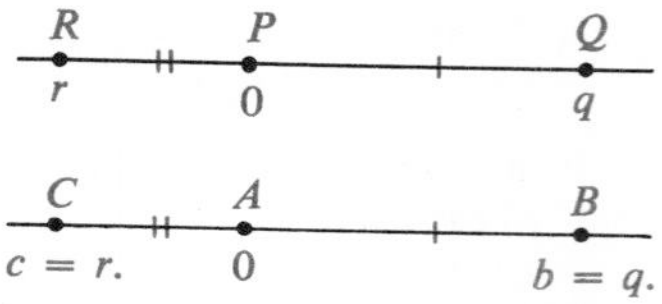

Diagram 524

Proof

There exists a coordinate system in line PQ in which the coordinate of P is zero and the coordinate of Q is the positive number q. Let r denote the coordinate of R.

388

In line AB, there is a coordinate system in which the coordinate of A is zero and the coordinate of B is the positive number b. In line AB, there is a point C with the coordinate $c = r$.

Because $d(A, B) = b$ and $d(P, Q) = q$ and it is given that $d(A, B) = d(P, Q)$,

1 $q = b$.

Then

2 $d(A, C) = |r| = d(P, R)$,

and

3 $d(B, C) = |b - r| = |q - r| = d(Q, R)$.

So there is a point C in line AB that satisfies the conditions of the theorem.

Now let C' with coordinate c' denote any point of AB such that

4 $d(A, C') = d(P, R)$ and $d(B, C') = d(Q, R)$.

Because neither $d(P, R)$ nor $d(Q, R)$ is zero, neither $d(A, C')$ nor $d(B, C')$ is zero. Hence, C' is neither A nor B, which implies that c' is neither zero nor b. From statements 2, 3, and 4, we have

5 $d(A, C') = d(A, C)$ and $d(B, C') = d(B, C)$.

Hence

6 $|c'| = |c|$ and $|b - c'| = |b - c|$.

If c' is negative, then A is between C' and B. Then statement 5 implies that A is between C and B. Therefore, 0 is between c and b. This implies that c is negative, since b is positive. Thus, if c' is negative, c also is negative. Conversely, if c is negative, then A is between C and B, and statement 5 implies that C' is between A and B. Then 0 is between c' and b, and, since b is positive, this implies that c' is negative. Thus c and c' cannot have opposite signs. Thus, $|c'| = |c|$ implies that $c' = c$ and, therefore, that $C' = C$.

Consequently, there is only one point of AB that satisfies the conditions of the theorem.

Theorem 191/7

In a distance-preserving mapping, the image of a line is a line.

Proof

Let Γ denote a distance-preserving mapping, and, in the domain of Γ, let P and Q denote two points in line t. The images of P and Q, the points P' and Q', are distinct and determine a line $P'Q'$. If R is any third point of t, then one of the points P, Q, or R is between the other two. Since this relation is invariant under Γ (Theorem 190/7), one of the three image points P', Q', or R' is between the other two. Thus, the three image points are collinear and this means that R' belongs to $P'Q'$. Because every point of t maps onto a point of $P'Q'$, it follows that $t\Gamma$ is in $P'Q'$, that is, $t\Gamma \subset P'Q'$.*

Let $\overline{R}$ denote any point of the line $P'Q'$ other than P' or Q'. Because $\overline{P'Q'} \cong \overline{PQ}$, then by Lemma 191/7, there is one point R in t whose distances from P and from Q are the same as the distances of $\overline{R}$ from P' and from Q'. Because Γ preserves distances, R maps onto a point R' in $P'Q'$ whose distances from P' and from Q' are the same as those of $\overline{R}$. But, by Lemma 191/7, there is only one point in line $P'Q'$ whose distances from P' and Q' are $d(\overline{R}, P')$ and $d(\overline{R}, Q')$. Therefore, $R' = \overline{R}$.

Since P', Q', and any other point $\overline{R}$ of line $P'Q'$ are the images of points in t, it follows that $P'Q' \subset t\Gamma$.

Finally, from $t\Gamma \subset P'Q'$ and $P'Q' \subset t\Gamma$, it follows that $P'Q' = t\Gamma$ and, hence, that Γ maps lines onto lines.

Corollary 191/7
In a distance-preserving mapping, segments, open rays, and closed rays are mapped respectively onto segments, open rays, and closed rays, and like-directed collinear rays are mapped onto like-directed collinear rays.

Theorem 192/7
In a distance-preserving mapping, the image of a plane is a plane. (D525)

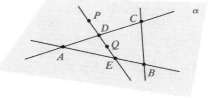

Diagram 525

Proof
Let Γ denote a distance-preserving mapping, and let $\alpha(A, B, C)$ denote a plane in the domain of Γ, where A, B, and C are noncollinear. Then the image points A', B', and C' are noncollinear and so determine a plane $\beta(A', B', C')$.

We propose to show that $\alpha\Gamma \subset \beta$ and that $\beta \subset \alpha\Gamma$ and, hence, that $\beta = \alpha\Gamma$.

Let P denote any point in the plane $\alpha(A, B, C)$. A point Q exists that is distinct from P and is in the interior of $\triangle ABC$. Line PQ intersects $\triangle ABC$ in two points D and E. By Theorem 191/7, the lines AB, BC, and CA map onto the lines $A'B'$, $B'C'$, and $C'A'$ respectively in $\beta(A', B', C')$. Because D and E belong to $\triangle ABC$, it follows that D' and E' are in β. Hence, line DE maps onto line $D'E'$ in β. Because P is in DE, its image P' is in $D'E'$ and, hence, is in β. Thus, every point of α has an image in β and, therefore, $\alpha\Gamma \subset \beta$.

---

* See Appendix 1, Topic 1, for a review of the subset symbol " $\subset$."

If X is any point of β, there exists a point Y that is
distinct from X and is interior to $\triangle A'B'C'$, and line XY
intersects $\triangle A'B'C'$ in two points G' and H'. Points G'
and H' are the images of two points G and H in α because
$\triangle A'B'C'$ is the image of $\triangle ABC$. By Theorem 191/7, line GH
maps onto line $G'H'$. Therefore, X and Y in line $G'H'$ are
the images of points in α. Since every point of β is the
image of a point in α, it follows that $\beta \subset \alpha\Gamma$.

Since each of the sets $\alpha\Gamma$ and β contains the other,
$\beta = \alpha\Gamma$.

Because a distance-preserving mapping maps lines onto lines
and planes onto planes, and preserves betweenness for points and
the intersection of sets, several corollaries follow easily.

Corollary 192a/7

A distance-preserving mapping maps open and closed half-planes
onto open and closed half-planes respectively.

Corollary 192b/7

A distance-preserving mapping maps parallel lines onto
parallel lines, parallel planes onto parallel planes, a line
and a plane that are parallel onto a line and a plane that
are parallel, and rays that are like directed onto rays
that are like directed.

Theorem 193/7

In a distance-preserving mapping, the image of a triangle is
a congruent triangle, and the image of an angle is a
congruent angle.

Proof

Let Γ denote a distance-preserving mapping. If $\triangle ABC$ is in
the domain of Γ, then the noncollinear points A, B, and C
have noncollinear images A', B', C'. Because Γ preserves
betweenness for points, Γ maps $\overline{AB}$, $\overline{BC}$, and $\overline{CA}$ onto $\overline{A'B'}$,
$\overline{B'C'}$, and $\overline{C'A'}$ respectively. From $d(A, B) = d(A', B')$,
$d(B, C) = d(B', C')$, and $d(C, A) = d(C', A')$, it follows that
$\triangle ABC \cong \triangle A'B'C'$ by the side, side, side congruence theorem.

If $\measuredangle PQR$ is in the domain of Γ, the closed rays $\overrightarrow{QP}$ and $\overrightarrow{QR}$
map onto the closed rays $\overrightarrow{Q'P'}$ and $\overrightarrow{Q'R'}$ respectively. Because
P, Q, and R are noncollinear, P', Q', and R' are
noncollinear. From the congruence $\triangle PQR \cong \triangle P'Q'R'$, it
follows that $\measuredangle PQR \cong \measuredangle P'Q'R'$.

Corollary 193/7

Perpendicularity of lines, of planes, and of lines and planes
is invariant in a distance-preserving mapping.

As a result of the properties that we have established for a distance-preserving mapping, we make the following definition.

Definition 131/7 *Congruent sets*

If set S is the image of set R in a distance-preserving mapping, then R and S are said to be congruent sets.

Convention

The fact that sets R and S are congruent will be denoted by the sentence $R \cong S$.

Definition 131/7 raises a question. If two polygons are congruent in the way that we first defined congruence, then is there a distance-preserving mapping of one polygon onto the other? We will see that there is such a mapping and that our definitions agree when, in the next section, we consider particular ways of producing distance-preserving mappings.

Exercises

1 Let Γ denote a distance-preserving mapping of space onto itself. Let A' denote $A\Gamma$, let B' denote $B\Gamma$, and so forth. Which of the following statements are necessarily correct? *Answer*

a If $\langle C, F, X \rangle$, then $\langle C', F', X' \rangle$.

b If $\langle A', C', F' \rangle$, then $\langle F, C, A \rangle$.

c If $\langle A, B', C \rangle$, then $\langle A', B, C' \rangle$.

d $AB = A'B'$.

e $AB \cong A'B'$.

f $(AB)\Gamma = A'B'$.

g $(AB)\Gamma \cong A'B'$.

h $AB \perp CD$ implies $A'B' \perp C'D'$.

i $AB \perp \alpha(D, E, F)$ implies $A'B' \perp D'E'$.

j $AB \perp \alpha(B, E, F)$ implies $A'B' \perp B'F'$.

k $\alpha(A, B, C)\Gamma = \beta(A', B', C')$.

l $\alpha(A, B, C) \cong \beta(A', B', C')$.

m $\sphericalangle EFG° = \sphericalangle G'F'E'°$.

n $d(A, B) + d(B, C) = d(A', C')$.

o If the image of AB is CD, then the image of A is either C or D.

2 Let A and B denote two points of line t and let a denote $d(A, B)$. To each point P of t, there corresponds an ordered pair of nonnegative numbers (x, y) such that $x = d(P, A)$, $y = d(P, B)$, and one of the numbers x, y, and a is the sum of the other two. Conversely, if x, y, and a are nonnegative numbers such that one is the sum of the other two, then there is just one point P

392

of t to which (x, y) corresponds. (This follows from Lemma 191/7.)

a Point B corresponds to $(a, 0)$. What is the ordered pair for A? For the midpoint of $\overline{AB}$? *Answer*

b Where, in relation to A and B, is the point P that corresponds to $(5a, 4a)$? The point Q that corresponds to $(4a, 5a)$?

c If P corresponds to (x, y), what is the locus of points P for which $x + a = y$ and $y > x$?

d If $x = \dfrac{2a}{3}$, what are the possible values of y?

3 Why is any set of points S congruent to itself?

4 If Γ is a distance-preserving mapping of space onto itself, then, by Theorem 191/7, the image of a line t in a plane α is a line t' in the plane $\alpha' = \alpha\Gamma$. If P and Q are two points of α in the same side of t, prove that P' and Q' cannot be in opposite sides of t'.

5 Assume that in a distance-preserving mapping Γ, the closed rays $\overrightarrow{AB}$ and $\overrightarrow{CD}$ are two like-directed rays with images $\overrightarrow{A'B'}$ and $\overrightarrow{C'D'}$. Explain why $\overrightarrow{A'B'}$ and $\overrightarrow{C'D'}$ must be like directed.

6 Let Γ denote a distance-preserving mapping of space onto itself. If C is in $\overrightarrow{AB}$ and D is in the image $\overrightarrow{A'B'}$ and C and D are such that $d(A, C) = d(A', D)$, prove that $D = C'$. *Answer*

7 If $\triangle A'B'C'$ is the image of $\triangle ABC$ in a distance-preserving mapping of space onto itself, and if D and E are in $\overrightarrow{AC}$ and $\overrightarrow{A'C'}$ respectively and are such that $\overline{AD} \cong \overline{A'E}$, prove that $\triangle ABD \cong \triangle A'B'E$.

8 Prove that, in a distance-preserving mapping of space, the image of a circle $C(P, r)$ is a circle $C(P', r)$. *Answer*

9 In working with a distance-preserving mapping Γ, it often is convenient to use the fact that $A \rightarrow A'$ and $B \rightarrow B'$ imply $AB \rightarrow A'B'$, and also the fact that $s \rightarrow s'$ and $t \rightarrow t'$ imply $s \cap t \rightarrow s' \cap t'$. If M, N, and O are the midpoints of the sides of $\triangle ABC$ and are in sides opposite to A, B, and C respectively, show that the centroid of $\triangle ABC$ must map onto the centroid of $\triangle A'B'C'$.

♦ 10 If a distance-preserving mapping Γ leaves the two points A and B fixed, explain why Γ leaves every point of line AB fixed.

♦ 11 Use exercise 10 to show that, if a distance-preserving mapping leaves three noncollinear points A, B, and C fixed, then this mapping leaves every point in the plane of A, B, and C fixed.

♦ 12 From exercises 10 and 11, what would you guess is the nature of a distance-preserving mapping of space that leaves fixed each of four noncoplanar points A, B, C, and D?

Now that we have seen some of the many invariants common to
all distance-preserving mappings, we turn to the question of how
to produce such mappings. We will find that a few basic types of
these mappings can be defined very simply and that combinations
of them will give us all of the distance-preserving mappings.

Definition 132/7 *Reflection in a plane*

The reflection of a point P in a plane α is P itself if P
belongs to α. If P does not belong to α, the reflection of P
in α is the point Q such that the midpoint of $\overline{PQ}$ is the foot of P
in α. The reflection of a set $\mathcal{R}$ in α is the mapping
in which the image of each point of $\mathcal{R}$ is its reflection
in α. (D526)

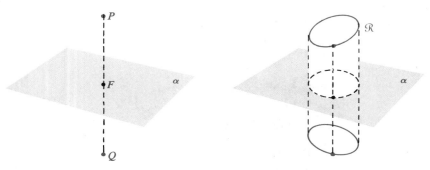

Diagram 526

Comment

If Q is the reflection of P in α, then P is the reflection
of Q in α.

Definition 133/7 *Plane of symmetry*

If the reflection of a set $\mathcal{R}$ in a plane α maps $\mathcal{R}$ onto itself,
then α is a plane of symmetry of the set. (D527)

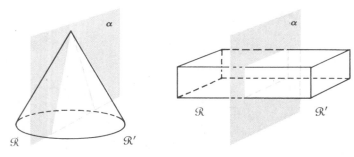

Diagram 527

For each of these exercises, assume that a reflection
in a plane is distance preserving.

1 Let Γ denote the reflection of space in plane α.

   a For what lines t is it true that $t\Gamma = t$? *Answer*

   b For what planes β is it true that $\beta\Gamma = \beta$?

   c What rays are mapped onto oppositely directed rays?

   d What rays are mapped onto like-directed rays?

   e What segments are invariant under Γ?

   f What mapping of space onto itself is Γ^2?

   g Where is α in relation to β and βΓ if $\alpha \neq \beta$?

2 If $\mathcal{R}'$ denotes the reflection of set $\mathcal{R}$ in plane α, why
must α be a plane of symmetry to the two sets $\mathcal{R} \cup \mathcal{R}'$
and $\mathcal{R} \cap \mathcal{R}'$? What are the two sets if $\mathcal{R} \subset \alpha$?

Definition 134/7 *Reflection in a line*

The reflection of a point P in a line t is P itself if P
belongs to t. If P does not belong to t, the reflection
of P in t is the point Q such that the midpoint of $\overline{PQ}$ is
the foot of P in t. The reflection of a set $\mathcal{R}$ in t is the
mapping in which the image of each point of $\mathcal{R}$ is its
reflection in t. (D528)

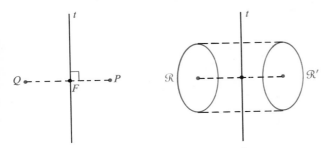

Diagram 528

Comment

If Q is the reflection of P in t, then P is the reflection of Q in t.

Definition 135/7 *Line of symmetry*

If the reflection of a set $\mathcal{R}$ in a line t maps $\mathcal{R}$ onto itself,
then t is a line of symmetry of the set.

Definition 136/7 *Reflection in a point*

The reflection of a point P in a point O is O itself
if $P = O$. If $P \neq O$, then the reflection of P in O
is the point Q such that point O is the midpoint
of $\overline{PQ}$. (D529) The reflection of a set $\mathcal{R}$ in point O is
the mapping in which the image of each point
of $\mathcal{R}$ is its reflection in point O.

Diagram 529

Comment

If Q is the reflection of point P in point O, then P
is the reflection of point Q in O.

Definition 137/7 *Center of symmetry*

If the reflection of a set $\mathcal{R}$ in a point O maps $\mathcal{R}$
onto itself, then O is a center of symmetry
of $\mathcal{R}$. (D530)

Definition 138/7 *Translation*

A translation of a point P in the direction of $\overrightarrow{AX}$
by the positive number k is the point Q such
that $\overrightarrow{PQ}$ has the direction of $\overrightarrow{AX}$ and $d(P, Q) = k$.
The translation of a set $\mathcal{R}$ in the direction of $\overrightarrow{AX}$
by the positive number k is the mapping in which
the image of each point of $\mathcal{R}$ is its translation
in the direction $\overrightarrow{AX}$ by the positive number k.
(D531)

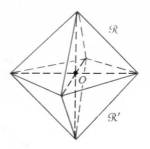

Diagram 530

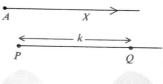

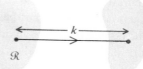

Diagram 531

Exercises

For these exercises, assume that the mappings
are distance preserving.

1 Let Γ denote the reflection of space in line t.

  a What lines are invariant under Γ? *Answer*

  b What planes are invariant under Γ?

  c What rays map onto like-directed rays? Onto
  oppositely directed rays?

  d For any set $\mathcal{R}$, is t a line of symmetry of $\mathcal{R} \cup \mathcal{R}\Gamma$
  and $\mathcal{R} \cap \mathcal{R}\Gamma$?

  e Is the set of points A, B, $A\Gamma$, and $B\Gamma$ necessarily coplanar?

2 If A and B denote two points, how many lines t exist
  such that B is the reflection of A in t? How many
  planes α exist such that B is the reflection of A in α? *Answer*

3 Let Γ denote the reflection of space in point O.

  a What lines and planes are invariant under Γ?

  b What rays map onto like-directed rays? Onto
  oppositely directed rays?

  c For any set $\mathcal{R}$, must point O be a center of symmetry
  of the set $\mathcal{R} \cup \mathcal{R}\Gamma$ and of the set $\mathcal{R} \cap \mathcal{R}\Gamma$?

  d Must A, B, $A\Gamma$, and $B\Gamma$ be coplanar?

4 Let Γ denote the reflection of plane α in the point O
  of α. Let t denote a line that belongs to α and passes
  through O. Let Ψ denote the reflection of α in t.
  Make a drawing to show the position of $P\Gamma$, $P\Gamma\Psi$,
  $P\Psi$, and $P\Psi\Gamma$ for P not in t and also for a point P
  in t. What does your drawing suggest about the products
  $\Gamma\Psi$ and $\Psi\Gamma$? What are the fixed points of $\Gamma\Psi$?

5 What are the lines of symmetry of a circle? What are the planes of symmetry? What are the centers of symmetry? *Answer*

6 Does an angle ever have a center of symmetry? A line of symmetry? A plane of symmetry?

7 We have defined a center of a closed convex curve $\mathscr{B}$ as a point that is in the interior of the curve and that bisects every chord of the given curve through the point. Why is such a center automatically a center of symmetry of $\mathscr{B}$?

8 Describe the centers of symmetry, the lines of symmetry, and the planes of symmetry of a right circular cylinder. *Answer*

9 a Is the intersection of two lines of symmetry of a set $\mathscr{S}$ necessarily a center of symmetry of $\mathscr{S}$? (Hint: Consider the case where $\mathscr{S}$ is an equilateral triangle.)

b Prove that two perpendicular lines of symmetry of a planar set $\mathscr{T}$ intersect in a center of symmetry of the set $\mathscr{T}$.

10 Let Γ denote a translation of space by the positive number k in the direction of $\overrightarrow{AB}$.

a What are the invariant points of the mapping? What are the invariant lines? What are the invariant planes?

b What rays map onto like-directed rays? Onto oppositely directed rays?

11 In plane α, triangle $\triangle ABC$ is a right triangle with hypotenuse $\overline{AB}$. The mappings Γ, Ψ, and Φ are respectively the reflection of α in point B, the reflection of α in line CB, and the translation of α in the direction $\overrightarrow{BC}$ by the number $2d(B, C)$. What is the intersection set of right triangle $\triangle ABC$ and $(\triangle ABC)\Gamma\Psi\Phi$?

We have not yet defined the mappings that correspond to the rotation of a set about a point through a general angle. Mappings of this kind are more complicated than those we have defined so far. We commonly speak of something rotating "around a point," for example, when a ray turns in a plane about a fixed origin. But, more accurately, every rotation is a rotation about a line.

The line is called the *axis of rotation*. If $\overrightarrow{AB}$ is a closed ray that is rotated to a different position $\overrightarrow{AC}$ not opposite $\overrightarrow{AB}$, then points A, B, and C determine a plane, and there is a line t that is perpendicular to this plane at A (D532). Line t is the axis about which the rotation takes place.

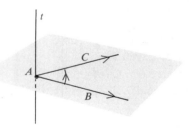

Diagram 532

To define a rotation in space, one has not only the problem of defining the motion in relation to an axis of rotation but also the problem of making clear which direction of turning about the line is intended. One way of handling these difficulties lies in the fact that rotations can be produced by forming the products of reflections. In fact, one can base all of the theory on reflections.

Let us first look at the situation in a plane. Suppose that $\angle AOB$ is an acute angle of measure $2r$ in plane α and that we wish to define a mapping of α onto itself that has the properties we associate with turning the plane about O so that $\overrightarrow{OA}$ moves through the interior of $\angle AOB$ to the position $\overrightarrow{OB}$. Let $\overrightarrow{OX}$ be the ray bisecting $\angle AOB$. Then the desired mapping should not only map $\overrightarrow{OA}$ onto $\overrightarrow{OB}$ but it also should map $\overrightarrow{OX}$ onto $\overrightarrow{OX'}$ such that $\overrightarrow{OB}$ is the bisector of $\angle XOX'$ (D533a). If Γ is the reflection

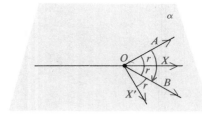

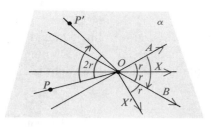

Diagram 533a   533b

in line OX, then Γ maps $\overrightarrow{OA}$ onto $\overrightarrow{OB}$, where we want it, but $\overrightarrow{OX}$ is fixed. However, if Ψ is the reflection of α in line OB, then ray $\overrightarrow{OB}$, which is $(\overrightarrow{OA})\Gamma$, stays fixed while $\overrightarrow{OX}$ maps onto the correct position $\overrightarrow{OX'}$. Thus, the product $\Gamma\Psi$ moves $\overrightarrow{OA}$ onto $\overrightarrow{OB}$ and $\overrightarrow{OX}$ onto $\overrightarrow{OX'}$ as the desired rotation should. Further study of the product shows that each point P distinct from O maps onto $P' = P\Gamma\Psi$ so that $d(O, P) = d(O, P')$ and $\angle P'OP° = 2r$.

The reflection of α in $\overrightarrow{OX}$ followed by the reflection in $\overrightarrow{OA}$ (rather than in $\overrightarrow{OB}$) maps $\overrightarrow{OB}$ onto $\overrightarrow{OA}$ and $\overrightarrow{OX}$ onto $\overrightarrow{OX''}$ so that $\overrightarrow{OA}$ is the bisector of $\sphericalangle XOX''$. This product is the rotation of α about O again by an angle of measure $2r$, but this rotation has the opposite sense to the previous one. (Actually this rotation is the inverse of the other.)

To follow this same process in space, let t denote the line perpendicular to α at O (D534a), where $\sphericalangle AOB$ is the same acute angle defined in the previous example. Let β denote the plane of t and OA, let γ denote the plane of t and OB, and let π denote the plane of t and OX. Thus, π is a bisector of an acute dihedral angle formed by β and γ.

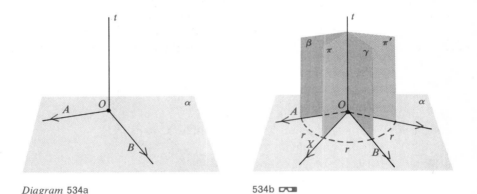

Diagram 534a   534b

Now let Γ denote the reflection of space in plane π and let Ψ denote the reflection of space in plane γ. The product $\Gamma\Psi$ is the same mapping of α onto itself as before and maps $\overrightarrow{OA}$ onto $\overrightarrow{OB}$. But now Γ maps the whole plane β onto γ, leaving π fixed. Then Ψ leaves γ fixed, but maps π onto π' so that γ is the bisector of a dihedral angle formed by π and π'. The product $\Gamma\Psi$ of the two plane reflections is a rotation of space about the axis of rotation t and by the angle of measure $2r$. The reflection in π followed by the reflection in β is the inverse of the previous rotation and maps γ onto β.

Though we will not give a proof here, it can be shown that all of the distance-preserving mappings of space can be expressed as the product of reflections in planes. Let us temporarily use the notation Γ_α to denote the reflection of space in the plane α. Then, if α and β are two intersecting planes, the product $\Gamma_\alpha\Gamma_\beta$ is a rotation about their line of intersection t. If α and β are perpendicular, then $\Gamma_\alpha\Gamma_\beta$ is the reflection of space in line t. If α and β are parallel planes (D535), then $\Gamma_\alpha\Gamma_\beta$ is the translation of space in a direction perpendicular to the planes and from α toward β, and by an

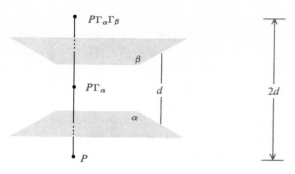

Diagram **535**

amount that is twice the distance between the planes. Finally, if α, β, and γ are three planes that are concurrent at point O and each two of these planes are perpendicular, then the product of Γ_α, Γ_β, and Γ_γ, in any order, is the reflection of space in point O.

Exercises

1 Let t be a coordinatized line in which point A has coordinate a. Let Γ denote the mapping $(x, 2a - x)$ of t onto itself. That is, any point X with coordinate x maps onto $X' = X\Gamma$ with coordinate $x' = 2a - x$.

  a Show that A is the only fixed point. *Answer*

  b Show that $d(A, X) = d(A, X')$.

  c Why do exercises 1a and 1b imply that, for $X \neq A$, point A is the midpoint of $\overline{XX'}$? From this exercise, it follows that Γ is the reflection of t in point A.

2 If k is a positive number and t is a coordinatized line, what type of mappings are $x \to x + k$ and $x \to x - k$? How are the mappings related to each other? *Answer*

3 In a coordinatized line, let A and B have coordinates a and b respectively. Use exercise 1 to indicate by coordinates the product mappings $\Gamma\Psi$ and $\Psi\Gamma$, where Γ is the reflection of t in A and Ψ is the reflection of t in B. Show that these products are the translations of the line in the directions $\overrightarrow{AB}$ and $\overrightarrow{BA}$ by the number $k = 2\,d(A, B)$.

4 Let s and t denote two parallel lines in plane α, with $d(s, t) = k$. Let A in s have F as its foot in t. Make a diagram that pictures P between s and t, and with Q and R in opposite sides of the strip between s and t. Construct the images of these points under the product $\Gamma_s\Gamma_t$, where Γ_s and Γ_t are the reflection of α in s and in t respectively. Show that the ray from each point to its image has the direction of $\overrightarrow{AF}$ and that the distance between each point and its image is $2k$.

400

5 Let α denote the plane of an angle $\sphericalangle ABC$ that has the measure 30. Assume that the mapping Γ_s is the reflection of α in $s = BA$, and that Γ_t is the reflection of α in $t = BC$. Then, for every P in α, where $P \neq B$, $\sphericalangle PBP'^\circ = 60$ if $P' = P\Gamma_s\Gamma_t$. Make a careful drawing that shows $\sphericalangle PBP'$ in relation to $\sphericalangle ABC$ for two different positions of P.

6 Given two points A and P in a plane α and a rotation Φ of α about A, how many pairs of lines s and t exist in α such that $P\Gamma_s\Gamma_t = P\Phi$, where Γ_s and Γ_t denote reflections of α in s and t respectively?

7 Let s and t denote two lines in plane α.
a If $s \parallel t$, define a product of reflections of α in lines that translates s onto t.
b If s intersects t, define a product of reflections of α in lines that rotates s onto t.

8 A mapping Γ of a set onto itself that is not the identity mapping but is such that Γ^2 is the identity is called an *involution*. Is the reflection of space in a point, a line, or a plane an involution? Is a translation of space an involution? Is there any n such that the nth power of a translation of space is the identity?

In the previous exercises we have assumed that translations and reflections preserve distance. We want to look briefly at what is involved in proving these facts, but first we will introduce a term that is useful.

Definition 139/7 *Motion of a set*
A distance-preserving mapping of a set onto itself will be called a motion of the set.

By defining reflections, rotations, and translations on space as the domain set, one obtains motions of space. When the domain and range of such mappings is a plane or a line, then the mappings become motions of the plane or of the line respectively. As we mentioned before, it can be shown that every motion of space is either a reflection or the product of reflections.

To establish all of the properties we have been discussing informally presents no real difficulty. To show, for example, that a reflection or a translation is a distance-preserving mapping, we need to look only at two points A and B and their images A' and B' for a few essentially different cases. In these cases, a proof that $d(A, B) = d(A', B')$ then establishes that the mapping is distance preserving for any domain whatsoever. We illustrate this for the reflection in a point.

Theorem 194/7
The reflection of space in a point is a motion of space.

Proof

Let O denote a point, and let Γ denote the reflection of space in O. Let A and B denote two points, and let $A' = A\Gamma$, $B' = B\Gamma$. First, there are two possibilities; either the two points A and B are both different from O or exactly one of them is O. If the two points are different from point O, then either A, B, and O are noncollinear or they are collinear. Thus, we can treat all possibilities in three cases.

Case I A, O, and B are three noncollinear points. Then A, O, and B determine a plane α, and, by the definition of Γ, $\sphericalangle AOB$ and $\sphericalangle A'OB'$ are opposite angles in α. Therefore,

1    $\sphericalangle AOB \cong \sphericalangle A'OB'$.

By the definition of Γ, we also have

2    $\overline{AO} \cong \overline{OA'}$ and $\overline{BO} \cong \overline{OB'}$.

Then, by the side, angle, side congruence theorem,

3    $\triangle AOB \cong \triangle A'OB'$.

Therefore, $\overline{AB}$ and $\overline{A'B'}$ are congruent corresponding sides, and

4    $d(A, B) = d(A', B')$.

Case II A, O, and B are three collinear points. There is a coordinate system in the line t of A, O, and B in which O is the origin, A has a coordinate a, and B has a coordinate b. By the definition of Γ, the coordinate of A' is $-a$ and the coordinate of B' is $-b$. Therefore,

5    $d(A, B) = |b - a|$

and

6    $d(A', B') = |-b - (-a)| = |a - b|$.

Since $|b - a| = |a - b|$, we have $d(A, B) = d(A', B')$.

Case III   One of the points A and B, say A, is point O. By the definition of Γ, point O is the midpoint of $\overline{BB'}$. Hence, $d(O, B) = d(O, B')$. Since $A = O$, then $A' = O$, and $d(A, B) = d(O, B) = d(O, B') = d(A', B')$. Since, in all cases, $d(A, B) = d(A\Gamma, B\Gamma)$, the reflection Γ is a motion of space.

Corollary 194a/7
The reflection of any set in a point is a distance-preserving mapping. The reflection of a plane in one of its points is a motion of the plane. The reflection of a line in one of its points is a motion of the line.

Corollary 194b/7

A reflection in a point O maps a closed ray $\overrightarrow{AX}$ onto an oppositely directed ray $\overrightarrow{A'X'}$ that is parallel to $\overrightarrow{AX}$ if A, O, and X are noncollinear. (D536)

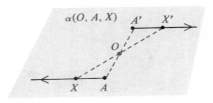

Proof

By the definition of a reflection Γ in a point O, the closed rays $\overrightarrow{AX}$ and $(\overrightarrow{AX})\Gamma = \overrightarrow{A'X'}$ are oppositely directed

Diagram 536

collinear rays if A, O, and X are collinear. If A, O, and X are noncollinear, the congruence $\triangle AOX \cong \triangle A'OX'$ gives $\sphericalangle OAX \cong \sphericalangle OA'X'$. And since $\overline{XX'}$ intersects line AA' at point O, the points X and X' are in opposite sides of AA' in $\alpha(A, O, X)$. Thus, by Theorem 88/4, AX and $A'X'$ are parallel lines, and $\overrightarrow{AX}$ and $\overrightarrow{A'X'}$ are oppositely directed.

Exercises

1 Which of the following statements are necessarily correct if Ψ is a motion of the set $\mathcal{R}$? *Answer*

  a Ψ is distance preserving.

  b If $\mathcal{S}$ is the range of Ψ, then $\mathcal{R} = \mathcal{S}$.

  c For all A in $\mathcal{R}$, $A\Psi = A$.

  d For all A and B in $\mathcal{R}$, $d(A, B) = d(A\Psi, B\Psi)$.

  e If P is in $\mathcal{R}$, then $P\Psi$ is in $\mathcal{R}$.

  f For every A in $\mathcal{R}$, there is some C in $\mathcal{R}$ such that $C\Psi = A$.

  g If $(\overline{AB})\Psi = \overline{AB}$, then the midpoint of $\overline{AB}$ is a fixed point.

2 Let Γ denote the reflection of space in point O and let $A'B'C'D'$ denote the image of the square $ABCD$ under Γ.

  a What is the range of Γ?

  b Must point O be in the plane of $ABCD$?

  c If $D = B\Gamma$, where is point O?

  d For what positions of point O would it be true that $d(A, A') = 2\,d(A, B)$? *Answer*

3 Let A, B, and C denote three noncollinear points in space, let Γ denote the reflection of space in a point D, and let Ψ denote the reflection of space in a point E. Prove that $(\triangle ABC)\Gamma\Psi$ is congruent to $\triangle ABC$.

4 For exercise 3, make a careful drawing of $\triangle ABC$ and $(\triangle ABC)\Gamma\Psi$ for D and E in the plane of $\triangle ABC$. From the triangle and its image, what mapping does $\Gamma\Psi$ appear to be?

5 Suppose that each vertex of a triangle $\triangle ABC$ is reflected in the midpoint of the opposite side so that A is reflected onto A', point B is reflected onto B', and C is reflected onto C'. Explain why $\triangle ABC$ is the midpoint triangle of $\triangle A'B'C'$.

♦ **6** Line t, point M, and $\triangle ABC$ are given and are coplanar. Under what conditions is M the midpoint of a segment determined by some point in t and some point in the triangle? How could such a pair of points be found? *Answer*

To see how one can use a motion, let us prove a three-space extension of the fact that the diagonals of a parallelogram bisect each other.

Theorem 195/7

The diagonals of a parallelepiped are concurrent at a point that is the midpoint of all of the diagonals and is a center of symmetry of the parallelepiped. (D537)

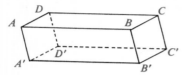

Diagram 537a

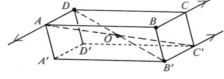

537b

Proof

Let $ABCD$ and $A'B'C'D'$ denote the parallelograms that are the boundaries of the two parallel bases and are such that $\overline{AA'}$, $\overline{BB'}$, $\overline{CC'}$, and $\overline{DD'}$ are parallel edges. Then $AA'D'D$ and $BB'C'C$ are parallelograms in opposite faces, and $AA'B'B$ and $DD'C'C$ are parallelograms in opposite faces.

Let O denote the midpoint of the diagonal $\overline{DB'}$, and let Γ denote the reflection of space in O. Then Γ interchanges D and B'. The closed ray $\overrightarrow{B'C'}$ has the direction of $\overrightarrow{BC}$ ($BB'C'C$ is a parallelogram), and $\overrightarrow{BC}$ has the opposite direction of $\overrightarrow{DA}$ ($ABCD$ is a parallelogram). Thus $\overrightarrow{B'C'}$ and $\overrightarrow{DA}$ are oppositely directed rays and must be interchanged by Γ, since their origins B' and D are interchanged by Γ. But $\overline{B'C'} \cong \overline{BC} \cong \overline{DA}$, so Γ must interchange A and C'. Therefore, the diagonal $\overline{AC'}$ also has midpoint O.

The same argument shows that Γ must interchange $\overrightarrow{DD'}$ and $\overrightarrow{B'B}$, and, from $\overline{DD'} \cong \overline{AA'} \cong \overline{BB'}$, Γ interchanges D' and B. Hence, O is the midpoint of diagonal $\overline{D'B}$. In the same way, point O is the midpoint of $\overline{A'C}$.

Now, because all of the vertices are interchanged in pairs, Γ must interchange opposite faces, and so maps the polyhedron onto itself. But then O is a center of symmetry, and so every chord of the polyhedron that contains O is bisected by O.

404

Theorem 195/7 gives a great deal of extra information about different parts of the parallelepiped. Just as opposite sides of a parallelogram are congruent, the opposite full parallelograms of a parallelepiped are congruent. We also know, for example, that $\sphericalangle DAB \cong \sphericalangle B'C'D'$ because they are interchanged. We know that the dihedral angle of the polyhedron with edge AD is congruent to that with edge $C'B'$ because these angles are interchanged.

It is worth noting that, since we used triangle congruences to prove that the reflections and translations are distance preserving, we can always prove, by triangle congruences, any fact we obtain with motions. What we have in mappings, then, is not something basically different, but a natural and powerful extension of our previous methods and an extension that gives an infinite number of congruences simultaneously.

The following theorems, which we have starred, have proofs very similar to the proof of Theorem 194/7.

* Theorem 196/7
The reflection of any set in a line or in a plane is a distance-preserving mapping.

* Theorem 197/7
The translation of any set in a direction $\overrightarrow{AX}$ and by the positive number k is a distance-preserving mapping.

Exercises

1 Perpendicular lines s and t in space intersect at point F and determine a plane α. Let Ψ denote the reflection of space in a point F, let Φ_t denote the reflection of space in the line t, and let Φ_s denote the reflection of space in the line s.
  a What is the locus of all points P in α such that $P\Psi = P\Phi_s$?
  b What is the locus of all points P in α such that $P\Psi = P\Phi_s\Phi_t$? Such that $P\Psi = P\Phi_t\Phi_s$?
  c What is the locus of all points P in α such that $P\Psi\Phi_s\Phi_t = P$? *Answer*
2 Line t is perpendicular to line AB at F, and the two lines determine plane α. If Γ is a translation of α by $d(A, B)$ in the direction $\overrightarrow{AB}$ and Ψ is the reflection of α in t, answer the following questions.
  a What are the fixed points of $\Gamma\Psi$?
  b What are the fixed points of $\Psi\Gamma$?
  c What lines of α are invariant under $\Gamma\Psi$? *Answer*

405

3 To prove that a reflection in a plane is distance preserving (Theorem 196/7), one has to show that, if A and B are two points of space and A' and B' are their reflections in a plane α, then $d(A, B) = d(A', B')$. A proof might be subdivided into the following four cases: (1) A and B are in α. (2) Just one of the points A and B is in α. (3) Neither A nor B is in α and $AB \perp \alpha$. (4) Neither A nor B is in α, and AB is not perpendicular to α.

  a Prove that, in cases 1 and 2, $d(A, B) = d(A', B')$.

  b How does case 3 follow from the fact that the reflection of a line in one of its points is distance preserving?

  c In case 4, what type of polygon is $AA'B'B$ if A and B are in the same side of α?

4 Let Γ denote a translation of space by the amount $d(X, Y)$ in a direction $\overrightarrow{XY}$. If A and B are two points such that AB is not parallel to XY, which theorem about parallelograms implies that $d(A, B) = d(A\Gamma, B\Gamma)$?

5 If Γ denotes a motion of space, how much information about the images of certain points will completely determine the mapping Γ in each of the following cases?

  a Γ is a reflection in some point. *Answer*

  b Γ is a reflection in some line.

  c Γ is a reflection in some plane.

  d Γ is a translation of space.

6 If $C(P, r)$ is a circle in plane α, then a reflection of α in P or in any line of α through P clearly reflects $C(P, r)$ onto itself. Explain why, in either case, a tangent to $C(P, r)$ must map onto a tangent line to $C(P, r)$.

7 Let P denote a point in the plane α of $C(A, r)$ and in the exterior of the circle. Use the ideas of exercise 6 to justify the construction in D538 for the lines through P and tangent to $C(A, r)$. Let Q denote the intersection of $C(A, r)$ and $\overline{AP}$, and let t denote the line that is in α and is perpendicular to AP at Q. Line t intersects the circle with center A and radius $d(A, P)$ at B and C. The open rays $\overrightarrow{AB}$ and $\overrightarrow{AC}$ intersect $C(A, r)$ at D and E respectively. Lines PD and PE are tangent at D and E to $C(A, r)$.

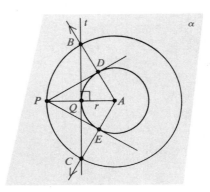

Diagram 538

(Hint: Consider the reflection of α in the line through A and the midpoint of $\overline{PB}$.)

8 Let A and B denote two points in the same side of line t in a plane α (D539). It is desired to find the point X in line t for which the sum $d(A, X) + d(X, B)$ will have the least possible value. If Γ is the reflection of α in t, prove that, for any X in t, $d(A, X) + d(X, B)$ equals $d(A\Gamma, X) + d(X, B\Gamma)$. From this proof, show how the desired position of X can be found.

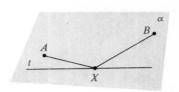

Diagram 539

9 In D540, $\overline{XY}$ represents a bridge that is perpendicular to the parallel banks of a river. The bridge was built to provide a route for traffic from A to B. If Γ translates X onto A and $Y' = Y\Gamma$, explain why the route from A to B via X and Y is the same length as going from A to B via Y' and Y. Is Y' the same point for all positions of X? Find the position of the bridge for which the path from A to B via X and Y has the least length.

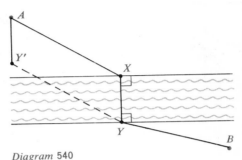

Diagram 540

10 A road is to be built from a town A to a town B that is on the opposite side of a river and downstream from A (D541). The river is very straight and has parallel banks. Each town shares evenly in the cost of the bridge (built perpendicularly to the river banks), but each town must pay for all the road on its side of the river. Determine where the bridge must be built so that each town pays for the same amount of road.

Diagram 541

11 Lines a, b, and c are coplanar and parallel in α, and line b is between a and c. A construction for points A, B, and C in a, b, and c respectively such that $\triangle ABC$ is equilateral is shown in D542. Point A is any point of a, and F is the foot in b of A. Point F' is constructed so that $\sphericalangle FAF'^\circ = 60$ and $\overline{AF'} \cong \overline{AF}$. Line b' is perpendicular to $\overline{AF'}$ at F' and intersects c at C. The open ray $\overrightarrow{AX}$ is constructed so that $\sphericalangle CAX^\circ = 60$ and F' and X are in opposite sides of AC. Point B is the

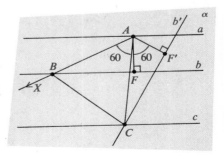

Diagram 542

intersection of $\overrightarrow{AX}$ and b. Let Γ denote a rotation of plane α about A that maps $\overrightarrow{AF}$ onto $\overrightarrow{AF'}$.

a Why is $F' = F\Gamma$?
b Why is $b' = b\Gamma$?
c Is $\overrightarrow{AC} = (\overrightarrow{AX})\Gamma$?
d Since $B = \overrightarrow{AX} \cap b$, then $B\Gamma = (\overrightarrow{AX})\Gamma \cap b\Gamma$.
Therefore, what does $B\Gamma$ equal?
e Why is $\overline{AB} \cong \overline{AC}$?
f Why does $\overline{AB} \cong \overline{AC}$ imply that $\triangle ABC$ is equilateral?

The translations and reflections of space imply that every set has infinitely many copies that can be obtained by moving a set to any point of space and turning it there to any desired attitude. This freedom of motion can be used to show that our new, general meaning for congruence of sets includes, as a special case, our definition of congruent polygons. A careful proof of this fact requires more time than we wish to take, but we easily can see how such a proof could be obtained.

Suppose that $\triangle ABC \cong \triangle DEF$, where $\alpha(A, B, C)$ is the plane of one triangle and $\beta(D, E, F)$ is the plane of the other. To show that there is a motion of space in which $\triangle DEF$ is the image of $\triangle ABC$, we use the fact that the product of two motions is again a motion.

To begin a proof, we can move α onto β. For if α and β are parallel, then the midparallel plane can be taken as the plane of reflection. (See Theorem 151/4.) If α and β intersect, then a plane bisecting one of their dihedral angles can be taken as the plane of reflection. (See Theorem 150/4.) So the problem is reduced to considering $\triangle ABC$ and $\triangle DEF$ in the same plane β.

Let $s = AB$ and let $t = DE$. There is a motion of plane β that maps s onto t. For if s and t are parallel, then the reflection in their midparallel line will do. If s and t intersect, then a line that bisects one of their angles can be taken as a line of reflection. So the problem is reduced to coplanar triangles with AB and DE in the same line t.

Next we can move A onto D. We can do this by the identity mapping if $A = D$ or by a translation if $A \neq D$. This motion maps β onto itself and maps t onto itself. Now we can keep the point $A = D$ fixed and map B onto E. To do this, we can use the identity mapping if B is already in E. If $B \neq E$, we can use the reflection in A.

At this stage, if C and F are in the same side of line t, then each of these points has the same distance from A and the same distance from B. Consequently, C and F are the same point. (See Corollary 62/3.) If C and F are in opposite sides of t, then a reflection in t leaves A and B fixed. Hence, by Corollary 62/3, a reflection in t maps C onto F.

The argument we have described for triangles can be extended to show that, if two polygons are congruent, then there is a motion of space in which one polygon is the image of the other. On the other hand, any motion of one polygon onto another clearly establishes a correspondence of the two polygons that is a congruence in the sense we first defined.

We will not carry our study of motions any further since we want to look briefly at the mappings that generalize similarity in the way that motions generalize congruence. However, in the study of volumes that we will consider later in this book, we will need a fact that we now state as a starred theorem.

---

* Theorem 198/7

For any planes α and β, there exists a motion of space that maps α onto β and maps a given side of α onto a given side of β.

Exercises

1 Segments $\overline{AB}$ and $\overline{CD}$ in D543 are congruent and in a plane α. Describe in words and show by diagrams a series of motions of α onto itself whose product maps A onto C and B onto D. Can this be done in more than one way?

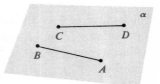

Diagram 543

2 **a** In D544, $\triangle RST$ and $\triangle HJK$ are in the plane α, and $\triangle RST \cong \triangle HJK$. Describe and show by diagrams a series of motions of α onto itself whose product maps H onto R, J onto S, and K onto T.

b For what position of $\triangle HJK$ in relation to $\triangle RST$ will the reflection of α in HK followed by the reflection of α in T map H, J, and K onto R, S, and T respectively?

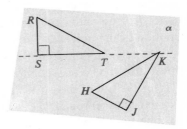

Diagram 544

3 **a** If $\triangle ABC$ is a given triangle, describe the locus of all points X such that $\triangle ABC \cong \triangle ABX$. *Answer*

b If $ABCD$ is a tetrahedron, describe the locus of all points X such that $ABCD \cong ABCX$.

4 If A and B are two points of a plane α, then, by Corollary 62/3, there is at most one point of α in a given side of AB that is a given distance from A and a given distance from B. What kind of space analogue of this corollary is suggested by exercise 3b?

5 Assume that the angles $\sphericalangle ABC$ and $\sphericalangle DBE$ are acute, congruent, and coplanar in α. If the reflection of α in BA followed by the reflection in BC is the same rotation of α as the reflection in BD followed by the reflection in BE, what are the relative positions of the following rays?

a $\overrightarrow{BC}$ and $\overrightarrow{BE}$ if $\overrightarrow{BA} = \overrightarrow{BD}$

b $\overrightarrow{BA}$ and $\overrightarrow{BE}$ if $\overrightarrow{BC} = \overrightarrow{BD}$ *Answer*

c $\overrightarrow{BC}$ and $\overrightarrow{BE}$ if $\overrightarrow{BA}$ and $\overrightarrow{BD}$ are opposite rays

d $\overrightarrow{BC}$ and $\overrightarrow{BD}$ if $\overrightarrow{BA}$ and $\overrightarrow{BE}$ are opposite rays

6 In a plane α, lines t_1 and t_2 are perpendicular and intersect at point O. Let Γ_1 denote the reflection of α in t_1, let Γ_2 denote the reflection of α in t_2, let Ψ denote the reflection of α in point O, and let I denote the identity mapping of α onto itself. Each of the paired products of these transformations is equal to one of the four defined transformations. Fill in the *transformation table* in D545 by assuming that the first transformation is from the left (vertical) column and the second is from the top (horizontal) row. (For example, the product of Γ_2 and Ψ is Γ_1.)

	I	Γ_1	Γ_2	Ψ
I				
Γ_1				
Γ_2				Γ_1
Ψ				

Diagram 545

7 A fact that we have not proved but one that seems reasonable is that, if a motion of a plane maps the set of vertices of a polygon onto itself, then the motion of the plane is a motion of the polygon and also of the full polygon. Similarly, if a motion of space maps the set of vertices of a polyhedron onto itself, then the motion of space is a motion of the polyhedron and also of the solid polyhedron. Conversely, any motion of a polygon or of a polyhedron must map the vertex set onto itself.

To see the use of the preceding ideas, let $\mathcal{S}$ denote a regular tetrahedron $ABCD$. Let O denote a center of symmetry of $\mathcal{S}$ (if one exists), and let Γ denote the reflection of space in O.

a Why cannot O be a vertex? *Answer*

b Since Γ must interchange vertices in pairs, say, A with B and C with D, which two different points would point O have to be?

Exercises 7a and 7b show that $\mathcal{S}$ has no center of symmetry. Next, let t denote a line of symmetry of $\mathcal{S}$ (if one exists), and let Ψ denote the reflection of space in t (D546).

c Why cannot Ψ leave one vertex fixed or three vertices fixed?

d Why cannot Ψ leave all vertices fixed or just two vertices fixed?

e The only possibility left is that Ψ leaves no vertices fixed. It, therefore, must interchange the vertices in pairs, say, A with B and C with D. Then t is forced to be what line of symmetry? Is this line perpendicular to both $\overline{AB}$ and $\overline{CD}$?

f The reflection in t is the mapping $\{(A, B), (B, A), (C, D), (D, C)\}$. What is $(\overline{AD})\Psi$? What is $(\overline{BC})\Psi$? In this mapping, what happens to the midpoints M of $\overline{AD}$ and N of $\overline{BC}$? What is the relation of t to line MN?

g What is the third line of symmetry that is perpendicular to both t and MN?

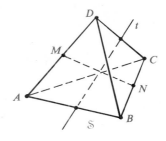

Diagram 546

Now let α denote a plane of symmetry of $\mathbb{S}$ (if one exists) and let Φ denote the reflection in α.

h Explain why the number of vertices fixed under Φ cannot be any of the numbers 0, 1, 3, and 4. *Answer*

i If, under Φ, A and B are fixed and C is interchanged with D, plane α must be what plane?

j If each edge determines a plane of symmetry, how many such planes are there?

k The product of two motions is always a motion (perhaps the identity). By checking how $\Psi\Phi$ maps the vertex set, identify this product mapping.

♦ **8** The collection of all the motions of a set onto itself can be said to form its *motion group*. The number of these motions sometimes is called the *order* of the motion group, and the identity mapping is always counted as one motion. For example, the order of the motion group for an isosceles triangle is 2, that is, there are two ways to fit such a triangle onto itself. What is the order of the motion group for each of the following?

a A scalene triangle (a triangle that has no two congruent sides)

b An equilateral triangle *Answer*

c A cube

d A regular tetrahedron

e A sphere

411

9 If Γ is a mapping of a set $\mathscr{R}$ onto itself and if n is the least positive integer such that Γ^n is the identity mapping of $\mathscr{R}$ onto itself, then n is called the *period* of the mapping. Thus the identity mapping has period 1. A reflection of $\mathscr{R}$ onto itself is a mapping of period 2.

a Is there a motion of a plane onto itself that is a mapping of period 9?

b Find the period of the mapping
$\{(A, B), (B, C), (C, A), (D, E), (E, D)\}$.

• 10 If Γ is a motion of a plane α and if Γ interchanges two points A and B so that $A\Gamma = B$, $B\Gamma = A$, prove that Γ is the reflection of α either in the midpoint M of $\overline{AB}$ or in the line of α that is the perpendicular bisector of $\overline{AB}$.

11 Let $\mathscr{C}'$ denote a side of plane α, and let $\mathscr{B}'$ denote a side of a second plane β. Define a motion of space that maps α onto β and $\mathscr{C}'$ onto $\mathscr{B}'$ if each of the following is true.

a $\alpha \parallel \beta$ and $\alpha \subset \mathscr{B}'$; plane β is not contained in $\mathscr{C}'$.

b $\alpha \parallel \beta$; $\alpha \subset \mathscr{B}'$; $\beta \subset \mathscr{C}'$.

c Line $t = \alpha \cap \beta$, and $\mathscr{C}' \cap \mathscr{B}'$ is the interior of the acute dihedral angle $\sphericalangle \alpha't\beta'$, where α' and β' are open half-planes determined by t.

**Similarity 30/7
mappings** When we first considered a correspondence of two triangles, say, $ABC \leftrightarrow DEF$, we defined it in terms of vertices corresponding with vertices, sides with sides, and angles with angles. We then found conditions under which the correspondence was a congruence. From our present point of view, if $\triangle ABC$ is in the domain of any distance-preserving mapping Γ and if (A, D), (B, E), and (C, F) belong to Γ, then not only is $ABC \leftrightarrow DEF$ a congruence but also any subset $\mathscr{C}$ of $\triangle ABC$ is congruent to its image set $\mathscr{C}\Gamma$ in $\triangle DEF$.

Since correspondences were used to define similar triangles and polygons, it is natural to think that there should be mappings of space that map figures onto similar figures in much the same way that distance-preserving mappings map figures onto congruent figures. From the side, side, side similarity theorem for triangles, one would expect, for example, that a mapping of space that tripled all distances would have to map any triangle onto a similar triangle. We use this idea to define mappings called *similarities*.

Definition 140/7 *Similarity mapping**

A mapping Γ is a similarity mapping if there exists a
positive number k such that, for every pair of points P and
Q in the domain of Γ, $d(P\Gamma, Q\Gamma) = k\, d(P, Q)$. The
number k is called the "similarity ratio," or simply the "ratio,"
of the mapping.†

From the definition of a similarity mapping, Theorem 199/7
is at once apparent.

Theorem 199/7

If Γ is a similarity mapping of ratio k, then Γ^{-1} is a
similarity mapping of ratio $\dfrac{1}{k}$.

Proof

Let A and B denote two points in the domain of Γ^{-1}. These
are the respective images under Γ of two points P and Q in
the domain of Γ. Because Γ is a similarity mapping
of ratio k,

1 $d(P\Gamma, Q\Gamma) = d(A, B) = k\, d(P, Q).$

Therefore, since $k \neq 0$,

2 $d(P, Q) = \dfrac{1}{k} d(A, B).$

But from the relation of Γ and Γ^{-1}, points P and Q are the
images of A and B under Γ^{-1}. Therefore, statement 2
can be expressed as

3 $d(A\Gamma^{-1}, B\Gamma^{-1}) = \dfrac{1}{k} d(A, B),$

which shows that Γ^{-1} is a similarity mapping of ratio $\dfrac{1}{k}$.

Now all of the theory that we saw in the previous sections
for distance-preserving motions holds again for similarities.
Theorem 200/7 is an example of this.

Theorem 200/7

If Γ is a similarity mapping of ratio k, then point C is
between A and B in the domain of Γ if and only if its
image point $C\Gamma$ is between the images $A\Gamma$ and $B\Gamma$.

---

* Such a mapping also is called a *similitude*.
† The similarity ratio also is called the *proportionality constant* of the mapping.

Proof

Let A' denote $A\Gamma$, let B' denote $B\Gamma$, and let C' denote $C\Gamma$.
By Corollary 59/3 and the definition of betweenness for
points, C is between A and B if and only if
1 $d(A, C) + d(C, B) = d(A, B)$;
and, therefore, if and only if
2 $k\,d(A, C) + k\,d(C, B) = k\,d(A, B)$;
and, therefore, if and only if
3 $d(A', C') + d(C', B') = d(A', B')$;
and, therefore, if and only if C' is between A' and B'.

Theorem 200/7 implies that, in a similarity mapping Γ, the
image of a line AB is contained in the line $A'B'$. The fact that
$(AB)\Gamma$ is the whole line $A'B'$ will follow from a lemma just as it
did before.

* Lemma 201/7

If P, Q, and R are three collinear points and if $d(A, B) = k\,d(P, Q)$,
where k is a positive number, then there is exactly one point C
in line AB such that $d(A, C) = k\,d(P, R)$ and $d(B, C) = k\,d(Q, R)$.

Theorem 201/7

The image of a line in a similarity mapping is a line.

Proof

Let Γ denote a similarity mapping of ratio k and let P, Q,
and R denote three points in a line t in the domain of Γ.
Then one of the points is between the other two. And,
by Theorem 200/7, its image is between the images of the
other two points. Therefore, the set $t' = t\Gamma$ is contained
in the line $P'Q'$, where P' and Q' are the images of P and Q.

Let W denote a point of $P'Q'$ that is distinct from P'
and Q'. Then one of the numbers $d(P', Q')$, $d(P', W)$, and
$d(Q', W)$ is the sum of the other two. So one of the numbers
$\frac{1}{k}d(P', Q')$, $\frac{1}{k}d(P', W)$, and $\frac{1}{k}d(Q', W)$ is the sum of
the other two. From this and the fact that
$d(P, Q) = \frac{1}{k}d(P', Q')$, it follows, from Lemma 201/7, that
there is a point H in line PQ such that
1 $d(P, H) = \frac{1}{k}d(P', W)$ and $d(Q, H) = \frac{1}{k}d(Q', W)$.

Point H has an image $H' = H\Gamma$, and because
$d(P', H') = k\,d(P, H)$ and $d(Q', H') = k\,d(Q, H)$, it follows
from statement 1 that
2 $d(P', H') = d(P', W)$ and $d(Q', H') = d(Q', W)$.

414

By Lemma 191/7, there is only one point in line $P'H'$ at the distance $d(P', W)$ from P' and also at the distance $d(Q', W)$ from Q'. Therefore, $W = H'$, so W is the image of a point in t. Since every point of line $P'Q'$ is the image of a point in t, line $P'Q'$ is the image of t.

Corollary 201/7

In a similarity mapping, segments, open rays, and closed rays are mapped respectively onto segments, open rays, and closed rays.

Exercises

1 A similarity mapping Ψ of ratio 3 maps the noncollinear points A, B, and C onto A', B', and C'.

a What is the length of $\overline{A'B'}$ if $d(A, B) = 1$? If $d(A, B) = \frac{1}{10}$? If $d(A, B) = 8\pi$? *Answer*

b What is the length of $\overline{AB}$ if $d(A', B') = 18$? If $d(A', B') = 10$? If $d(A', B') = \sqrt{2}$?

c What is the perimeter of $\triangle A'B'C'$ if the perimeter of $\triangle ABC$ is 11? Is 100? Is $\pi\sqrt{5}$?

d By what similarity theorem is $\triangle A'B'C' \sim \triangle ABC$?

e Is $\measuredangle A'B'C'^\circ = 3\measuredangle ABC^\circ$?

2 Let the set of positive numbers $\{a, b, c\}$ be called a *linear set* if one of the numbers is the sum of the other two. Let this set be called a *triangular set* if the sum of each two is greater than the third.

a Give an example of a linear set, of a triangular set, and of a set that is neither linear nor triangular.

b If k is a positive number, prove that $\{a, b, c\}$ and $\{ka, kb, kc\}$ are both linear, are both triangular, or are both neither linear nor triangular.

c If A, B, and C are three points and if $a = d(B, C)$, $b = d(C, A)$, and $c = d(A, B)$, must $\{a, b, c\}$ be either linear or triangular? Why?

d If A', B', and C' are the images of A, B, and C in a similarity mapping of ratio k and if $a' = d(B', C')$, $b' = d(C', A')$, and $c' = d(A', B')$, must $\{a, b, c\}$ and $\{a', b', c'\}$ both be linear? Must they both be triangular? Why?

3 In plane α, let $ABCD$ denote a quadrilateral that is in the domain of a similarity mapping Γ of ratio k, and let A', B', C', and D' denote the images of A, B, C, and D respectively. Use this information and exercise 2 in connection with the following questions.

a Why must the number set $\{d(A', B'), d(B', C'), d(C', A')\}$ be triangular? Does this conclusion imply that A', B', and C' are noncollinear?

415

b Let β be the plane of A', B', and C'. If $M = AC \cap BD$, why is $\{d(A', M'), d(M', C'), d(A', C')\}$ a linear triple? Does this imply that M' is a third point of line $A'C'$?

c Under the conditions given in exercise 3b, why is $\{d(B', M'), d(M', D'), d(B', D')\}$ a linear triple? Why does this conclusion imply that D' is in β?

d For each point P in $\overline{CD}$, the distance set $\{d(P, A), d(P, B), d(A, B)\}$ is triangular. How does this fact imply that $(\overline{CD})\Gamma$ cannot intersect line $A'B'$? (This reasoning shows that points in the C-side of AB must map onto points in the C'-side of $A'B'$.)

4 Let s and t denote two transversals of a family of parallel lines. A mapping Γ of s onto t is defined in which the image of any point X in s is the point X' in t that is the corresponding point to X. Let A and B denote two particular points of s, and let k be defined by $k = \dfrac{d(A', B')}{d(A, B)}$. If X and Y are any two points of s, prove that $d(X', Y') = k\, d(X, Y)$. Hence, show that Γ is a similarity mapping of s onto t.

5 If Γ is a similarity mapping of ratio k and Ψ is a similarity mapping of ratio m, then $\Gamma\Psi$, if it exists, is a similarity mapping of ratio km. Prove this fact for the special case where Γ is the mapping of A, B, and C onto D, E, and F respectively and where Ψ is the mapping of D, E, and F onto G, H, and I respectively.

6 a Use exercise 5 to explain why the product, if it exists, of a distance-preserving mapping and a similarity is a similarity.

b Under what conditions could the product of a similarity and a similarity be a distance-preserving mapping?

7 a Show that the mapping of a line onto itself given in coordinates by $x \to 3x - 5$ is a similarity mapping of ratio 3. *Answer*

b Show that any mapping of a line onto itself given in coordinates by $x \to ax + b$, where a and b are real numbers, and $a \neq 0$, is a similarity mapping. What is its ratio?

c Show that, if the mapping in exercise 7b is not distance preserving, then the mapping has a fixed point.

8 Let Γ_1 and Γ_2 denote similarity mappings of a line onto itself given in coordinates by $x\Gamma_1 = 3x + 2$ and $x\Gamma_2 = 5x - 1$. Express the similarity mapping $\Gamma_1\Gamma_2$ in coordinates. What are the fixed points of Γ_1, of Γ_2, and of $\Gamma_1\Gamma_2$? *Answer*

◆ **9** Show that, if the similarity mappings Γ_1 and Γ_2
of a line onto itself have the same ratio k
and one fixed point A in common, then the
similarity mappings Γ_1 and Γ_2 are not necessarily
the same similarity mapping.

In Theorem 192/7, we used the fact that a distance-preserving
mapping maps lines onto lines to prove that it also maps planes
onto planes. Now we have the fact that a similarity mapping maps
lines onto lines, and by a proof almost identical to that of
Theorem 192/7, one can prove that a similarity mapping also
maps planes onto planes.

---

* Theorem 202/7

In a similarity mapping, the image of a plane is a plane.

* Corollary 202a/7

A similarity mapping maps open and closed half-planes
onto open and closed half-planes respectively.

* Corollary 202b/7

A similarity mapping maps parallel lines onto parallel lines,
parallel planes onto parallel planes, a parallel line and
plane onto a parallel line and plane, and like-directed rays
onto like-directed rays.

Theorem 203/7

In a similarity mapping, the image of a triangle is a similar
triangle, and the image of an angle is a congruent angle.

Proof

Let Γ denote a similarity mapping of ratio k. If $\triangle ABC$ is in
the domain of Γ, then A, B, and C are noncollinear points
and so have noncollinear image points A', B', and C'
respectively. Since Γ preserves betweenness for points,
Γ maps $\overline{AB}$, $\overline{BC}$, and $\overline{CA}$ onto $\overline{A'B'}$, $\overline{B'C'}$, and $\overline{C'A'}$ respectively.
Thus $\triangle A'B'C' = (\triangle ABC)\Gamma$. From the definition of Γ,

1 $\dfrac{d(A', B')}{d(A, B)} = \dfrac{d(B', C')}{d(B, C)} = \dfrac{d(C', A')}{d(C, A)} = k.$

So, by the side, side, side similarity theorem,

2 $\triangle A'B'C' \sim \triangle ABC.$

If $\sphericalangle PQR$ is in the domain of Γ, then P, Q, and R are
noncollinear. As a result, their images P', Q', and R'
also are noncollinear. From the similarity
just established,

3 $\triangle P'Q'R' \sim \triangle PQR.$

Statement 3 implies

4 $\sphericalangle P'Q'R' \cong \sphericalangle PQR.$

Therefore, $\sphericalangle PQR$ is mapped by Γ onto a congruent angle.

Corollary 203/7

Perpendicularity of lines, of planes, and of lines and planes
is invariant in a similarity mapping.

Because of the properties we now have for similarity mappings,
we make the following definition.

Definition 141/7 *Similar sets*

If a set $\mathcal{S}$ is the image of a set $\mathcal{R}$ in a similarity mapping,
then $\mathcal{R}$ and $\mathcal{S}$ are similar sets.

Convention

We will denote that two sets $\mathcal{R}$ and $\mathcal{S}$ are similar sets by
the sentence $\mathcal{R} \sim \mathcal{S}$.

To establish the agreement of this general meaning of similarity with our previous one, we would have to show that there
always is a similarity mapping of a polygon onto a similar polygon.
This can be proved by an argument that resembles the one we
described for congruence.

The only similarity of space we will define in the formal system
is the following type, which is called an *expansion* or a *contraction*
at a point. However, it can be proved that every similarity of
space is either of this type or is a mapping of this type followed
or preceded by a motion of space.

Definition 142/7 *Expansion or contraction of space at a point*

Corresponding to a point O and a positive number k, an
expansion or a contraction of space at O is a mapping
defined as follows:
Point O is its own image, and P different
from O is mapped onto P' in the closed
ray $\overrightarrow{OP}$ such that $d(O, P') = k\, d(O, P)$.
If $k > 1$, the mapping is an expansion.
If $k < 1$, the mapping is a contraction.
For $k = 1$, the mapping is the identity.
The number k is the ratio of
expansion or contraction. (D547)

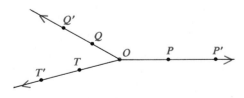

Diagram 547

Theorem 204/7

An expansion or a contraction of space at a point is a
similarity mapping.

Proof

Let Γ denote an expansion of space at point O with ratio k.
We will prove that Γ is a similarity mapping without using
the fact that $k > 1$. In this way, the same proof will hold
for contractions or for $k = 1$.

Let A and B denote two points with images $A' = A\Gamma$ and $B' = B\Gamma$. The points A, B, and O are either collinear or noncollinear.

Case ɪ The points A and B are collinear with O.

In the line t of O, A, and B, there is a coordinate system in which O is the origin and has coordinate zero. Points A and B have coordinates a and b respectively. Let a' and b' denote the coordinates of A' and B' respectively.

Since $d(O, A) = |a|$, $d(O, A') = |a'|$, and, by the definition of Γ, $d(O, A') = k\, d(O, A)$, we have

1 $|a'| = k|a|$.

Therefore, $a' = ka$ or $a' = -ka$. But because $\overrightarrow{OA}$ and $\overrightarrow{OA'}$ are like-directed closed rays, a and a' have the same sign. And since k is positive, it follows that

2 $a' = ka$.

The relation of statement 2 also is correct if $A' = O$, for then $A = O$, $a' = 0$, $a = 0$, and $a' = ka$.

By the same reasoning,

3 $b' = kb$.

Then

4 $d(A', B') = |b' - a'| = |kb - ka| = k|b - a| = k\, d(A, B)$.

Case ɪɪ Points A and B are noncollinear with O. (ᴅ548a)

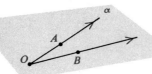

Diagram 548a   548b

Then A, O, and B determine a plane α, which is the plane of $\sphericalangle AOB$. By the definition of Γ, A' is in $\overrightarrow{OA}$ and B' is in $\overrightarrow{OB}$. Because

5 $\dfrac{d(O, A')}{d(O, A)} = \dfrac{d(O, B')}{d(O, B)} = k,$

it follows, from the side, angle, side similarity theorem, that

6 $\triangle A'OB' \sim \triangle AOB$.

Therefore,

7 $\dfrac{d(A', B')}{d(A, B)} = \dfrac{d(O, A')}{d(O, A)} = \dfrac{d(O, B')}{d(O, B)} = k.$

So

8 $d(A', B') = k\, d(A, B)$.

Since, in all cases, $d(A', B') = k\, d(A, B)$, the mapping Γ is a similarity mapping of ratio k.

By using the expansions and contractions of space in combination with motions, we can produce copies of a set to any scale we choose and at any location in space. As just one example, the familiar situation of projecting a slide onto a parallel screen now can be regarded as just part of an expansion of space at the source of the light (D549). The ratio of expansion k of the mapping gives

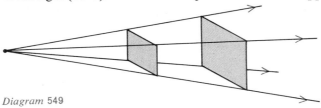

Diagram 549

you the similarity ratio between the image picture and the picture on the slide. This also is the ratio of the distances of the screen and the slide from the light.

Exercises

1 If Γ denotes a similarity mapping of ratio k from domain $\mathcal{R}$ to range $\mathcal{S}$, and A' denotes $A\Gamma$, which of the following statements are necessarily correct?

  a $d(A, B) = k\, d(A', B')$.

  b Γ^{-1} is a similarity mapping of ratio $\dfrac{1}{k}$.

  c If $<A', B', C'>$, then $<A, B, C>$.

  d $AB = A'B'$.

  e $AB \sim A'B'$.

  f $(AB)\Gamma \cong A'B'$.

  g $\{A, B, C\} \sim \{A', B', C'\}$.

  h $\alpha(A, B, C)\Gamma = \beta(A', B', C')$.

  i If $AB \parallel CD$, then $A'B' \parallel C'D'$.

  j $\triangle ABC \cong \triangle A'B'C'$.

  k $\sphericalangle EFG \cong \sphericalangle E'F'G'$.

  l $\sphericalangle EFG \sim \sphericalangle E'F'G'$.

  m $\mathcal{R} \sim \mathcal{S}$.

  n $d(A', B') + d(B', C') = k\, d(A, C)$.

2 In a coordinatized line let the points A, B, C, and D have the respective coordinates $a = 1$, $b = -3$, $c = 5$, and $d = 6$. If Γ, Φ, and Ψ are respectively the mappings

$x \rightarrow -x$, $x \rightarrow x + 6$, and $x \rightarrow \dfrac{x}{4} + \dfrac{15}{4}$, check that $a\Gamma\Phi\Psi = c$

and that $b\Gamma\Phi\Psi = d$. Show that $\Gamma\Phi\Psi$ is a similarity of the line onto itself. With diagrams, show the steps by which the similarity mapping $\Gamma\Phi\Psi$ takes $\overline{AB}$ onto $\overline{CD}$.

420

3 Suppose that it is desired to find the distance from A to B across the lake pictured in D550. Let C denote a point outside the lake such that a contraction at C in the ratio k maps A onto A' and B onto B' so $\overline{A'B'}$ is outside the lake. How does $d(A', B')$, which can be measured directly, provide a way to find $d(A, B)$?

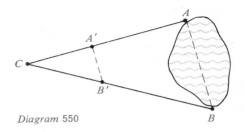

Diagram 550

4 a If $C(P, r)$ is a given circle and $\triangle ABC$ is a given coplanar triangle, use mappings to prove that there exists a triangle that is inscribed in the circle and is similar to $\triangle ABC$.

b Explain why any two circles or any two spheres are similar sets.

5 Let the mapping Γ of a line t onto itself be expressed in coordinates by $x \rightarrow kx + (1 - k)a$ where a is any real number and k is a positive number.

a Show that Γ is the identity mapping if and only if $k = 1$.

b If $k \neq 1$, show that point A with coordinate a is the only fixed point. *Answer*

c Show that, if $x > a$, then $x\Gamma > a$. Also show that, if $x < a$, then $x\Gamma < a$. Hence, show that each side of A in t maps onto itself.

d Show that $d(A, X') = k\,d(A, X)$. Hence, Γ is either the expansion or the contraction of t at A in the ratio k.

6 a In terms of coordinates, define the mapping Γ that is the contraction of a coordinatized line t at the point with coordinate -1 in the ratio $\frac{1}{2}$.

b If Ψ is the mapping of t onto itself given in coordinates by $x \rightarrow 4x - 12$, show that Ψ is an expansion of t. Find the coordinate of the fixed point and the ratio of expansion. *Answer*

c Is $\Gamma\Psi$ an expansion or a contraction of t? If it is an expansion or a contraction, what is its ratio and what is the coordinate of the fixed point?

7 Let P denote a point interior to $\angle AOB$ (D551). Justify the following argument of the statement "There are two circles that pass through P and are tangent to both of the lines OA and OB."

Let Q denote any point in $\overrightarrow{OX}$ that bisects $\angle AOB$. Let F denote the foot in OB of Q.

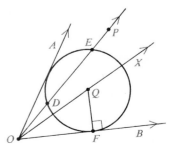

Diagram 551

421

The circle $C(Q, r)$, where $r = d(Q, F)$, is tangent to OA and
OB and is intersected by $\overrightarrow{OP}$ in two points D and E.
The expansion or the contraction of the plane at O that maps
D onto P and the expansion or contraction that maps E onto P
map $C(Q, r)$ onto circles that pass through P and are tangent to OA
and OB. Since the images of $C(Q, r)$ are different under the
two mappings, there are two solution circles.

8 If Γ is the expansion or the contraction of space at O
in the ratio k, $k > 0$, and if Ψ is the reflection of
space in O, the product $\Gamma\Psi$ sometimes is called a
reversed contraction or expansion.

  a Is $\Gamma\Psi$ the same mapping as $\Psi\Gamma$?

  b What points, lines, and planes are invariant under Γ? Under $\Gamma\Psi$?

  c Find the reversed expansion of a coordinatized line at
the point A with coordinate $a = 3$ in the ratio $k = 2$. *Answer*

♦ **9 a** Prove that, if F is a foot in set $\mathcal{S}$ of point P and Γ
is a similarity mapping, then $F\Gamma$ is a foot in $\mathcal{S}\Gamma$ of $P\Gamma$. *Answer*

  b Does a similarity mapping Γ map a point, a line, or
a plane of symmetry of $\mathcal{S}$ onto a corresponding point,
line, or plane of symmetry of $\mathcal{S}\Gamma$?

♦ **10** From Lemma 201/7, it follows that a similarity mapping Γ
of line s onto line t is completely determined if
two points in s have known images in line t. Let Γ
denote a similarity mapping of a coordinatized line
onto itself. In this mapping, points A and B with
coordinates $a = 4$ and $b = 5$ map onto points A' and B'
with coordinates $a' = 2$ and $b' = -1$. Find the expression
for Γ in the following ways.

  a As the product $\Psi\Phi$, where Ψ is the reflection in the point C
with coordinate $c = 3$ and Φ is the expansion at A' in the ratio 3

  b As the product $\Psi_1\Psi_2\Psi_3$, where Ψ_1 is the
translation of A onto A', Ψ_2 is the expansion at A'
in the ratio 3, and Ψ_3 is the reflection in A'

  c Define a product different from those in exercises 10a
and 10b that will produce Γ.

Some other 31/7
    uses of We want to mention just a few of the places where you again will
  mappings encounter mappings if you continue the study of mathematics.

    Functions A mapping in which the domain and the range are sets of num-
bers is a special type of function. If the mapping is the set of
ordered pairs (C, F), where $F = \frac{9}{5}C + 32$, the set is a mapping

of centigrade temperatures onto Fahrenheit. The inverse mapping is the set of pairs (F, C) given by $C = \frac{5}{9}(F - 32)$. This mapping is called the inverse function. Functions have properties other than those we have considered, but the mapping notion enters naturally and can be extended to define general functions.

Vectors   By associating, in turn, each two directions $\overset{\cdot\rightarrow\cdot}{AB}$ and $\overset{\cdot\rightarrow\cdot}{BA}$ with the segment $\overline{AB}$, we can define two directed segments that are determined by A and B. These are denoted by $\overrightarrow{AB}$ and $\overrightarrow{BA}$ and are called *vectors*.*

A translation of space Γ can be represented by a vector $\overrightarrow{AB}$ with the understanding that the direction of the translation is that of the vector and the amount of the translation is the length of the vector. Any other vector of the same length and direction would then represent the same translation, and two such vectors are *equivalent*. If $\overrightarrow{AB}$ represents one translation Γ of space and $\overrightarrow{CD}$ represents another translation Ψ, then there is a vector $\overrightarrow{BE}$ that is equivalent to $\overrightarrow{CD}$ (D552). Since Γ maps A onto B and Ψ maps

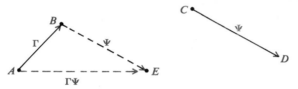

Diagram 552

B onto E, the product $\Gamma\Psi$ maps A onto E. Because a translation is completely determined by one point and its image, the product $\Gamma\Psi$ is represented by $\overrightarrow{AE}$. This is a general way of combining two vectors geometrically, and $\overrightarrow{AE}$ is called the *resultant*, or the *vector sum*, of $\overrightarrow{AB}$ and $\overrightarrow{CD}$.

If a vector $\overrightarrow{AF}$ is equivalent to $\overrightarrow{CD}$, then, by the properties of parallelograms, $\overrightarrow{FE}$ is equivalent to $\overrightarrow{AB}$ (D553). Therefore, the resultant of $\overrightarrow{AB}$ and $\overrightarrow{AF}$ is $\overrightarrow{AE}$. We know that, in general, $\Gamma\Psi \neq \Psi\Gamma$.

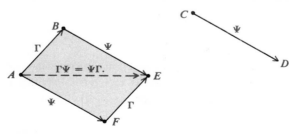

Diagram 553

---

* The symbol $\overrightarrow{AB}$ is a standard notation for the vector from A to B. This is one reason why we did not use this symbol for denoting a ray.

423

However, D553 clearly shows that for translations the product ΓΨ is the product ΨΓ. (The product of translations is commutative.)

In physics, vectors often are used to represent forces. In such cases, the length of the vector gives the amount of a force, and the direction of the vector gives the direction in which the force acts. The parallelogram *AFEB* then is a representation of the *parallelogram law* for combining two forces $\overrightarrow{AB}$ and $\overrightarrow{AF}$ (D553). The diagonal vector $\overrightarrow{AE}$ represents the magnitude and the direction of a single force that has the same effect as the two forces $\overrightarrow{AB}$ and $\overrightarrow{AF}$.

Vectors can be defined in an independent way, and their uses to represent translations or forces are just particular applications. In geometry, vectors are particularly useful in the study of surfaces and the study of curves that are not in a plane, for example, a circular staircase.

Projective geometry Let O denote a point that is not in either of two parallel planes α and β. For each X in α, the line OX intersects β at a point X', and the mapping $X \rightarrow X'$ is a similarity mapping of α onto β (D554). But suppose that α and β are any two intersecting planes

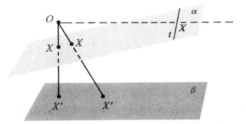

Diagram 554

and that point O is in neither of these planes. A general line through O intersects α at X and intersects β at X'. If X' is taken as the image of X, you get a *projective mapping* of points of α onto points of β. This is not quite a mapping of α onto β, since there is a line t of points X in α for which OX is parallel to β. These points X have no image. However, for points in α that do have images, the mapping preserves collinearity, but it does not preserve distance or the ratio of distances.

The study of properties that are invariant under such mappings is the subject of projective geometry. Distance plays no part in this geometry, and the theorems deal with properties of lines, curves, and surfaces that are expressed entirely by intersections of sets (which are invariant in all one-to-one mappings). To give an example of a projective theorem, consider the following: If A, B, and C are three points of line s in plane α and A', B', and C' are three points of line t in α (D555), then the intersection of

AB' and *A'B*, of *BC'* and *B'C*, and of *CA'* and *C'A* will be collinear if the intersections exist (Theorem of Pappus).

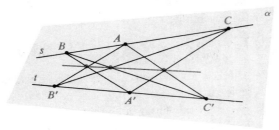

Diagram 555

Conformal One can define an *angle between two curves* as an angle between
mappings the lines tangent to the curves at a point of intersection of the
curves. There are mappings called *conformal* that preserve angles
in this sense, though they may not preserve distances or collinearity. These mappings play an important part in applied
mathematics, for example, in physics and in engineering.

To give an example of how angles may be unchanged in a very
general mapping, suppose that $\overline{AB}$ is a diameter of a sphere
$S(P, r)$ and that α is the plane through P that is perpendicular to
$\overline{AB}$ (D556). Let each point X of the sphere in the B-side of α be
mapped onto the point X' in which the line AX intersects α.

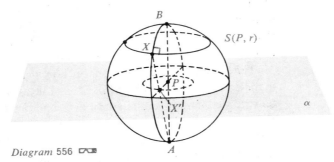

Diagram 556

If α is thought of as the plane of the equator, then the plane
sections of the sphere in planes parallel to α correspond to the
circles of latitude (small circles of the sphere). All of these circles
map onto circles in α with center P. The plane sections of the
sphere in planes through line AB correspond to the circles of
longitude (great circles of the sphere). The halves of these great
circles in the B-side of α map onto segments in α with center P.
Each circle of latitude is perpendicular to each circle of longitude,*
and this is still true of their images.

---

* Two curves that meet so that their tangent lines form a right angle are said to be *orthogonal*
curves.

425

Groups Suppose that one has a collection $\mathcal{S}$ of elements $a, b, c, \ldots$ and has some way of combining pairs of elements to form a new element, say, $a \otimes b$. Then $\mathcal{S}$ is said to form a *group* with respect to the combining rule "$\otimes$" if the following are true.

1) For each pair a and b in $\mathcal{S}$, the combination $a \otimes b$ also is in $\mathcal{S}$. (Closure property)
2) There is an element e in $\mathcal{S}$, called an identity element, such that for every a in $\mathcal{S}$, $e \otimes a = a$. (Identity property)
3) For each element a in $\mathcal{S}$, there exists an element a', called the inverse of a, such that $a' \otimes a = e$. (Inverse property)
4) For any elements a, b, and c in $\mathcal{S}$, it is correct that $a \otimes (b \otimes c) = (a \otimes b) \otimes c$. (Associative property)

It is easy to verify that the collection of all the mappings of a set $\mathcal{R}$ onto itself forms a group if the rule of combining two mappings is to form their product. Since this product is again a mapping of $\mathcal{R}$ onto itself, the closure property is satisfied. The element e of the identity property is the identity mapping I. The inverse of any mapping Γ is Γ^{-1}, and this satisfies the inverse property. By the definition for products of mappings, the associative property is correct.

To give a different example, the set of real numbers forms a group when the rule for combining two of these numbers is to form their sum, that is, when the rule is $a \otimes b = a + b$. The identity element is 0, since $0 + a = a$, and the inverse of any element a is $(-a)$, since $(-a) + a = 0$. The associative property is just the fact that $a + (b + c) = (a + b) + c$.

The motions of Euclidean space form a group, and the mathematician Felix Klein pointed out that Euclidean geometry could be regarded simply as the study of properties that are invariant under motions of this group. He suggested that other parts of mathematics also might be classified in terms of the invariants of different groups. A program to carry out this classification that was called the *Erlanger program* had tremendous importance in showing mathematicians the unity in different subjects and in revealing unsuspected connections between different parts of mathematics.

Topology If $\mathcal{S}$ denotes a set of points and if the interior of every sphere centered at P contains in its interior a point of $\mathcal{S}$ that is not P, then P is defined as a *limit point* to the set $\mathcal{S}$. For example, every boundary point of a plane convex figure is a limit point to the figure and also to the set of interior points of the figure.

If a mapping Γ and its inverse are one-to-one mappings that preserve limit points, that is, if each mapping maps any limit point to a set onto a limit point to the image set, then they are said to be *topological mappings*. The study of the invariants of these mappings is called *topology*. If you think of an object $\mathcal{C}$ made of rubber and call the object $\mathcal{C}'$ after it has been stretched and twisted in some manner, then each point P in $\mathcal{C}$ has a position P' in $\mathcal{C}'$ and the mapping $P \rightarrow P'$ is a topological mapping of $\mathcal{C}$ onto $\mathcal{C}'$. For this reason, topology is sometimes called "rubber geometry."

One can get an idea of the generality of topology in the following way. Let $\mathcal{S}$ denote the set of all one-to-one mappings of Euclidean space onto itself. Then $\mathcal{S}$ is a group with respect to combining two mappings by forming their product. All of the mappings in $\mathcal{S}$ that are motions of space form a group $\mathcal{S}_1$. All of the motions in $\mathcal{S}$ that are similarity mappings form a group $\mathcal{S}_2$. All of the mappings in $\mathcal{S}$ that are topological mappings form a group $\mathcal{S}_3$.

Every motion is a similarity mapping, but not conversely. Therefore, $\mathcal{S}_1$ is called a *proper subgroup* of $\mathcal{S}_2$. Each of the similarity mappings is a topological mapping, but not conversely. Consequently, $\mathcal{S}_2$ is a proper subgroup of $\mathcal{S}_3$. In turn, $\mathcal{S}_3$ is a proper subgroup of $\mathcal{S}$.

Any invariant of a group automatically is an invariant of all the subgroups. As you proceed to larger and larger groups, you find fewer invariants but, in a sense, "deeper" ones. And you get a truer perspective of the part of mathematics to which a property really belongs when you find the largest group in which it is an invariant. To give an example of this, consider the following. Suppose that $C(P, r)$ is any circle and that $\triangle ABC$ is any triangle. Then there exists a triangle that is similar to $\triangle ABC$ and is such that all three vertices belong to the circle. But this also can be proved if $C(P, r)$ is replaced by any simple, closed, plane curve

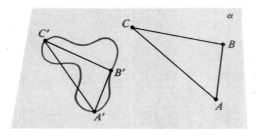

Diagram 557

(D557). So the property does not really "belong" to circles, but is a topological property of all simple, closed, plane curves.

427

Chapter review

1 In each of the following, what is the value of x if Γ is the mapping of a line onto itself expressed in terms of coordinates by the set of all pairs $(x, 2x + 8)$?

a $x\Gamma = 8.$ e $(\frac{1}{2})\Gamma = x.$

b $10\Gamma = x.$ f $\pi\Gamma = x^2.$

c $x\Gamma = -1.$ g $x\Gamma > 0.$

d $x\Gamma = x.$ h $x\Gamma = 2x + 8.$

2 Consider a mapping of the set of all positive odd integers $D = \{1, 3, 5, 7, \ldots\}$ onto the set of all positive even integers $R = \{2, 4, 6, 8, \ldots\}$. In this mapping, each number x in D is mapped onto the number $x + 1$ in R.

a Is this mapping the set of all ordered pairs (x, y) such that $y = x + 1$ and x is a number in D?

b Does this mapping preserve betweenness? (That is, if x, y, and z are numbers in D, does $\langle x, y, z \rangle$ imply $\langle x + 1, y + 1, z + 1 \rangle$?)

c Let *3-divisibility* of two numbers a and b be defined to mean that $\dfrac{a + b}{3}$ is a positive integer. Name the two least numbers of D that have 3-divisibility. Is 3-divisibility of number pairs preserved by this mapping?

d What is the image of 47? Of set D?

3 Assume that a mapping Ψ is defined by $\{(A, A), (B, C), (C, B), (D, E), (F, F)\}$. Select from the list "$\{A, F\}, \{A, B, C, D, F\}, \{A, C, B, E, F\}, \{A, B, C, F\}, B, C$" those sets or points that correctly complete the following statements.

a Each point of the set ~~~ is a fixed point of Ψ.

b The set ~~~ is an invariant set of Ψ.

c The set ~~~ is a pointwise invariant set of Ψ.

d The domain of the inverse of Ψ is the set ~~~.

e $C\Psi^{-1} = $ ~~~.

4 What is the value of x in each of the following if the mappings Γ and Ψ are defined on the set of real numbers as $x\Gamma = x^2 + 1$ and $x\Psi = 3x - 5$?

a $3\Gamma\Psi = x.$ d $2\Psi\Gamma\Psi = x.$

b $(-2)\Psi\Gamma = x.$ e $x\Gamma = x\Psi + x^2.$

c $x\Gamma\Psi = 46.$ f $x\Gamma - 4 = x\Psi.$

5 Let Ψ be a mapping of a line t onto itself given in coordinates by the ordered pairs $(x, 2x + 1)$. Also, with each set $\mathcal{D}$ of two points A and B in t, associate the measure $m(\mathcal{D}) = d(A, B)$.

a If the coordinates of A and B are $a = 4$ and $b = 6$ respectively, what are the values of $a\Psi$ and $b\Psi$?

b What is $m(\mathfrak{D})$ if the coordinates of A and B in t are -5 and 8 respectively?

c If $\mathfrak{D}\Psi = \{A\Psi, B\Psi\}$ and the coordinates of A and B in t are 4 and 6 respectively, what is $m(\mathfrak{D}\Psi)$?

d Is $m(\mathfrak{D})$ invariant under Ψ?

6 If the two points P and Q are both in the domains of the distance-preserving mappings Γ and Ψ, which of the following are necessarily true (T), possibly true (P), or necessarily false (F)?

a $d(P, Q) = d(Q\Gamma, P\Gamma)$.

b $d(P, P\Psi) = d(Q, Q\Psi)$.

c $d(P, Q) = d(P\Gamma, Q\Psi)$.

d $d(P\Gamma, Q\Gamma) = d(P\Gamma\Psi, Q\Gamma\Psi)$.

e If the product $\Gamma\Psi$ exists, it is a distance-preserving mapping.

f Ψ^{-1} is a distance-preserving mapping.

g If R is in the domain of Γ, then $\langle P, Q, R \rangle$ if and only if $\langle P\Gamma, Q\Gamma, R\Gamma \rangle$.

7 Points R, P, and Q in line PQ have coordinates -10, -3, and 8 respectively, and points A and B in line AB have coordinates -2 and -13 respectively.

a Is $d(A, B) = d(P, Q)$?

b How many points C are there in AB such that $d(P, R) = d(A, C)$ and $d(Q, R) = d(B, C)$? Find the coordinate of each such point.

8 Lines AB and CD are parallel in plane α, and Γ is a motion of space. From the list "line, lines, plane, planes, $A\Gamma$, $B\Gamma$, $C\Gamma$, $D\Gamma$, $X\Gamma$, $A\Gamma B\Gamma$, $(AC)\Gamma$, $(CD)\Gamma$, $(AD)\Gamma$," select each item that correctly completes the following statements.

a $(AB)\Gamma$ is a $\sim\sim\sim$.

b $\alpha\Gamma$ is a $\sim\sim\sim$.

c $(AB)\Gamma$ and $(CD)\Gamma$ are parallel $\sim\sim\sim$.

d $AB \cong \sim\sim\sim$ and $\sim\sim\sim \cong C$.

e If AC is perpendicular to CD, then $\sim\sim\sim$ is perpendicular to $\sim\sim\sim$.

f $\triangle ABD$ is congruent to the triangle determined by $\sim\sim\sim$, $\sim\sim\sim$, and $\sim\sim\sim$.

g If point X is between A and D, then $\sim\sim\sim$ is between $\sim\sim\sim$ and $\sim\sim\sim$.

9 If Φ denotes the reflection of $\triangle ABC$ in a plane α, which of the following statements are necessarily correct?

a If $A = A\Phi$, then A is in α.

b If $A \neq A\Phi$, then α bisects the segment $\overline{AA\Phi}$.

c If $C\Phi = B$, then $CB \perp AB$.

d If $\overline{CC\Phi} \cong \overline{BB\Phi}$, then $\overline{CB} \parallel \overline{C\Phi B\Phi}$.

e If $d(A, A\Phi) = d(B, B\Phi) = d(C, C\Phi)$, then the plane of $\triangle ABC$ either is α or is parallel to α.

10 Point A is in the circle $C(P, 8)$ and Ψ denotes the translation of space in the direction $\overrightarrow{PA}$ by the positive number k.

a If $P\Psi$ is in the segment $\overline{PA}$, what is the greatest possible value of k?

b If the circles $C(P, 8)$ and $C(P\Psi, 8)$ do not intersect in two points, what is the least possible value of k?

c If $k = 5$, then $d(P\Psi, A\Psi) = $ ~~~.

d If $d(P, A\Psi) = 14$, then $k = $ ~~~.

e If $BP \perp PA$ and $(B\Psi)A \perp PA$, then $k = $ ~~~.

11 The two points A and B are in a circle $C(P, 3)$ contained in a plane α and $\sphericalangle BPA^\circ = 60$. Let Φ denote a rotation of α about P such that $(\overrightarrow{PA})\Phi$ and $\overrightarrow{PB}$ are in the same side of PA. Let $\sphericalangle(A\Phi)PA^\circ = x$.

a What is the length of $\overline{AB}$? Of $\overline{A\Phi B\Phi}$? Are these two segments congruent for all possible values of x?

b What points of α are invariant under Φ?

c If $x = 5$, what is the measure of $\sphericalangle(B\Phi)P(A\Phi)$? Of $\sphericalangle BP(A\Phi)$?

d If $\sphericalangle(B\Phi)PA^\circ = 90$, what is $d(B\Phi, A)$?

12 Points A, B, C, D, and E in a line t have coordinates -2, -100, -7, 11, and 0 respectively. If Γ denotes a reflection of t in point A and Ψ denotes a reflection of t in point C, what are the coordinates of the following points?

a $D\Gamma$ **d** $B\Psi\Gamma$

b $E\Psi$ **e** $A\Gamma\Psi$

c $C\Gamma\Psi$ **f** $D\Psi\Gamma\Psi\Gamma$

13 If Γ denotes a similarity mapping of space of ratio $\frac{1}{2}$, which of the following are necessarily correct?

a $d(A, B) = \frac{1}{2} d(A\Gamma, B\Gamma)$ for any two points A and B in space.

b Γ^{-1} is a similarity mapping of space of ratio $(\frac{1}{2})^{-1}$.

c If $<A\Gamma, B\Gamma, C\Gamma>$, then $<A, B, C>$.

d The image of a line t is a line.

e $\sphericalangle ABC^\circ = \frac{1}{2}(\sphericalangle A\Gamma B\Gamma C\Gamma^\circ)$ for any angle $\sphericalangle ABC$.

f $\mathcal{R} \sim \mathcal{R}\Gamma$ for any set $\mathcal{R}$ in space.

14 If polygon $ABCD$ is a square in space and Φ denotes an expansion of space at point A of ratio 3, which of the following polygons are squares? Which are trapezoids? Find the maximum and minimum widths for each figure.

a $AB(C\Phi)D\Phi$ **c** $(ABCD)\Phi$

b $(A\Phi)(B\Phi)(C\Phi)D\Phi$ **d** $(A\Phi)B(C\Phi)D$

Cumulative review

1 The circle $C(O, r)$ is in a plane β. The three points A, B, and C are in the circle and $<A, O, B>$. If point D is in β, identify each of the following as a radius, a diameter, a chord, a secant, or a tangent of the circle.

   a $\overline{OC}$ d $\overline{AC}$

   b $\overline{AB}$ e AD if $AD \perp AB$

   c AC f $\overline{BD}$ if $d(B, O) + d(O, D) = 2r$

2 Let a, b, and c denote the lengths of the sides of a triangle and let p denote its perimeter. Which of the following are correct?

   a If $a = 2$ and $b = 3$, then $c > 5$.

   b If $a = 8$ and $b = 7$, then $c < 15$.

   c If $p = 20$, $a = 4$, and $b < 13$, then $c > 3$.

   d If $a > b > 3$, then $p > 9$.

   e If $a < 1$ and $b < 2$, then $p < 6$.

3 The ordered set of six points (A, B, C, D, E, F) are successive in a line t in that order and the successive segments $\overline{AB}$, $\overline{BC}$, $\overline{CD}$, $\overline{DE}$, and $\overline{EF}$ have the same length. The mappings Γ and Ψ are reflections of t onto itself in the points C and D respectively.

   a What point is $A\Gamma\Psi$?

   b Are any of the six points fixed in the mapping $\Psi\Gamma$?

   c What points of t are fixed in the mapping $\Psi\Gamma$?

   d Describe how $\Gamma\Psi\Psi\Gamma$ maps the six points.

   e For what integer n is F the midpoint of E and $A(\Gamma\Psi)^n$?

4 The two lines CC' and AA' intersect at B such that $<C', B, C>$, $<A', B, A>$, and $\angle ABC° = x$. The closed rays $\overrightarrow{BD}$ and $\overrightarrow{BE}$ bisect $\angle ABC$ and $\angle A'BC$ respectively.

   a If $\overrightarrow{BC}$ is the initial ray of a ray coordinate system for the A-side of CC', what is the coordinate of $\overrightarrow{BD}$? Of the ray opposite $\overrightarrow{BE}$?

   b If $\overrightarrow{BC}$ is the initial ray of a ray coordinate system for the A'-side of CC', what is the coordinate of $\overrightarrow{BA'}$? Of $\overrightarrow{BE}$?

   c If $\overrightarrow{BE}$ is the initial ray of a ray coordinate system for the C-side of BE, what is the ray coordinate of $\overrightarrow{BD}$? Of $\overrightarrow{BA}$?

5 The lengths of the sides $\overline{BC}$, $\overline{AB}$, and $\overline{AC}$ of $\triangle ABC$ are 6, 3, and 8 respectively. Point D in $\overrightarrow{CA}$ is such that $d(C, D) = 5$ and E in $\overline{BD}$ is such that $\overrightarrow{AE}$ bisects $\angle BAC$.

   a Prove that $\triangle BEA \cong \triangle DEA$.

   b If $\angle EAD° = x$, what is the measure of $\angle BDC$? Of $\angle EBA$?

   c Must $d(E, D)$ be greater than 1? Must $d(E, D)$ be less than $\frac{11}{2}$?

6 Indicate whether each of the following statements is necessarily true (T), possibly true (P), or necessarily false (F).

a The line through a vertex of a triangle and the midpoint of the opposite side is perpendicular to that side and bisects the vertex angle.

b Three angles of a triangle are congruent if and only if three sides are congruent.

c The three points A, B, and C are collinear if $d(A, B) = d(A, C)$.

d If the hypotenuse of $\triangle ABC$ is congruent to the hypotenuse of $\triangle DEF$ and $\measuredangle A \cong \measuredangle D$, then $\triangle ABC \cong \triangle DEF$.

e In the plane of $\triangle DEF$, point F is the only point whose distances from D and E are the numbers $d(F, D)$ and $d(F, E)$ respectively.

f The intersection of two closed half-planes is a ray.

7 The two lines r and s intersect at A and, in their plane, lines r' and s' are perpendicular to r and s at B and C respectively.

a Must r' intersect s'?

b Could $A = B$? Could $A = B = C$?

c If C is in r', must A, B, and C be noncollinear?

d If r' intersects s' at point D, could $ABCD$ be a rectangle? Could $ABCD$ be a trapezoid?

8 Assume that the distance between the two parallel lines AB and CD is 4, $d(A, B) = 3$, and $d(C, D) = 7$.

a If $d(A, C) = 5$, what are the possible values of $d(B, C)$?

b If $d(A, C) = 5$, what are the possible values of $d(B, D)$?

9 Consider the following possible conditions for a quadrilateral.

Condition 1: All of the sides are congruent.

Condition 2: All of the angles are congruent.

Condition 3: Each pair of opposite sides is parallel.

Condition 4: The diagonals are perpendicular.

a Which of these conditions imply that a quadrilateral is a parallelogram?

b Which of the other conditions are implied by condition 1?

c Which of the other conditions are implied by condition 4?

d Do conditions 2 and 3 together imply either condition 1 or condition 4?

10 From the information given in D558, which of the following statements are necessarily correct?

a $DE \parallel FG$.

b $FG \parallel BC$.

c $DE \parallel BC$.

d $\triangle ADE \sim \triangle ABC$.

e $\triangle AFG \sim \triangle ABC$.

f $\triangle ADE \sim \triangle AFG$.

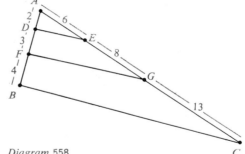

Diagram 558

432

11 The three points A, B, and C are collinear and DC is perpendicular to BC. If segments $\overline{AD}$, $\overline{BC}$, and $\overline{DC}$ have lengths $4\sqrt{5}$, 3, and 4 respectively, what are the possible values of $d(A, B)$?

12 If α and β denote parallel supporting lines of a tetrahedron $\mathcal{T}$, then the sets $\alpha \cap \mathcal{T}$ and $\beta \cap \mathcal{T}$ can be which of the following?

  a A point and a segment respectively

  b Each a point

  c Each a segment

  d A point and a full triangle respectively

13 The lengths of the sides $\overline{AB}$, $\overline{AC}$, and $\overline{BC}$ of $\triangle ABC$ are 8, 8, and 2 respectively. Let m and n denote two parallel supporting lines of $\triangle ABC$.

  a What is the maximum possible value of $d(m, n)$?

  b If $m = BC$, what is $d(m, n)$?

  c If $n = AC$, what is $d(m, n)$?

  d If $n \perp BC$, what is $d(m, n)$?

  e What is the minimum width of $\triangle ABC$?

14 Segments $\overline{AB}$ and $\overline{CD}$ are perpendicular diameters of the circle $C(O, 3)$ in a plane α. The mappings Γ, Ψ, and Φ are defined as follows.

  Γ: reflection of plane α in line AB

  Ψ: translation of α in the direction $\overrightarrow{OB}$ by the positive number 4

  Φ: expansion of α at O of ratio 5

Find the distance from C to each of the following points.

  a $C\Gamma$ **d** $C\Gamma\Phi$

  b $C\Gamma\Psi$ **e** $C\Psi\Phi$

  c $C\Phi$ **f** $C\Gamma\Psi\Phi$

Area **32/8**

The notion of the area of a plane figure S grew out of the need to have some way of expressing the amount of the plane "taken up" or "covered" by S. In physical terms, for example, this need was an obvious requirement in the buying and selling of land. To obtain some numerical measure of area, a particular type of region, usually a full square with unit sides, was taken to be a region of unit area. The area of a general region S then was the number of these unit regions that were contained in S in such a way that, roughly speaking, no two of them overlapped.

It is easy to see why an exact mathematical treatment of this idea is complicated. Think of the plane covered by unit squares (D559a). If S is a plane convex figure, then a certain number of the unit squares will be contained in S. However, in general,

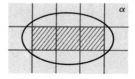

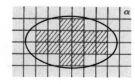

Diagram 559a   559b

these unit squares will not exactly cover S. If the plane is divided into nonoverlapping squares one-half unit on each side, then those squares inside the boundary of S will more nearly cover S than before. Again, though, the coverage need not be exact. One can see that, no matter how small a square is used, the boundary of the union of these squares will not be a smooth curve but will be made up of segments. So in the general case, one can never expect to get an exact coverage.

To see that a curved boundary is not the only reason for the difficulties, consider a full rectangle ^+ABCD where $d(A, B) = x = 3$ and $d(B, C) = y = 2$ (D560). Then the product $xy = 6$ gives the number of full unit squares that exactly cover the full rectangle.

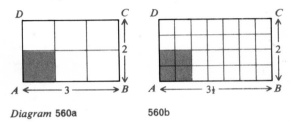

Diagram 560a   560b

But suppose that $x = 3\frac{1}{2}$ and $y = 2$. If squares that are one-half on each side are used, then exactly twenty-eight of these smaller squares cover the rectangle. Since it takes four of these smaller squares to cover a unit square, we can say that the area is $\frac{28}{4} = 7$ unit squares. Again, this number is just the product xy.

Now consider the case of a general rectangle whose sides have lengths x and y. If we can find a number z such that $\frac{x}{z} = m$ and $\frac{y}{z} = n$, where m and n are integers, then a full square with sides of length z can be used mn times to cover the full rectangle exactly. But if x and y are incommensurable, then, for every choice of z, one of the numbers, $\frac{x}{z}$ or $\frac{y}{z}$, is not an integer. For example, a rectangle with $x = \sqrt{2}$ and $y = 1$ cannot be covered exactly by placing whole squares side by side, no matter what size square is used.

All of these ideas point to the fact that one cannot treat area (or volume) problems in an exact mathematical way and with any real generality without using a theory of limits for sets of numbers. Since such a theory is beyond the purposes of this book, we will deal with area and volume in a formal way only for certain special figures and by means of some special axioms. In some other cases, we will indicate informally what the area and the volume formulas are when they are obtained by limit arguments.

We first will consider area for plane convex figures, and later we will extend the notion to other types of sets.

Axiom 16/8 *Additive area axiom*

Corresponding to a plane convex figure S, there is exactly one positive number that is the area of S. If S is the union of a finite number of plane convex figures, no two of which have an interior point in common, then the area of S is the sum of the areas of these plane convex figures.

Convention

We will denote the area of a general plane convex figure S by the notation $Ar(S)$. (D561) To simplify language and notation, the area of a polygon always will mean the area of the full polygon, and the area of the full polygon $^+P_1P_2P_3\ldots P_n$ will be denoted by the symbolism $Ar(P_1P_2P_3\ldots P_n)$.

$$Ar(S) = Ar(S_1) + Ar(S_2) + Ar(S_3) + Ar(S_4).$$

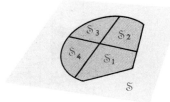

Convention

The sum or the product of segments always will mean the sum or the product of the lengths of the segments.

Diagram 561

We now assume the area formula for a rectangle, which, of course, is actually the formula for the area of a full rectangle.

Axiom 17/8

The area of a rectangle is the product of the lengths of two adjacent sides of the rectangle.

Comment

If one side of a rectangle is selected as the base, either of the adjacent sides is called the height. Therefore, the area of a rectangle often is said to be the product of the base and the height.

Since we have seen that mathematical congruence plays the role that corresponds to fitting one figure exactly on another, certainly the area of congruent figures should be the same. If we assume that this is true for congruent triangles, then we could prove that it is true for congruent polygons. However, we may as well assume the fact for general plane convex figures.

Axiom 18/8

If two plane convex figures have congruent boundaries, then the two figures have the same area.

From the area axioms, we now can easily obtain an area formula for right triangles. Then we can use the formula for right triangles to obtain an area formula for general triangles.

Theorem 205/8

The area of a right triangle is one half the product of its legs.* (D562)

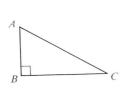

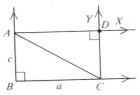

Diagram 562a   562b

Proof

Let $\triangle ABC$ denote a right triangle with hypotenuse $\overline{AC}$. Let $c = d(A, B)$, and let $a = d(B, C)$. The closed ray $\overrightarrow{AX}$ in the direction of $\overrightarrow{BC}$ and the closed ray $\overrightarrow{CY}$ in the direction of $\overrightarrow{BA}$ intersect at a point D so that $ABCD$ is a rectangle. The triangles $\triangle ABC$ and $\triangle CDA$ are congruent. Thus, by Axiom 18/8,

1 $Ar(\triangle ABC) = Ar(\triangle CDA)$.

Since the full rectangle $^{+}ABCD$ is the union of the full triangles $^{+}\triangle ABC$ and $^{+}\triangle CDA$ and these triangles intersect only in side $\overline{AC}$, by Axioms 16/8 and 17/8, we have

2 $Ar(\triangle ABC) + Ar(\triangle CDA) = Ar(ABCD) = ac$.

Then, from statement 1,

3 $2\, Ar(\triangle ABC) = ac$.

And so

4 $Ar(\triangle ABC) = \frac{1}{2}ac$.

Theorem 206/8

The area of a triangle is one half the product of any side and the altitude to that side. (D563)

Case 1

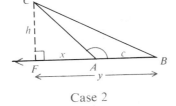

Case 2

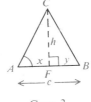

Case 3

Diagram 563

---

* Again recall that it is the full right triangular region that has area.

437

Proof

Let F denote the foot in line AB of the vertex C of $\triangle ABC$.
Let $h = d(C, F)$, $c = d(A, B)$, $x = d(A, F)$, and $y = d(F, B)$.

Case I   If F is A or B, then $\triangle ABC$ is a right triangle and $\overline{AB}$
and $\overline{CF}$ are its legs. So by Theorem 205/8,

1 $Ar(\triangle ABC) = \frac{1}{2}ch$.

Case II   If F is in the open ray opposite $\overrightarrow{AB}$, then A is
between F and B; so

2 $x + c = y$

and

3 $^+\triangle CFB = {}^+\triangle CFA \cup {}^+\triangle CAB$.

The interiors of $\triangle CFA$ and $\triangle CAB$ do not intersect. Therefore,

4 $Ar(\triangle CFB) = Ar(\triangle CFA) + Ar(\triangle CAB)$.

Applying Theorem 205/8 to the right triangles $\triangle CFB$ and $\triangle CFA$,
statement 4 can be expressed as

5 $\frac{1}{2}yh = \frac{1}{2}xh + Ar(\triangle CAB)$.

From statements 5 and 2, we obtain

6 $Ar(\triangle CAB) = \frac{1}{2}yh - \frac{1}{2}xh = \frac{1}{2}h(y - x) = \frac{1}{2}hc$.

Case III   If F is between A and B, then

7 $x + y = c$

and

8 $^+\triangle CAB = {}^+\triangle CAF \cup {}^+\triangle CFB$.

Since the interiors of $\triangle CAF$ and $\triangle CFB$ do not intersect,

9 $Ar(\triangle CAB) = Ar(\triangle CAF) + Ar(\triangle CFB)$.

Applying Theorem 205/8, we have

10 $Ar(\triangle CAB) = \frac{1}{2}xh + \frac{1}{2}yh = \frac{1}{2}h(x + y)$.

Statements 7 and 10 imply that

11 $Ar(\triangle CAB) = \frac{1}{2}hc$.

If F is in the open ray opposite $\overrightarrow{BA}$, the argument is
similar to the case when F is in the open ray opposite $\overrightarrow{AB}$.
In all cases, then,

12 $Ar(\triangle CAD) = \frac{1}{2}ch$.

Comment

If a side of a triangle is selected as a base, then the length
of the altitude to that side is called the height in relation
to the base, and the area of the triangle often is said
to be one half the base times the height.

Exercises

1 In each of the following, the lengths of two adjacent sides
   of a rectangle are given. What is the area of the rectangle?

   a 39 and 41   d $\sqrt{6}$ and $\sqrt{21}$ *Answer*
   b $2\frac{3}{4}$ and $5\frac{1}{3}$ e 0.09 and 0.012
   c π and $3\sqrt{7}$ f 1.06 and .5

2 Each number given below is the length of one side of a square. In each case, what is the area of the square?

a 63

b $7\frac{1}{3}$

c $9\sqrt{5}$ *Answer*

d $\pi\sqrt{\pi}$

e 0.001

f $1.5\sqrt{3}$

3 If the measure of a kitchen floor tile is 9 in. by 9 in., how many tiles are needed to cover a floor that is 12 ft. wide and 13 ft. long? Will a whole number of these tiles cover this floor exactly? What is the maximum size, in inches, that a square tile can be so that a whole number of them will cover the floor exactly?

4 a What is the area of a square $ABCD$ whose sides have length x?

b What is the area of a square $A'B'C'D'$ if its sides have length $2x$? Have length $3x$?

c How is the area of a square changed if its sides are doubled in length? If they are tripled in length? If they are divided by two?

5 What is the ratio of the area of a rectangle of base b and height h to the area of a rectangle that has the height and the base that are given in each of the following?

a Height, $2h$; base, b

b Base, $2b$; height, $2h$ *Answer*

c Base, $2b$; height, $3h$

6 The hypotenuse of right triangle $\triangle ABC$ is $\overline{AB}$, and the sides opposite A, B, and C have lengths a, b, and c respectively. Find the area of $\triangle ABC$ for each of the following cases.

a $a = 5; b = 8.$

b $a = \frac{1}{2}; b = \frac{1}{3}.$ *Answer*

c $c = 5; b = 4.$

d $\angle A° = 30; a = 4.$

e $\angle B° = 45; c = 6\sqrt{2}.$

f $\angle B° = 60; a = 3.$

7 What are the lengths of the three altitudes of a triangle if the sides of the triangle have lengths 3, 4, and 5? Verify that the product of each base and the corresponding height is the same number. (That is, verify that this product is twice the area.)

8 Use the dimensions given in D564 to compute the length of the altitude of $\triangle HJK$ that is perpendicular to the side $\overline{KJ}$. Then compute the length of the altitude to the side $\overline{HK}$.

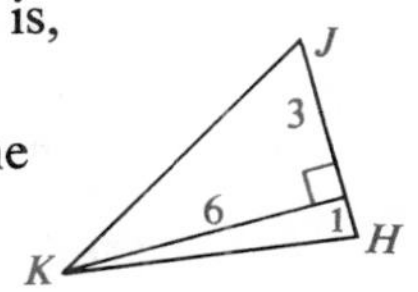

Diagram 564

9 If the lengths of the segments shown in D565 are a, b, c, h, x_1, and x_2, find the area of $\triangle ABC$ for each of the following cases.

a $x_1 = 3; x_2 = 7; h = 5.$

b $x_1 = 4; h = 4; a = 5.$ *Answer*

c $b = 25; h = 20; a = 25.$

d $a = \sqrt{28}; b = \sqrt{19}; h = \sqrt{3}.$

e $b = 2; x_1 = \sqrt{3}; a = 3.$

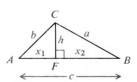

Diagram 565

439

10 a If x is the length of each side of an equilateral triangle $\triangle ABC$, show that a formula for the area of $\triangle ABC$ is $Ar(\triangle ABC) = \dfrac{x^2}{4}\sqrt{3}$.

b What is the area of an isosceles right triangle whose hypotenuse has length 6? Has length π? *Answer*

c If x is the length of the hypotenuse of an isosceles right triangle $\triangle DEF$, show that a formula for the area of $\triangle DEF$ is $Ar(\triangle DEF) = \dfrac{x^2}{4}$.

11 Using the information given in D566, find the area of $\triangle ABC$ and of $\triangle DEF$.

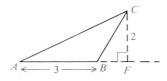 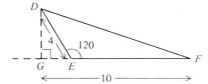

Diagram 566

12 Which of the following statements are necessarily correct?

a If $ABCD \cong EFGH$, then $Ar(ABCD) = Ar(EFGH)$.

b If $Ar(\triangle ABC) = Ar(\triangle XYZ)$, then $\triangle ABC \cong \triangle XYZ$.

c There exists a square whose area is $\sqrt{3}$.

d Corresponding to a positive number k, there is exactly one plane convex figure $\mathcal{S}$ whose area is the positive number k.

e Every square $\mathcal{S}$ such that $Ar(\mathcal{S})$ is a rational number has a side whose length is rational.

f There exists a rectangle $ABCD$ such that $Ar(ABCD) = 8\sqrt{7}$ and $d(A, B)$ is a rational number.

g If the sides of a right triangle $\triangle ABC$ have lengths a, b, and c, then a^2, b^2, and c^2 are each greater than $Ar(\triangle ABC)$.

h There exists $\triangle DEF$ such that $Ar(\triangle DEF) = \pi$.

13 Show that the area of $\triangle ABC$ equals $\dfrac{(a + b)^2 - c^2}{4}$ if $\measuredangle C$ is a right angle and a, b, and c denote the lengths of the sides opposite $\measuredangle A$, $\measuredangle B$, and $\measuredangle C$ respectively.

14 If lines AB and CD are parallel, what point P in AB makes $Ar(\triangle PCD)$ a maximum? Explain your answer.

♦ 15 Consider a full equilateral triangle, one unit on each side, as a region of unit area, and call this unit of area a "trinch."

a What is the area in "trinches" of an equilateral triangle that is 2 units on a side? That is 3 units on a side?

440

b What is the formula for the area in "trinches" of equilateral triangles that are x units on a side?

c The region of a plane that is covered by a unit square is the same as that covered by how many "trinches"? *Answer*

d If a rectangle has sides of lengths x and y, what is its area in "trinches"?

◆ 16 A first-century mathematician named Hero (or Heron) found that the area of any triangle $\triangle ABC$ whose sides have lengths a, b, and c could be found from the formula $Ar(\triangle ABC) = \sqrt{s(s-a)(s-b)(s-c)}$, where $s = \frac{1}{2}(a+b+c)$. (In the formula, s is called the *semi-perimeter*.)

a Check the formula for the 3, 4, 5 right triangle.

b Prove the formula for right triangles.

c Find the area of a triangle whose sides have lengths 5, 8, and 11.

d Prove that the radius length r of the inscribed circle of a triangle is $r = \sqrt{\dfrac{(s-a)(s-b)(s-c)}{s}}$.

◆ 17 Point P is interior to an equilateral triangle $\triangle ABC$ whose sides have length a. Prove that the sum of the distances of P from the sides of the triangle is the same for all positions of P. Then find this sum.

18 Triangle $\triangle ABC$ is equilateral, and each side has length a. Triangle $\triangle PQR$ is isosceles, and the two congruent sides each have length a. If $\triangle ABC$ and $\triangle PQR$ have the same area, what is the length of the base of $\triangle PQR$? *Answer*

19 From the distributive property of real numbers, $a(b+c) = ab + ac$, we get the familiar rule for finding the product of two expressions such as $(x + y + z)$ and $(a + b)$. If the dimensions of a rectangle are $x + y + z$ and $a + b$, explain why the distributive property is necessary for the consistency of Axioms 16/8 and 17/8.

Using the area formula for triangles, one can easily obtain the area formula for parallelograms and trapezoids.

---

* Theorem 207/8

The area of a parallelogram is the product of the length of any side and the distance between the line of that side and the parallel line of the opposite side. (D567)

Diagram 567

441

Comment

If a side of a parallelogram is selected
as the base, then, in relation to this
base, the height of the parallelogram
is the distance between the line of
the base and the line of the opposite
side. The area of the parallelogram is
then said to be the base times the height.
(D568)

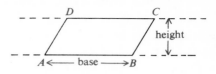

Diagram **568**

Definition 143/8 *Height of a trapezoid*

The distance between the lines of the two parallel bases
of a trapezoid is called the height of the trapezoid.

* Theorem 208/8

The area of a trapezoid is one half the product of its height
and the sum of the lengths of its bases. (D569)

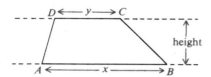

Diagram **569**

Exercises

1 If $ABCD$ is a parallelogram and lines $AB, DC, AD,$ and BC
are denoted by $r, s, n,$ and m respectively, find
$Ar(ABCD)$ in each of the following cases.
 a $d(A, B) = 7$; $d(r, s) = 5$.
 b $d(A, B) = 5$; $d(B, C) = 3$; $d(m, n) = 4$.
 c $d(A, D) = 9$; $d(D, C) = 20$; $d(r, s) = 6$.
 d $d(A, B) = \sqrt{2}$; $d(n, m) = 1$; $d(r, s) = \frac{5}{2}\sqrt{2}$;
 $d(A, D) = 5$. *Answer*
 e $d(A, D) = d(A, B) = d(r, s) = \pi$.

2 Use the information given in exercise 1 and Theorem 207/8
to find $d(r, s)$ if $d(A, B), d(A, D),$ and $d(m, n)$ are
10, 5, and 8 respectively.

3 For a parallelogram $ABCD$, prove that $d(A, B) > d(B, C)$
implies that $d(AB, CD) < d(BC, DA)$, and conversely.

4 Assume that the full parallelogram $ABCD$ is the intersection
of two closed strips whose widths are 5 and 7. What
is the length of a shorter side of the
parallelogram if the length of a longer side is 8? *Answer*

5 Find the base and the height of a parallelogram $ABCD$
whose area is 288 and whose height is 12 less than
3 times its base.

6 As D570 indicates, $ABCD$ and $ABEF$ are parallelograms with a common base $\overline{AB}$. The respective opposite sides $\overline{CD}$ and $\overline{EF}$ are in a line parallel to AB. If w, x, y, and z denote the areas of the regions indicated in the diagram, justify the following argument. (This argument is essentially one that Euclid used.)

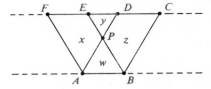

Diagram 570

1 $x + y = y + z$. (Why?)
2 $\therefore x = z$.
3 $\therefore x + w = z + w$.
4 $\therefore Ar(ABFE) = Ar(ABCD)$. (Why?)

7 Let $ABCD$ denote a parallelogram. For each of the following cases, find $Ar(ABCD)$.

   a $\sphericalangle A° = 45$; $d(A, D) = 6\sqrt{2}$; $d(D, C) = 10$.
   b $\sphericalangle D° = 60$; $d(A, D) = 10$; $d(A, B) = 29$. *Answer*
   c $d(B, C) = 5$; $d(D, C) = 10$; $\sphericalangle B° = 150$.
   d $d(A, D) = d(D, C) = 4$; $d(A, C) = 2\sqrt{15}$.

8 For trapezoid $ABCD$, let b, b', and h denote the lengths of the bases and the height respectively (D571).

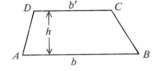

Diagram 571

   a Find $Ar(ABCD)$ if $b = 10$, $b' = 8$, and $h = 3$.
   b Find $Ar(ABCD)$ if $b = \frac{1}{2}$, $b' = \frac{1}{3}$, and $h = \frac{1}{4}$. *Answer*
   c Find h if $Ar(ABCD) = 1000$, $b = 20$, and $b' = 10$.
   d Find b if $Ar(ABCD) = 4$, $h = 1$, and $b' = 3$.
   e Find b, b', and h if $Ar(ABCD) = 216$ and $b = 2b' = 2h$.

9 Assume that polygon $ABCD$ is an isosceles trapezoid whose bases are $\overline{AB}$ and $\overline{CD}$.

   a Find $Ar(ABCD)$ if $\sphericalangle A° = 60$, $d(A, D) = 6$, and $d(D, C) = 4$. *Answer*
   b Find $Ar(ABCD)$ if $\sphericalangle B° = 45$, $d(A, D) = 5\sqrt{2}$, and $d(A, B) = 11$.

10 Prove that the area of a rhombus is equal to one half the product of its diagonals.

11 Polygon $EFGH$ is a trapezoid with $EF \parallel HG$. Use the information in D572 to find the area of $EFGH$. *Answer*

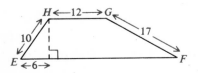

Diagram 572

443

12 Let $\triangle ABC$ denote a triangle that is inscribed in the circle $C(P, r)$ and is such that $\triangle ABC$ has the greatest possible area.

a Explain why the tangent to the circle at C must be parallel to AB.

b From exercise 12a, it follows that the tangent at each vertex of the triangle is parallel to the opposite side. Why does this imply that no two of these three tangents are parallel?

c Why is it also true that no side of the triangle is a diameter and that the diameter parallel to a side is between that side and the opposite vertex of the triangle?

d In the plane of $\triangle ABC$ and $C(P, r)$, why must the perpendicular bisector of $\overline{BC}$ and the line perpendicular at A to the tangent at A be the same line? Why does this imply that $\overline{AB} \cong \overline{BC}$?

e Why must $\triangle ABC$ be equilateral?

◆ **13** Let $\triangle ABC$ denote a triangle that is inscribed in the circle $C(P, r)$ and is such that $\overline{AC}$ is a diameter of the circle and the area of $\triangle ABC$ is as great as possible. Show that $\triangle ABC$ is an isosceles right triangle.

◆ **14** Let $ABCD$ denote a rectangle inscribed in the circle $C(P, r)$ such that the area of $ABCD$ is as great as possible.

a Why is $\overline{AC}$ a diameter?

b If $\triangle ACQ$ is inscribed in $C(P, r)$ and Γ is the reflection of the plane in P, prove that $AQCQ'$, where $Q' = Q\Gamma$, is a rectangle inscribed in $C(P, r)$ and that the area of $AQCQ'$ is twice the area of $\triangle ACQ$.

c How does it follow from exercises 14a and 14b, along with exercise 13, that $ABCD$ is a square?

We now will extend the class of point sets to which area applies by the following definitions.

Definition 144/8 *Area sum*

If set S is the union of a finite number of plane convex figures such that no two of these figures have an interior point in common, then the sum of the areas of these figures is defined to be the area of S. (D573)

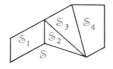

$$S = S_1 \cup S_2 \cup S_3 \cup S_4.$$
$$Ar(S) = Ar(S_1) + Ar(S_2) + Ar(S_3) + Ar(S_4).$$

Diagram 573

444

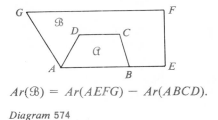

Definition 145/8 *Area difference*

If $\mathcal{C}$ is a plane convex figure and if $\mathcal{C} \cup \mathcal{B}$ is a different plane convex figure such that no interior point of $\mathcal{C}$ belongs to $\mathcal{B}$, then the area of $\mathcal{B}$ is defined to be the area of $\mathcal{C} \cup \mathcal{B}$ minus the area of $\mathcal{C}$. (D574)

$$Ar(\mathcal{B}) = Ar(AEFG) - Ar(ABCD).$$

Diagram 574

The preceding definitions, which specify the area for sets that are not necessarily convex, raise a natural question. If we "break up" a set in different ways, say, $\mathcal{R} = \mathcal{S}_1 \cup \mathcal{S}_2$ and $\mathcal{R} = \mathcal{S}_3 \cup \mathcal{S}_4$, and if the pieces have different areas, might it not be the case that we could obtain different area sums for $\mathcal{R}$? For example, the region $\mathcal{R}$ that has for its boundary the segment circuit determined by (A, B, C, D, E, A) is the union of $\mathcal{S}_1$ and $\mathcal{S}_2$ and also of $\mathcal{S}_3$ and $\mathcal{S}_4$ (D575). Moreover, $\mathcal{R} \cup {}^+\triangle BCD = {}^+ABDE$.

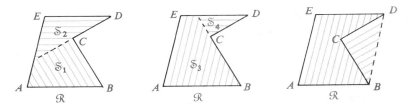

Diagram 575

Thus, we should have the same number for $Ar(\mathcal{S}_1) + Ar(\mathcal{S}_2)$, for $Ar(\mathcal{S}_3) + Ar(\mathcal{S}_4)$, and for $Ar(ABDE) - Ar(BDC)$. How do we know that we will, in fact, obtain the area for $\mathcal{R}$ in these different ways? Our intuitive feeling, of course, is that you do not change the amount of material in a cloth by cutting it up in different pieces, and regardless of how you cut it, you will always get the same sum for the pieces.

Despite our intuitive feelings concerning this question of area, a mathematical answer to the question not only is not obvious, it is beyond the scope of this book. Even establishing the consistency of area for general polygons, which can be done by elementary methods, requires more time and detail than we can afford. But, of course, we could not use the axioms and the definitions with any confidence if no deeper theory about their consistency existed.

Exercises

1 Points E, F, G, and H are in the exterior of the square $ABCD$. When these points are

paired with segments $\overline{AD}$, $\overline{AB}$, $\overline{BC}$, and $\overline{CD}$ respectively, they form four equilateral triangles (D576). Let $\mathcal{R}$ denote the union of the full square and the four full triangles.

a Is $\mathcal{R}$ a convex set?

b Is $\mathcal{R}$ the union of a finite number of plane convex figures?

c Do any of the triangles and/or the square share a common interior point?

d What is $Ar(\mathcal{R})$ if $d(A, B) = 6$? *Answer*

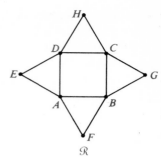

Diagram 576

2 The figure "N" pictured in D577 could be considered either as the union of two rectangles and a parallelogram or as the union of two trapezoids and a parallelogram. From the dimensions given, show that the area of the figure remains constant, regardless of which union is considered. (Hint: Unknown dimensions can be obtained by using the Pythagorean theorem and the method of similar triangles.)

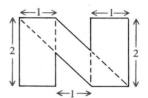

Diagram 577

3 Assume that the figures shown in D578 are coplanar. Let $\mathcal{T}_1$ denote $^+\triangle P_1OP_2$, let $\mathcal{T}_2$ denote $^+\triangle P_2OP_3$, let $\mathcal{T}_3$ denote $^+\triangle P_3OP_4$, and so on. Let $\mathcal{S}_1 = \mathcal{T}_1$, let $\mathcal{S}_2 = \mathcal{T}_1 \cup \mathcal{T}_2$, let $\mathcal{S}_3 = \mathcal{T}_1 \cup \mathcal{T}_2 \cup \mathcal{T}_3$, and so on.

a Find $Ar(\mathcal{S}_1)$, $Ar(\mathcal{S}_2)$, $Ar(\mathcal{S}_3)$, and $Ar(\mathcal{S}_4)$. *Answer*

b Does the pattern of answers for exercise 3a suggest a formula for $Ar(\mathcal{S}_n)$? Explain your answer.

c Would you think that, for some integer n, the sets $\mathcal{S}_n$ and $\mathcal{S}_1$ share some common interior points?

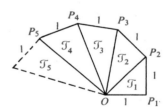

Diagram 578

4 The polygon $ABCD$ pictured in D579 is a square, and the segments whose union forms the star-shaped figure are congruent. Find the area of the star-shaped figure in terms of x and y. *Answer*

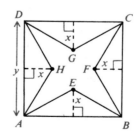

Diagram 579

◆ **5** Use D579 to find $Ar(EFGH)$ in terms of x and y.

6 The drawing in D580 shows a metal faceplate designed for a particular machine. What is the area of this faceplate if the shaded regions denote sections cut out of the metal? (Certain essential dimensions have not been given but these can be calculated from those that are indicated.) *Answer*

446

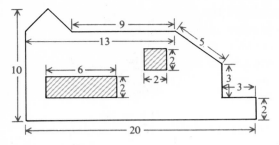

Diagram 580

7 Assume that polygon $ABCD$ is a trapezoid whose bases are $\overline{AB}$ and $\overline{CD}$ (D581). If the diagonals of the trapezoid intersect at point E, prove that $Ar(\triangle ADE) = Ar(\triangle BCE)$.

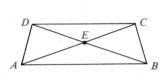

Diagram 581

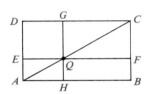

Diagram 582

8 Polygon $ABCD$ shown in D582 is a rectangle; $\overline{EF} \parallel \overline{AB}$; $\overline{GH} \parallel \overline{DA}$; $\overline{EF}$ and $\overline{GH}$ intersect at Q in $\overline{AC}$. Prove that $Ar(DGQE) = Ar(QFBH)$.

9 In $\triangle ABC$, $\overline{AE}$ and $\overline{BD}$ are medians (D583). If these medians intersect at point F, prove that $Ar(\triangle ABF) = Ar(DFEC)$.

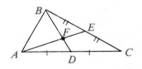

Diagram 583

10 If each of two parallel lines contains a side of parallelogram $\mathscr{P}_1$ and a side of parallelogram $\mathscr{P}_2$, prove that the areas of $\mathscr{P}_1$ and $\mathscr{P}_2$ are proportional to the lengths of the sides that are in the parallel lines.

11 Parallelograms $ABCD$ and $AB'C'D'$ have $\measuredangle A$ in common, D' is between A and D, and point B' is between A and B (D584).

Prove that $\dfrac{Ar(ABCD)}{Ar(AB'C'D')} = \dfrac{d(A, B)\,d(A, D)}{d(A, B')\,d(A, D')}$.

(Hint: Let $\overrightarrow{D'C'}$ intersect $\overline{BC}$ at X, and use the result of exercise 10.)

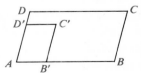

Diagram 584

12 Triangles $\triangle ABC$ and $\triangle AB'C'$ have $\measuredangle A$ in common, C' is between A and C, and B' is between A and B. Prove:

$$\frac{Ar(\triangle ABC)}{Ar(\triangle AB'C')} = \frac{d(A, B)\,d(A, C)}{d(A, B')\,d(A, C')}.$$

447

‣ **13** If a line t separates a full parallelogram into two regions of equal areas, prove that t contains the center of the parallelogram.

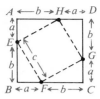

Diagram 585

‣ **14** Consider a square $ABCD$ whose edges are each of length $a + b$. Points E, F, G, and H are selected in the square as indicated in D585.

   a Prove that $EFGH$ is a square.

   b Let $d(E, F) = c$ and show, by the additive area axiom, that $c^2 = a^2 + b^2$.

   (Theorem of Pythagoras)

‣ **15** The polyhedron shown in D586 is a cube. If the length of each side of the cube is x, what is the area of $\triangle DGE$ in terms of x? *Answer*

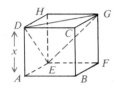

Diagram 586

We now want to establish some properties of regular polygons. These properties are useful in themselves and also will allow us to explain (not prove) a reasonable formula for the area of a circle.

Theorem 209/8

For every regular polygon, there exists a circumcircle, and the circumcenter is equidistant from all the sides of the polygon. (D587)

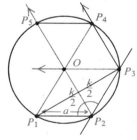

Proof

Let $\mathscr{P} = P_1P_2P_3 \ldots P_n$ denote a regular n-gon. Let a denote the common length of all of the sides of the polygon; let k denote the common measure of all of the angles; and let $C(O, r)$ be the circumcircle of $\triangle P_1P_2P_3$ (Corollary 116b/4). Then

  1 $r = d(O, P_1) = d(O, P_2) = d(O, P_3)$.

Statement 1, together with the fact that $a = d(P_1, P_2) = d(P_2, P_3)$, implies that

  2 $\triangle OP_2P_1 \cong \triangle OP_2P_3$

Diagram 587

and, therefore, as corresponding angles of a congruence, that

  3 $\measuredangle OP_2P_1 \cong \measuredangle OP_2P_3$.

The congruent angles in statement 3 are acute, since each is a base angle of an isosceles triangle. Hence, the congruence of statement 3 implies that $\overrightarrow{P_2O}$ is the closed ray that bisects $\measuredangle P_1P_2P_3$. Thus, O is interior to $\measuredangle P_1P_2P_3$ and so is in the P_1-side of line P_2P_3. Also

  4 $\measuredangle P_3P_2O° = \dfrac{k}{2}$.

From the definition of the polygon $\mathscr{P}$, the open ray $\overrightarrow{P_3P_4}$ is in the P_1-side of P_2P_3 and

  5 $\measuredangle P_2P_3P_4° = k$.

448

Because the open ray $\overrightarrow{P_3O}$ is in the P_1-side of P_2P_3 and

6 $\sphericalangle P_2P_3O° = \sphericalangle P_3P_2O° = \dfrac{k}{2}$,

it follows that $\overrightarrow{P_3O}$ is the bisector of $\sphericalangle P_2P_3P_4$. Then, from

7 $\sphericalangle OP_3P_4 \cong \sphericalangle OP_3P_2$,

8 $\overline{OP_3} \cong \overline{OP_3}$,

and

9 $\overline{P_3P_4} \cong \overline{P_3P_2}$,

it follows, by the side, angle, side congruence axiom, that

10 $\triangle OP_3P_4 \cong \triangle OP_3P_2$.

And, therefore, as corresponding parts,

11 $\overline{OP_3} \cong \overline{OP_4}$; so $d(O, P_4) = r$.

Thus, P_4 also is in the circle $C(O, r)$.

By the same argument, one can show that

12 $\triangle OP_4P_5 \cong \triangle OP_4P_3$,

so

13 $d(O, P_5) = d(O, P_4) = r$.

Continuing in this way,* it follows that $C(O, r)$ passes
through all of the vertices of the polygon, and so $C(O, r)$
is the circumcircle of the polygon.

If $\overline{P_iP_{i+1}}$ and $\overline{P_jP_{j+1}}$ are any two sides
of the polygon (D588), the isosceles triangles
$\triangle OP_iP_{i+1}$ and $\triangle OP_jP_{j+1}$ are congruent
by the side, side, side congruence theorem.
If M is the midpoint of $\overline{P_iP_{i+1}}$ and N is
the midpoint of $\overline{P_jP_{j+1}}$, it follows that
$\triangle OMP_i$ and $\triangle ONP_j$ are congruent right
triangles and that $d(O, M) = d(O, N)$. Thus,
M is the foot in line P_iP_{i+1} of O; point N is the foot in
line P_jP_{j+1} of O; and point O is equidistant from these lines
of the sides of the polygon.

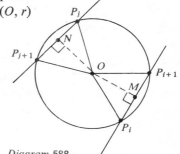

Diagram 588

Definition 146/8 *Apothem*

The distance from the circumcenter of a regular polygon to the line
of each of its sides is the apothem of the regular polygon. (D589)

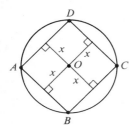

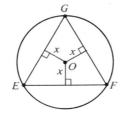

Diagram 589

---

* For a completely accurate proof, of course, we would have to use mathematical induction.

Theorem 210/8

The area of a regular polygon is one half the product
of the apothem and the perimeter of the polygon. (D590)

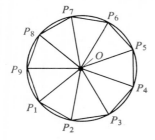 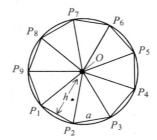

Diagram 590a   590b

Proof

If $\mathcal{P} = P_1P_2P_3 \ldots P_n$ denotes a regular polygon, the argument
of the proof for Theorem 209/8 shows that the circumcenter O
of the polygon is in each ray that is a bisector of an
angle of the polygon. From this it follows that O belongs
to each closed half-plane that contains $\mathcal{P}$ and whose edge
contains a side of $\mathcal{P}$. And, since O is not in any side
because it is equidistant from all of the sides, O is
interior to the polygon. The full polygon is the union
of the full central triangles, $^+\triangle OP_1P_2$, $^+\triangle OP_2P_3$,
$^+\triangle OP_3P_4, \ldots, ^+\triangle OP_nP_1$. Since no two of these triangles
intersect except in a side,

1 $Ar(\mathcal{P}) = Ar(\triangle OP_1P_2) + Ar(\triangle OP_2P_3) + \ldots + Ar(\triangle OP_nP_1)$.

But each of the central triangles has the apothem, say h,
as its height relative to the side of the polygon as base.
So if a is the common length of the sides, then the area
of each triangle in statement 1 is $\frac{1}{2}ah$. Thus,

2 $Ar(\mathcal{P}) = \frac{1}{2}ah + \frac{1}{2}ah + \frac{1}{2}ah + \ldots + \frac{1}{2}ah$ (n addends)

or

3 $Ar(\mathcal{P}) = n(\frac{1}{2}ah)$.

But there are n sides of $\mathcal{P}$, each of length a. Therefore, na
is the perimeter p of the polygon. So, statement 3
can be expressed as

4 $Ar(\mathcal{P}) = \frac{1}{2}hp$,

which we wished to show.

If you start with a regular polygon, say, a square $P_1P_2P_3P_4$
with circumcircle $C(O, r)$, then there are four congruent central
triangles with O as the central vertex (D591a). The four rays that

450

bisect the four central vertex angles intersect the circle, and these intersection points, together with P_1, P_2, P_3, and P_4, are the vertices of a regular 8-gon inscribed in $C(O, r)$. There then are eight central triangles. If we again bisect the central vertex angles, we can obtain a regular inscribed polygon of sixteen sides.

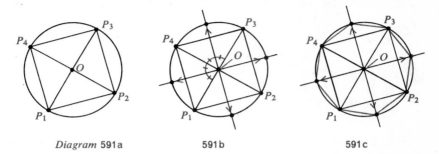

Diagram 591a   591b   591c

In the process just described, suppose that $\mathcal{P}_n$ is the regular inscribed polygon, that p_n is its perimeter, and that h_n is the apothem. As n continues to double, the full polygon more nearly covers the circle. Thus, the area of the polygon should give closer and closer approximations of the area of the circle. It can be shown that there is a real number, denoted by π, such that the number $\dfrac{Ar(\mathcal{P}_n)}{r^2}$ gets closer and closer to π as greater and greater values of n are taken. If we use an arrow to mean "approaches as n increases indefinitely," then $\dfrac{Ar(\mathcal{P}_n)}{r^2} \to \pi$. In other words, $\dfrac{Ar(\mathcal{P}_n)}{r^2}$ approaches π as n increases indefinitely. Hence, $Ar(\mathcal{P}_n) \to \pi r^2$. And since $Ar(\mathcal{P}_n) \to Ar[C(O, r)]$, we get the area formula for a circle, the formula $Ar[C(O, r)] = \pi r^2$.

The number π is irrational and cannot be expressed exactly in decimal form. Various approximations of this number were known even in very ancient times, and $\frac{22}{7}$ and 3.1416 are rational approximations that commonly are used.

We have not defined the length of a curve.* But, taking the *circumference* of the circle $C(O, r)$ to be the number p that is the limit of the perimeters p_n in our process, we easily can make a reasonable guess at the circumference. Since $Ar(\mathcal{P}_n) \to \pi r^2$, then, by Theorem 205/8,

1) $\frac{1}{2}h_n p_n \to \pi r^2$.

But, by assumption, $p_n \to p$, and the apothems $h_n \to r$. Consequently,

2) $\frac{1}{2}h_n p_n \to \frac{1}{2}rp$.

* Curve length is discussed briefly in Chapter 9.

From statements 1 and 2, we obtain

3) $\frac{1}{2}rp = \pi r^2$,

or

4) $p = 2\pi r$.

Statement 4 gives the formula for the circumference of circle $C(O, r)$:

$$\text{Circumference of } C(O, r) = 2\pi r.$$

From the formula for the circumference, it follows that the ratio of the circumference of a circle to the diameter of the circle is π. This ratio does not depend in any way on the size of the circle and is probably the simplest way of remembering one meaning of π.

Exercises

1 Let $\mathscr{P} = P_1P_2P_3 \ldots P_n$ denote a regular polygon, and let $C(O, r)$ denote its circumcircle.

a Find the apothem, the perimeter, and the area of $\mathscr{P}$ if $n = 4$ and $r = 10\sqrt{2}$. *Answer*

b Find the apothem, the perimeter, and the area of $\mathscr{P}$ if $n = 6$ and $r = 4$.

c What is the area and the perimeter of $\mathscr{P}$ if $n = 3$ and the apothem of $\mathscr{P}$ is 6?

2 If a denotes the area of a regular polygon $\mathscr{P} = P_1P_2P_3 \ldots P_{20}$ and m denotes the length of $\overline{P_1P_2}$, what is the apothem of $\mathscr{P}$ in terms of a and m? If O denotes the circumcenter of $\mathscr{P}$, what is the length of $\overline{OP_1}$ in terms of a and m? *Answer*

3 a If $C(O, r)$ is the circumcircle of a square $\mathbb{S}$, prove that $Ar(\mathbb{S}) = 2r^2$.

b If x denotes the length of each side of a regular hexagon $\mathcal{H}$, prove that $Ar(\mathcal{H}) = \dfrac{3x^2}{2}\sqrt{3}$.

4 Polygon $ABCDE$ is a regular 5-gon, and $\overline{OF}$ is the segment determined by the circumcenter O of the polygon and its foot F in the side $\overline{AB}$ (D592). Hence, $x = d(O, F)$ is the apothem of the pentagon. Construct a regular pentagon $A'B'C'D'E'$ whose apothem is the length of the given segment $\overline{XY}$.

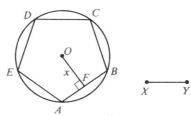

Diagram 592

5 Quadrilateral $ABCD$ (D593) is circumscribed about the circle $C(O, 6)$. If the perimeter of $ABCD$ is 48, what is $Ar(ABCD)$? (Hint: Use

the fact that a point P external to a circle is equidistant from the contact points of the two tangent lines through P. See exercise 3, page 217. For example, $\overline{AX} \cong \overline{AY}$.) *Answer*

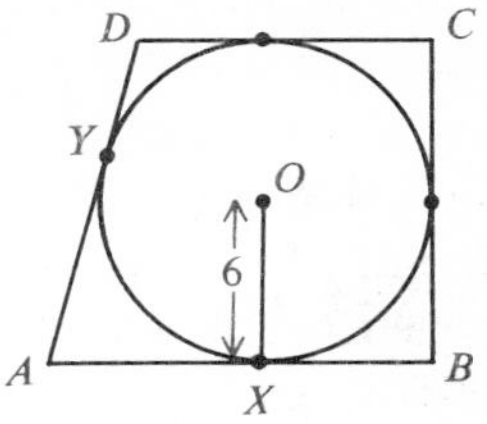

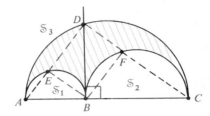

Diagram 593

6 Exercise 5 suggests a general formula for the area of a polygon that has an incircle. What is this formula (which generalizes Theorem 210/8)?

◆ **7** Assume that point B is between A and C and that $\mathbb{S}_1$, $\mathbb{S}_2$, $\mathbb{S}_3$ are semicircles with diameters $\overline{AB}$, $\overline{BC}$, and $\overline{AC}$ respectively (D594). If the semicircles are coplanar in the same closed half-plane of AB, the region they bound (which is shaded in the diagram) is called a *shoemaker's knife*. A perpendicular to AC at B intersects $\mathbb{S}_3$ at D. Point E between A and D is in $\mathbb{S}_1$, and point F between C and D is in $\mathbb{S}_2$.

Diagram 594

a Show that $BFDE$ is a rectangle.

b Show that the area of the shoemaker's knife is the same as that of the circumcircle of $BFDE$.

◆ **8** Show that the length of each side of a regular octagon inscribed in a circle of radius 1 is $\sqrt{2 - \sqrt{2}}$.

(Hint: First consider an inscribed square.)

9 Find the ratio of the apothem to the perimeter for regular polygons of 3, 4, and 6 sides.

◆ **10** Repeat exercise 9 for regular polygons of 8 and 5 sides. (Hint: Consider Theorem 163/5.)

11 The value of π correct to ten decimal places is given by the decimal 3.1415926536.

a Is $\frac{22}{7}$ greater than or less than π?

b Find the difference of π and $\frac{22}{7}$, and express the difference correct to 5 decimal places.

c Since π is irrational, why must $\sqrt{\pi}$ be irrational?

12 Using 3.14 as an approximation of π, find the corresponding approximate area and circumference of each of the following circles.

a $C(P, 1)$ **c** $C(H, 2)$

b $C(B, 10)$ *Answer*   **d** $C(J, \frac{1}{3.14})$

13 a In terms of π, what is the radius of a circle whose area is 1?

453

b In terms of π, what is the diameter of a circle whose perimeter is $2\pi^2 + 2\pi\sqrt{2}$? *Answer*

c What is the radius of a circle if its area equals its circumference?

14 One of the following numbers is the exact area of the circle $C(P, 2)$, while the other two numbers are different approximations of the area. Which number is the exact area, and which of the other two numbers is the better approximation of the area?

    a $12\frac{4}{7}$ **b** 4π **c** 12.5664

• 15 Consider a full circle of radius 1 as a region of unit area, and call this unit of area a "cinch."

    a What is the area in "cinches" of the circle $C(P, 2)$? Of the circle $C(H, 10)$?

    b What is a formula for the area in "cinches" of a circle of radius r?

    c What is the area in "cinches" of a square in which each side has length 3? *Answer*

    d What is a formula for the area in "cinches" of a rectangle whose sides have lengths x and y?

16 By definition, concentric circles are circles in the same plane that have the same center. In D595, the circles $C(P, r_1)$ and $C(P, r_2)$, where $r_1 < r_2$, are examples of concentric circles.

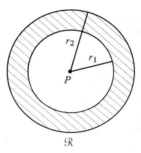

Diagram 595

    a What is the area of the shaded ring in terms of π if $r_1 = 3$ and $r_2 = 5$? *Answer*

    b Let $\mathcal{R}$ denote the shaded region. What is a formula for $Ar(\mathcal{R})$ in terms of π, r_1, and r_2?

    c What is a formula for $Ar(\mathcal{R})$ in the special case where $r_2 = r_1 + 1$?

17 The three circles $C(O, 1)$, $C(O, 2)$, and $C(O, 3)$ that are shown in D596 are concentric. What is the total area of the shaded regions in terms of π?

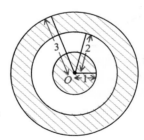

Diagram 596

• 18 A leather belt connects two rotating wheels that each have the radius 5 in. The belt has no sag, and the centers of the wheels are 3 ft. apart. How long is the belt in inches?

• 19 The wheels on an old steam engine were 7 ft. in diameter. How many revolutions per minute would such a wheel have to make for the steam engine to travel 60 mi. per hour? Use $\frac{22}{7}$ as an approximation of π. *Answer*

20 a What is the ratio of the areas of two circles if their radii are 3 and 7 respectively?

b The circumferences of two circles are 5 and 13 respectively. What is the ratio of the areas of these circles?

c If the ratio of the areas of two circles is 16 to 25, what is the ratio of their circumferences? Of their radii? Of their diameters?

21 If the area of the region bounded by the inscribed and the circumscribed circles of a square is 9π, what is the area of the square?

22 Planes α and β intersect the sphere $S(P, 10)$ in such a way that $d(P, \alpha) = 1$ and $d(P, \beta) = 9$. What is the ratio of the areas of the two circles formed by these intersections?

23 Show that no square and circle have the same perimeter and the same area.

24 By methods of calculus, it can be shown that $\pi = 4(1 - \frac{1}{3} + \frac{1}{5} - \frac{1}{7} + \frac{1}{9} - \ldots)$. Use the first four of these terms to calculate the decimal approximation of π to four places.

Since a similarity mapping of ratio k changes all lengths by the factor k, it maps a rectangle $\mathcal{R}$ whose sides have lengths a and b onto a rectangle $\mathcal{R}'$ whose sides have lengths ka and kb. The area of $\mathcal{R}'$ then is $(ka)(kb) = k^2ab$. So the area of $\mathcal{R}'$ is k^2 times the area of $\mathcal{R}$. As one might suppose, the more general fact is that, if two plane convex figures are similar in a ratio k, then the area of one is k^2 times the area of the other. Let us see how we can prove this for polygons. First we establish the following fact.

Theorem 211/8

If two triangles are similar, then the ratio of altitudes to corresponding sides is the same as the ratio of the corresponding sides.

Proof

Let $\triangle ABC \sim \triangle A'B'C'$ denote a similarity of triangles in which the ratio of a side of $\triangle A'B'C'$ to the corresponding side of $\triangle ABC$ is k. (D597) Let F denote the foot in line AB of C, and let F' denote the foot in line $A'B'$ of C'.

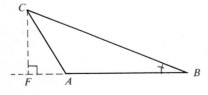

Diagram **597**

455

If $\angle B$ is acute, then the congruent angle $\angle B'$ is acute.
So F is in $\overrightarrow{BA}$ and F' is in $\overrightarrow{B'A'}$. Because $\angle CFB \cong \angle C'F'B'$
(both are right angles),

1 $\triangle CFB \sim \triangle C'F'B'$

by Theorem 160/5. Therefore,

2 $\dfrac{d(C', F')}{d(C, F)} = \dfrac{d(C', B')}{d(C, B)} = k.$

If $\angle A$ is acute, then the congruent angle $\angle A'$ is acute.
(D598) So F is in $\overrightarrow{AB}$ and F' is in $\overrightarrow{A'B'}$. In $\triangle CFA$
and $\triangle C'F'A'$, the angles at A and A' are given
congruent and those at F and F' are right angles.
Hence,

3 $\triangle CFA \sim \triangle C'F'A'$;

and, therefore,

4 $\dfrac{d(C', F')}{d(C, F)} = \dfrac{d(C', A')}{d(C, A)} = k.$

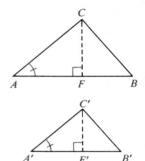

Diagram 598

Since either $\angle A$ is acute or $\angle B$ is acute, either the
relation of statement 2 or of statement 4 is true.
In either case, the ratio of the altitude $\overline{C'F'}$ to the
altitude $\overline{CF}$ is k.

Corollary 211a/8
The corresponding altitudes in a congruence of triangles
are congruent.

Corollary 211b/8
If the ratio of corresponding sides of similar triangles is k,
the ratio of the areas of these triangles is k^2.

Proof
Let $\triangle ABC \sim \triangle A'B'C'$ denote a similarity of triangles
such that

1 $\dfrac{d(A', B')}{d(A, B)} = \dfrac{d(B', C')}{d(B, C)} = \dfrac{d(C', A')}{d(C, A)} = k.$

If $\overline{CF}$ is the altitude of $\triangle ABC$ from vertex C and if $\overline{C'F'}$ is the
altitude of $\triangle A'B'C'$ from vertex C', then, by Theorem 211/8,

2 $\dfrac{d(C', F')}{d(C, F)} = k.$

By Theorem 205/8, we have

3 $Ar(\triangle ABC) = \tfrac{1}{2} d(B, C) d(C, F)$;
4 $Ar(\triangle A'B'C') = \tfrac{1}{2} d(B', C') d(C', F')$.

Substituting in statement 4 from statements 1 and 2,

5 $Ar(\triangle A'B'C') = \tfrac{1}{2}[k \, d(B, C)] [k \, d(C, F)]$.

Comparing statement 5 with statement 3, we have

6 $Ar(\triangle A'B'C') = k^2 Ar(\triangle ABC)$.

Theorem 212/8
If the ratio of corresponding sides of similar polygons is k,
then the ratio of the areas of the polygons is k^2.

456

Proof

Let $P_1P_2P_3 \ldots P_n \sim Q_1Q_2Q_3 \ldots Q_n$ denote a similarity cf two
n-gons in which the ratio of side $\overline{Q_iQ_{i+1}}$ to $\overline{P_iP_{i+1}}$ is k.

The successive full triangles at vertex P_1,
$^+\triangle P_1P_2P_3, {}^+\triangle P_1P_3P_4, \ldots, {}^+\triangle P_1P_{n-1}P_n$, are such that
no one of them contains an interior point of another and
their union is the full polygon $^+P_1P_2P_3 \ldots P_n$. So,
by Axiom 16/8,

1 $Ar(P_1P_2P_3 \ldots P_n) = Ar(\triangle P_1P_2P_3) + Ar(\triangle P_1P_3P_4) + \ldots + Ar(\triangle P_1P_{n-1}P_n)$.

In the same way,

2 $Ar(Q_1Q_2Q_3 \ldots Q_n) = Ar(\triangle Q_1Q_2Q_3) + Ar(\triangle Q_1Q_3Q_4) + \ldots + Ar(\triangle Q_1Q_{n-1}Q_n)$.

But by Corollary 170a/5, each of the successive triangles
at Q_1 is similar to its corresponding triangle at P_1, and k
also is the ratio of the sides in these triangle similarities.
Then, by Corollary 211b/8, each of the triangles at Q_1 has
area k^2 times the area of its corresponding triangle at P_1.
Thus, statement 2 can be expressed as

3 $Ar(Q_1Q_2Q_3 \ldots Q_n) = k^2 Ar(\triangle P_1P_2P_3) + k^2 Ar(\triangle P_1P_3P_4) + \ldots + k^2 Ar(\triangle P_1P_{n-1}P_n)$.

Statements 1, 2, and 3 imply that

4 $Ar(Q_1Q_2Q_3 \ldots Q_n) = k^2 Ar(P_1P_2P_3 \ldots P_n)$,

which we wished to show.

Exercises

1 The triangle $\triangle ABC$ has area x, and the sides
opposite A, B, and C have the lengths a, b, and c
respectively (D599). The triangle $\triangle DEF$ has
area y, and the sides opposite D, E, and F have
the lengths d, e, and f respectively. Also,
$\triangle ABC \sim \triangle DEF$.

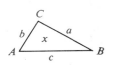

a If $a = 4$ and $d = 7$, what is the ratio $\dfrac{x}{y}$?

b If $c = 4$, $x = 10$, and $y = 30$, what is f?

c If $\dfrac{b}{e} = \dfrac{3}{2}$, what is the ratio $\dfrac{f}{c}$?

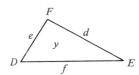

Diagram 599

d If $\dfrac{d}{a} = \dfrac{1}{8}$ and $x = 5$, what is y? *Answer*

2 Segment $\overline{AB}$ is the hypotenuse of the right triangle
$\triangle ABC$, and $\overline{AB}$ has length c (D600). Sides $\overline{AC}$ and
$\overline{BC}$ have lengths b and a respectively. Let F denote
the foot in $\overline{AB}$ of C and let x, y, and z
denote the areas of $\triangle BCF$, $\triangle CFA$, and $\triangle ABC$
respectively. Justify the following relations.

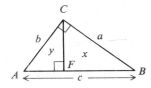

a $z = x + y$.   b $x = \left(\dfrac{a}{c}\right)^2 z$.   c $y = \left(\dfrac{b}{c}\right)^2 z$.

Diagram 600

3 From the relations that you justified for exercise 2, obtain the Pythagorean theorem $c^2 = a^2 + b^2$.

4 Let $\mathscr{P}_1$, $\mathscr{P}_2$, and $\mathscr{P}_3$ denote regular n-gons whose sides have lengths a, b, and c respectively and that have areas x, y, and z respectively. If $c^2 = a^2 + b^2$, justify the following relations.

a $\dfrac{x}{z} = \left(\dfrac{a}{c}\right)^2$.   **b** $\dfrac{y}{z} = \left(\dfrac{b}{c}\right)^2$.   **c** $z = x + y$.

(Hence, show that, if regular n-gons and not just squares are constructed in the hypotenuse and on the sides of a right triangle, then the area of the regular n-gon on the hypotenuse is the sum of the areas of those on the sides.)

5 The diameter of circle $\mathcal{S}_3$ is the hypotenuse of a right triangle. Circles $\mathcal{S}_1$ and $\mathcal{S}_2$ have the other two sides of the right triangle as respective diameters. Since any two circles are similar figures, the argument of exercises 2, 3, and 4 would indicate that the area of $\mathcal{S}_3$ is the sum of the areas of $\mathcal{S}_1$ and $\mathcal{S}_2$. Check this result directly by using the formula for the area of a circle.

6 A line that passes through the centroid of $\triangle ABC$ and is parallel to AB intersects $\overline{AC}$ at D and intersects $\overline{BC}$ at E. If the area of trapezoid $ABED$ is 10, what is the area of $\triangle ABC$? *Answer*

7 Let $\triangle RST \sim \triangle MNX$ denote a similarity of triangles in which the ratio of a side of $\triangle RST$ to its corresponding side in $\triangle MNX$ is 3. What is the area of each triangle if the sum of their areas is 100? If the product of their areas is 225? If the difference of their areas is 9696?

8 If $\triangle ABC$ and $\triangle DEF$ are equilateral triangles with areas x and y respectively, and if an altitude of $\triangle ABC$ has the same length as a side of $\triangle DEF$, what is the ratio of x to y?

9 If a square and an equilateral triangle have the same perimeter, what is the ratio of their areas? *Answer*

◆ **10 a** Given $\triangle ABC$, construct the line t that is parallel to $\overline{AB}$ and that divides $\triangle ABC$ into two regions of equal area.

b Given $\triangle ABC$, construct the two parallel lines m and n that are parallel to $\overline{AB}$ and that divide $\triangle ABC$ into three regions of equal area.

11 a The lengths of two corresponding sides of similar polygons are 3 and 27. What is the ratio of their areas? Of their perimeters? *Answer*

b If the areas of two similar polygons are 36 and 121, what is the ratio of two corresponding sides?

c Two similar polygons have areas of 20 and 180. If the length of one side of the first polygon is 3, what is the length of the corresponding side of the second polygon?

12 a Given two segments of lengths x and y, construct a third segment of length a such that $a^2 = xy$. (Hint: Consider the altitude to the hypotenuse of a right triangle.) *Answer*

b Given a parallelogram $ABCD$ that is a rectangle, construct a square $EFGH$ such that
$Ar(ABCD) = Ar(EFGH)$.

13 a Given a quadrilateral $ABCD$, construct a triangle $\triangle EFG$ such that $Ar(ABCD) = Ar(\triangle EFG)$.

b Given a quadrilateral $GHJK$ that is not a parallelogram, construct a square $WXYZ$ such that
$Ar(GHJK) = Ar(WXYZ)$.

14 Given $\triangle ABC$ and a segment of length x, construct a triangle $\triangle DEF$ such that $\triangle ABC \sim \triangle DEF$ and the perimeter of $\triangle DEF$ is x.

◆ 15 Given a scalene triangle $\triangle ABC$, construct an equilateral triangle $\triangle DEF$ such that $Ar(\triangle DEF) = Ar(\triangle ABC)$.

◆ 16 If a full n-gon $^+\mathscr{P}$ is expressed as the union of full triangles whose vertices are also vertices of $^+\mathscr{P}$, prove that there are $n - 2$ triangles in this union and that each of the $n - 2$ diagonals of $^+\mathscr{P}$ is a side of some triangle in the union (D601).

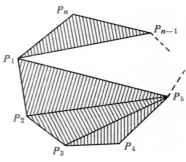

Diagram 601

Note: It can be shown that, if an n-gon $\mathscr{P}$ has a circumcircle, then its area exceeds that of any n-gon that has sides of the same lengths (in any order) as those of $\mathscr{P}$ but that has no circumcircle. Among all n-gons of given perimeter, the regular n-gon has a strictly greatest area. (For elementary proofs, see *Convex Figures* by I. Yaglom and V. Boltyanskiĭ.)

Volume 33/8

Just as the area of a plane figure is the measure of its extent in terms of the number of nonoverlapping unit squares that it contains, so the volume of a solid figure is the measure of the amount of space it occupies in terms of the nonoverlapping unit cubes that it contains. Volume is another subject that we really cannot handle formally, since limit concepts are involved. But we can get some ideas about volume by following the pattern we used for area; that is, by working with a few very strong axioms.

459

Corresponding to a convex solid $\mathcal{R}$, there is just one positive
number that is the volume of $\mathcal{R}$. If $\mathcal{R}$ is the union of a
finite number of convex solids, no two of which have an
interior point in common, then the volume of $\mathcal{R}$ is the sum
of the volumes of the solids in the union.

Convention

We will denote the volume of a convex solid $\mathcal{R}$ by the notation
$Vol(\mathcal{R})$. The volume of a polyhedron $P_1 P_2 P_3 \ldots P_n$ always
will mean the volume of the solid polyhedron, and we will
denote this volume by the notation $Vol(P_1 P_2 P_3 \ldots P_n)$.

Axiom 20/8

If two convex solids have congruent boundaries, then the
solids have the same volume.

Definition 147/8 *Height of a right rectangular parallelepiped*

With respect to any face chosen as base the distance
between that face and the opposite parallel face is
the height of the parallelepiped. (D602)

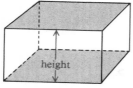

height

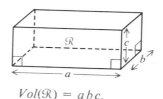

$$Vol(\mathcal{R}) = abc.$$

Diagram 602

Diagram 603

Axiom 21/8

The volume of a solid, right, rectangular parallelepiped is the product
of the area of the base and the height of the parallelepiped. (D603)

Comment

Axiom 21/8 implies that, using any face as the base and using the height
relative to that base, we will always obtain the same volume.

In a physical sense, a rectangular parallelepiped is just a
rectangular box. Suppose that the three edges at a corner have
lengths a, b, and c. Then the volume is the product abc, since
one term in the product is the height, and the product of the other
two terms is the area of the rectangular base.

We will make one more assumption about volumes.

Axiom 22/8 *Cavalieri's principle*

If two convex solids $\mathcal{R}$ and $\mathcal{S}$ have two parallel supporting
planes in common and if every plane that is parallel to

these planes and between them intersects $\mathcal{R}$ and $\mathcal{S}$ in plane convex figures with equal areas, then the solids $\mathcal{R}$ and $\mathcal{S}$ have the same volume. (D604)*

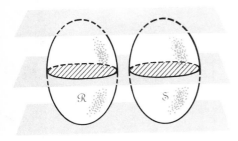

Diagram 604 ◫

An interpretation of Cavalieri's principle is the following. If a physical solid is made of one substance so that all parts have the same density, then the volume is directly proportional to the weight. If you slice the solid into very thin parallel slabs, all having the same thickness, then the weight of each of these slabs will be almost proportional to the area of the flat face of the slab. So if you do this for two solids with matching slabs of the same face area (Axiom 22/8 suggests one way of setting up the matching), then the corresponding pieces will have approximately the same weight and, hence, the same volume, regardless of the difference in shape of the flat faces. Since each solid is the union of its pieces, and the corresponding pieces have equal weights, the two solids have the same total weight and, hence, the same total volume.

This intuitive interpretation is not a justification of Cavalieri's principle. It is merely a way of seeing that it is not unreasonable to suppose that, if the number of matching slabs in the two solids is increased so that each piece gets thinner, then the approximation to the correct volume will improve. That this principle will give the correct result in the limit is what is being assumed in place of a mathematical justification that uses limits.

We now have all that we need to obtain volume formulas for some special classes of solids.

---

* It can be proved that, if two full polygons have the same area, then each can be expressed as the union of a finite number of full triangles so that there is a one-to-one correspondence of the two sets of triangles in which corresponding triangles are congruent. It is not necessarily correct, however, that, if two polyhedra have the same volume, then there is a decomposition of each of the polyhedra into the same finite number of congruent tetrahedra. This is the basic reason why a Cavalieri principle or some equivalent principle is necessary in treating volume.

Every plane section of a solid prism that is parallel to
the bases has the same area as each of the bases. (D605)

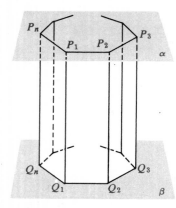

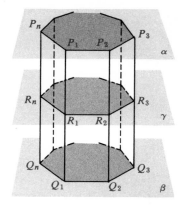

Diagram 605a   605b 🐂

Proof

Let a prism have the full congruent n-gons $^+P_1P_2P_3 \ldots P_n$ and
$^+Q_1Q_2Q_3 \ldots Q_n$ as its bases in the parallel planes α and β
respectively, where $P_1P_2P_3 \ldots P_n \cong Q_1Q_2Q_3 \ldots Q_n$. Let γ
denote any plane that is between α and β and is parallel
to them. Let $R_1, R_2, R_3, \ldots, R_n$ denote the intersections
of γ with the respective lateral edges $\overline{P_1Q_1}, \overline{P_2Q_2}, \ldots, \overline{P_nQ_n}$
of the prism. Then, from convexity, the plane section in γ
is the full n-gon $^+R_1R_2R_3 \ldots R_n$. Because β and γ are
parallel, each face of the prism intersects β and γ in
parallel segments. And since all of the lateral edges
of the polyhedron are parallel to each other, it follows that
the part of each face that is in the closed solid strip
between β and γ is a full parallelogram. That is,
$Q_1Q_2R_2R_1, Q_2Q_3R_3R_2, \ldots, Q_{n-1}Q_nR_nR_{n-1}$ are all
parallelograms.

   Let $k = d(R_1, Q_1)$ and let Γ denote the translation
of space in the direction of $\overrightarrow{R_1Q_1}$ and by the amount k.
This translation maps R_1 onto Q_1. Since $\overrightarrow{R_2Q_2}$ has the
direction of $\overrightarrow{R_1Q_1}$ and $d(R_1, Q_1) = d(R_2, Q_2) = k$, the
translation Γ maps R_2 onto Q_2. By the same argument, Γ maps
$R_3, \ldots, R_n$ onto $Q_3, \ldots, Q_n$ respectively and so maps the
plane section γ onto the base of the prism. The plane section
and the base of the prism, therefore, are congruent and so
have the same area by Axiom 18/8.

Definition 148/8 *Height of a prism*

The distance between the parallel base planes of a prism is the height of the prism. This distance also is the height of the solid prism.

Theorem 214/8

The volume of a solid prism is the product of the area of the base and the height of the prism. (D606)

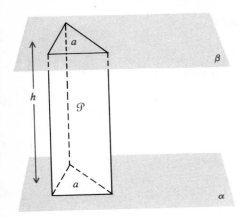

Diagram 606a

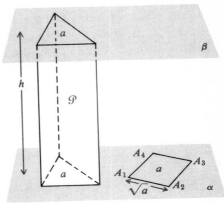

606b

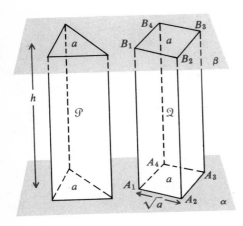

606c

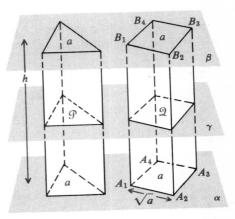

606d ⌦

Proof

Let $\mathcal{P}$ denote a solid prism with parallel base planes α and β.
Let a denote the area of each base, and let h denote the height of $\mathcal{P}$.

In the base plane α, there exists a square $A_1A_2A_3A_4$, each of whose sides has length $\sqrt{a}$. So

1 $Ar(A_1A_2A_3A_4) = \sqrt{a}\,\sqrt{a} = a.$

463

Lines t_1, t_2, t_3, and t_4, which are perpendicular to α at
A_1, A_2, A_3, and A_4 respectively, intersect β at points B_1,
B_2, B_3, and B_4 respectively.

Then α and β are common parallel planes of support to $\mathscr{P}$
and to the solid right rectangular parallelepiped $\mathscr{Q}$ whose
bases are the full squares $^+A_1A_2A_3A_4$ and $^+B_1B_2B_3B_4$.
The height of $\mathscr{Q}$ also is h.

Let γ be any plane between α and β and parallel to them.
By Theorem 213/8, the section of $\mathscr{P}$ in plane γ has the
same area as the base of $\mathscr{P}$, and the section of $\mathscr{Q}$ in γ has
the same area as the base of $\mathscr{Q}$. Since $\mathscr{P}$ and $\mathscr{Q}$ have bases
of the same area, the sections of $\mathscr{P}$ and $\mathscr{Q}$ in γ have the
same area. So, by Axiom 22/8, $\mathscr{P}$ and $\mathscr{Q}$ have the same volume.
By Axiom 21/8,

2 $Vol(\mathscr{Q}) = ah$.

Therefore,

3 $Vol(\mathscr{P}) = ah$.

Since a is the area of the base of $\mathscr{P}$ and h is the height of $\mathscr{P}$,
the theorem is established.

The following terms will be convenient in combining exercises
concerning area with those concerning volume.

Definition 149/8 *Surface area of a polyhedron*
The surface area of a polyhedron is the sum of the areas
of its faces.

Definition 150/8 *Lateral face, lateral area*
Each nonbase face of a pyramid or prism $\mathscr{P}$ is a lateral face of $\mathscr{P}$.
The sum of the areas of the lateral faces is the lateral area of $\mathscr{P}$.

Exercises

1 Let $\mathscr{R}$ denote a solid rectangular parallelepiped whose
  height is h and whose base has sides of lengths b and b'.
  a What is $Vol(\mathscr{R})$ if $b = 2$, $b' = 3$, and $h = 4$?
  b What is $Vol(\mathscr{R})$ if $b = b' = 7$ and $h = 10$?
  c If $Vol(\mathscr{R}) = 10\frac{1}{2}$, $b = 3$, and $h = 7$, what is b'? *Answer*
  d What is h if $Vol(\mathscr{R}) = 363$, $b = 3$, and $b' = h$?
2 The convex solids $\mathscr{R}$ and $\mathscr{S}$ have two parallel supporting
  planes α and β in common, and δ is a plane that is
  between α and β and is parallel to them. If the plane
  sections formed by δ intersecting $\mathscr{R}$ and $\mathscr{S}$ are denoted
  by $\mathscr{A}$ and $\mathscr{B}$ respectively, which of the following
  statements are necessarily correct?
  a The solids $\mathscr{R}$ and $\mathscr{S}$ have equal diameters.
  b The number $d(\alpha, \beta)$ is less than or equal to the diameter of $\mathscr{R}$.

464

c The number $d(\alpha, \delta)$ is less than the number $d(\beta, \delta)$.

d $Vol(\mathcal{R}) = Vol(\mathcal{S})$.

e The regions $\mathcal{A}$ and $\mathcal{B}$ are convex.

f $Ar(\mathcal{A}) = Ar(\mathcal{B})$.

g If the boundary of $\mathcal{R}$ is congruent to the boundary of $\mathcal{S}$, then $Vol(\mathcal{R}) = Vol(\mathcal{S})$.

h By Cavalieri's principle, if $Ar(\mathcal{A}) = Ar(\mathcal{B})$, then $Vol(\mathcal{R}) = Vol(\mathcal{S})$.

3 Let $\mathcal{P}$ denote the right rectangular parallelepiped $ABC \ldots H$ whose dimensions are indicated in D607. What is the area of the section of $\mathcal{P}$ in plane α if α contains the following points?

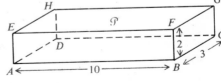

Diagram 607

a A, B, E, and F

b A, E, and G *Answer*

c E, F, and C

d A, F, and G

4 Consider a right circular cylinder $\mathcal{C}$ (D608) whose bases are the circles $C(O, 4)$ and $C(O', 4)$ and $d(O, O') = 10$.

a If a plane α intersects $\mathcal{C}$ and is perpendicular to the axis OO', what is the area of the plane section of $\mathcal{C}$ in α?

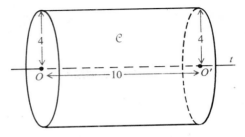

Diagram 608

b Suppose that a plane β intersects $\mathcal{C}$ and is parallel to the line $t = OO'$. What is the area of the plane section if $d(t, \beta) = 1$? *Answer*

5 Show that the square of the length of the longest diagonal of a right rectangular parallelepiped is equal to the sum of the squares of the lengths of any three edges that meet at a vertex.

6 a Find the volume of a cube if its surface area is 5046.

b What is the length of an edge of a cube whose surface area equals its volume? *Answer*

7 The lengths of the three edges at a corner of a right rectangular parallelepiped $\mathcal{P}$ are in the ratio 7 to 5 to 4.

a If $Vol(\mathcal{P})$ is 1120, find the dimensions of $\mathcal{P}$.

b If the surface area of $\mathcal{P}$ is 4150, find $Vol(\mathcal{P})$.

8 What is the volume of a cube if the length of a face diagonal is $5\sqrt{2}$? If the length of a diagonal of the cube is $\sqrt{12}$?

9 Find the volume and the surface area of a cube if a plane section containing two parallel face diagonals has the area $17\sqrt{2}$.

10 a Express the surface area S of a cube in terms of its volume V.

b Express the volume V of a cube in terms of the area K of one of its faces. *Answer*

11 The volume of a right rectangular parallelepiped is 720, and its surface area is 484. If the height of the solid is 10, what are the dimensions of the base? (Hint: Form two equations in two variables.)

12 Find the volume of a triangular prism $\mathcal{T}$ whose height is 12 and whose base is a 3, 4, 5 right triangle.

13 What is the length of a base edge of a square prism $\mathcal{S}$ if its height is 17 and $Vol(\mathcal{S}) = 68$?

14 What is the volume of a regular hexagonal prism $\mathcal{H}$ if its height is 13 and the length of a base edge is $2\sqrt{3}$? *Answer*

15 Assume that the base of a prism is a regular hexagon whose perimeter is $6e$. Give a formula for the volume V of the prism in terms of e and the height h of the prism. Solve the formula for h and simplify your solution.

16 Find the lateral area S of the following right prisms.

a Base: a square, each edge of length 9; height 4

b Base: equilateral triangle, each side of length 8; height 10

c Base: regular hexagon, each side of length 10; height 12 *Answer*

17 What is the volume of a right square prism if its lateral surface area is 72 and its height is 3?

18 What are the base dimensions of a right square prism if its lateral area equals its volume? Do the given conditions determine the height? Explain. *Answer*

19 The base of a triangular prism is equilateral. The height of the prism is 13 and its volume is $832\sqrt{3}$. What is the perimeter of the base of the prism?

20 The base of a solid prism $\mathcal{S}$ is a full regular 66-gon $P_1P_2P_3 \ldots P_{66}$ whose apothem is x and whose edges have length y. What is the volume of $\mathcal{S}$ in terms of x and y if the height is π?

21 State an area analogue to Cavalieri's principle for volume. Illustrate the analogue's correctness for two triangles with equal base length and equal height.

We now want to find the volume formula for pyramids. Then, from this formula, we will be able to find, in an informal way, the volume formula for circular cones. First we will add some standard terms to the formal system.

The distance from the vertex of a pyramid to the base plane is
the height of the pyramid (and also of the solid pyramid).
The distance from the vertex of a circular cone to the base
plane is the height of the cone (and also of the solid cone). (D609)

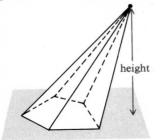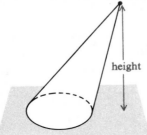

Diagram 609

Convention

Like prisms, pyramids often are classified by the type of base they
have. Thus, a pyramid is rectangular or hexagonal depending
on whether its base is a rectangle or a hexagon. (D610)

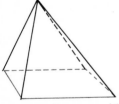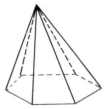

rectangular pyramid   hexagonal pyramid

Diagram 610

Definition 152/8 *Right pyramid, slant height*
A pyramid whose vertex is equidistant from the vertices of
the *n*-gon base is a right pyramid. The distance from the vertex
to its foot in any side of the base is called the slant height
of the right pyramid. (D611)

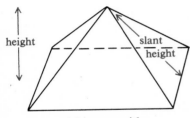

right pyramid

Diagram 611

Our goal is to prove the theorem that the volume of any pyramid is one third its height times the area of its base. We first will show that this is a correct formula for triangular pyramids. Then we will extend the formula to general pyramids. To do this, we need the properties of the next two theorems.

Theorem 215/8

If a pyramid $\mathcal{P}$ with base plane α has base area b and height h and if a pyramid $\mathcal{R}$ has the same vertex as $\mathcal{P}$ and its base is a section of $\mathcal{P}$ contained in a plane parallel to α, then

the base b' and height h' of $\mathcal{R}$ are such that $\dfrac{b'}{b} = \left(\dfrac{h'}{h}\right)^2$. (D612)

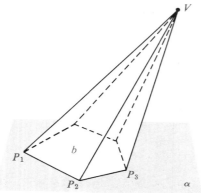

Diagram 612a

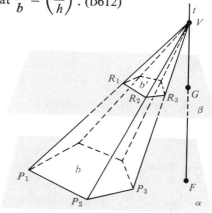

612b

Proof

Let $^{+}P_1P_2P_3 \ldots P_n$ denote the full n-gon in plane α that is the base of the pyramid $\mathcal{P}$, and let V denote the vertex of $\mathcal{P}$. Let β denote a plane that is parallel to α and is such that V and α are in opposite sides of β. Let $R_1, R_2, R_3, \ldots, R_n$ be the intersections of β with the segments $\overline{VP_1}, \overline{VP_2}, \overline{VP_3}, \ldots, \overline{VP_n}$ respectively. Let $\mathcal{R}$ denote the pyramid whose vertex is V and whose base is the full n-gon $^{+}R_1R_2R_3 \ldots R_n$.

Let t denote the line through V that is perpendicular to α at F and to β at G. Then

1 $h = d(V, F)$ and $h' = d(V, G)$.

Define

2 $k = \dfrac{h'}{h} = \dfrac{d(V, G)}{d(V, F)}$.

Let Γ denote the contraction of space at V in the ratio k. The image of F then is the point F' in the closed ray $\overrightarrow{VF}$ such that

3 $d(V, F') = k\, d(V, F)$.

468

Substituting in statement 3 the value of k defined in statement 2 gives

4 $d(V, F') = \dfrac{d(V, G)}{d(V, F)} \cdot d(V, F) = d(V, G).$

Since G is in the closed ray $\overrightarrow{VF}$, statement 4 implies that

5 $F' = G.$

Because Γ maps F onto G, it also maps the plane α, which is perpendicular to t at F, onto the plane perpendicular to t at G, which is β. Thus, a general point A of α is mapped onto the point in β in which $\overrightarrow{VA}$ intersects β. Thus $P_1, P_2, P_3, \ldots, P_n$ are mapped by Γ onto $R_1, R_2, R_3, \ldots, R_n$ respectively. Hence, the base of $\mathscr{P}$ is mapped onto the base of $\mathscr{R}$.

It follows, by Theorem 204/7, that

6 $R_1 R_2 R_3 \ldots R_n \sim P_1 P_2 P_3 \ldots P_n$

and that k is the ratio of similarity. So by Theorem 212/8,

7 $Ar(R_1 R_2 R_3 \ldots R_n) = k^2 \, Ar(P_1 P_2 P_3 \ldots P_n).$

Thus,

8 $b' = k^2 b,$

or

9 $\dfrac{b'}{b} = k^2 = \left(\dfrac{h'}{h}\right)^2,$

which we wished to show.

By using Theorem 215/8 and Cavalieri's principle, we now can show that the volume of a pyramid is completely determined by the height and the base area.

Theorem 216/8

If two pyramids have the same height and have bases with the same area, then they have the same volume. (D613)

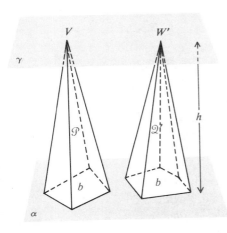

Diagram 613a

613b

469

Proof

Let $\mathscr{P}$ and $\mathscr{Q}$ denote two pyramids each with height h and base area b. Let V and W and α and β denote the vertices and the base planes of $\mathscr{P}$ and $\mathscr{Q}$ respectively.

By Theorem 198/7, there is a motion of space Γ that maps β onto α and maps V onto $W' = W\Gamma$ in the V-side of α. The motion maps $\mathscr{Q}$ onto a congruent pyramid $\mathscr{Q}' = \mathscr{Q}\Gamma$. By Axiom 20/8,

1 $Vol(\mathscr{Q}) = Vol(\mathscr{Q}')$.

From the properties of a motion, the height of the pyramid $\mathscr{Q}'$ is h, since it is the same as that of $\mathscr{Q}$. Similarly, the base of $\mathscr{Q}'$ has area b.

The pyramids $\mathscr{Q}'$ and $\mathscr{P}$ are in the closed solid strip between α and the plane γ that passes through V and W' and is parallel to α.

Consider any plane δ between α and γ that is parallel to both and at a distance x from γ. The section of $\mathscr{P}$ in δ, $\mathscr{P} \cap \delta$, is a full polygon. This is the base of a pyramid with vertex V and height x. If Theorem 215/8 is applied to this pyramid and $\mathscr{P}$, it follows that

2 $\dfrac{Ar(\mathscr{P} \cap \delta)}{b} = \left(\dfrac{x}{h}\right)^2.$

By the same reasoning, the section of $\mathscr{Q}'$ in δ, $\mathscr{Q}' \cap \delta$, is a full polygon that is the base of a pyramid with vertex W' and height x. So by Theorem 215/8,

3 $\dfrac{Ar(\mathscr{Q}' \cap \delta)}{b} = \left(\dfrac{x}{h}\right)^2.$

Comparing statements 2 and 3, it follows that

4 $Ar(\mathscr{P} \cap \delta) = Ar(\mathscr{Q}' \cap \delta).$

So by the Cavalieri principle, Axiom 22/8,

5 $Vol(\mathscr{P}) = Vol(\mathscr{Q}').$

Then, from statements 1 and 5, we obtain

6 $Vol(\mathscr{P}) = Vol(\mathscr{Q}).$

We now can get a formula for the volume of a triangular pyramid, that is, for a tetrahedron.

Theorem 217/8

The volume of a triangular pyramid is one third the product of the area of the base and the height of the pyramid. (D614)

Proof

Let $^+\triangle ABC$ denote the base of a triangular pyramid $\mathscr{P}$ with vertex C'. Let α denote the plane of $\triangle ABC$, and let α' denote the plane through C' that is parallel to α. In α', let $\overrightarrow{C'X}$

470

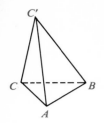 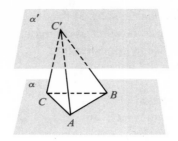 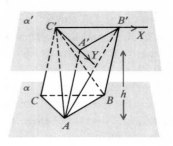

Diagram 614a   614b   614c

denote the closed ray in the direction of $\overset{\rightarrow}{CB}$, and let B'
denote the point in this ray such that
1 $d(C', B') = d(C, B)$.
Let $\overset{\rightarrow}{C'Y}$ denote the closed ray in α' in the direction of $\overset{\rightarrow}{CA}$,
and let A' denote the point in this ray such that
2 $d(C', A') = d(C, A)$.

Now $CBB'C'$ is a parallelogram and $CAA'C'$ is a
parallelogram. Therefore, $\overline{AA'}$ and $\overline{BB'}$ are both parallel
to $\overline{CC'}$, and so they are parallel to each other. Also,
$\overline{AA'} \cong \overline{CC'} \cong \overline{BB'}$; so $ABB'A'$ is a parallelogram.
By the side, side, side congruence theorem,
3 $\triangle ABC \cong \triangle A'B'C'$.

The full triangles $^+\triangle ABC$ and $^+\triangle A'B'C'$ are the bases
of a triangular prism $\mathcal{R}$. If h denotes the distance
between the planes α and α', then h is the height of
both $\mathcal{P}$ and $\mathcal{R}$, and, by Theorem 214/8,
4 $Vol(\mathcal{R}) = Ar(\triangle ABC)h$.

Now consider the triangular pyramid $\mathcal{P}'$ with base $^+\triangle A'B'C'$
in α' and with vertex A. Because $\mathcal{P}$ and $\mathcal{P}'$ have the same
height h and congruent bases, then, by Theorem 216/8,
5 $Vol(\mathcal{P}) = Vol(\mathcal{P}')$.

Also, the interiors of $\mathcal{P}$ and $\mathcal{P}'$ are in opposite sides of
the plane of A, B, and C'; so $\mathcal{P}$ and $\mathcal{P}'$ have no interior
point in common.

Now let $\mathcal{P}''$ denote the triangular pyramid with base $^+\triangle BC'B'$
and vertex A. The height h' of this pyramid is the
distance of A from plane $\beta(B, C', B')$.

Now the pyramid $\mathcal{P}$ also can be regarded as a pyramid
with base $^+\triangle C'BC$ and vertex A. From the parallelogram
$CBB'C'$, we have
6 $\triangle BC'B' \cong \triangle C'BC$.
The pyramid $\mathcal{P}$ with $^+\triangle C'BC$ as its base has the same base area
as $\mathcal{P}''$, and its height is also h', the distance of A
from the plane β. Therefore, by Theorem 216/8,
7 $Vol(\mathcal{P}) = Vol(\mathcal{P}'')$.

471

The interiors of $\mathcal{P}$ and $\mathcal{P}''$ also are in opposite sides of the plane of A, B, and C'; so they have no interior point in common.

Finally, the interiors of $\mathcal{P}'$ and $\mathcal{P}''$ are in opposite sides of the plane of A, B', and C'; so $\mathcal{P}$ and $\mathcal{P}''$ have no interior point in common.

Since the triangular prism $\mathcal{R}$ is the union of $\mathcal{P}$, $\mathcal{P}'$, and $\mathcal{P}''$, and no two of these three pyramids have an interior point in common, the volume of the prism is the sum of the volumes of the pyramids. Since, by statements 5 and 7, the pyramids have equal volume,

8 $Vol(\mathcal{R}) = 3\,Vol(\mathcal{P})$.

From statements 8 and 4, it follows that

9 $Vol(\mathcal{P}) = \frac{1}{3}\,Vol(\mathcal{R}) = \frac{1}{3}h\,Ar(\triangle ABC)$,

which we wished to show.

Now we can establish the volume formula for general pyramids.

Theorem 218/8

The volume of a pyramid is one third the product of the area of the base and the height of the pyramid. (D615)

Proof

Let $^{+}P_1P_2P_3 \ldots P_n$ denote the full n-gon that is the base of a pyramid $\mathcal{P}$ with vertex V and height h. Each of the successive full triangles at P_1, $^{+}\triangle P_1P_2P_3$, $^{+}\triangle P_1P_3P_4$, $\ldots$, $^{+}\triangle P_1P_{n-1}P_n$, is the base of a triangular pyramid with vertex V and height h. The pyramid is the union of these $n - 2$ pyramids. Since no two of these pyramids have an interior point in common,

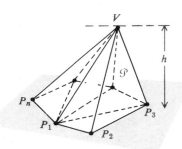

Diagram 615

1 $Vol(\mathcal{P}) = \frac{1}{3}h\,Ar(\triangle P_1P_2P_3) + \frac{1}{3}h\,Ar(\triangle P_1P_3P_4) + \ldots + \frac{1}{3}h\,Ar(\triangle P_1P_{n-1}P_n)$

or

2 $Vol(\mathcal{P}) = \frac{1}{3}h[Ar(\triangle P_1P_2P_3) + Ar(\triangle P_1P_3P_4) + \ldots + Ar(\triangle P_1P_{n-1}P_n)]$.

But the sum in statement 2 is just the area of the full n-gon that is the base of $\mathcal{P}$; so

3 $Vol(\mathcal{P}) = \frac{1}{3}h[Ar(P_1P_2P_3 \ldots P_n)]$.

Now it is easy to see that the volume of a circular cone also should be one third the area of the base times the height. If the base of the circular cone is a circle of radius r, then a regular n-gon can be inscribed in the circular base (D616). If V is the vertex of the cone, then the pyramid that has V as its vertex and the full n-gon as its base is contained in the cone. As the number

472

of sides of the *n*-gon base is increased, the area of the base of the pyramid approaches the area of the base of the cone, and the

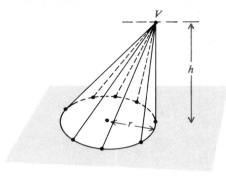

Diagram 616

volume of the pyramid approaches the volume of the cone. This helps to explain the formula for the volume of a circular cone, which is $Vol(\text{Cone}) = \frac{1}{3}\pi r^2 h$.

Exercises

1 A pyramid $\mathcal{P}$ whose vertex is point V is intersected by a plane β that is parallel to the base of the pyramid. Let b and h denote the base area and the height of $\mathcal{P}$ respectively. Let b' denote the area of the section of $\mathcal{P}$ in β, and let h' denote $d(V, \beta)$. If $h' \neq 0$, which of the following statements are necessarily correct?

a $h' < h$.

b The boundary of the section of $\mathcal{P}$ in β is similar to the boundary of the base of $\mathcal{P}$.

c $b' \geqq b$.

d If α denotes the base plane of $\mathcal{P}$, then $d(V, \beta) + d(\beta, \alpha) = h$.

e $\dfrac{b'}{b} = \dfrac{h'}{h}$.

f The section of $\mathcal{P}$ in β is in the V-side of the base plane of $\mathcal{P}$.

g If δ is a plane that passes through V and is parallel to β, then the intersection of $\mathcal{P}$ and the solid strip determined by δ and β is a full pyramid whose vertex is V.

2 In this exercise, use the definitions in exercise 1 for b, b', h, and h'.

a Find h' if $b' = 1$, $b = 4$, and $h = 6$.

b Find b' if $b = 25$, $h' = 2$, and $h = 10$.

c Find b if $b' = 3$, $h = 5$, and $h' = 3$.

d Find h if $b' = h' = 6$ and $b = 10$. *Answer*

e Solve for h in terms of b, b', and h'.

473

3 Three pyramids $\mathcal{P}_1$, $\mathcal{P}_2$, and $\mathcal{P}_3$ have base areas b_1, b_2, and b_3 respectively. Each pyramid has its vertex in a plane α and its base in a plane β. If $\alpha \parallel \beta$, which of the following statements are necessarily correct?

a $b_1 = b_2 = b_3$.

b $Vol(\mathcal{P}_1) = Vol(\mathcal{P}_2) = Vol(\mathcal{P}_3)$.

c The height of $\mathcal{P}_1$ equals the height of $\mathcal{P}_2$ and the height of $\mathcal{P}_3$.

d If $\mathcal{P}_1 \cong \mathcal{P}_2$, then $Vol(\mathcal{P}_1) = Vol(\mathcal{P}_2)$.

e If $Vol(\mathcal{P}_1) = Vol(\mathcal{P}_2)$, then $\mathcal{P}_1 \cong \mathcal{P}_2$.

f The vertices of $\mathcal{P}_1$, $\mathcal{P}_2$, and $\mathcal{P}_3$ are collinear.

g If $b_1 = b_3$, then $Vol(\mathcal{P}_1) = Vol(\mathcal{P}_3)$.

h If $Vol(\mathcal{P}_1) = Vol(\mathcal{P}_3)$, then $b_1 = b_3$.

i If $Vol(\mathcal{P}_2) = Vol(\mathcal{P}_3)$, then $\mathcal{P}_2$ and $\mathcal{P}_3$ have congruent bases.

4 Find the volume of a triangular pyramid if its height is 20 and its base is a right triangle whose legs have measures of 9 and 6 respectively. *Answer*

5 Find the volume of a pyramid if its height is 12 and its base is a triangle whose sides have measures of 10, 10, and 12.

6 The figure in D617 is a cube, and $d(A, B) = 4$. If point V is the center of $EFGH$, what is the volume of the pyramid determined by V, A, B, C, and D?

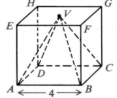

Diagram 617

7 What is the slant height, the lateral area, and the total surface area of the pyramid described in exercise 6?

8 What is the volume of a pyramid if its height is 3 and if its base is a regular hexagon whose sides each have length 4? *Answer*

◆ **9** Prove that the n-gon base of a right pyramid has a circumcircle whose center is the foot in the base plane of the vertex of the pyramid.

10 What are the dimensions of the base of a square pyramid if its volume is 539 and its height is 33?

11 The volume of a pyramid $\mathcal{P}$ with vertex V is 6. The area of the base is 1.

a If the base of $\mathcal{P}$ is fixed, what is the locus of all possible points of V? *Answer*

b What is the maximum possible value of the lateral area?

c If $\mathcal{P}$ is a right pyramid, must the base be a regular n-gon?

12 Find the volume of a right square pyramid whose lateral area is $32\sqrt{13}$ and whose square base has a measure of 8 on each side.

474

13 Find the volume, the lateral area, and the surface area of a right pyramid whose height is 5 and whose base is a regular hexagon with sides of length 10.

14 Let h denote the height of a circular cone, and let $C(P, r)$ denote its circular base. Using $\frac{22}{7}$ as an approximation of π, find the volume of the cone for each of the following values of h and r.

a $h = 3$ and $r = 7$. *Answer*

b $h = 21$ and $r = 5$.

c $r = h = 2\frac{1}{3}$.

15 Using $\frac{22}{7}$ as an approximation of π, find the base radius of a circular cone whose volume is 132 and whose height is 14.7.

16 Using 3.14 as an approximation of π, find the volume of a circular cone whose base radius is 1.4 and whose height is 1.1.

17 What is the volume of a circular cone whose base radius and height are $2\sqrt{3}$ and $5\sqrt{2}$ respectively? *Answer*

18 If $\mathscr{P}$ is a pyramid with vertex V and base plane α, and if β is a plane that is parallel to α and is between V and α, then the intersection of $\mathscr{P}$ with the closed solid strip between α and β is a solid polyhedron $\mathscr{F}$ that is called a *frustum* of the pyramid $\mathscr{P}$ (D618). The distance between α and β is the height of $\mathscr{F}$, and the plane sections of $\mathscr{P}$ in α and β are the bases of $\mathscr{F}$. A frustum of a right pyramid is a right frustum. Let b denote the area of the base common to $\mathscr{F}$ and $\mathscr{P}$, let b' denote the area of the other base of $\mathscr{F}$, and let h denote the height of $\mathscr{F}$. Then the volume of the frustum is given by the formula

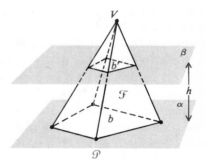

Diagram **618**

$Vol(\mathscr{F}) = \frac{1}{3}h(b + b' + \sqrt{bb'})$.

a Calculate the volume of $\mathscr{F}$ if $b = 36$, $b' = 16$, and $h = 12$.

b Use the information given in exercise 18a to find the height x of the pyramid $\mathscr{P}$. (Hint: See Theorem 215/8.)

c If $\mathscr{P}$ is a right square pyramid, use the information given in exercise 18a to find the lengths of all the edges in $\mathscr{F}$.

◆ 19 Prove the formula given in exercise 18 for the volume of a frustum $\mathscr{F}$ of a pyramid $\mathscr{P}$. (Hint: Let x denote the height of the pyramid $\mathscr{P}$. Express the volume of $\mathscr{F}$ as the difference in volume of two pyramids and use Theorem 215/8.)

475

20 Find the volume of a frustum of a pyramid if the height of the frustum is 15 and the bases are equilateral triangles whose perimeters are 24 and 12.

◆ **21** The nonbase faces of a frustum of a pyramid are known as its *lateral faces*, and the sum of their areas is the *lateral area* of the frustum. Find the lateral area of a frustum of a right square pyramid if the height of the frustum is 4 and the square bases have edge lengths of 16 and 10 respectively. (Hint: Draw top and side views of the frustum.) *Answer*

◆ **22** The frustum of a right square pyramid is shown in D619. If $d(A, B) = 12\sqrt{2}$, $d(A, A') = 10$, and the height of the frustum is 6, what is the volume of the frustum? What is the lateral area?

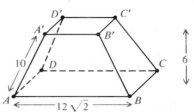

Diagram **619**

◆ **23** If a right circular cone $\mathcal{C}$ with vertex V has base radius r and height h, we can make a reasonable guess concerning the *lateral surface area* of $\mathcal{C}$* (which excludes the base area) as follows (D620). The segments that join V to the circular boundary of the base are congruent and have a common length s (the slant height of $\mathcal{C}$). If the cone is slit along one of these edges and the lateral surface is rolled out in a plane, it covers a region $\mathcal{S}$ contained in the full circle $^+C(V, s)$. The region $\mathcal{S}$ is bounded by two radial segments and part of the circle $C(V, s)$. This circular part has length $2\pi r$, since it is the former circular boundary of the cone's base. If we assume that the areas of $\mathcal{S}$ and of $^+C(V, s)$ are in the same ratio as the lengths of their circular boundaries,

we have $\dfrac{Ar(\mathcal{S})}{\pi s^2} = \dfrac{2\pi r}{2\pi s}$ or

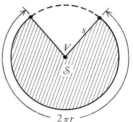

Diagram **620**

$Ar(\mathcal{S}) = $ lateral $Ar(\mathcal{C}) = \pi r s = \pi r \sqrt{r^2 + h^2}$.

a Find the total surface area of a right circular cone whose height is 7 and whose base has radius 4.

b If a right circular cone has a lateral surface area of 35π and a slant height of 7, what is the height of the cone?

---

* We have not defined this area in any formal way, and this is a purely intuitive exercise about a reasonable guess for an area formula.

• 24 A right circular cone $\mathcal{C}$ of height h has vertex V. In terms of h, how far from V is a plane that is parallel to the base of $\mathcal{C}$ and that divides the cone into two parts of equal volume?

We will conclude this very brief treatment of volume with only a few more comments. First, following the pattern for area, we can extend the class of sets having volume by making additional definitions.

Definition 153/8 *Volume sum*

If $\mathcal{S}$ is the union of a finite number of convex solids such that no two of the solids have an interior point in common, then the sum of their volumes is defined to be the volume of $\mathcal{S}$.

Definition 154/8 *Volume difference*

If $\mathcal{R}$ is a convex solid and $\mathcal{R} \cup \mathcal{S}$ is a different convex solid such that no interior point of $\mathcal{R}$ belongs to $\mathcal{S}$, then the volume of $\mathcal{S}$ is defined to be the volume of $\mathcal{R} \cup \mathcal{S}$ minus the volume of $\mathcal{R}$.

In neither of the definitions just given do we require $\mathcal{S}$ to be convex.

Two particular figures, the cylinder and the sphere, are so standard that they are worth mentioning here. The height of a circular cylinder is defined to be the distance between its parallel base planes. Let $^+P_1P_2P_3, \ldots, P_n$ and $^+Q_1Q_2Q_3, \ldots, Q_n$ denote full, congruent regular n-gons that are inscribed in the respective circular bases and are such that the segments $\overline{P_iQ_i}$ are all parallel (D621). The points P_i and Q_i are vertices of a

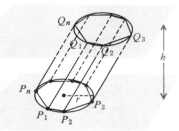

Diagram 621

prism contained in the cylinder. The prism and the cylinder have the same height. As n, the number of sides in the n-gons, is increased, the base area of the prism approaches the base area of the cylinder. Each prism has a volume that is the product of the base area and the height. So, as one would suppose,

Vol(Cylinder) = (base area) × (height) = $\pi r^2 h$, where r is the radius of the circular base and h is the height of the cylinder.

Without attempting any formal proof, we also can give a reasonable argument for the volume of a sphere. Consider a half-sphere, or hemisphere, S with radius r and with its base circle in a plane α (D622a). Also consider a right circular cylinder C_y whose base in α is a full circle with radius r and whose

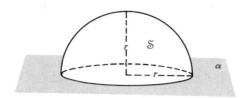

Diagram 622a

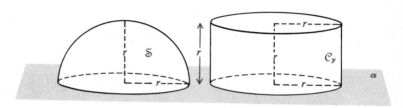

622b

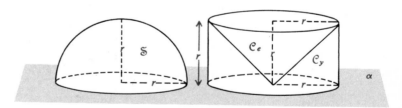

622c

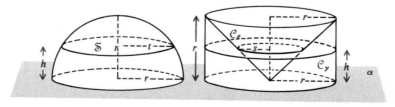

622d ◻▱▮

height also is r. Finally, let C_e denote the right circular cone whose base is the top base of the cylinder C_y and whose vertex is the center of the base of the cylinder in α. The plane of the top base

478

of the cylinder is a supporting plane of the cone and is tangent
to the hemisphere at its topmost point.

Let a plane at distance h from α cut the hemisphere, cylinder,
and cone. The section of the hemisphere in this plane is a full
circle with radius t, and, by the Pythagorean theorem, $t^2 = r^2 - h^2$.
So the area of the section is $\pi t^2 = \pi(r^2 - h^2)$. The section of the
cylinder $\mathcal{C}_y$ is a full circle with radius r and with area πr^2. The
section of the cone is a full circle with radius s. A plane that
contains the common axis of the cone and the cylinder cuts the
cone in an isosceles right triangle (D623). From the similar right
triangles formed, it follows that $s = h$.

The plane section of the cone, therefore, is a full circle whose
area is πh^2.

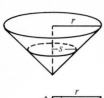

Diagram 623

Now let $\mathcal{R}$ denote the set of points of the cylinder that are
not interior to the cone. The plane section of $\mathcal{R}$ is a circular
ring bounded by concentric circles with radii r and s respectively.
The area of the ring region is the difference area of the two full
concentric circles. Therefore, the area of the plane section of
$\mathcal{R}$ is $\pi r^2 - \pi h^2 = \pi(r^2 - h^2)$.

Comparing this last formula with the formula $\pi t^2 = \pi(r^2 - h^2)$,
it follows that the plane sections of the hemisphere have the same
area as the plane sections of $\mathcal{R}$. If, as seems reasonable, we apply
the Cavalieri principle,* the volume of the hemisphere $\mathcal{S}$ should be
the same as the volume of $\mathcal{R}$. But the volume of $\mathcal{R}$ should be the
difference of the volume of the cylinder and the volume of the
cone. Taking $Vol(\mathcal{C}_y) = \pi r^2 \cdot r = \pi r^3$ and $Vol(\mathcal{C}_e) = \frac{1}{3}\pi r^2 \cdot r = \frac{1}{3}\pi r^3$, we get $Vol(\mathcal{R}) = Vol(\mathcal{S}) = \pi r^3 - \frac{1}{3}\pi r^3 = \frac{2}{3}\pi r^3$. Then the
volume of a sphere, being twice that of the hemisphere, is given
by the formula $Vol[\text{Sphere } S(O, r)] = \frac{4}{3}\pi r^3$.

Exercises

1 For each of the following, find the volume of the
circular cylinder whose base has radius r and whose
height is h. Use $\frac{22}{7}$ as an approximation of π.

  a $h = 7$ and $r = 2$.   **c** $r = h = \frac{7}{22}$. *Answer*

  b $r = 7$ and $h = 10$.   **d** $r = .17$ and $h = 0.1$.

2 What is the diameter of the base of a circular cylinder
whose volume is 648π and whose height is 8? *Answer*

3 The formula $V = \pi r^2 h$ gives the volume V of a circular
cylinder in terms of its base radius r and its height h.
What is the formula for V in terms of the base
circumference c and the height h?

---

* Since $\mathcal{R}$ is not a convex solid, the argument involves an extension of Cavalieri's principle
to a new type of set.

• **4** The surface area of that portion of a cylinder between the base planes is called the *lateral area* of the cylinder. If a right circular cylinder has a base radius r and a height h, explain why a reasonable formula for the lateral area is the following:
Lateral area of right circular cylinder $= 2\pi rh$.
(Hint: See exercise 23, page 476.)

5 Using the formula given in exercise 4, find the lateral area of the following right circular cylinders with base radius r and height h. Use $\frac{22}{7}$ as an approximation of π.

    a $r = 7$ and $h = 5$.   **c** $r = 10$ and $h = 42$. *Answer*
    b $r = \frac{7}{22}$ and $h = 1$.   **d** $r = h = 14$.

6 If the lateral area of a right circular cylinder is 160π and its height is 16, what is its volume? *Answer*

7 If the lateral area and the volume of a right circular cylinder are equal, what is the radius of the base of the cylinder? Is the height of the cylinder a constant? Explain your answer.

8 Find the radius and the height of a right circular cylinder whose volume and lateral area are 294π and 84π respectively.

9 Using $\frac{22}{7}$ as an approximation of π, find the volume of the following spheres.

    a $S(P, 7)$ **b** $S(H, \frac{3}{4})$ **c** $S(C, 2)$

10 A right circular cylinder is *inscribed* in a sphere if both of its bases are contained in the sphere. If a right circular cylinder that has height 6 and base radius 4 is inscribed in a sphere, what is the volume of the sphere?

11 If an expansion of space at a point maps a sphere onto another sphere with a volume twice as great, what is the ratio of expansion?

12 A sphere is inscribed in a cube if it is tangent to all six faces of the cube. What is the ratio of the volume of the cube to the volume of its inscribed sphere? *Answer*

13 If a hemisphere and a right circular cone have the same base and the vertex of the cone is in the hemisphere, prove that the cone has one half the volume of the hemisphere.

14 The "ice-cream cone" in D624 is the union of a right circular cone and a hemisphere that has the same base circle $C(O, r)$ as the cone. What is the height of the cone, in terms of r, if the cone and the hemisphere have the same volume?

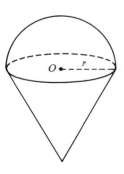

Diagram 624

480

♦ **15** A sphere is inscribed in a regular tetrahedron, that is, the sphere is tangent to all four faces of the tetrahedron. If an edge of the pyramid measures 12, what is the volume of the sphere?

♦ **16** A special case of a discovery by Pappus can be described as follows. Let S denote a plane convex figure that has a center O, and let t denote a line that is in the plane of S but does not intersect the interior of S. If space is rotated about line t, then S sweeps out a solid R in making a complete revolution and returning to its initial position. The center O describes a circle of radius $d(O, t)$, and the formula of Pappus is the following: $Vol(R) = 2\pi[d(O, t) \, Ar(S)]$. Thus, the product of the area of S and the circumference of the circle traversed by O gives the volume of R.

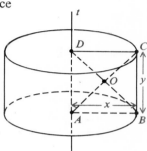

a A full rectangle ^+ABCD revolved about line $t = AD$ generates a right circular cylinder of height $d(B, C) = y$ and base radius $d(A, B) = x$. Use the Pappus formula to find the volume of this cylinder (D625).

b In the plane of the full rectangle ^+ABCD, let t denote the line that is parallel to AD and is such that $d(t, AD) = z$ and $d(t, BC) = x + z$ (D626). Find the volume of the region swept out by ^+ABCD in a revolution of space about t. (Compare the result obtained from the Pappus formula with the result obtained by finding the difference in volume of the two cylinders.) *Answer*

Diagram 625

c Assume that the nearest point of a circular inner tube from the center of symmetry to the tube is r_1 and that the farthest point is r_2. (The nearest and farthest points are the inner and outer radii of the tube.) Using the Pappus formula, find a formula for the volume of the tube. (Such a solid, obtained by revolving a full circle about a line, is called a *torus*.)

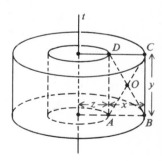

Diagram 626 ▭▪

With the notions of area and volume added to the formal system, we have completed a fairly broad foundation for a three-dimensional Euclidean space. We have defined a large class of plane and solid figures in this space. We have introduced into the system many basic geometrical ideas and have established a number of important relations. We could now go on to apply the ideas and methods we have to different figures and to different types of problems. And the known theorems that we could now prove, without any new axioms, would fill several books.

However, this book is intended to be only an introduction to some of the most important ideas of geometry. And in terms of that purpose we are nearly through. In the next chapter we will prove a few of the basic properties of circles because these are so standard and useful they should not be omitted.

Chapter review

1 Assume that segment $\overline{AB}$ is the hypotenuse of the right triangle $\triangle ABC$ and E is the foot in $\overline{AB}$ of C. Find the measures of the following angles and segments if $d(A, B) = 20$ and $Ar(\triangle ABC) = 100$.

   a $\overline{CE}$ b $\overline{BE}$ c $\measuredangle ECA$ d $\measuredangle EBC$

2 Show that the area of $\triangle ABC$ equals $\dfrac{b}{4}\sqrt{4a^2 - b^2}$ if

$d(A, B) = d(A, C) = a$ and $d(B, C) = b$.

3 Which *one* of the following statements is necessarily false if polygon $ABCD$ is a parallelogram?

   a $Ar(ABCD) = Ar(\triangle ABC) + Ar(\triangle ACD)$.
   b $Ar(ABCD) = d(A, B)\, d(AB, CD)$.
   c $d(A, B)\, d(B, C) \geq Ar(ABCD)$.
   d $Ar(ABCD) = d(C, B)\, d(BC, AD)$.
   e $d(D, C)\, d(A, D) < Ar(ABCD)$.

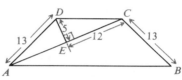

4 From the information given in D627, find the area of the trapezoid $ABCD$.

Diagram 627

5 Each side of $\triangle ABC$ has length x and sides $\overline{PR}$ and $\overline{RQ}$ of $\triangle PQR$ also have length x.

   a If $d(P, Q) = x$, is $Ar(\triangle ABC) = Ar(\triangle PQR)$? Why?
   b Show that $Ar(\triangle ABC) = Ar(\triangle PQR)$ does not necessarily imply that $d(P, Q) = x$.

6 Let $C(O, r)$ denote the circumcircle of $\triangle ABC$, each side of which has length 6.

   a Find r.
   b What is the apothem of $\triangle ABC$?
   c Assuming the formula for the area of a circle, find the area of the plane convex figure bounded by BC and that part of $C(O, r)$ that is not in the A-side of BC.

7 Points D and E are in $\overline{AB}$ and $\overline{AC}$ of $\triangle ABC$ respectively and are such that $DE \parallel BC$ and $\dfrac{d(A, D)}{d(D, B)} = \tfrac{1}{4}$.

   a Are $\overline{AE}$ and $\overline{AC}$ commensurable segments?
   b Does a rotation about A, followed by an expansion or a contraction at A, exist that will map $\overline{AB}$ onto $\overline{AC}$?
   c What is the ratio of $\overline{DE}$ to $\overline{BC}$?
   d If $\overline{DX}$ and $\overline{BY}$ are corresponding altitudes of $\triangle ADE$ and $\triangle ABC$, what is the ratio of $\overline{DX}$ to $\overline{BY}$?

e What is the ratio of $Ar(\triangle ADE)$ to $Ar(\triangle ABC)$?

f What is the ratio of $Ar(BCED)$ to $Ar(\triangle ADE)$?

8 The distance from the vertex V of a right circular cone $\mathcal{C}$ to its base $C(O, 2)$ is 3. Find the area of a section of $\mathcal{C}$ in plane α if each of the following statements is true.

   a Plane α contains points O and V.

   b Plane α is perpendicular to line VO and $d(O, \alpha) = 1$.

9 Segments $\overline{AC}$ and $\overline{AB}$ are two face diagonals of a cube $\mathcal{C}$. If the plane section of $\mathcal{C}$ that contains $\overline{AC}$ and $\overline{AB}$ has an area of $50\sqrt{3}$, what is the volume and the surface area of $\mathcal{C}$?

10 Let V-$ABCD$ denote a square right pyramid, let h denote its height, and let x denote the length of each side of the square base.

   a Find the volume of this pyramid in terms of h and x.

   b Find the lateral surface area of this pyramid in terms of h and x.

   c Find h and x if the volume and the lateral surface area are numerically equal.

11 A tent is to have a canvas floor and is to be in the form of a right circular cone. The circular base is to have a diameter of 12 ft. and the height of the cone is to be 10 ft. If 1% of the material is wasted in the cutting and sewing, how many square yards in all are required for the tent? (Hint: See exercise 23, p. 476.)

12 A subway tunnel is to be $\frac{1}{2}$ mi. long and is to have a cross section shaped like a semicircle with a diameter of 20 ft. If an average of 10π cu. yd. of dirt are removed each working day, how many such days will it take to remove the dirt that is necessary to form the tunnel?

13 A nonsquare rectangle $\mathcal{R}$ has sides of lengths x and y, where $x > y$. A square $\mathcal{S}$ has sides of length $z = \dfrac{x + y}{2}$.

   a Show that $\mathcal{R}$ and $\mathcal{S}$ have equal perimeters.

   b Show that $x > z > y$.

   c Show that, if $a = x - z$, then $a = z - y$.

   d Using exercise 13c, show that $Ar(\mathcal{R}) = z^2 - a^2$ and, hence, that $Ar(\mathcal{S}) > Ar(\mathcal{R})$. (This proves that, for all rectangles of a given perimeter, the square has the greatest area.)

14 Show that the ratio of the volume of a sphere to the volume of the right circular cylinder circumscribed about the sphere is $\frac{2}{3}$.

15 Indicate whether each of the following statements is necessarily true (T), possibly true (P), or necessarily false (F).

   a The area of parallelogram $HJKG$ is $d(H, J)\, d(K, G)$.

   b If the length of the hypotenuse of a right triangle is x, then the area of the triangle is less than $(\frac{1}{2})x^2$.

   c For every polygon, there exists a circumcircle.

d If $\overline{AX}$ is a median of the equilateral triangle $\triangle ABC$, then the apothem of $\triangle ABC$ equals $\frac{1}{3}d(A, X)$.

e The area of an equilateral triangle is greater than its perimeter.

f If $\triangle ABC \sim \triangle DEF$, then altitudes $\overline{AX}$ and $\overline{DY}$ have the same ratio as altitudes $\overline{BG}$ and $\overline{EH}$.

g $\pi > \frac{22}{7}$.

h If the ratio of corresponding sides of two triangles is $\frac{1}{4}$, then the ratio of their areas is $\frac{1}{16}$.

i If two convex solids have two parallel supporting planes in common, and if a plane that is parallel to these planes and between them intersects the two solids in plane convex figures with areas equal to each other, then the two solids have the same volume.

j If two pyramids have the same base and the same height, they have the same volume.

k Among all rectangles with the same area, the square has the greatest perimeter.

Cumulative review

1 Assume that the two points A and B in line t have coordinates a and b respectively. For each of the following values of a and b, find the value, or the values, that the coordinate of the midpoint of $\overline{AB}$ may have.

a $a = -81$ and $b = -3$.

b $a = -\frac{3}{4}$ and $b = \frac{5}{11}$.

c $a = 0$ and the altitudes of equilateral triangle $\triangle ABC$ have length $6\sqrt{3}$.

d $a = \pi$ and $d(A, B) = 7$.

e $b = -2$ and the diagonal length of square $ABCD$ is 6.

f $a = 3$ and $\overline{AB}$ is a diameter of the circle $C(B, \frac{4}{3})$.

2 a If sides $\overline{AC}$ and $\overline{BC}$ of $\triangle ABC$ are congruent, what is the locus of all points X such that $\triangle ABX \cong \triangle ABC$?

b If sides $\overline{AC}$ and $\overline{BC}$ of $\triangle ABC$ are not congruent, what is the locus of all points X such that $\triangle ABX \cong \triangle ABC$?

3 Let a triangle determined by 3 of the 8 vertices of a cube be called a *cube-triangle*. Not all such triangles are congruent, but many of them are. If $\mathcal{S}$ is a set of triangles and every cube-triangle of a particular cube is congruent to some member of $\mathcal{S}$, what is the least number of triangles in $\mathcal{S}$?

4 Explain what the following notations represent.

a $d(\alpha, \beta)$

b $\measuredangle \alpha' \, t \, \beta''$

c $t \perp \alpha$

d $ABCD \sim EFGH$

e $S(A, 7)$

f $d(A, \mathcal{S})$

g $A\Gamma$

h $+HJKLM$

i $\mathcal{R} \cong \mathcal{R}\Gamma$

j $\measuredangle X\text{-}AB\text{-}Y$

k Ψ^{-1}

l $(P_1, P_2, P_3, \ldots, P_n)$

5 Let $C(D, d)$, $C(E, e)$, and $C(F, f)$ denote the three excircles of $\triangle ABC$, and let P denote its centroid.

  a Is P necessarily the centroid of $\triangle DEF$?

  b If each side of $\triangle ABC$ has length 6, what is the length of $\overline{PD}$?

  c In exercise 5b, what is the ratio of $\overline{CP}$ to $\overline{EP}$?

6 Assume that the two planes α and β intersect in the line t that separates the two planes into the open half-planes α', α'', β', and β''. If $\measuredangle ABC$ is a plane angle of a dihedral angle between α and β, indicate whether each of the following statements is necessarily true (T), possibly true (P), or necessarily false (F).

  a $\overline{AB} \perp t$.

  b $\overline{AB} \perp \alpha$.

  c $\measuredangle ABC^\circ = (\measuredangle \alpha \ t \ \beta)^\circ$.

  d $t \perp \overline{AC}$.

  e If $\measuredangle ABC^\circ = 90$, then $\alpha \perp \beta$.

  f If $\alpha \perp \beta$, then $\measuredangle ABC^\circ = 90$.

  g $t \perp \theta(A, B, C)$.

  h $\overline{AC} \perp \overline{BC}$.

  i If $\measuredangle A'BC \cong \measuredangle ABC$, then $\overrightarrow{BA} = \overrightarrow{BA'}$.

  j $\overline{AB} \perp \overline{BC}$.

  k If $\measuredangle RST$ is a plane angle of a dihedral angle between α and β, then $\measuredangle RST$ is either congruent or supplementary to $\measuredangle ABC$.

7 Quadrilateral $\mathfrak{Q}_1$ has sides of lengths x, $x + 1$, $2x$, and $4x - 3$ in order of increasing size. Quadrilateral $\mathfrak{Q}_2$ has sides of lengths $y + 1$, $2y - 4$, $2y + 2$, and $3y + 3$ in order of increasing size. What are the dimensions of $\mathfrak{Q}_1$ and $\mathfrak{Q}_2$ if they are similar polygons?

8 In a plane α, line t is perpendicular to three parallel lines a, b, and c at points A, B, and C respectively. If $<C, B, A>$, $d(C, B) = 3$, and $d(B, A) = 2$, which product of the three mappings defined below maps a onto c and c onto b?

  Γ: translation of α by distance 5 in the direction $\overrightarrow{AB}$

  Ψ: reflection of α in line a

  Φ: contraction of α at point C of ratio $\frac{3}{5}$

9 If P does not belong to a set $\mathfrak{S}$ but has a foot F in $\mathfrak{S}$, then which of the following statements are correct?

  a $d(P, \mathfrak{S}) = d(P, F)$.

  b $\mathfrak{S}$ must be a bounded set.

  c There exists a sphere $S(P, r)$ such that none of its interior points belongs to $\mathfrak{S}$.

  d $\overrightarrow{PF}$ intersects $\mathfrak{S}$ in at least two points.

e Point F is a boundary point of S.

f For all other points X of S, $d(P, X) \geq d(P, F)$.

g Line PF cannot be a supporting line of S.

10 Use D628 to help you match each "part" of the pyramid in the column at the left with its correct name in the column at the right.

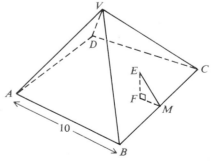

column 1	*column* 2
a V	A Diagonal
b $\not{\triangleleft} VAC$	B Supporting plane
c $^+\triangle ABC$	C "The" vertex
d α	D Base
e $\overline{VB}$	E Edge
f $\not{\triangleleft} A\text{-}VC\text{-}B$	F Face angle
	G Dihedral angle

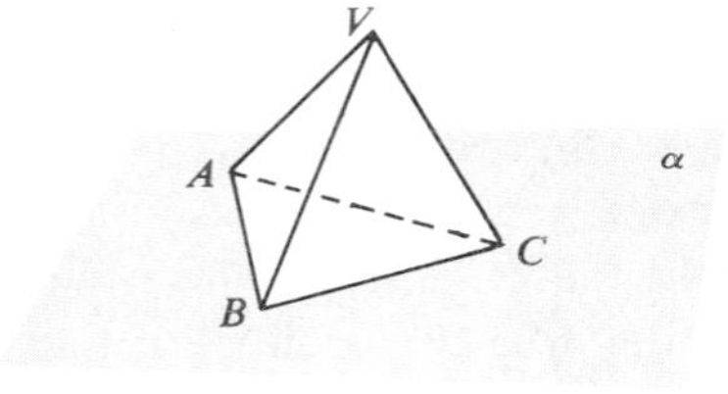

Diagram **628**

11 Point M is between the two parallel planes α and β, and $\triangle ABC$ is contained in α. A mapping Γ of α onto β is defined in the following way: For all points X in α, $X\Gamma$ (denoted X') in β equals the intersection of β and the open ray $\overrightarrow{XM}$.

a If $\overline{AM} \cong \overline{MA'}$, must M be in the midplane of α and β?

b Is $AC \parallel A'C'$? Are all lines in α parallel to their image lines?

c Are the open rays $\overrightarrow{BC}$ and $\overrightarrow{B'C'}$ like directed or oppositely directed?

d Must $\triangle ABC$ and $\triangle A'B'C'$ be congruent? Must they be similar?

e Is the ratio of $\overline{CB}$ to $\overline{C'B'}$ equal to the ratio of $\overline{CM}$ to $\overline{C'M'}$?

12 Point P is interior to $\triangle XYZ$ and is 2 units from XZ, 5 units from YZ, and 7 units from XY. If the measures of $\not{\triangleleft} Y$ and $\not{\triangleleft} Z$ are 90 and 60 respectively, what is the area of $\triangle XYZ$?

13 The pyramid $V\text{-}ABCD$, with vertex V, has a full square for a base and full equilateral triangles for faces (D629). Point E is the centroid of $\triangle VBC$, point F is the foot of E in ^+ABCD, and M is the midpoint of $\overline{BC}$. If all the edges of the pyramid have length 10, what is the area of $\triangle EFM$?

Diagram **629**

14 Let e denote the length of an edge of a regular tetrahedron.

a Find the volume of the tetrahedron in terms of e.

b Find the surface area of the tetrahedron in terms of e.

Chapter **9**

Circles and circular arcs

Angle and arc properties of circles

34/9

In this chapter, we want to establish some of the standard properties of circles that are particularly useful. However, so many properties of circles are known that we will be able to deal with only a few of them.

We will begin with the notion of two opposite arcs in a circle.

Definition 155/9 *Opposite circular arcs*

If A and B are two points of a circle $C(O, r)$, the points of the circle in one side of the secant line AB form an open circular arc of the circle. The points of the circle in the other side of AB form an opposite open circular arc. Each arc with the two points A and B is a closed circular arc, and the two arcs are opposite closed arcs. Points A and B are the endpoints of all four arcs, and chord $\overline{AB}$ is the endpoint chord of all four arcs.

Conventions

Unless otherwise stated, the term *arc* will mean a closed circular arc. In some cases, we will indicate the two opposite closed arcs with endpoints A and B by the notation $\widehat{AB}'$ and $\widehat{AB}''$.

Sometimes, however, an arc will be indicated by its endpoints and a third point of the arc. (D630) Thus, the notation $\overparen{APB}$ will denote an arc that has endpoints A and B and that passes through point P. Point P is said to be between A and B in the arc, and, in the notation $\overparen{APB}$, the letter P always is placed between the letters for the endpoints. Thus $\overparen{APB}$ and $\overparen{BPA}$ are the same closed arc. Clearly, if R is any other point of arc $\overparen{APB}$ that is between A and B, then $\overparen{APB} = \overparen{ARB}$. If $\overparen{APB}$ and $\overparen{AQB}$ are different arcs of the same circle, then they are opposite arcs. An arc $\overparen{APB}$ and its endpoint chord $\overline{AB}$ are said to *subtend* each other. Each three points A, P, and B in a circle $C(O, r)$ are noncollinear, and $C(O, r)$ is the circumcircle of $\triangle APB$. Because the three points A, P, and B determine the circle, we will denote the circle that contains arc $\overparen{APB}$ by the notation $\odot APB$. Thus, the fact that $\overparen{APB}$ is contained in $C(O, r)$ is equivalent to $C(O, r) = \odot APB$.

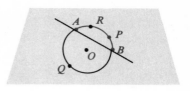

Diagram 630

Definition 156/9 *Minor arc, major arc*

An arc $\overparen{APB}$ is a minor arc if P and the center of $\odot APB$ are in opposite sides of the secant AB. (D631) An arc that is not a minor arc is a major arc.

Definition 157/9 *Semicircle*

A major arc $\overparen{AQB}$ whose endpoints are collinear with the center of $\odot AQB$ is a semicircle. (D632) ($\overline{AB}$ is a diameter.)

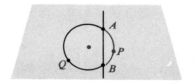

Diagram 631

Comment

The opposite arc of a minor arc is always a major arc. The opposite arc of a major arc is a minor arc unless the major arc is a semicircle, in which case both of the opposite arcs are semicircles.

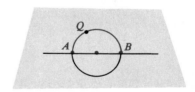

Diagram 632

Exercises

1 In a plane α, if the circle $C(O, r)$ is intersected by a line t in the two points P and Q, which of the following statements are necessarily true? *Answer*

a In $C(O, r)$, the line t determines two opposite open arcs and two opposite closed arcs.

b Chord $\overline{PQ}$ is the endpoint chord for the four arcs determined by the secant line t.

c Any two points in $C(O, r)$ determine an endpoint chord for two opposite closed arcs.

488

d If P and Q are endpoints of a major arc, then they are not endpoints of a minor arc.

e If $\overparen{PAQ}$ is a minor arc, then $\overline{PQ}$ is not a diameter.

f If $\overparen{PAQ}$ is a minor arc, its opposite arc is a major arc.

g The opposite arc of a major arc is always a minor arc.

h The union of a closed arc and its opposite arc is always the circle of the arcs.

i The intersection of two open arcs is always an open arc.

j The union of two open arcs is always an open arc.

2 In a plane β, circle $C(O, r)$ is intersected by a line m in the two points H and J (D633). If points C and D in $C(O, r)$ are in one side of m and points A and B in $C(O, r)$ are in the opposite side of m, which of the following statements are necessarily true?

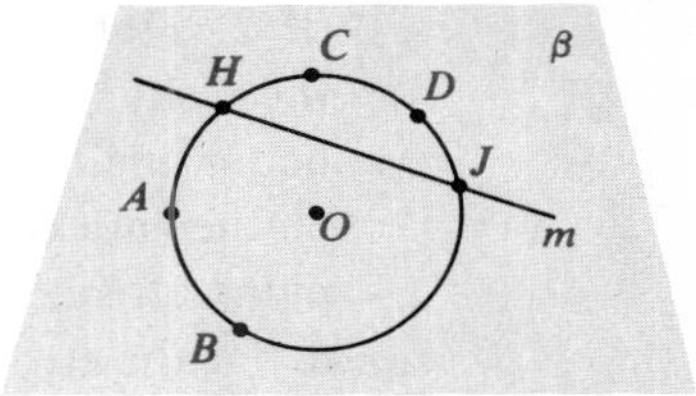

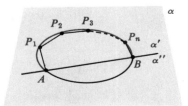

a $\overparen{HCJ} = \overparen{HDJ}$.

b $\overparen{HAJ} = \overparen{HBD}$.

c $\odot AHC = \odot BJD$.

d $C(O, r) = \odot BDH$.

e $d(C, m) < r$.

f $d(H, J) \leq 2r$.

Diagram 633

g If $d(H, J) = 2r$, then $\overparen{HCJ}$ is a semicircle.

h If $\overparen{HAJ}$ is a major arc, then $\overparen{HCJ}$ is a minor arc.

i If $<H, O, J>$, then both $\overparen{HBJ}$ and $\overparen{HDJ}$ are major arcs.

j If $\overparen{HAJ} = \overparen{HQJ}$, then Q is in the A-side of m.

k If $\overparen{HBJ}$ is a minor arc, then $\overparen{HCJ}$ is a major arc.

l Chord $\overline{HB}$ subtends $\overparen{HAB}$ and $\overparen{HJB}$.

m If $\overparen{HB'}$ denotes $\overparen{HAB}$, then $\overparen{HB''}$ denotes $\overparen{HJB}$.

n The union of $\overparen{HD'}$ and $\overparen{HD''}$ is $C(O, r)$.

In the last chapter, we talked, in a descriptive way, about the circumference of a circle. However, we have not yet given any formal definition of the length of an arc of a curve. Such a definition usually is based on the following ideas. Let A and B denote two points of a closed convex curve that is in a plane α (D634). Let α' and α'' denote the sides in α of line AB. The two points A and B and all points of the curve that are in AB or in α' form a set $\mathcal{S}$ that is an arc of the curve. If $P_1, P_2, P_3, \ldots, P_n$

Diagram 634

489

are n points in S and none of these points is A or B, one can define what it means for the ordered set $(A, P_1, P_2, \ldots, P_n, B)$ to be successive in S in that order. This definition corresponds to the notation of going from A to B along S and passing through the points $(P_1, P_2, P_3, \ldots, P_n)$ in that order. The ordered set of segments $(\overline{AP_1}, \overline{P_1P_2}, \overline{P_2P_3}, \ldots, \overline{P_nB})$ form a segment path from A to B that is "attached" to arc S. This segment path has a length, a real number x, that is the sum of the lengths of the segments in the path.

If the path just described happens to be the arc S, it is natural to define x as the length of S. If the path is not S, there are two rather natural requirements for whatever number a we take for the length of the arc. One is that the number a, which is the length of S, should be greater than x. The second requirement is that there should be segment paths attached to S whose lengths give better and better approximations of a. To express these ideas in a mathematical way, we consider *all* the paths from A to B that are paths attached to S and whose vertices are successive in S. We define the arc length a to be the least number such that no segment path from A to B (of the proper type) has a length greater than a.

To treat arc length with accuracy, one first has to determine which arcs have length; that is, one has to determine when the number a of the definition given in the paragraph above actually exists.* To settle this basic question and to obtain even simple properties of arc length require the use of limits. For this reason, we will not consider the subject of arc lengths in any formal way.

In the special case of a circular arc, however, it is possible to define an *angular measure* of an arc that is not its length but that acts as a useful substitute for length.

Definition 158/9 *Central angle of a circle*

An angle that is in the plane of a circle and whose vertex is the center of the circle is a central angle of the circle. The arc whose endpoints are in a central angle and whose open arc is interior to the angle is the arc that subtends the central angle. (D635)

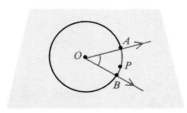

$\overset{\frown}{APB}$ subtends central angle $\measuredangle AOB$.

Diagram 635

Definition 159/9 *Angular arc measure*

The angular measure of a minor arc $\overset{\frown}{APB}$ in a circle $C(O, r)$ is the measure of the central angle $\measuredangle AOB$ that the arc $\overset{\frown}{APB}$ subtends.

---

* If a does exist, the arc is said to be *rectifiable*. Though convex arcs are rectifiable, there exist curves with arcs that are not rectifiable.

The angular measure of an arc that is a semicircle is 180.
The angular measure of a major arc $\overset{\frown}{APB}$ that is not a
semicircle is 360 minus the angular measure of the minor arc
opposite $\overset{\frown}{APB}$.

Convention

We will denote the angular measure of the circular arc $\overset{\frown}{APB}$
by the notation $\overset{\frown}{APB}°$. Unless otherwise stated, the measure
of an arc will be understood to mean the angular measure
of a circular arc. (D636)

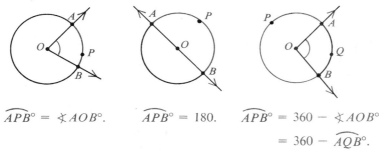

$\overset{\frown}{APB}° = \angle AOB°.$ $\overset{\frown}{APB}° = 180.$ $\overset{\frown}{APB}° = 360 - \angle AOB°$

$= 360 - \overset{\frown}{AQB}°.$

Diagram 636

Comment

From the definition of angular arc measure, it follows that
the sum of the measure of two opposite arcs is 360.

The angular measure of an arc clearly does not tell us the
length of the arc. But, as we would suppose, we can define conditions under which arcs of the same measure are congruent and so
must have properties that we would expect for arcs of the same
length. Also, we can obtain an additive property for angular
measure that tells us that the measure of $\overset{\frown}{APB}$ is the sum of the
measures of the arcs $\overset{\frown}{AP}$ and $\overset{\frown}{PB}$ that are contained in $\overset{\frown}{APB}$. Thus,
the angular measure of arcs gives us a way of comparing arcs
without using the actual lengths of the arcs.

The foundation properties of arcs and their angular measures
form a pattern very much like the pattern we encountered with
segments. For example, it seems clear, from D637, that the sum of
the measures of the arcs $\overset{\frown}{AP}$ and $\overset{\frown}{PB}$ that are contained in $\overset{\frown}{APB}$ is
the measure of $\overset{\frown}{APB}$. If $\overset{\frown}{APB}$ is a minor arc that subtends the
central angle $\angle AOB$, the proof of the relation is straightforward.
The measure of $\angle AOB$ is the measure of $\overset{\frown}{APB}$ and also is the
sum of the measures of $\angle AOP$ and $\angle POB$. Since the measures
of $\angle AOP$ and $\angle POB$ also are the measures of $\overset{\frown}{AP}$ and $\overset{\frown}{PB}$,
$\overset{\frown}{APB}° = \overset{\frown}{AP}° + \overset{\frown}{PB}°.$

491

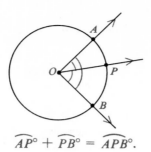

$$\overarc{AP}^\circ + \overarc{PB}^\circ = \overarc{APB}^\circ.$$

Diagram 637

If $\overarc{APB}$ is a semicircle with center O, then, by definition, $\overarc{APB}^\circ = 180$ and also, by Theorem 28/2, $\sphericalangle AOP^\circ + \sphericalangle POB^\circ = 180$ (D638). Since $\overarc{AP}^\circ = \sphericalangle AOP^\circ$ and $\overarc{PB}^\circ = \sphericalangle POB^\circ$, we again get $\overarc{APB}^\circ = \overarc{AP}^\circ + \overarc{PB}^\circ$.

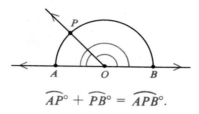

$$\overarc{AP}^\circ + \overarc{PB}^\circ = \overarc{APB}^\circ.$$

Diagram 638

The relation also is correct if $\overarc{APB}$ is a major arc that is not a semicircle. However, a proof for such an arc requires the use of the relation established for minor arcs and semicircles and the consideration of several different positions of P in arc $\overarc{APB}$. The idea of a proof for one case is shown in D639.

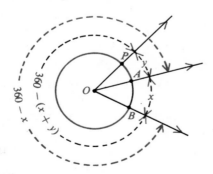

$$360 - x = y + [360 - (x + y)].$$
$$\overarc{APB}^\circ = \overarc{AP}^\circ + \overarc{PB}^\circ.$$

Diagram 639

What is true of this particular basic relation of arcs is true of some of their other simple properties. That is, while the relations are easy to see, the proofs require considerable time and detail. Instead of taking the time and space to prove these relations, we will state a number of them as starred theorems.

Definition 160/9 *Subarc, adjacent arcs*

An arc that is contained in another arc is said to be a subarc of the other. Two arcs that are contained in the same circle and that have only an endpoint in common are said to be adjacent arcs of the circle.

* Theorem 219/9

Corresponding to each point P between A and B in arc $\overarc{AB}$, there are two adjacent subarcs $\overarc{AP}$ and $\overarc{PB}$ such that $\overarc{APB}$ is the union of these arcs, and the measure of $\overarc{APB}$ is the sum of the measures of $\overarc{AP}$ and $\overarc{PB}$. That is, $\overarc{APB}° = \overarc{AP}° + \overarc{PB}°$.

* Corollary 219/9

Each of the subarcs $\overarc{AP}$ and $\overarc{PB}$ of $\overarc{APB}$ has a measure that is less than the measure of $\overarc{APB}$.

Exercises

1 The four points A, B, C, and D are in circle $C(O, r)$, and no two of these points are collinear with O (D640).

  a Which of the angles $\sphericalangle AOB$, $\sphericalangle DCB$, $\sphericalangle CBO$, and $\sphericalangle DOC$ are central angles of $C(O, r)$?

  b Must $P = O$ if $\sphericalangle BPC$ is a central angle of $C(O, r)$?

  c Must M and N be in $C(O, r)$ if $\sphericalangle MON$ is a central angle of $C(O, r)$?

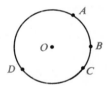

Diagram 640

  d For all points R and S, is $\sphericalangle ROS$ a central angle of $C(O, r)$? *Answer*

  e From the information given in D640, which arc subtends the central angle $\sphericalangle AOC$?

2 The minor arc $\overarc{APB}$ subtends the central angle $\sphericalangle AOB$ of circle $C(O, r)$, and Q is in the arc opposite $\overarc{APB}$ (D641).

  a What is the measure of $\overarc{APB}$ if $\sphericalangle AOB° = 36$? If $\sphericalangle AOB° = \pi$? If $\sphericalangle AOB° = 179$?

  b What is the measure of $\overarc{AQB}$ if $\sphericalangle AOB° = 90$? If $\sphericalangle AOB° = 1$? If $\sphericalangle AOB° = 179$? If $\sphericalangle AOB° = \pi$? *Answer*

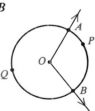

Diagram 641

  c What is the measure of $\overarc{APB}$ and $\overarc{AQB}$ if A, O, and Q are collinear and $\sphericalangle BQO° = 35$? *Answer*

  d What is the length of $\overline{AB}$ if $\overarc{APB}° = 60$? If $\overarc{APB}° = 90$?

e What is x if $x = \overset{\frown}{APB}° + \overset{\frown}{BQA}°$?

f Under the conditions stated, which of the following sets could be collinear: $\{A, O, P\}$, $\{B, Q, O\}$, $\{Q, P, O\}$, and $\{Q, A, B\}$?

3 If points $A, B, C, \ldots, H$ are in circle $C(O, r)$ and are located as shown in D642, which of the following statements are necessarily true?

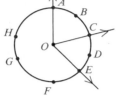

a $\overset{\frown}{ABC}$ is a subarc of $\overset{\frown}{ABD}$.

b $\overset{\frown}{BCD}$ is a subarc of $\overset{\frown}{AEF}$.

c $\overset{\frown}{ACF}$ is a subarc of $\overset{\frown}{DEG}$.

d $\overset{\frown}{ABC}$ and $\overset{\frown}{BCD}$ are adjacent arcs.

e $\overset{\frown}{AEF}$ and $\overset{\frown}{FGH}$ are adjacent arcs.

f $\overset{\frown}{ABC}$ and $\overset{\frown}{CDB}$ are adjacent arcs.

g $\overset{\frown}{ABC}$ and $\overset{\frown}{CDA}$ are adjacent arcs.

Diagram 642

4 Using D642, decide which arc has measure x if each of the following is true.

a $\overset{\frown}{ACE}° = \overset{\frown}{ABC}° + x$.

b $\overset{\frown}{HAD}° - \overset{\frown}{BCD}° = x$.

c $\overset{\frown}{HGC}° + x = 360$.

d $\overset{\frown}{AHG}° + \overset{\frown}{GFE}° = x - \overset{\frown}{CDE}°$.

e $x = \sphericalangle AOD°$. *Answer*

5 Use the information given in exercise 3 to answer the following questions.

a Does $x < \overset{\frown}{ABD}°$ imply $x < \overset{\frown}{ABC}°$?

b If $\overset{\frown}{ABD}° = 95$ and $\sphericalangle COD° = 35$, what is the value of $\overset{\frown}{ABC}°$? *Answer*

c If $\overset{\frown}{ACF}° = \overset{\frown}{AHF}°$ and $<C, O, G>$, must $\overset{\frown}{CDF}$ and $\overset{\frown}{GHA}$ have the same measure?

d Which has the greater measure, $\overset{\frown}{AGC}$ or the arc opposite $\overset{\frown}{ADE}$?

We already have observed that any two circles are similar and any two circles that have equal radii are congruent. Suppose that $\overset{\frown}{AB'}$ is a minor arc of a circle $C(X, r)$ with opposite major arc $\overset{\frown}{AB''}$ and that $\overset{\frown}{CD'}$ is a minor arc of a circle $C(Y, s)$ with opposite major arc $\overset{\frown}{CD''}$ (D643). If $\overset{\frown}{AB'}$ and $\overset{\frown}{CD'}$ have the same measure, then $\overset{\frown}{AB''}$

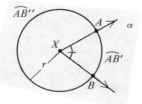
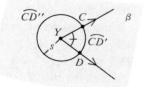

Diagram 643

494

and $\overset{\frown}{CD''}$ also have the same measure. The central angles $\sphericalangle AXB$ and $\sphericalangle CYD$ are congruent. Also there is a motion of space Γ that maps X onto Y, $\overrightarrow{XA}$ onto $\overrightarrow{YC}$, and $\overrightarrow{XB}$ onto $\overrightarrow{YD}$ (D644). Then

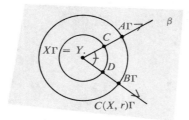

Diagram 644

Γ maps $C(X, r)$ onto a circle that is concentric with $C(Y, s)$ and is such that Y, C, and $A\Gamma$ are collinear and Y, D, and $B\Gamma$ are collinear. Now there clearly is an expansion or a contraction of space, say Ψ, that maps the circle $C(X, r)\Gamma$ onto $C(Y, s)$. Under the product $\Gamma\Psi$, which is a similarity of space, $\overset{\frown}{AB'}$ maps onto $\overset{\frown}{CD'}$ and $\overset{\frown}{AB''}$ maps onto $\overset{\frown}{CD''}$. So the arcs of equal measure are similar. Also, if $r = s$, these arcs are congruent.

Since the kind of argument that was just given can be applied to semicircles, we have the following basic theorem.

---

* Theorem 220/9

Two arcs are similar if and only if they have the same measure. They are congruent if and only if they have the same measure and belong to congruent circles.

* Corollary 220a/9

Arcs that are opposite congruent arcs are congruent.

* Corollary 220b/9

The endpoint chords of congruent arcs are congruent.

Conventions

That arcs $\overset{\frown}{APB}$ and $\overset{\frown}{CQD}$ are similar will be denoted by the sentence $\overset{\frown}{APB} \sim \overset{\frown}{CQD}$. That these arcs are congruent will be denoted by the sentence $\overset{\frown}{APB} \cong \overset{\frown}{CQD}$.

Comment

In particular, it should be noted that $\overset{\frown}{APB}° = \overset{\frown}{CQD}°$ implies only similarity of the arcs. It does not imply congruence of the arcs unless $\odot APB$ and $\odot CQD$ are congruent circles. But from this it follows that, if $\overset{\frown}{APB}$ and $\overset{\frown}{CQD}$ are arcs of the same circle, then $\overset{\frown}{APB}° = \overset{\frown}{CQD}°$ does imply $\overset{\frown}{APB} \cong \overset{\frown}{CQD}$.

By using the motions of space, one can also establish the following theorem.

If $\overset{\frown}{AB}$ and $\overset{\frown}{CD}$ are congruent chords of congruent circles, then either the opposite minor and major arcs in the pair $\overset{\frown}{AB'}$ and $\overset{\frown}{AB''}$ are congruent to the opposite minor and major arcs in the pair $\overset{\frown}{CD'}$ and $\overset{\frown}{CD''}$ respectively, or all four of the arcs are congruent semicircles.

Exercises

1 Consider the three relations $\overset{\frown}{AB} = \overset{\frown}{CD}$, $\overset{\frown}{AB} \sim \overset{\frown}{CD}$, and $\overset{\frown}{AB} \cong \overset{\frown}{CD}$.

   a Which relation implies the other two? *Answer*
   b Which relation implies one of the others but not both?

2 Make a diagram to illustrate a situation in which $\overset{\frown}{AB}{}^\circ = \overset{\frown}{CD}{}^\circ$ but where $\overline{AB}$ is not congruent to $\overline{CD}$.

3 If $\overset{\frown}{APB}$ and $\overset{\frown}{AQB}$ are two circular arcs such that P and Q are coplanar with AB and are in the same side of AB, must the arcs be congruent? Explain your answer.

4 If $\overset{\frown}{APB}$ denotes a given circular arc, explain why there is one and only one circle that contains this arc.

5 Must similar arcs of the same circle be congruent? *Answer*

6 Is the following statement a theorem? "If the arcs $\overset{\frown}{APB}$ and $\overset{\frown}{CQD}$ belong to similar circles and if $\overline{AB} \cong \overline{CD}$, then $\overset{\frown}{APB}$ is similar either to $\overset{\frown}{CQD}$ or to the arc opposite $\overset{\frown}{CQD}$."

7 Which of the following statements are necessarily correct?

   a If two arcs are similar, then their opposite arcs are similar.
   b If two arcs have equal angular measure, then their opposite arcs have equal angular measure.
   c If two arcs have equal angular measure, then the chords they subtend are congruent.
   d If two arcs of the same circle have the same angular measure, then the chords they subtend are congruent.
   e If two arcs of the same circle subtend congruent chords, then the arcs are congruent.

8 Circles $C_1(O, 4)$ and $C_2(O, 7)$ are concentric. The closed rays $\overset{\cdot\cdot\rightarrow}{OA}$ and $\overset{\rightarrow}{OB}$ intersect C_1 and C_2 in points X and A and in points Y and B respectively so that $\sphericalangle AOB^\circ = 60$ (D645). Let $\overset{\frown}{XY'}$ and $\overset{\frown}{AB'}$ denote minor arcs of C_1 and C_2 respectively.

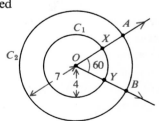

Diagram 645

   a What is the measure of the arcs $\overset{\frown}{XY'}$ and $\overset{\frown}{AB'}$? Of the arcs $\overset{\frown}{XY''}$ and $\overset{\frown}{AB''}$? *Answer*
   b Is $\overset{\frown}{XY'} \sim \overset{\frown}{AB'}$? Is $\overset{\frown}{XY'} \cong \overset{\frown}{AB'}$?
   c What is the length of $\overline{XY}$? Of $\overline{AB}$? Is $XY \parallel AB$?
   d What is the ratio of $\overline{XY}$ to $\overline{AB}$? Of $\overline{OX}$ to $\overline{OA}$? Of $\overline{OY}$ to $\overline{XA}$?

The following lemma, which combines several earlier results, is particularly useful in dealing with circles. Use this lemma to prove the theorem given next.

Lemma

If two isosceles triangles have sides of the same length but do not have congruent bases, then the vertex angles are not congruent and the altitudes to the bases are not congruent; the longer base, the greater vertex angle, and the shorter of the two altitudes are all in the same triangle. (D646)

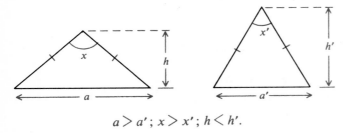

$$a > a'; x > x'; h < h'.$$

Diagram 646

9 *Theorem*

If $\overline{AB}$ subtends the minor arc $\overset{\frown}{APB}$ in circle $C(X, r)$ and $\overline{CD}$ subtends the minor arc $\overset{\frown}{CQD}$ in the congruent circle $C(Y, r)$, then each of the following is true:

a $d(A, B) > d(C, D)$ implies that $\overset{\frown}{APB}° > \overset{\frown}{CQD}°$ and that $d(X, AB) < d(Y, CD)$.

b $\overset{\frown}{APB}° > \overset{\frown}{CQD}°$ implies that $d(A, B) > d(C, D)$ and that $d(X, AB) < d(Y, CD)$.

c $d(X, AB) < d(Y, CD)$ implies that $d(A, B) > d(C, D)$ and that $\overset{\frown}{APB}° > \overset{\frown}{CQD}°$.

(That is, in the same or congruent circles, the greater of two minor arcs subtends the greater chord, and the greater chord is nearer to the center than is the lesser chord.)

10 *Theorem*

If $\overline{AB}$ subtends the minor arc $\overset{\frown}{APB}$ in $C(X, r)$ and $\overline{CD}$ subtends the minor arc $\overset{\frown}{CQD}$ in the congruent circle $C(Y, r)$, then each of the conditions $\overline{AB} \cong \overline{CD}$, $\overset{\frown}{APB}° = \overset{\frown}{CQD}°$, $d(X, AB) = d(Y, CD)$ implies the other two. (That is, in the same or congruent circles, congruent minor arcs subtend congruent chords that are equidistant from the centers of the circles.)

Proof idea

Prove directly or as a corollary of the theorem in exercise 9.

497

The next theorem shows that the line of each diameter of a circle is a line of symmetry of the circle.

Theorem 222/9

The reflection of a circle in the line of a diameter maps the circle onto itself. (D647)

Proof

In the plane α of circle $C(O, r)$, let t
denote a line that passes through O.
The mapping Γ, which is the reflection
in line t, maps α onto itself and maps
any point P in $C(O, r)$ onto a point
$P' = P\Gamma$ in α. Since O in t is a fixed
point, $d(O, P) = d(O\Gamma, P\Gamma) = d(O, P')$.
Therefore, P' is in $C(O, r)$.
Thus, every point of $C(O, r)$ has an image in $C(O, r)$. But P
in $C(O, r)$ also is the image under Γ of P'. Since $C(O, r)$
contains its image and is contained in its image, it is
its own image, and Γ maps $C(O, r)$ onto itself.

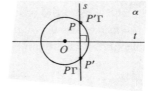

Diagram 647

From the last theorem, we can obtain a midpoint property for arcs. First we define a midpoint of an arc in terms of the measures of subarcs.

Definition 161/9 *Midpoint of an arc*

The point M is a midpoint in arc $\overset{\frown}{AB}$ if it is between A and B
in the arc and if the subarcs $\overset{\frown}{AM}$ and $\overset{\frown}{MB}$ have equal measure.

Theorem 223/9

If M is a midpoint of arc $\overset{\frown}{AB}$, then $\overset{\frown}{AM}° = \overset{\frown}{MB}° = \frac{1}{2}\overset{\frown}{AB}°$.

Proof

By assumption, $\overset{\frown}{AM}° = \overset{\frown}{MB}°$. By Theorem 219/9,
$\overset{\frown}{AM}° + \overset{\frown}{MB}° = \overset{\frown}{AB}°$. Therefore,
$\overset{\frown}{AM}° = \frac{1}{2}\overset{\frown}{AB}°$, and $\overset{\frown}{BM}° = \frac{1}{2}\overset{\frown}{AB}°$.

Theorem 224/9

An arc has at most one midpoint.

Proof

If M is a midpoint in $\overset{\frown}{AB}$ and P is any other point of the arc
between A and B, then P is in either the subarc $\overset{\frown}{AM}$ or the
subarc $\overset{\frown}{MB}$. If P is between A and M in $\overset{\frown}{AM}$, then, by
Corollary 219/9, $\overset{\frown}{AP}° < \overset{\frown}{AM}°$. Hence, $\overset{\frown}{AP}° < \frac{1}{2}\overset{\frown}{AB}°$, and P is not
a midpoint of $\overset{\frown}{AB}$. If P is in $\overset{\frown}{MB}$, then $\overset{\frown}{BP}° < \overset{\frown}{BM}°$.
Consequently, $\overset{\frown}{BP}° < \frac{1}{2}\overset{\frown}{AB}°$, and P is not a midpoint of $\overset{\frown}{AB}$.
Since no point P of $\overset{\frown}{AB}$, other than M, is a midpoint, there
is at most one midpoint of the arc.

Theorem 225/9

Every arc has exactly one midpoint, and the midpoints of
opposite arcs are collinear with the center of the circle.
(D648)

Proof

Let $\overset{\frown}{AB'}$ and $\overset{\frown}{AB''}$ denote opposite arcs
in $C(O, r)$, and let t denote the line
through O that is perpendicular to line AB.
Let M denote the intersection of t
with $\overset{\frown}{AB'}$, and let N denote its intersection
with $\overset{\frown}{AB''}$. The reflection of the plane
of the circle in line t leaves M and N
fixed and interchanges A and B. The
reflection maps each side of line AB

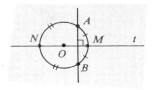

Diagram 648

onto itself and maps the circle onto itself (Theorem 222/9).
Hence, it maps each of the arcs $\overset{\frown}{AB'}$ and $\overset{\frown}{AB''}$ onto itself.
The subarcs $\overset{\frown}{AM}$ and $\overset{\frown}{MB}$ of $\overset{\frown}{AMB}$ are interchanged and, hence,
are congruent. Since they are adjacent arcs whose union
is $\overset{\frown}{AMB}$, point M is a midpoint of $\overset{\frown}{AMB}$. Then, by
Theorem 224/9, M is *the* midpoint of $\overset{\frown}{AMB}$. By the same kind
of argument, point N is the midpoint of $\overset{\frown}{ANB}$.

Corollary 225/9

The line through the center of a circle and the midpoint of
a chord is the bisector of the two opposite arcs that subtend
the chord.

The reflection of a circle in a diameter line also gives an easy
proof of the following property.

Theorem 226/9

The arcs of a circle that are between two parallel secants
and that have endpoints in the secants are congruent. (D649)

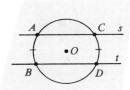

Diagram 649a

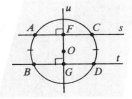

649b

Proof

Let s and t denote parallel secants of a circle $C(O, r)$,
with $\overline{AC}$ denoting the chord in s and $\overline{BD}$ denoting the chord

in t. Let u denote the line through O that is perpendicular to s at F and is perpendicular to t at G. Then F is the midpoint of $\overline{AC}$, and G is the midpoint of $\overline{BD}$. Also, we will suppose that the notation has been chosen so that A and B are in the same side of u. The reflection of the plane of $C(O, r)$ in the line u interchanges A with C and B with D and maps $C(O, r)$ onto itself. In this mapping, the t-side of s maps onto itself and the s-side of t maps onto itself; so the strip between A and B maps onto itself. But the opposite sides of u are interchanged. Hence, the arcs $\overset{\frown}{AB}$ and $\overset{\frown}{CD}$ are interchanged and so are congruent.

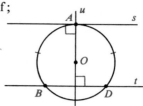

Corollary 226/9

The arcs of a circle that are between a tangent and a parallel secant are congruent. (D650)

Diagram 650

Exercises

1 Let B denote the midpoint of the minor arc $\overset{\frown}{AC}$ of the circle $C(O, r)$. If D and E are the midpoints of the minor arcs $\overset{\frown}{BC}$ and $\overset{\frown}{AB}$ respectively and $\sphericalangle AOC^\circ = 80$, what are the measures of the minor arcs $\overset{\frown}{AB}$, $\overset{\frown}{DC}$, and $\overset{\frown}{EC}$? *Answer*

2 If point M is the midpoint of the minor arc $\overset{\frown}{AB'}$ of circle $C(O, r)$, prove each of the following.
  a $\overline{AM} \cong \overline{MB}$.
  b $\overrightarrow{OM}$ bisects $\sphericalangle AOB$.
  c $OM \perp AB$.

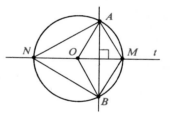

Diagram 651

3 Let $\overset{\frown}{AB'}$ and $\overset{\frown}{AB''}$ denote opposite arcs in $C(O, r)$, and let t denote the line that passes through O and is perpendicular to line AB (D651). If M and N are the intersections of t with $\overset{\frown}{AB'}$ and $\overset{\frown}{AB''}$ respectively, prove that $\triangle AON \cong \triangle BON$ and that $\triangle AMN \cong \triangle BMN$.

4 Let $\overline{AB}$ and $\overline{CD}$ denote parallel chords of $C(O, r)$. If M is the midpoint of an arc determined by C and D, prove the following (D652).
  a $\triangle ACM \cong \triangle BDM$. *Answer*
  b $\triangle ADB \cong \triangle BCA$.

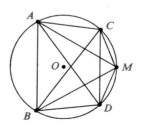

Diagram 652

5 Points A and B in $C(O, r)$ are in opposite sides of the line of diameter $\overline{MN}$ and are such that M and O are in the same side of line AB. If $\overrightarrow{MN}$ bisects $\sphericalangle AMB$, prove each of the following.
  a $\sphericalangle AON \cong \sphericalangle BON$. b $\overline{AN} \cong \overline{BN}$. c $\overline{MA} \cong \overline{MB}$.

6 Points A and B in $C(O, r)$ are in opposite sides of the line of the diameter $\overline{MN}$ and are such that $\overline{MA} \cong \overline{MB}$. Prove that $\overline{NA} \cong \overline{NB}$. *Answer*

500

7 If $\overline{AB}$ is a diameter of $C(O, r)$ and D and C are in $C(O, r)$ such that chord $\overline{AC}$ is parallel to radial segment $\overline{OD}$, prove that $\widehat{BD}° = \widehat{DC}°$. (Hint: Do D and C have to be in the same side of AB?)

8 Point P is the midpoint of the minor arc $\widehat{APB}$ of $C(O, r)$, and Q is the midpoint of the chord $\overline{AB}$. Prove each of the following.

  a $PQ \perp AB$.   **b** Line PQ contains O.

9 Prove each of the following.

  a If the diameter $\overline{MN}$ of $C(O, r)$ bisects chords $\overline{AB}$ and $\overline{CD}$, which are not diameters, then $\overline{AB} \parallel \overline{CD}$.

  b If the diameter $\overline{MN}$ of $C(O, r)$ bisects a chord $\overline{AB}$ that is not a diameter, then $\overline{MN}$ bisects any chord $\overline{CD}$ of $C(O, r)$ that is parallel to $\overline{AB}$.

10 **a** Why are the arcs of a circle that are between parallel tangents congruent?

  b Prove Corollary 226/9.

11 **a** Given a minor arc $\widehat{AB}$ of $C(O, r)$, find, by construction, the midpoint of $\widehat{AB}$.

  b Given a major arc $\widehat{CD}$ of $C(O, r)$, find, by construction, its midpoint M.

12 Prove that any trapezoid inscribed in a circle is isosceles.

13 If trapezoid $ABCD$ is inscribed in $C(O, r)$ and $\overline{AB}$ is its longer base, prove that $\angle A$ and $\angle B$ are congruent. *Answer*

14 In D653, rectangle $ABCD$ is inscribed in $C(O, r)$. Find the measure of each of the following in terms of x, where x is the measure of the minor arc $\widehat{AD}$.

  a Minor arc $\widehat{BC}$

  b $\widehat{ABC}$

  c Minor arc $\widehat{DC}$

  d $\angle DOA$

  e $\angle OBC$ *Answer*

  f $\angle ODC$

Diagram 653

15 Assume that trapezoid $ABCD$ is inscribed in $C(O, r)$ and that $\overline{AB}$ is its longer base. If CO is perpendicular to $\overline{DB}$, prove that $\overline{AD} \cong \overline{DC}$.

We now can use angular arc measures, which are related to the central angles of a circle, to get information about other angles related to a circle. The most important of these are the so-called *inscribed angles* of a circle.

Definition 162/9 *Inscribed angle*

An angle $\angle APB$ is said to be inscribed in the arc $\widehat{APB}$ of $\odot APB$ and to subtend the arc of $\odot APB$

opposite $\overparen{APB}$ (D654). Thus, an angle is inscribed in an arc if it contains the endpoints of the arc and if its vertex is in the arc and between the endpoints. An angle inscribed in an arc also is said to be an inscribed angle of the circle to which the arc belongs.

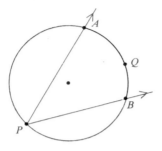

Diagram 654

From the definition of an inscribed angle, the relation of Theorem 227/9 is apparent.

Theorem 227/9

If $\overrightarrow{PX}$ is an open ray interior to the angle $\sphericalangle APB$ inscribed in $\odot APB$, then $\overrightarrow{PX}$ intersects the arc opposite $\overparen{APB}$ in a point between A and B in the arc. (D655)

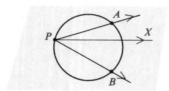
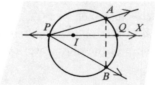

Diagram 655a   655b

Proof

By the definition of $\sphericalangle APB$ inscribed in $\odot APB$, the triangle $\triangle APB$ is inscribed in the circle and its interior is contained in the interior of the circle. Since $\overrightarrow{PX}$ contains a point I interior to the triangle, it contains a point interior to the circle. By Theorem 168/5, the ray opposite $\overrightarrow{IP}$ intersects the circle at some point Q. Because $\overrightarrow{PX}$ is interior to $\sphericalangle APB$, Q is interior to $\sphericalangle APB$. But no point of arc $\overparen{AP}$ or $\overparen{PB}$ in $\overparen{APB}$ is interior to $\sphericalangle APB$. Therefore, Q belongs to the arc opposite $\overparen{APB}$ and clearly is neither A nor B.

We already know from Theorem 119/4 that every angle inscribed in a semicircle is a right angle. Experimenting with other

502

cases should convince one that all the angles inscribed in the
same circular arc are congruent to each other (D656). The measure common to all such angles is described in the next theorem.

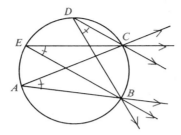

Diagram 656

Theorem 228/9

The measure of an inscribed angle of a circle is one half
the measure of the arc that subtends the angle.

Proof

Let $\sphericalangle APB$ denote an angle inscribed in arc $\overset{\frown}{APB}$ of $\odot APB$, and let
$\overset{\frown}{AQB}$ denote the arc that is opposite $\overset{\frown}{APB}$ and is subtended
by $\sphericalangle APB$. Also, let O denote the center of $\odot APB$.

Case I   The center O is in $\sphericalangle APB$. (D657) Then
either $\overline{PA}$ or $\overline{PB}$ is a diameter, and we will suppose
that the notation has been chosen so that $\overline{PB}$ is a
diameter. Then $\overset{\frown}{APB}$ contains the semicircle in
the side of PB that is opposite A. So the arc $\overset{\frown}{AQB}$
that is opposite $\overset{\frown}{APB}$ is a minor arc whose
central angle is $\sphericalangle AOB$. Therefore,

1 $\sphericalangle AOB° = \overset{\frown}{AQB}°.$

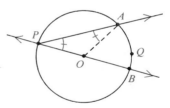

Diagram 657

Since $\overset{\leftarrow\!\!\rightarrow}{OB}$ and $\overset{\leftarrow\!\!\rightarrow}{OP}$ are opposite closed rays, $\sphericalangle AOB$ is
an exterior angle at O of $\triangle AOP$. Consequently,
by the exterior angle corollary, Corollary 91b/4,

2 $\sphericalangle AOB° = \sphericalangle APO° + \sphericalangle PAO°.$

Because $\triangle AOP$ is an isosceles triangle with congruent
base angles at P and A, statement 2 can be expressed as

3 $\sphericalangle AOB° = 2\sphericalangle APO° = 2\sphericalangle APB°.$

Therefore, from statements 3 and 1,

4 $\sphericalangle APB° = \tfrac{1}{2}\sphericalangle AOB° = \tfrac{1}{2}\overset{\frown}{AQB}°,$

which shows that the measure of $\sphericalangle APB$ is one half
the measure of its subtended arc.

Case II   The center O is interior to $\sphericalangle APB$. (D658)
In this case, $\overset{\rightarrow}{PO}$ is interior to $\sphericalangle APB$ and
intersects the circle at D between A and B in
$\overset{\frown}{AQB}$ (Theorem 227/9). Consequently, $\overset{\frown}{AQB} = \overset{\frown}{ADB}.$

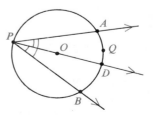

Diagram 658

By Theorem 220/9,

5 $\widehat{AQB}° = \widehat{ADB}° = \widehat{AD}° + \widehat{DB}°$,

where both $\widehat{AD}$ and $\widehat{DB}$ are contained in $\widehat{ADB}$.
Because the center O belongs to $\angle APD$ and also
to $\angle DPB$, we have from Case I,

6 $\angle APD° = \frac{1}{2}\widehat{AD}°$

and

7 $\angle DPB° = \frac{1}{2}\widehat{BD}°$.

And since $\overrightarrow{PO}$ is interior to $\angle APB$, then, by Axiom 11/2,

8 $\angle APB° = \angle APD° + \angle DPB°$.

Thus, from statements 6, 7, and 8,

9 $\angle APB° = \frac{1}{2}\widehat{AD}° + \frac{1}{2}\widehat{BD}° = \frac{1}{2}(\widehat{AD}° + \widehat{BD}°)$.

Substituting from statement 5 in statement 9 gives

10 $\angle APB° = \frac{1}{2}\widehat{AQB}°$.

Case III The center O is in neither $\angle APB$ nor its interior. (D659)
Then both the open rays $\overrightarrow{PA}$ and $\overrightarrow{PB}$ are in the same
side of line PO. Again, let D denote the point
in which $\overrightarrow{PO}$ intersects the circle, and so $\overline{PD}$ is
a diameter. Then, by Theorem 23/2, one of the
closed rays $\overrightarrow{PA}$ or $\overrightarrow{PB}$ is between the other and ray $\overrightarrow{PD}$.
We will suppose that $\overrightarrow{PB}$ is between $\overrightarrow{PA}$ and $\overrightarrow{PD}$. Now
$\angle APD$ is an inscribed angle of the circle and
contains the center. Hence, by Case I,

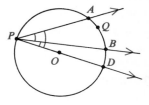

Diagram 659

11 $\angle APD° = \frac{1}{2}\widehat{ABD}°$.

The angle $\angle BPD$ is an inscribed angle that contains
the center O. Therefore, by Case I,

12 $\angle BPD° = \frac{1}{2}\widehat{BD}°$,

where $\widehat{BD}$ is contained in $\widehat{ABD}$, since $\overrightarrow{PB}$ is interior to $\angle APD$.
Also, because $\overrightarrow{PB}$ is interior to $\angle APD$,

13 $\angle APD° = \angle APB° + \angle BPD°$.

Substituting from statements 11 and 12 in statement 13 gives

14 $\frac{1}{2}\widehat{ABD}° = \angle APB° + \frac{1}{2}\widehat{BD}°$.

But, by Theorem 219/9,

15 $\widehat{ABD}° = \widehat{AQB}° + \widehat{BD}°$.

As a result, statement 14 can be expressed as

16 $\frac{1}{2}(\widehat{AQB}° + \widehat{BD}°) = \angle APB° + \frac{1}{2}\widehat{BD}°$.

Statement 16 can be simplified to

17 $\frac{1}{2}\widehat{AQB}° = \angle APB°$.

Thus, in all cases, the measure of $\angle APB$ is one half
the measure of the subtended arc $\widehat{AQB}$.

Corollary 228a/9

Two angles that are inscribed in the same arc are congruent.

Proof

The angles have the same measure, since they both subtend the
same arc, that is, the arc opposite the arc in which they are inscribed.

Corollary 228b/9

If *ABCD* is a quadrilateral inscribed in a circle, then its diagonally opposite angles are supplements. (D660)

Proof

$\angle A$ of *ABCD* subtends $\overparen{BCD}$, so

1 $\angle A° = \frac{1}{2}\overparen{BCD}°$.

The diagonally opposite angle, $\angle C$, subtends $\overparen{DAB}$, so

2 $\angle C° = \frac{1}{2}\overparen{DAB}°$.

But *A* and *C* are in opposite sides of the diagonal line *BD*, so $\overparen{BCD}$ and $\overparen{DAB}$ are opposite arcs and the sum of their measures is 360. From statements 1 and 2, we have

3 $\angle A° + \angle C° = \frac{1}{2}(\overparen{BCD}° + \overparen{DAB}°) = \frac{1}{2}(360) = 180$.

Therefore, $\angle A$ and $\angle C$ are supplements.

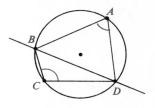

Diagram 660

This last corollary suggests the answer to an interesting question. Unlike triangles, quadrilaterals do not necessarily have circumcircles. The question then is "Which quadrilaterals do have circumcircles?" Corollary 228b/9 suggests the following theorem.

* Theorem 229/9

There exists a circumcircle to the quadrilateral *ABCD* if and only if the diagonally opposite angles of the quadrilateral are supplements.

Exercises

1 If points *A, B, C, ..., H* are in *C(O, r)* as shown in D661, which of the following statements are correct? *Answer*

 a $\angle ADF$ is inscribed in arc $\overparen{ADF}$.

 b $\angle ADF$ subtends arc $\overparen{ADF}$.

 c $\angle EBH$ is an inscribed angle of *C(O, r)* and subtends arc $\overparen{HGE}$.

 d $\angle HBF$ is inscribed in arc $\overparen{HDF}$.

2 We can define *n* points $P_1, P_2, P_3, \ldots, P_n$ of a circle to be *cyclic in the order* $(P_1, P_2, P_3, \ldots, P_n)$ if $P_1P_2P_3 \ldots P_n$ is a convex polygon.

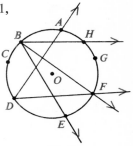

Diagram 661

Then clearly the reverse order $(P_n, P_{n-1}, P_{n-2}, \ldots, P_2, P_1)$ is a cyclic order. Also, the shift of a cyclic order $(P_1, P_2, P_3, \ldots, P_n)$ to $(P_2, P_3, P_4, \ldots, P_n, P_1)$ produces another cyclic order. Let *A, B, C,* and *D* be cyclic in *C(O, r)* in the order *(A, B, C, D)*.

 a If $\angle BAD° = 20$, what is the value of $\overparen{BAD}°$?

 b Is it possible that $\overparen{DAC}° \leq 320$ if $\overparen{BAD}° = 20$?

 c If $\overparen{CBA}° = 80$, what is the value of $\overparen{ADC}°$?

 d If $\angle CDB° = 18$, what is the value of $\angle BAC°$?

505

3 The triangle $\triangle ABC$ is inscribed in a circle, and $\overparen{AB}$, $\overparen{BC}$, and $\overparen{CA}$ denote the arcs subtending $\angle C$, $\angle A$, and $\angle B$ respectively.

  a Find the numerical measures of the angles if $\overparen{AB}° = 110$ and $\overparen{AC}° = 90$.

  b Find the numerical measures of the angles if $\overparen{AB}° = 320$ and the triangle is isosceles.

  c Find the arc measures if $\angle A° = 4$ and $\angle B° = 88$. *Answer*

  d Find the angle measures if $\overparen{AB}° = \frac{1}{2}\overparen{BC}° = \frac{1}{3}\overparen{CA}°$.

4 Isosceles trapezoid $ABCD$ is inscribed in $C(O, r)$ and $\overline{AB}$ is a diameter. Find the measures of the following arcs and angles if $\angle DAB° = 80$.

  a $\overparen{DCB}$ **c** $\overparen{CBA}$ **e** $\angle DOB$ *Answer*

  b Minor arc $\overparen{DC}$ **d** $\angle DBC$ **f** $\angle ACD$

5 Segment $\overline{MN}$ is a diameter of $C(O, r)$, and P is a point in the circle such that $\angle NOP° = 60$. Find the lengths of $\overline{MP}$ and $\overline{NP}$ in terms of r. *Answer*

6 Quadrilateral $ABCD$ is inscribed in circle $C(O, r)$. If $\overline{AB} \cong \overline{AD}$ and $\overline{CB} \cong \overline{CD}$, prove that $\overline{AC}$ is a diameter.

7 Two chords $\overline{AB}$ and $\overline{CD}$ of $C(O, r)$ intersect at point P such that P is interior to the circle and $\overparen{BD} \cong \overparen{CB}$. Prove that $\triangle APD \sim \triangle ACB$.

◆ **8** Assume that, in the plane of the circular arc $\overparen{ABC}$, the points P and B are in opposite sides of line AC. Prove each of the following.

  a If P is interior to $\odot ABC$, then $\angle APB° > \frac{1}{2}\overparen{ABC}°$.

  b If P is exterior to $\odot ABC$, then $\angle APB° < \frac{1}{2}\overparen{ABC}°$.

9 Use the results in exercise 8 to prove Theorem 229/9.

10 Circles $C(O, x)$ and $C(O, y)$ are concentric and $x > y$. Suppose that $\overline{AB}$ is a diameter of $C(O, y)$ and C and D are in opposite sides of AB and in $C(O, x)$ so that $\overline{AC}$ is perpendicular to $\overline{AB}$ and $\overline{BD}$ is perpendicular to $\overline{AB}$. Prove that C, O, and D are collinear (D662).

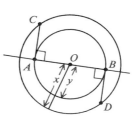

Diagram 662

11 An acute isosceles triangle $\triangle ABC$, with base $\overline{AB}$, is inscribed in $C(O, r)$. Points D and E in $C(O, r)$ are such that D is the midpoint of minor arc $\overparen{AB}$ and $\overline{AE}$ is perpendicular to $\overline{BC}$. Prove that $\overparen{BE}° = \overparen{AD}°$.

12 Diameter $\overline{MN}$ of circle $C(O, r)$ is perpendicular to chord $\overline{XY}$ at point F.

  a Show that $[d(X, Y)]^2 = 4d(M, F)d(F, N)$. *Answer*

  b What is the measure of minor arc $\overparen{MY}$ if $d(M, X) = r$? *Answer*

13 If $C(O, r)$ is the circumcircle of the equilateral triangle $\triangle ABC$ and point P is in the arc that subtends $\sphericalangle A$, prove that $d(A, P) = d(B, P) + d(P, C)$.

14 If P is a point of the circle $C(O, r)$ and if $0 < s < 2r$, then the coplanar circle $C(P, s)$ intersects $C(O, r)$ at two points A and B (D663). Also, the circle $C(B, s)$ intersects $C(P, s)$ at Q interior to $C(O, r)$ and intersects $C(O, r)$ at a second point D. If line DQ intersects $C(O, r)$ at a second point H, prove that $d(Q, H) = r$.

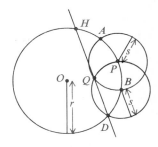

Diagram 663

From the information we now have about the central and inscribed angles of a circle, we can obtain relations for still other angles that are associated with a circle.

Definition 163/9 *Intercepted arc*

An arc of a circle is said to be intercepted by an angle if each arm of the angle contains an endpoint of the arc and if the open arc is interior to the angle. Thus, a central angle and an inscribed angle intercept the arc subtending them. (D664)

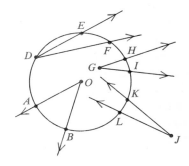

Theorem 230/9

The measure of an angle that is in the plane of a circle and whose vertex is interior to the circle is equal to one half the sum of the measures of the arcs intercepted by the angle and its opposite angle. (D665)

Diagram 664

Proof

Let $\overset{\frown}{AB}$ denote the arc of circle $C(O, r)$ intercepted by $\sphericalangle APB$, where P is interior to the circle. Let A' and B' denote the intersection of the circle with rays opposite $\overset{\longrightarrow}{PA}$ and $\overset{\longrightarrow}{PB}$ respectively so that $\overset{\frown}{A'B'}$ is the arc intercepted by the angle opposite $\sphericalangle APB$. Then $\sphericalangle AA'B$ subtends $\overset{\frown}{AB}$, and

1 $\sphericalangle PA'B° = \sphericalangle AA'B° = \frac{1}{2}\overset{\frown}{AB}°$.

The angle $\sphericalangle B'BA'$ subtends the arc $\overset{\frown}{B'A'}$, and so

2 $\sphericalangle PBA'° = \sphericalangle B'BA'° = \frac{1}{2}\overset{\frown}{B'A'}°$.

Because $\sphericalangle APB$ is an exterior angle at P of $\triangle PA'B$, the exterior angle theorem implies that

3 $\sphericalangle APB° = \sphericalangle PA'B° + \sphericalangle PBA'°$.

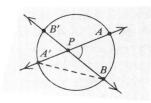

$\sphericalangle APB° = \frac{1}{2}(\overset{\frown}{AB}° + \overset{\frown}{A'B'}°)$.

Diagram 665

507

Substituting from statements 1 and 2 in statement 3 gives

4 $\angle APB° = \frac{1}{2}(\overparen{AB°} + \overparen{B'A'°})$,

which we wished to show.

Theorem 231/9

If $\overline{AB}$ and $\overline{CD}$ are two chords of a circle that
intersect at an interior point P, then
$\triangle PAC \sim \triangle PDB$. (Also, $\triangle PAD \sim \triangle PCB$.)
(D666)

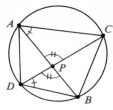

Diagram 666

Proof

The angles $\angle CAB$ and $\angle CDB$ subtend the same arc $\overparen{CB}$ and so
are congruent (Corollary 224b/9). Since $\angle CAB = \angle CAP$
and $\angle CDB = \angle PDB$, angle $\angle A$ of $\triangle PAC$ is congruent to $\angle D$
of $\triangle PDB$. Since $\angle APC$ and $\angle DPB$ are opposite angles,
they are congruent. Therefore, $\angle P$ of $\triangle PAC$ is congruent
to $\angle P$ of $\triangle PDB$. It follows, from the angle, angle
similarity theorem, Theorem 160/5, that $\triangle PAC \sim \triangle PDB$,
which we wished to show.

From our last theorem we have the following corollary.

Corollary 231/9

The chords of a circle that are concurrent at an interior
point P are each separated by P into two segments
such that the product of the lengths of the two
segments is the same for each chord. (D667)

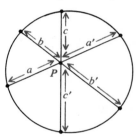

Proof

From Theorem 231/9, it follows that
$\dfrac{d(P, A)}{d(P, D)} = \dfrac{d(P, C)}{d(P, B)}$. Therefore,

$$aa' = bb' = cc'.$$

$d(P, A)\, d(P, B) = d(P, C)\, d(P, D).$

Diagram 667

Definition 164/9 *Power of a point interior to a circle*

The chords of a circle that are concurrent at an interior
point P are each separated by P into two segments such
that the product of the lengths of the two segments
is the same for each chord. The power of P with
respect to the circle is the common value of
this product.

Comment

The power of the center of the circle is clearly r^2, where r is the
radius. As P comes nearer to the circle, its power
becomes less. Points in the circle sometimes are regarded
as points of zero power.

The idea of the power of a point with respect to a circle can be
extended to points exterior to the circle.

If P is exterior to a circle and $\overset{\cdot\cdot\rightarrow}{PX}$ intersects the circle at A
and C and $\overset{\rightarrow}{PY}$ intersects the circle at B and D so that $\measuredangle XPY$
intercepts arcs $\overarc{AB}$ and $\overarc{CD}$, then $d(P, A)\, d(P, C) = d(P, B)\, d(P, D)$,
and the measure of $\measuredangle XPY$ is one half the positive difference
of the measures of the arcs intercepted by the angle.

Proof

We will suppose that the notation has been chosen so
that A is between P and C and B is between P and D. (D668a)

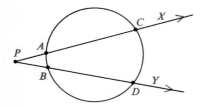

Diagram 668a   668b

Then $\measuredangle PCB$ is inscribed in the circle and subtends the
arc $\overarc{AB}$ intercepted by $\measuredangle XPY$. Also, $\measuredangle PDA$ is inscribed in the
circle and subtends the same arc $\overarc{AB}$. Therefore,

1 $\measuredangle PCB° = \frac{1}{2}\overarc{AB}° = \measuredangle PDA°.$

Since $\measuredangle P$ is common to $\triangle PCB$ and $\triangle PDA$ and, from
statement 1, the angle at C is congruent to the angle at D, then

2 $\triangle PCB \sim \triangle PDA.$

Hence,

3 $\dfrac{d(P, C)}{d(P, D)} = \dfrac{d(P, B)}{d(P, A)}.$

4 $\therefore\ d(P, A)\, d(P, C) = d(P, B)\, d(P, D),$

which proves the first part of the theorem.

If $\overset{\rightarrow}{BZ}$ is an open ray in the direction
of $\overset{\cdot\cdot\rightarrow}{PX}$, it is interior to $\measuredangle CBD$. (D669)
Then, by Theorem 227/9, $\overset{\rightarrow}{BZ}$ intersects $\overarc{CD}$
at a point E between C and D. Therefore,

5 $\measuredangle DBE° = \frac{1}{2}\overarc{ED}° = \frac{1}{2}(\overarc{CD}° - \overarc{CE}°).$

Because $\overline{AC}$ and $\overline{BE}$ are parallel chords, it
follows, from Theorem 226/9, that

6 $\overarc{AB} \cong \overarc{CE}.$

Thus, statement 5 also can be expressed as

7 $\measuredangle DBE° = \frac{1}{2}(\overarc{CD}° - \overarc{AB}°).$

But $\measuredangle XPY$ and $\measuredangle EBD$ are corresponding angles
formed by the parallel lines PX and BZ
and the transversal PY, so

8 $\measuredangle XPY \cong \measuredangle EBD.$

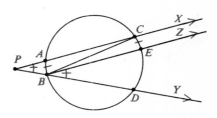

Diagram 669

Statement 8, together with statement 7, gives

9 $\angle XPY° = \frac{1}{2}(\overgroup{CD}° - \overgroup{AB}°)$.

Definition 165/9 *Power of a point exterior to a circle*

If P is exterior to a circle and t is a secant through P
that intersects the circle at A and C, then the power of P
with respect to the circle is $d(P, A)d(P, C)$.

Comment

From Theorem 232/9, it follows that the power of P is the
same number for all secants through P.

In the next set of theorems about angle relations of a circle, we
have outlined the proofs and left some of the details as exercises.

Theorem 233/9

If line PX is tangent to circle $C(O, r)$ at P and
if B is any other point of the circle, then
the measure of $\angle XPB$ is one half the measure
of the arc $\overgroup{PQB}$ where Q is interior to the angle.

Proof idea

Case I $\angle XPB$ is acute. (D670) Then
$\angle POB° = \overgroup{PQB}°$ (Why?).
$\angle XPB° = 90 - \angle BPO°$ (Why?) and
$\angle POB° = 180 - 2\angle BPO°$ (Why?).
Therefore, $\frac{1}{2}\angle POB° = 90 - \angle BPO°$.
Hence, $\angle XPB° = \frac{1}{2}\angle POB°$ so $\angle XPB° = \frac{1}{2}\overgroup{PQB}°$.

Case II $\angle XPB° = 90$. Then $\overgroup{PQB}° = 180$ (Why?).
Therefore, $\angle XPB° = \frac{1}{2}\overgroup{PQB}°$.

Case III $\angle XPB$ is obtuse. (D671) Let $\overrightarrow{PY}$ denote
the closed ray opposite $\overrightarrow{PX}$ and let $\overgroup{PRB}$
denote the arc opposite $\overgroup{PQB}$. Then $\angle YPB$ is
acute (Why?). By Case I, $\angle YPB° = \frac{1}{2}\overgroup{PRB}°$
(Why?). Then $\angle XPB° = 180 - \frac{1}{2}\overgroup{PRB}°$ (Why?).
But $\overgroup{PRB}° = 360 - \overgroup{PQB}°$ (Why?). So
$\frac{1}{2}\overgroup{PRB}° = 180 - \frac{1}{2}\overgroup{PQB}°$. Therefore,
$\angle XPB° = 180 - (180 - \frac{1}{2}\overgroup{PQB}°) = \frac{1}{2}\overgroup{PQB}°$.

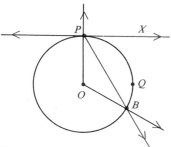

Diagram 670

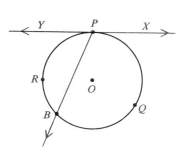

Diagram 671

Theorem 234/9

The measure of an angle formed at a point
external to a circle by a ray tangent to
the circle and a ray that intersects the
circle in two points is one half the positive
difference of the measures of the arcs
intercepted by the angle. (D672)

Proof idea

Let PA denote a line tangent to circle $C(O, r)$
at A and let $\overrightarrow{PX}$ denote an open ray

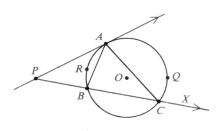

Diagram 672

510

intersecting the circle at B and C with B
between P and C. Further, let $\overset{\frown}{ARB}$ and $\overset{\frown}{AQB}$
denote the arcs intercepted by $\angle P$, where R
is interior to $\triangle PAB$. Then $\angle ABC° = \angle PAB° + \angle P°$
(Why?). Therefore, $\angle P° = \angle ABC° - \angle PAB°$.
But $\angle ABC° = \frac{1}{2}\overset{\frown}{AQC}°$ (Why?), and $\angle PAB° = \frac{1}{2}\overset{\frown}{ARB}°$ (Why?).
Hence, $\angle P° = \frac{1}{2}(\overset{\frown}{AQC}° - \overset{\frown}{ARB}°)$. Also,

$$\triangle PAB \sim \triangle PCA \text{ (Why?), so } \frac{d(P, A)}{d(P, C)} = \frac{d(P, B)}{d(P, A)}$$

or $d(P, B)\, d(P, C) = d(P, A)^2$.

Corollary 234/9

If point P is external to a circle and if a tangent line
through P intersects the circle at A, then the power of P
with respect to the circle is $d(P, A)^2$.

Theorem 235/9

If P is external to circle $C(O, r)$ and if
PA and PB are two lines tangent to the
circle at A and B respectively, then the
segments $\overline{PA}$ and $\overline{PB}$ are congruent and the
measure of $\angle APB$ is one half the positive
difference of the measures of the
opposite arcs $\overset{\frown}{AB'}$ and $\overset{\frown}{AB''}$. (D673)

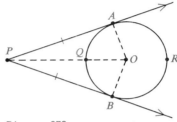

Diagram 673

Proof idea

Let Q and R denote the points of the circle
in line PO, with Q between P and O.
$\triangle AOP \cong \triangle BOP$ (Why?), so $\overline{PA} \cong \overline{PB}$. $\angle OPA° = \frac{1}{2}\overset{\frown}{AR}° - \frac{1}{2}\overset{\frown}{AQ}°$
(Why?), and $\angle OPB° = \frac{1}{2}\overset{\frown}{RB}° - \frac{1}{2}\overset{\frown}{BQ}°$ (Why?). Then
$\angle P° = \angle OPA° + \angle OPB° = \frac{1}{2}(\overset{\frown}{AR}° + \overset{\frown}{RB}°) - \frac{1}{2}(\overset{\frown}{AQ}° + \overset{\frown}{BQ}°)$,
or $\angle P° = \frac{1}{2}(\overset{\frown}{ARB}° - \overset{\frown}{AQB}°)$.

Exercises

1 Diagram 674 shows points $A, B, C, \ldots, G$ in
$C(O, r)$, point P in the interior of
$C(O, r)$, $P \neq O$, and Q in the exterior of
$C(O, r)$.
 a Which arc of $C(O, r)$ is intercepted by $\angle APF$?
By $\angle FOD$? By $\angle BAE$? *Answer*
 b Name the two arcs of $C(O, r)$ that are
intercepted by $\angle AQF$.
 c If $\angle AMB$ intercepts arc $\overset{\frown}{AB}$ of $C(O, r)$, must
M be in the plane of $C(O, r)$? Explain your answer.
 d Is F contained in the arc intercepted by $\angle BAF$?
 e If QX and QY are tangent to $C(O, r)$ at X and Y
respectively, name all points of $C(O, r)$ that are not
in arcs intercepted by $\angle XQY$.

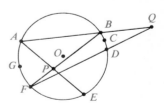

Diagram 674

2 Assume that chords $\overline{AB}$ and $\overline{CD}$ of $C(O, r)$
intersect at an interior point P (D675).

a What is the measure of $\angle APC$ if the measures
of the arcs intercepted by $\angle APC$ and $\angle DPB$
are 80 and 100 respectively? If the measures
are 6 and 200? If the measures are π and $\sqrt{7}$?

b What is the measure of $\angle APD$ if the measures
of the arcs intercepted by $\angle APC$ and $\angle DPB$
are 20 and 80 respectively? If the measures
are 1 and 3?

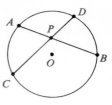

Diagram 675

c What is the measure of the arc
intercepted by $\angle DPB$ if $\widehat{AC}^\circ = 90$ and $\angle APC^\circ = 70$?

d What is the measure of $\angle APC$ if $\widehat{AD}^\circ = 60$ and $P = O$?

e What is the measure of $\angle APC$ if $\widehat{AC}^\circ = 2\widehat{DB}^\circ = 100$? *Answer*

3 Point P is exterior to $C(O, r)$ and secants PA
and PB intersect the circle in points C, A,
D, and B as shown in D676. Assume that
$\widehat{CD}$ and $\widehat{AB}$ denote the arcs intercepted
by $\angle APB$.

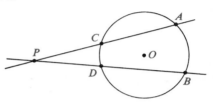

a What is the measure of $\angle APB$ if the
measures of $\widehat{CD}$ and $\widehat{AB}$ are 20 and 60
respectively? If the measures are 1 and
99? If the measures are $\sqrt{2}$ and $\sqrt{3}$?

Diagram 676

b What is $\widehat{CD}^\circ$ if $\widehat{AB}^\circ = 140$ and $\angle APB^\circ = 65$? *Answer*

c What is $\widehat{AB}^\circ$ if $\widehat{CD}^\circ = \angle APB^\circ = 30$?

d Find $\widehat{CD}^\circ$ in terms of x, where $\widehat{AB}^\circ = 3\angle APB^\circ = 6x$.

4 Line PX is tangent to $C(O, r)$ at P, and B is
any other point in the circle. Point Q
of $C(O, r)$ is interior to $\angle BPX$ (D677).

a What is the measure of $\angle BPX$ if the measure
of $\widehat{BQP}$ is 46? If the measure is 179?
If the measure is $2\pi + 38$?

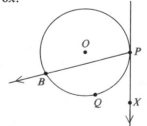

b What is the measure of arc $\widehat{BQP}$ if $\angle BPX^\circ$
is 17? If $\angle BPX^\circ$ is $\sqrt{19}$? If $\angle BPX^\circ$ is 90?

Diagram 677

c If OB is parallel to PX, must $\angle BPX^\circ = 45$?
Explain.

5 Point P is external to $C(O, r)$, the open ray
$\overrightarrow{PA}$ is tangent to the circle at A, and
the open ray $\overrightarrow{PC}$ intersects $C(O, r)$ at B
and C with B between P and C (D678).
Assume that $\widehat{AB}$ and $\widehat{AC}$ denote the arcs
intercepted by $\angle APC$.

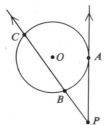

a What is $\angle P^\circ$ if $\widehat{AB}^\circ$ and $\widehat{AC}^\circ$ are 8 and 10
respectively? Are 20 and 96? Are $8\sqrt{7}$
and $20\sqrt{7}$?

Diagram 678

512

b What is $\overset{\frown}{AB}°$ if $\angle P° = 10$ and $\overset{\frown}{AC}° = 35$?

c What is the measure of $\overset{\frown}{AC}$ in terms of x
if $\angle P° = 3x$ and $\overset{\frown}{AB}° = 2x$? *Answer*

d What is $\angle P°$ if $\overline{BC}$ is a diameter and $\overset{\frown}{AB}° = \frac{4}{5}\overset{\frown}{AC}°$?

e What are the bounds for $\angle P°$ if $\overline{BC}$ is a diameter?

6 Point H is external to $C(O, r)$ and HA and HE
are two lines tangent to the circle at A
and E respectively. Secant HO intersects
$C(O, r)$ at P and Q with P between H and Q
(D679).

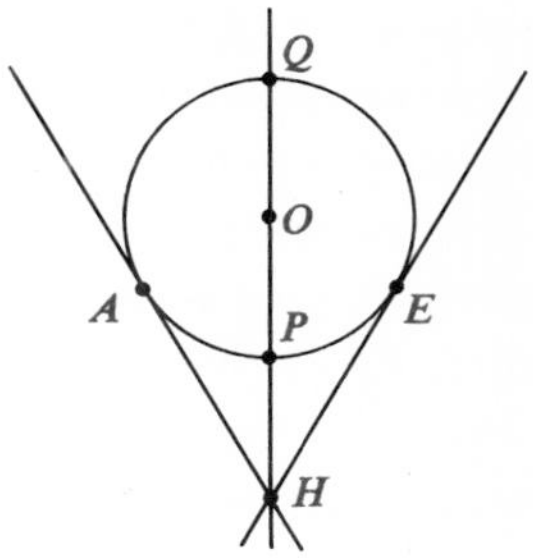

a What is the measure of $\angle AHE$ if $\overset{\frown}{APE}°$ is 30?
If $\overset{\frown}{APE}°$ is 176?

b What is the measure of $\angle AHE$ if $\overset{\frown}{AQE}°$ is 340?
If $\overset{\frown}{AQE}°$ is 100π?

c What is $\overset{\frown}{APE}°$ if $\angle AHE° = 100$? *Answer*

d If $\angle PQA° = 20$, what is $\angle AHE°$?

e Find $\angle EPQ°$ in terms of x if $\angle AHE° = x$.

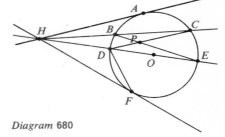

Diagram 679

7 Point H is external to $C(O, r)$ and lines
HA and HF are tangent to $C(O, r)$ at A
and F respectively. Lines HC and HE
are secants that intersect $C(O, r)$
at B, C, D, and E as shown in D680.
If $\overline{DE}$ is a diameter and if the
measures of $\overset{\frown}{AB}$, $\overset{\frown}{BD}$, and $\overset{\frown}{CE}$ are 47, 25,
and 45 respectively, what are the
measures of the following angles?

a $\angle CPE$ **d** $\angle AHF$

b $\angle CHE$ **e** $\angle EDF$

c $\angle AHC$

Diagram 680

8 Assume the conditions of exercise 2 and D675.

a What is the power of P with respect to $C(O, r)$ if
$d(A, P) = 5$ and $d(P, B) = 4$? If $d(C, P) = 3$ and
$d(C, D) = 5$? *Answer*

b If $\overline{CP}$, $\overline{CD}$, and $\overline{AB}$ have lengths 6, 9, and 19
respectively, what are the lengths of $\overline{AP}$ and $\overline{PB}$?

9 Assume the conditions of exercise 3 and D676.

a What is the power of P if $\overline{PC}$ and $\overline{CA}$ have lengths 3
and 4 respectively?

b What is the power of P if $d(P, D) = \sqrt{11}$ and
$d(P, B) = 5\sqrt{11}$? *Answer*

c If $\overline{PA}$, $\overline{CA}$, and $\overline{PB}$ have lengths 24, 16, and 16
respectively, what is the length of $\overline{PD}$?

10 Assume the conditions of exercise 5 and D678.

a What is the power of P with respect to the circle if
$d(P, A) = 7$? If $d(P, A) = 2\sqrt{3}$?

513

b What is the length of $\overline{PA}$ if $d(P, B) = 1$ and $d(B, C) = 2$?

c Find the length of $\overline{PC}$ if $d(P, A) = 6$ and $d(P, B) = 4$.

d Find the length of $\overline{PB}$ if $d(P, A) = 5$ and $d(B, C) = \frac{16}{3}$.

◆ **11** Assume that secants PR and PN intersect
$C(O, r)$ at points Q, R, M, and N as indicated
in D681. Let chords $\overline{RM}$ and $\overline{QN}$ intersect
at A and let $\widehat{RN}$ and $\widehat{QM}$ denote the arcs
intercepted by $\angle RPN$. If $\widehat{RN}° = 49$ and
$\angle RAN° = 3\angle P°$, what are the measures of
$\angle P$ and $\angle QNM$?

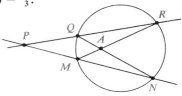

Diagram 681

12 Given a circle $C(O, r)$ and an external point P, construct
with a straightedge and compass the two tangent lines
PA and PB of $C(O, r)$. (Hint: Find the midpoint of $\overline{PO}$.)

13 Given a segment $\overline{AB}$, use Corollary 234/9 to
construct $\overline{CD}$ and $\overline{EF}$ such that $[d(A, B)]^2 = d(C, D)d(E, F)$.

14 Given two line segments $\overline{AB}$ and $\overline{CD}$, use Theorem 232/9
to construct two line segments $\overline{EF}$ and $\overline{GH}$ such that
$d(A, B)d(C, D) = d(E, F)d(G, H)$.

◆ **15** Given a line segment $\overline{AB}$ and an angle $\angle C$, construct a
circle $\odot DFE$ such that $\overline{DE} \cong \overline{AB}$ and $\angle DFE° = \angle C°$.
(Hint: Consider Theorem 228/9 and Theorem 233/9.)

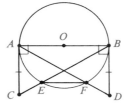

16 Line PA is tangent to $C(O, r)$ at A, and B is any
other point in the circle. If point R in
$C(O, r)$ is interior to $\angle PAB$ and the open ray $\overrightarrow{AR}$
bisects $\angle PAB$, prove that $\triangle AOR \cong \triangle ROB$.

Diagram 682

17 Segment $\overline{AB}$ is a diameter of $C(O, r)$ and the leg of
two right triangles, $\triangle CAB$ and $\triangle ADB$, as indicated
in D682. Assume that points E and F are the
intersections of the circle with $\overline{CB}$ and $\overline{AD}$
respectively. If $\overline{AC} \cong \overline{DB}$, prove that $\overline{EF} \parallel \overline{AB}$.

18 In D683, segment $\overline{MN}$ is a diameter of $C(O, r)$,
and secants PM and QM intersect the circle
at points R and S respectively so that
$<R, N, Q>$ and $<P, N, S>$. Show that $\angle P$ is
congruent to $\angle Q$. *Answer*

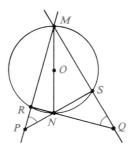

◆ **19** Segment $\overline{MN}$ is a diameter of $C(O, r)$, and line
PM is tangent to the circle at M. Also,
secant PN intersects $C(O, r)$ at Q and N
so that Q is between P and N. Prove that
$d(P, N)d(Q, N) = 4r^2$.

Diagram 683

◆ **20** Segment $\overline{MN}$ is a diameter of $C(O, r)$,
and line AB is tangent to the circle
at M so that M is between A and B.
If NA and NB intersect $C(O, r)$ at C
and D respectively so that $<A, C, N>$

and $\langle B, D, N \rangle$, prove that
$d(N, A)d(N, C) = d(N, B)d(N, D)$.

◆ **21** Line AB is tangent to $C(O, r)$ at N so
that N is between A and B (D684).
Segments $\overline{AO}$ and $\overline{BO}$ intersect the circle
at C and D respectively. Let a, b,
x, and y denote the lengths of $\overline{AN}$, $\overline{NB}$,
$\overline{AC}$, and $\overline{DB}$ respectively. Show that
$x(b^2 - y^2) = y(a^2 - x^2)$.

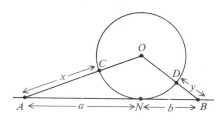

Diagram 684

Some tangency 35/9
properties of circles
We already have defined tangency of a line and a circle. Now we can use this tangency to define the tangency of one circle to another.

Definition 166/9 *Tangent circles*
Two circles are tangent if they are coplanar and are both
tangent to a line at the same point of the line.

Convention
If two coplanar circles $C(A, r)$ and $C(B, s)$ are tangent to a
line t at point P, then the circles are said to be tangent
to each other at P. The circles are said to be internally
tangent if the centers A and B are in the same side of t
and to be externally tangent if these centers are
in opposite sides of t. (D685)

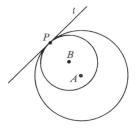

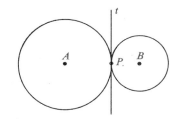

Diagram 685a   685b

Theorem 236/9
If two circles are tangent, their centers are collinear
with the point of tangency.

Proof
Let $C(A, r)$ and $C(B, s)$ denote two circles that are tangent
at P, and let t denote the line tangent to both circles at P.
Then, by Theorem 124/4, line PA is perpendicular to t at P
and line PB is perpendicular to t at P. But in the plane

515

of the circles, there is only one line that is perpendicular
to t at P. Therefore, PA and PB are the same line,
and P, A, and B are collinear.

Corollary 236a/9

Two tangent circles intersect only at their point of tangency.*

Proof

Assume that the circles intersect at Q distinct from P. Then,
by Corollary 75b/3, the line AB is the perpendicular bisector
of $\overline{PQ}$. This is impossible, since AB passes through P. Hence,
there is no second point of intersection Q.

Corollary 236b/9

If two circles are internally tangent, then, except for the point
of tangency, one circle is contained in the interior of the other.

Exercises

1 Let α' and α'' denote the open half-planes of plane α
determined by line t. If point P is in line t, which
of the following statements are necessarily correct? *Answer*

a The set of all points Q in α such that $C(Q, r)$ is
tangent to t at P is the plane α.

b The set of all points Q in α' such that $C(Q, r)$ is
tangent to t at P is an open ray in α' whose line
is perpendicular to t at P.

c The set of all points Q in space such that $C(Q, r)$ is tangent
to t at P is the plane β, where β is perpendicular to t at P.

d Given any point R in plane α, $R \neq P$, there exists a
circle $C(Q, r)$ that contains R and is tangent to t at P.

e Given a positive real number x, the set of all points Q
in space such that $C(Q, x)$ is tangent to t at P is
a circle $C(P, x)$ in a plane β perpendicular to α.

2 Which of the following statements are always correct if
$C(B, s)$ and $C(A, r)$ denote circles in space that are
tangent to line t at point P?

a Segment $\overline{AB}$ must intersect line t.

b Line AB must intersect line t.

c If AB contains P, circles $C(A, r)$ and $C(B, s)$ are coplanar.

d If $\overline{AB}$ does not contain P, the circles are not coplanar.

e If $d(A, B) > d(A, P)$ and the circles are coplanar,
then the circles are externally tangent.

f If the circles are coplanar and $d(B, P) > d(A, B) > d(A, P)$,
then the circles are internally tangent.

g If Q is a member of both circles, then $Q = P$.

---

* We could have used this property to define tangency for two coplanar circles.

h If line m is tangent to both circles at P, then m intersects t only at P.

i If t and A are in the plane α, then B is in the plane α.

3 Assume that circle $C(A, r)$ is tangent to line t at point P, and the coplanar circle $C(B, s)$ is tangent to t. If points A, P, and B are collinear, prove that $C(B, s)$ is tangent to t at P.

4 Prove Corollary 236b/9. *Answer*

5 Assume that the two circles $C(P, x)$ and $C(Q, y)$ are externally tangent. Let t denote the line tangent to both circles, and let B denote the common point of tangency. If M is a point in t other than B and if lines MX and MY are tangent to $C(P, x)$ and $C(Q, y)$ at X and Y respectively, where X and Y are not in t, prove that $d(M, X) = d(M, Y)$.

6 Given $C(A, r)$ in a plane α that is tangent to line t at point P, construct the circle $C(B, s)$ in α that is tangent to $C(A, r)$ at P and that contains a given point R in each of the following cases.

a R is in the side of t that does not contain A, and R is not in the line AP.

b R is between A and P.

7 Construct two coplanar circles that intersect in an angle of measure 60, that is, construct two coplanar circles whose tangent lines at a point of intersection form angles of measure 60 and 120.

8 Given two segments of lengths x and y, construct two coplanar circles $C(A, x)$ and $C(B, y)$ that are perpendicular in the sense that their tangent lines at a point of intersection are perpendicular. (Two circles with this kind of perpendicularity are said to be *orthogonal* to each other.)

♦ 9 Two intersecting coplanar circles that are not tangent intersect in two points, say, P and Q. Show that the angles of intersection at P are the same as those at Q. In other words, show that the two tangent lines at P form the same size angles of intersection as do the two tangent lines at Q.

10 The circles $C(A, 2)$ and $C(B, 3)$ are externally tangent, and line XY is tangent to $C(A, 2)$ and $C(B, 3)$ at X and Y respectively. If $X \neq Y$, find $d(X, Y)$. *Answer*

11 The circles $C(B, x)$ and $C(A, y)$ are internally tangent at P, and t denotes the line tangent to both circles. If T is in t such that $d(T, P) = 7$, $d(T, B) = \sqrt{85}$, and $d(T, A) = \sqrt{50}$, what is $d(B, A)$?

12 Two coplanar circles $C(A, 12)$ and $C(B, 6\sqrt{2})$ intersect at P and Q so that $\angle PAQ^\circ = 60$ and $\angle PBQ^\circ = 90$.

a What is the measure of $\angle APB$? *Answer*

b What is the measure of arc $\overset{\frown}{PQ}$ of $C(A, 12)$? Of arc $\overset{\frown}{PQ}$ of $C(B, 6\sqrt{2})$?

c Find $d(A, B)$.

It is apparent that, if point P is external to a circle, then a line rotating about P in the plane of the circle will pass through two positions of tangency to the circle. There are several ways of proving this, but we will give the proof that is most commonly used.

Theorem 237/9

If point P is external to a circle and in the plane of the circle, then there are exactly two lines through P that are tangent to the circle. (D686)

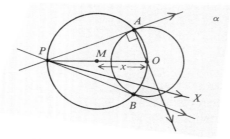

Diagram **686**

Proof

Let α denote the plane of $C(O, r)$, and let P be external to $C(O, r)$ in α. The circle in α whose center is the midpoint M of $\overline{PO}$ and whose radius is $x = d(O, M) = d(M, P)$ passes through O internal to $C(O, r)$ and passes through P external to $C(O, r)$. So $C(M, x)$, by Axiom 15/6, intersects $C(O, r)$ at two points A and B. Angle $\angle PAO$ is inscribed in a semicircle of $C(M, x)$ and, hence, is a right angle. Thus, line PA is perpendicular at A to the radial segment $\overline{OA}$ of $C(O, r)$ and, hence, is tangent to $C(O, r)$ at A. By the same argument, line PB is tangent to $C(O, r)$ at B. Consequently, there are at least two lines through P that are tangent to the circle.

Every point of $C(O, r)$ other than A or B is in the B-side of PA and in the A-side of PB. Hence, no point of $C(O, r)$ is exterior to $\angle PAB$. It follows that, if $\overrightarrow{PX}$ is any open ray in α distinct from $\overrightarrow{PA}$ and $\overrightarrow{PB}$, it is a ray that

518

intersects both $\overleftrightarrow{AB'}$ and $\overleftrightarrow{AB''}$ if it is interior to $\measuredangle APB$.
Otherwise, this ray fails to intersect $C(O, r)$ at any point.
Therefore, PA and PB are the only tangents to $C(O, r)$
that pass through P.

We now want to obtain the conditions under which a line is tangent to two different coplanar circles. Experimenting with diagrams would convince one of the following facts. If one circle is contained in the interior of another (D687), then there is no line that is tangent to both circles. If the circles are internally tangent, then there is just one line tangent to both of them. If the circles intersect in two points, there are two lines tangent to both circles.

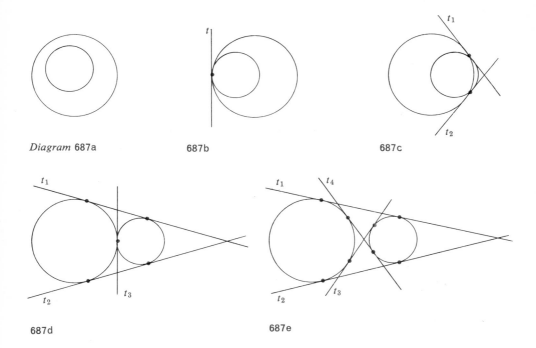

Diagram 687a   687b   687c

687d   687e

If the circles are externally tangent, there are three lines tangent to both circles. Finally, if the two circles are external to each other, then there are four lines that are tangent to both circles.

Theorem 238/9
If neither of two coplanar circles $C(A, x)$ and $C(B, y)$ is
internal or internally tangent to the other, then there are
two lines that are tangent to both circles and are such that
the two centers are in the same side of each tangent.
Either these two tangents t and t' intersect in the line
of centers or else they are parallel.

Proof

Let α denote the common plane of the two circles. Under the given conditions, the circles are not concentric, so $A \neq B$ and line $s = AB$ exists. Let $\overrightarrow{AX}$ denote a closed ray in α that is perpendicular to s at A and intersects $C(A, x)$ at C. Let $\overrightarrow{BY}$ denote the like-directed closed ray that is perpendicular to s at B and that intersects $C(B, y)$ at D.

Case I   The circles are congruent. (D688)

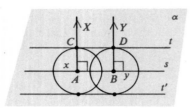
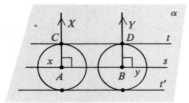

Diagram **688a**   **688b**

Then $x = y$ and $CABD$ is a rectangle. Since line $t = CD$ is perpendicular at C to the radial segment $\overline{AC}$ and is perpendicular at D to $\overline{BD}$, it is tangent to both circles and both centers are in the A-side of t. A reflection of the plane α in s maps each circle onto itself and maps t onto a line t' tangent to both circles and parallel to t.

Case II   The circles are not congruent. (D689)

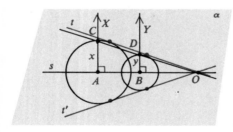
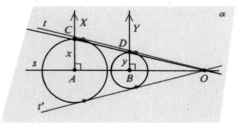

Diagram **689a**   **689b**

Then $x \neq y$, and we will suppose that $x > y$. In this case, $CABD$ is a trapezoid with parallel bases $\overline{CA}$ and $\overline{BD}$ and with $\overline{BD}$ the shorter base. Then line CD intersects s at a point O such that B is between A and O (Theorem 114/4). Because the right triangles $\triangle CAO$ and $\triangle DBO$ have an acute angle at O in common, it follows (Theorem 160/5) that

1 $\triangle DBO \sim \triangle CAO$.

Therefore,

$$2 \quad \frac{d(B, D)}{d(A, C)} = \frac{d(O, B)}{d(O, A)} = \frac{d(O, D)}{d(O, C)} = \frac{y}{x}.$$

We want to show that point O is exterior to $C(A, x)$.
To do so, let E denote the intersection of $\overrightarrow{AB}$ and $C(A, x)$.
Then $\triangle CAE$ is an isosceles right triangle. If $O = E$, then
$\triangle DBO$ is an isosceles right triangle, and $d(B, D) = d(B, O) = y$.
(D690) Then, because B is between A and O, $C(B, y)$ is

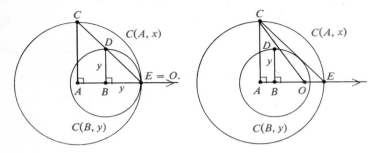

Diagram 690

internally tangent to $C(A, x)$, which contradicts the given
conditions. If O is between A and E, then it follows that
$d(B, D) < d(B, E)$ and $C(B, y)$ is contained in the interior
of $C(A, x)$, again, a contradiction.

Since point O in $C(A, x)$ or in its interior leads to a
contradiction, point O must be exterior to $C(A, x)$.
Therefore, by Theorem 237/9, there are two lines t and t'
that pass through O and are tangent to $C(A, x)$.

Let Γ be the contraction of the plane at point O in

the ratio $k = \dfrac{y}{x}$. Then A is mapped onto $A' = A\Gamma$ in $\overrightarrow{OA}$

such that $d(O, A') = k\,d(O, A)$. But from statement 2,
$d(O, B) = k\,d(O, A)$, and B is in $\overrightarrow{OA}$. Hence, $B = A\Gamma$.
Thus, Γ maps $C(A, x)$ onto a circle with center B. The
radius of the new circle is k times the radius of $C(A, x)$

and so is $kx = \left(\dfrac{y}{x}\right)x = y$. Therefore, Γ maps $C(A, x)$

onto $C(B, y)$. The line t that is tangent to $C(A, x)$ maps
onto a line $t\Gamma$ that is tangent to $C(B, y)$. But t passes
through O and so maps onto itself. Therefore, t is tangent
to both $C(A, x)$ and $C(B, y)$. By the same argument, t' is
tangent to both $C(A, x)$ and $C(B, y)$.

From the nature of Γ, it follows that O is also exterior
to $C(B, y)$ and that the centers of both circles are in
the same side of t and in the same side of t'.

Convention
The lines t and t' of Theorem 238/9 are called the common
external tangents of the two circles.

521

Theorem 239/9

If two coplanar circles $C(A, x)$ and $C(B, y)$ are nonintersecting
and are exterior to each other, then there exist two lines t
and t' that are tangent to both circles and are such that
the centers of the circles are in opposite sides of each
of the tangents.

Proof

Let α denote the plane of the circles
and let $s = AB$ denote the line of
centers. (D691) Let $\overrightarrow{AX}$ denote the
closed ray in α that is perpendicular
to s at A and intersects $C(A, x)$ at C.
Let $\overrightarrow{BZ}$ denote the oppositely directed
closed ray that has B as its endpoint
and intersects $C(B, y)$ at D. Since C
and D are in opposite sides of s,

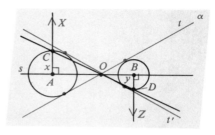

Diagram 691

line CD intersects s at O between A and
B. In the right triangles $\triangle CAO$ and $\triangle DBO$,
the angles at O are congruent opposite
angles. So, by Theorem 160/5,

1 $\triangle CAO \sim \triangle DBO$.

Hence,

2 $$\frac{d(A, C)}{d(B, D)} = \frac{d(O, A)}{d(O, B)} = \frac{d(O, C)}{d(O, D)} = \frac{x}{y}.$$

Because neither $C(A, x)$ and $C(B, y)$
nor their interiors have a point in
common, point O is exterior to at least
one of the circles, say, $C(B, y)$.
Then, by Theorem 237/9, there are two
lines t and t' through O that are
tangent to $C(B, y)$.

Let Γ denote the expansion or the
contraction of the plane at O in

the ratio $k = \dfrac{x}{y}$. (D692) (This ratio

could be the identity if $y = x$.)
This maps B onto a point $B' = B\Gamma$

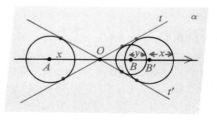

Diagram 692

in $\overrightarrow{OB}$ such that $d(O, B') = \dfrac{x}{y} d(O, B)$.

From statement 2, $d(O, A) = \dfrac{x}{y} d(O, B)$.

Consequently, O is the midpoint of $\overline{AB'}$.

The radius of the circle $C(B, y)\Gamma$ is $ky = \left(\dfrac{x}{y}\right)y = x$; so $C(B, y)\Gamma$

is the circle $C(B', x)$ that is congruent to $C(A, x)$.

Because the lines t and t' map onto themselves under Γ, they are tangent to both of the circles $C(B, y)$ and $C(B', x)$.

Now let Ψ denote the reflection of α in point O. Because O is the midpoint of $\overline{AB'}$, the reflection Ψ maps $C(B', x)$ onto the congruent circle $C(A, x)$. The reflection also maps t and t' onto themselves; so t and t' are both tangent to the image of $C(B', x)$, that is, they are both tangent to $C(A, x)$. Thus t and t' are tangent to both $C(B, y)$ and $C(A, x)$. From this it follows that O is external to both circles.

Under Γ, each half-plane of t maps onto itself. However, under Ψ, the half-planes of t are interchanged; so the centers of $C(A, x)$ and $C(B, y)$ are in opposite sides of t. For the same reasons, they are in opposite sides of t'.

Convention

The two lines t and t' of Theorem 239/9 are called the common internal tangents of the two circles.

By the same kind of arguments that have been used in the proofs of the preceding theorems, a great many other relations of the tangency of lines and circles can be established. A few of these relations are given in the next group of exercises.

Exercises

1 Lines *CJ, DG, EK,* and *FH* are tangent to the circles $C(A, x)$ and $C(B, y)$ at the points indicated in D693.

a Name the common external tangents of the two circles.

b Name the common internal tangents of the two circles.

c Are external tangents ever parallel? Are internal tangents ever parallel? *Answer*

d What kind of tangents do not intersect segment $\overline{AB}$?

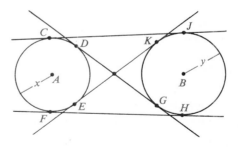

Diagram 693

2 Circles $C(P, x)$ and $C(Q, y)$ are tangent externally, and line t denotes their common internal tangent. If *AB* and *CD* are the common external tangents to the circles with *A* and *C* in $C(P, x)$ and *B* and *D* in $C(Q, y)$, prove that t bisects $\overline{AB}$ and $\overline{CD}$.

3 As indicated in D693, $C(A, x)$ and $C(B, y)$ are coplanar nonintersecting circles whose internal tangents *EK* and *DG* intersect $C(A, x)$ at *D* and *E* and intersect $C(B, y)$ at *K* and *G*. Their external tangents *CJ* and *FH* intersect

$C(A, x)$ at C and F and intersect $C(B, y)$ at J and H.

a Prove that $\overline{EK} \cong \overline{DG}$.

b Prove that $\overline{CJ} \cong \overline{FH}$.

4 In D694, point C is exterior to circle $C(O, r)$ and points A and B in the circle are such that CA and CB are tangents to the circle. Suppose that F is in the open arc $\overset{\frown}{AB}$ and E and D are in $\overline{BC}$ and $\overline{AC}$ respectively so that DE is tangent to $C(O, r)$ at F. Show that for all points F, the perimeter of $\triangle CDE$ is a constant.

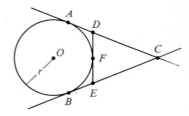

Diagram 694

5 Using the information in exercise 4, find the length of segment $\overline{OC}$ if $\sphericalangle C° = 60$ and $r = 10$. Also find the perimeter of $\triangle CDE$. *Answer*

♦ 6 Given two coplanar circles $C(A, x)$ and $C(B, y)$ that are exterior to each other, construct one of their common external tangents.

♦ 7 Given two coplanar circles $C(A, x)$ and $C(B, y)$ that are exterior to each other, construct one of their common internal tangents.

8 Diagram 695 shows two circles that are tangent internally at P with t as their common tangent. Chords $\overline{PQ}$ and $\overline{PR}$ of the larger circle intersect the smaller circle at S and T respectively. Show that $QR \parallel ST$.

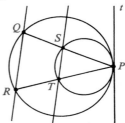

Diagram 695

9 If point P is interior to circle $C(O, r)$ and is not in diameter $\overline{AB}$, prove that $\sphericalangle APB° > 90$. *Answer*

10 The circles $C(P, r)$ and $C(Q, s)$ are tangent externally at point T, and line AB is an external tangent to the circles and intersects $C(P, r)$ and $C(Q, s)$ at A and B respectively (D696). Prove that $\sphericalangle ATB° = 90$. (Hint: Draw the common internal tangent to the two circles.)

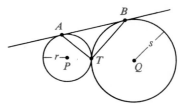

Diagram 696

11 Given three radii a, b, and c, construct three circles $C(A, a)$, $C(B, b)$, and $C(C, c)$ such that each circle is tangent externally to the other two. Is such a construction always possible?

♦ 12 In a given circle $C(O, r)$, inscribe three congruent circles that are each tangent to two of the congruent circles and to the given circle $C(O, r)$.

◆ **13** Given a point Q in line t and a circle $C(A, x)$ that is tangent to line t at point P that is not Q (D697), construct a circle $C(R, y)$ that is tangent to $C(A, x)$ and to line t at point Q.

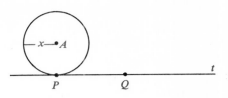

Diagram 697

14 Square $ABCD$ is inscribed in $C(O, r)$, and E is any point in the minor arc $\overset{\frown}{DC}$ other than points D and C. Trisect $\sphericalangle DEC$.

15 Circles $C(P, x)$ and $C(Q, x)$ are congruent and are tangent externally at B (D698). Segments $\overline{AB}$ and $\overline{BC}$ are collinear diameters of $C(P, x)$ and $C(Q, x)$ respectively, and E is in $C(P, x)$ such that CE is tangent to the circle. If CE intersects $C(Q, x)$ at D and D is between E and C, prove that $\overset{\frown}{AE}° = \overset{\frown}{BE}° + \overset{\frown}{DB}°$, assuming that $\overset{\frown}{AE}$, $\overset{\frown}{BE}$, and $\overset{\frown}{DB}$ denote arcs intercepted by $\sphericalangle ECA$.

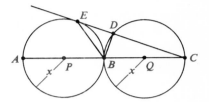

Diagram 698

16 Diagram 699 shows two pulleys connected by a tight belt. If the centers P and Q of the pulleys are 40 ft. apart and the radii of the pulleys are 4 ft. and 24 ft., what is the length of the belt? *Answer*

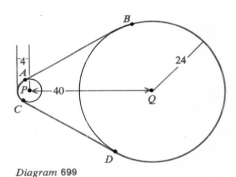

Diagram 699

◆ **17** In plane α, let t denote a line that is external to $C(O, r)$, and let F denote the foot in t of point O. Let FP denote a line tangent to $C(O, r)$ at P, and let E denote the intersection of $C\big(F, d(F, P)\big)$ and line OF. Prove that, for every point X in t, the circle in α with center X and passing through E intersects $C(O, r)$ in two points A and B such that XA and XB are the tangents to $C(O, r)$ through X.

Chapter review

1 Assume that the three points A, B, and C are points in a circle $C(O, r)$.

a What is the locus of all points F such that F is the foot in $\overset{\frown}{ABC}$ of point O?

b Must a foot of point O exist in chord $\overline{AC}$? Explain.

c Is the foot of B in line AC always between A and C? Explain.

2 Indicate whether each of the following statements is necessarily true (T), possibly true (P), or necessarily false (F).

a $C(O, r) = \odot APB$.

b If $\overline{AB}$ is a diameter of $\odot APB$, then arc $\overset{\frown}{ABP}$ is a semicircle.

c If $\overset{\frown}{ABC}$ of $C(O, r)$ is a minor arc, then $\overset{\frown}{ACB}$ is a major arc.

d The union of arcs $\overset{\frown}{ABC}$ and $\overset{\frown}{BAC}$ of circle $C(O, r)$ is $C(O, r)$.

e In $C(O, r)$, if $\overset{\frown}{ABD} = \overset{\frown}{ACD}$ and $B \neq C$, then the open ray $\overset{\rightarrow}{OC}$ is between the open rays $\overset{\rightarrow}{OB}$ and $\overset{\rightarrow}{OD}$.

f If $\overset{\frown}{ABC}$ of $C(O, r)$ is a major arc, then its opposite arc is a minor arc.

3 In plane α, let $\overline{AB}$ denote a diameter of $C(O, 5)$, and let α' denote a side of the line AB. The two points A and B and all points of $C(O, 5)$ in α' form a set $\mathcal{S}$ that is an arc of the circle. Let P_1, P_2, and P_3 denote three points of $\mathcal{S}$ such that none of these points is A or B.

a If $\overline{P_1O}$ is perpendicular to $\overline{AB}$, what is the length x of the segment path determined by the ordered set (A, P_1, B)?

b If $\measuredangle P_1OA° = \measuredangle P_2OB° = 60$, what is the length x of the segment path determined by the ordered set (A, P_1, P_2, B)?

c If $d(P_1, AB) = d(P_3, AB) = 4$ and $\overline{P_2O} \perp \overline{AB}$, what is the length x of the segment path determined by the ordered set (A, P_1, P_2, P_3, B)?

4 Assume that the minor arc $\overset{\frown}{ABC}$ subtends the central angle $\measuredangle AOC$ of $\odot ABC$ and that D is in the arc opposite $\overset{\frown}{ABC}$.

a What is the measure of $\overset{\frown}{ADC}$ if $\measuredangle AOC° = 72$?

b What is the measure of $\measuredangle AOB$ if $\overset{\frown}{ABC}° = 113$, $\overset{\frown}{ADC}° = 247$, and $\measuredangle BOC° = 27$?

c What is the measure of $\overset{\frown}{BDC}$ if $AO \perp OB$ and $\overline{BC} \cong \overline{OB}$?

5 Planes α and β are perpendicular and intersect in line t. The two circles $C(O, 7)$ and $C(P, 14)$ are in α and β respectively, and $\overline{AB}$ is a diameter of $C(P, 14)$ that is parallel to t. Assume that the mappings Γ, Φ, and Ψ are defined as follows:

Γ: rotation of space about AB through an angle of measure 90;

Φ: expansion of space at point P of ratio 2;

Ψ: translation of space in the direction $\overset{\rightarrow}{OP}$ by the amount $d(O, P)$.

Which of the product mappings listed below will map
$C(O, 7)$ onto $C(P, 14)$?

a $\Gamma\Psi\Phi$ c $\Phi\Psi\Gamma$

b $\Psi\Gamma\Phi$ d $\Psi\Phi\Gamma$

6 Assume that segments $\overline{AC}$, $\overline{DG}$, and $\overline{EF}$ are three diameters
of $C(B, r)$ and that C is in the E-side of DG.
What is the measure of $\sphericalangle DEF$ if each of the following
is true?

a $\sphericalangle BFG° = 52$.

b $\widehat{ECG}° = 122$.

c $\sphericalangle CBG° = 72$ and $\widehat{DE}° = 36$.

d $\widehat{ADE}° = 130$ and $\widehat{FG}° = 80$.

e $\widehat{DEA}° = 300$ and $\widehat{ECG}° = 130$.

7 From the information given in D700, which
of the following statements are
necessarily correct?

a $\sphericalangle NPJ° = \frac{1}{2}(\widehat{NAJ}° + \widehat{HBM}°)$.

b $\sphericalangle HPN° = (\frac{1}{2})\widehat{HCN}°$.

c $\sphericalangle HMN \cong \sphericalangle PJN$.

d $\triangle HPM \sim \triangle JPN$.

e $d(M, P)\,d(P, N) = d(J, P)\,d(P, H)$.

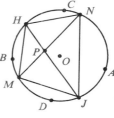

Diagram 700

8 Assume that point P is in the plane of the
circle $C(O, 6)$.

a What is the power of point P with respect to $C(O, 6)$
if $d(P, O) = \frac{1}{3}$? If $d(P, O) = \pi$? If $d(P, O) = 8$?

b What is $d(P, O)$ if the power of P with respect to
$C(O, 6)$ is equal to 108? Is equal to 640?

9 Circle $C(O, r)$ is inscribed in $\triangle ABC$ and intersects
$\triangle ABC$ at points D, E, and F as indicated in D701.
Arcs $\widehat{DHF}$ and $\widehat{FGE}$ are congruent and $\widehat{DJE}° = 100$.
Using D701, find the measure of each
of the following angles.

a $\sphericalangle DAF$ f $\sphericalangle FEB$

b $\sphericalangle DCE$ g $\sphericalangle DKE$

c $\sphericalangle OFK$ h $\sphericalangle KOF$

d $\sphericalangle FBE$ i $\sphericalangle DEK$

e $\sphericalangle DEC$

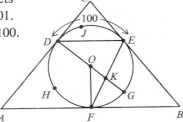

Diagram 701

10 For any triangle $\triangle ABC$, is it always possible to construct
three circles whose centers are A, B, and C such that
each circle is tangent to the other two? Explain.

11 What is the locus of the centers of all circles in space
tangent to each of the following?

a Two parallel lines r and s

b A line t at the point P

c Two intersecting lines m and n

d The circle $C(O, r)$ at the point P

e The concentric circles $C(P, 8)$ and $C(P, 10)$

f The two tangent circles $C(P, x)$ and $C(Q, y)$

12 Assume that the length of chord $\overline{AB}$ of $C(O, r)$ is 10 and that $d(O, \overline{AB}) = 6$. If the length of chord $\overline{CD}$ of $C(O, r)$ is 14, what is $d(O, \overline{CD})$?

13 Two circles $C(Q, 2)$ and $C(P, 6)$ are tangent externally (D702). The lines AC and AY are tangent to $C(P, 6)$ at C and Y respectively and are tangent to $C(Q, 2)$ at B and X respectively. What is the length of each of the following segments?

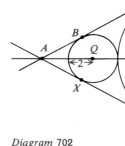

a $\overline{QP}$ **c** $\overline{AQ}$

b $\overline{BC}$ **d** $\overline{AB}$

Diagram 702

Cumulative review

1 The two points A and B in line t have coordinates 0 and 4 respectively, and r is a positive real number less than 1. Points X and Y are in t such that $<X, A, B>$ and $<A, Y, B>$.

a In terms of r, what are the coordinates of X and Y if

$$\frac{d(X, A)}{d(X, B)} = \frac{d(A, Y)}{d(Y, B)} = r?$$

b Use the coordinates from exercise 1a to show that the midpoint of $\overline{XY}$ is between X and A.

2 Points X and Y are in sides $\overline{AD}$ and $\overline{BC}$ of square $ABCD$, and $d(A, B) = 5$. If $d(A, X) = 2$ and $d(B, Y) = 4$, what is the distance from B to the line XY?

3 Segment $\overline{XY}$ is a chord of the square $GHJK$ and line XY is in the strip between KJ and GH. The lengths of $\overline{GX}$ and $\overline{GK}$ are 1 and 4 respectively. If Γ denotes a reflection of space in line XY, what is the length of the segment circuit determined by the ordered set $(G\Gamma, J, Y, K\Gamma)$?

4 Indicate whether each of the following statements is necessarily true (T), possibly true (P), or necessarily false (F).

a If $\triangle ABC \cong \triangle RSP$, then $\triangle BAC \cong \triangle PRS$.

b If $\triangle ABC \cong \triangle DEF$, there exists a motion of space such that $\triangle DEF$ is the image of $\triangle ABC$ under this motion.

c If CB bisects both $\sphericalangle C$ and side $\overline{AD}$ of $\triangle ADC$, then $\triangle ADC$ is isosceles.

d If line t intersects a plane β, then t is perpendicular to at least one line in β.

- If every point of a set S_1 is at the same distance from a set S_2, then every point of set S_2 must be at the same distance from S_1.

5 State at least two properties of triangles that contradict the measures given in D703.

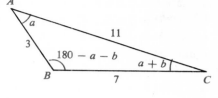

Diagram 703

6 Assume that circle $C(O, 6)$ is inscribed in the square $ABCD$. If E is the intersection of the circle and the ray $\overrightarrow{OC}$, then the distance from E to the square $ABCD$ is which of the following?

a $6(\sqrt{2} - 1)$ d $3(2\sqrt{2} - 1)$
b $3\sqrt{2}$ e $6 - 3\sqrt{2}$
c $12(\sqrt{3} - 1)$

7 Points $E, F, G,$ and H are the respective midpoints of sides $\overline{AB}, \overline{BC}, \overline{CD},$ and $\overline{DA}$ of quadrilateral $ABCD$. Form a one-to-one correspondence between the two lists below so that the matched names correctly complete the following sentence.
"If $ABCD$ is a $\sim\sim$, then $EFGH$ must be a $\sim\sim$."
a quadrilateral   A rhombus
b rhombus   B rectangle
c rectangle   C square
d square   D parallelogram

8 The medians of the equilateral triangle $\triangle ABC$ in a plane α intersect at Q, and each side of $\triangle ABC$ has length 7. If Ψ denotes a reflection of α in line AB, what is the area of polygon $A(Q\Psi)BQ$?

9 Let $a, b, c,$ and d denote real numbers. If $\dfrac{a}{b} = \dfrac{c}{d}$, which of the following equalities are necessarily correct?

a $\dfrac{a}{c} = \dfrac{b}{d}$.   d $ad = bc$.

b $ab = cd$.   e $\dfrac{a+b}{a-b} = \dfrac{c+d}{c-d}$.

c $\dfrac{a+c}{b} = \dfrac{c+b}{d}$.   f $\dfrac{a}{d} = \dfrac{c}{b}$.

10 If X is between A and B in side $\overline{AB}$ of $\triangle ABC$ and $\dfrac{d(A, X)}{d(A, B)} = r$, show that $\dfrac{Ar(\triangle AXC)}{Ar(\triangle ABC)} = r$. Why does this property imply that each median "bisects" the area of $\triangle ABC$?

11 If segments $\overline{AB}$ and $\overline{CD}$ are commensurable, there exists a segment $\overline{XY}$ such that $d(A, B) = md(X, Y)$ and

$d(C, D) = nd(X, Y)$, where m and n are integers.
For each of the following, indicate whether $\overline{AB}$ and $\overline{CD}$
are commensurable or not. If they are commensurable,
indicate the greatest possible value of $d(X, Y)$.

a $d(A, B) = \frac{1}{7}$ and $d(C, D) = \frac{5}{2}$.

b $d(A, B) = \sqrt{50}$ and $d(C, D) = \sqrt{75}$.

c $d(A, B) = \sqrt{72}$ and $d(C, D) = \sqrt{\frac{1}{2}}$.

12 Assume that segment $\overline{AB}$ is a diameter of the circle $C(O, r)$
in a plane α. Let α' denote one side of AB in α,
and let $\mathcal{R}$ denote the union of $\overline{AB}$ and the set of all
points that are interior to $C(O, r)$ in α'.

a Is $\mathcal{R}$ a bounded planar set? Is $\mathcal{R}$ a plane convex figure?

b Are all boundary points of $\mathcal{R}$ contained in $\mathcal{R}$? Do any
boundary points of $\mathcal{R}$ belong to $\mathcal{R}$?

c If all points of a circle $C(Q, x)$ are inner points
of $\mathcal{R}$, is Q an inner point of $\mathcal{R}$?

d If Φ denotes a contraction of α at point O, is
$\mathcal{R}\Phi \sim \mathcal{R}$?

e In exercise 12d, if Q is an inner point of $\mathcal{R}$, is
$Q\Phi$ an inner point of $\mathcal{R}$? If $H\Phi$ is an inner point
of $\mathcal{R}$, is H necessarily an inner point of $\mathcal{R}$?

13 If each side of $\triangle ABC$ in a plane α has length 2 and if
the mappings Γ and Ψ are the mappings defined below,
what is the area of the polygon determined by the
points $C, A\Gamma\Psi, B\Gamma, C\Gamma\Psi$, and $C\Gamma$?

Γ: expansion of α at A with ratio 3

Ψ: translation of α in the direction $\overrightarrow{AB}$ by amount 5

14 Circles $C(P, 9)$ and $C(Q, 2)$ are coplanar, and $d(P, Q) = 22$.
Point A of $C(P, 9)$ and point B of $C(Q, 2)$ are in opposite
sides of PQ. If line AB is tangent to both circles
and intersects $\overline{PQ}$ at F, what is the length of each
of the following segments?

a $\overline{PF}$ b $\overline{FQ}$ c $\overline{AF}$ d $\overline{AB}$

Sets **1**

A *set* is ordinarily determined in one of two ways, either by listing the elements in the set, such as the set of numbers {1, 2, 7},
or by listing properties that the elements of a set satisfy. In gen-
eral, we will use capital script letters, such as $\mathcal{R}$, $\mathcal{S}$, and $\mathcal{T}$, to
denote sets of numbers and sets of points. For example, $\mathcal{S}$ might
be the set of all real numbers; $\mathcal{R}$ might be the set of all points
in a plane; $\mathcal{T}$ might be the set of all lines in space that are parallel
to a given line. The set with no elements is the *empty set*, or the
null set.

Though we think of a set as a collection, aggregate, or assem-
blage of some kind of elements, we do not try to define the term
"set" in this book. We also take the notion of being an element
of a set as an undefined relation.

Subsets If $\mathcal{R}$ and $\mathcal{S}$ are sets, then $\mathcal{R}$ is a *subset* of $\mathcal{S}$, that is, $\mathcal{R}$ is contained
in $\mathcal{S}$ if every element that belongs to $\mathcal{R}$ also belongs to $\mathcal{S}$. This
relation is denoted by $\mathcal{R} \subset \mathcal{S}$, and $\mathcal{S}$ is also said to contain $\mathcal{R}$.
For example, if $\triangle ABC$ is contained in plane α, then $\triangle ABC \subset \alpha$.
In particular, for all sets $\mathcal{S}$, $\mathcal{S} \subset \mathcal{S}$. That is, every set is contained
in itself. The empty set is a subset of every set.

Equality To say that sets $\mathcal{R}$ and $\mathcal{S}$ are *equal* means that $\mathcal{R}$ and $\mathcal{S}$ are two
names for the same collection of elements.

The most common way of proving that $\mathcal{R} = \mathcal{S}$ is to prove
that $\mathcal{R} \subset \mathcal{S}$ and that $\mathcal{S} \subset \mathcal{R}$. To do this, one ordinarily considers
some arbitrary element of $\mathcal{R}$, say element x, and attempts to
show that x being in $\mathcal{R}$ implies that x must also be in $\mathcal{S}$. If this
can be shown for any x in $\mathcal{R}$, then, clearly, $\mathcal{R} \subset \mathcal{S}$. If a similar
argument can be carried through to show that $\mathcal{S} \subset \mathcal{R}$, then the
conclusion $\mathcal{R} = \mathcal{S}$ is established.

531

The set of all elements that belong to *both* set $\mathcal{R}$ and set $\mathcal{S}$ is called the *intersection set*, or simply the *intersection*, of $\mathcal{R}$ and $\mathcal{S}$. This intersection is denoted by either $\mathcal{R} \cap \mathcal{S}$ or $\mathcal{S} \cap \mathcal{R}$. It may be that there is no element common to $\mathcal{R}$ and to $\mathcal{S}$, in which case, $\mathcal{R} \cap \mathcal{S}$ is the empty set.

With the convention about the empty set as an intersection set, the intersection set $\mathcal{R} \cap \mathcal{S}$ always exists. So, when we speak of two "nonintersecting" lines, for example, we mean that their intersection is the empty set. This will always be the meaning of "nonintersecting" sets.

One can speak of the intersection of any number of sets. The intersection set $\mathcal{A} \cap \mathcal{B} \cap \mathcal{C} \cap \mathcal{D}$, for example, denotes the intersection of sets $\mathcal{A}$, $\mathcal{B}$, $\mathcal{C}$, and $\mathcal{D}$ and consists of those elements that belong to every one of the sets.

By its definition, an intersection set is contained in each of the sets whose intersection is being formed. That is, if $\mathcal{S} = \mathcal{A} \cap \mathcal{B} \cap \mathcal{C}$, then $\mathcal{S} \subset \mathcal{A}$, $\mathcal{S} \subset \mathcal{B}$, and $\mathcal{S} \subset \mathcal{C}$.

The set of all elements that belong to at least one of the sets $\mathcal{R}$ and $\mathcal{S}$ is called the *union* of $\mathcal{R}$ and $\mathcal{S}$ and is denoted by $\mathcal{R} \cup \mathcal{S}$ or $\mathcal{S} \cup \mathcal{R}$. As with intersection, one can speak of the union of any number of sets. Thus, $\mathcal{A} \cup \mathcal{B} \cup \mathcal{C} \cup \mathcal{D}$ is the set of all elements that belong to at least one of the sets $\mathcal{A}$, $\mathcal{B}$, $\mathcal{C}$, and $\mathcal{D}$.

By its definition, a union of sets contains each of the sets. That is, if $\mathcal{S} = \mathcal{A} \cup \mathcal{B} \cup \mathcal{C}$, then $\mathcal{A} \subset \mathcal{S}$, $\mathcal{B} \subset \mathcal{S}$, and $\mathcal{C} \subset \mathcal{S}$.

Some conventions about sets **2** If $\mathcal{S}$ is a set of real numbers, then a is the *maximum* of $\mathcal{S}$ if a is in $\mathcal{S}$ and if no number in $\mathcal{S}$ is greater than a. For example, the maximum of the set $\{1, 5, \frac{4}{3}, \sqrt{2}, 3\}$ is 5. The *minimum* of a numerical set $\mathcal{S}$ is the number b if b is in $\mathcal{S}$ and if no number in $\mathcal{S}$ is less than b. For example, 1 is the minimum of the set $\{1, 5, \frac{4}{3}, \sqrt{2}, 3\}$.

A numerical set may fail to have a maximum or a minimum. If, for example, $\mathcal{A}$, $\mathcal{B}$, and $\mathcal{C}$ are the respective sets of numbers x such that $-2 \leqq x < 5$, $-2 < x \leqq 5$, and $-2 < x < 5$; then $\mathcal{A}$ has -2 as its minimum but has no maximum, $\mathcal{B}$ has 5 as its maximum but has no minimum, and $\mathcal{C}$ has neither a maximum nor a minimum.

A basic property of any finite set of numbers is that it has both a maximum and a minimum.

A number *b* is said to be an *upper bound* to a numerical set S if no number in S is greater than *b*. Clearly, every number greater than *b* is also an upper bound to S. For example, if S is the set of real numbers *x* such that $x \leq \sqrt{3}$, then 2, 2.5, and 3 are upper bounds to S. The least number that is an upper bound to S, if one exists, is called the *least upper bound to* S. This number is commonly denoted by "L.U.B.(S)." The least upper bound to set S described above is $\sqrt{3}$. The least upper bound to a set may or may not belong to the set. If, for example, T is the set of real numbers such that $x < 7$, then L.U.B.(T) = 7, and 7 is not an element of T.

A number *c* is a *lower bound* to a numerical set S if no number in S is less than *c*. Clearly, every number less than *c* is also a lower bound to S. The greatest number that is a lower bound to S is called the *greatest lower bound to* S and is denoted by "G.L.B.(S)." The greatest lower bound to a set may or may not belong to the set. Consider, for example, the set R of real numbers *x* such that $\pi \leq x$. Such numbers as 3.1, $-\pi$, and $2\sqrt{2}$ are lower bounds of R. The G.L.B.(R) = π, which is an element of R. If, however, R is the set of numbers *x* such that $\pi < x$, then G.L.B.(R) = π, but π is not an element of R.

A numerical set S is said to be *bounded above* if an upper bound to S exists and to be *bounded below* if a lower bound to S exists. Ordinarily, the set is said to be *bounded* if both an upper and a lower bound exist.

One of the basic properties of all sets S of real numbers is that, if S is bounded above, that is, if an upper bound to S exists, then a least upper bound to S exists. Similarly, if a lower bound to S exists, then a greatest lower bound to S exists.

To find bounds to a set of numbers S is to find, if they exist, an upper bound and a lower bound. To find the "best bounds" to S is to find, if they exist, the L.U.B. and the G.L.B. to S.

Cardinality 3
of sets

There is a close connection between the notion of a one-to-one correspondence between two sets and the idea of comparing the number of elements in one set with the number of elements in another set. Consider a collection of objects, say a desk, a chair, a table, and a lamp. The act of counting these in a particular order, say one for the desk, two for the lamp, three for the table, and four for the chair, establishes a one-to-one correspondence between the set of objects and the set of successive positive integers {1, 2, 3, 4}. We say that the set has 4 elements and 4 is called the *cardinal number* of the elements in the set, or simply, the *cardinality* of the set. Similarly, if there exists a one-to-one correspondence between the elements of a set S and the set of successive positive integers $\{1, 2, 3, \ldots, n-2, n-1, n\}$, then the cardinality of S is n. Moreover, any set R that can be put into one-to-one correspondence with S also has cardinality n.

The previous ideas can be applied to sets that are not finite. If any two sets, finite or not, can be put into one-to-one correspondence with each other, then the sets are said to have the same cardinality. In particular, any set that has the same cardinality as the set of *all* positive integers $\{1, 2, 3, \ldots\}$ is said to be *denumerable*, or *countably infinite*. An infinite set that does not have the cardinality of the set of all positive integers is said to be *nondenumerable*, or *uncountably infinite*.

For finite sets $\mathcal{A}$ and $\mathcal{B}$, it is always true that if $\mathcal{A} \subset \mathcal{B}$ and $\mathcal{B}$ is not contained in $\mathcal{A}$ (so $\mathcal{A}$ is a *proper* subset of $\mathcal{B}$), then the cardinality of $\mathcal{A}$ is less than the cardinality of $\mathcal{B}$. However, this property does not hold for infinite sets. An infinite set always has the same cardinality as some of its proper subsets. In particular, every infinite set S of positive integers has the same cardinality as the set of all positive integers. One example for S might be the set of all positive integers that are squares (such as 1, 4, 9, and so on). The correspondence $n \leftrightarrow n^2$, where n is a positive integer, is a one-to-one correspondence between S and the set of all positive integers. So the set of square integers is denumerable, even though it is a proper subset of the set of positive integers.

It can be proved that the set of all rational numbers is denumerable and that the set of all irrational numbers is nondenumerable. Any *interval* of real numbers, such as the set of numbers x for which $1 \leq x \leq 2$, is a nondenumerable set.

One can see geometrically how a nondenumerable set may be put into one-to-one correspondence with a proper subset of itself. In D1 below, we have shown how a segment can be put into

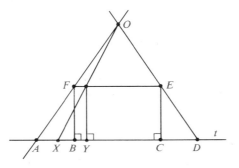

Diagram 1

one-to-one correspondence with a subset of itself. Let points A, B, C, and D be successive points in that order in line t, and let $BCEF$ denote a rectangle. Let O denote the intersection of lines AF and DE. To each point X in $\overline{AD}$, there corresponds a point Y in $\overline{BC}$ such that Y is the foot in t of the point $XO \cap FE$. The correspondence $X \leftrightarrow Y$ is a one-to-one correspondence of the nondenumerable set $\overline{AD}$ and its proper subset $\overline{BC}$.

Non-constructible numbers 4

Three famous problems posed by the ancient Greeks were the following straightedge and compass constructions.

a) To trisect any angle, that is, to construct an angle whose measure is one third that of any given angle
b) To double a cube, that is, to construct a cube whose volume is twice that of any given cube
c) To square a circle, that is, to construct a square whose area is equal to that of any given circle

Not until the nineteenth century were these problems settled. Then it was proved, by methods of modern algebra, that the third construction is never possible and that the other two are possible only in special cases.

In relation to each of these problems, compass and straightedge constructions are known that solve the problems in the sense that they produce an approximation of the desired solution. For example, given a circle, one can use a compass and straightedge to construct a square whose area differs from that of the circle by less than any preassigned positive number. There is no mathematical difficulty, for instance, about constructing a square whose area does not differ in the first million decimal places from the area of a given circle. Such constructions are constantly being rediscovered by people who do not understand the distinction between an *exact* and an *approximate* solution.

We cannot give here the proofs that settled the three famous construction problems. But we can indicate, in a very general way, what the proofs involved. Suppose that we start with a segment, which we arbitrarily take to be of unit length. Then, with a compass, we can mark a succession of unit segments along a line. So we can construct segments of length two, of length three, and so on. We can describe this by saying that any positive integer n is constructible. In these terms, a number x is constructible if, in some compass and straightedge construction, there is a segment of length x whose endpoints are the intersections of lines, or of circles, or of lines and circles in the construction.

Now consider, for example, the problem of doubling a cube. We can suppose that a cube of unit volume is given. Hence, we know the segments of unit length that are its edges. To construct a cube of volume 2, we must construct a cube whose edges have length $\sqrt[3]{2}$. So the question becomes "Is $\sqrt[3]{2}$ a constructible number?" It was discovered that, starting with a unit, *all* the constructible numbers (in compass and straightedge constructions) must have certain properties, that is, they must be numbers of a certain type. It was also found possible to prove that the particular number $\sqrt[3]{2}$ is not of this type and, hence, is not a constructible number. The conclusion, then, had to be that there is no compass and straightedge construction that will produce a cube whose volume is *exactly* twice that of a unit cube.

The area of a circle of radius 1 is π. A square with the same area has edges of length $\sqrt{\pi}$. It was proved that $\sqrt{\pi}$ is not in the set of constructible numbers that correspond to compass and straightedge constructions. Hence, one cannot "square the circle" with these tools.

A similar line of argument proved that there is no construction with these instruments for the trisection of general angles. Clearly, some particular angles, for instance, a right angle, can be trisected with a compass and straightedge construction.

A counting principle 5

There is a very simple principle that often is useful in solving problems that involve counting. If one thing can be done in x different ways and, afterwards, a second thing can be done in y different ways, and then a third thing can be done in z different ways, then the number of different ways of doing the three things in that succession is the product xyz.

To give an illustration, consider the problem of counting the number of orderings possible for four points A, B, C, and D. The number of possibilities for the first position in the ordering is 4; the number for the second position is 3; for the third position, 2; and for the fourth position, 1. Hence, the number of orderings is $4 \cdot 3 \cdot 2 \cdot 1 = 24$. The product $n \cdot n - 1 \cdot \ldots \cdot 3 \cdot 2 \cdot 1$ is often written $n!$ (read "n factorial"). Thus, there are 4! orderings of 4 different elements, and one can see that there are $n!$ orderings of n different elements.

For a different example, suppose that $P_1, P_2, P_3, \ldots, P_{10}$ are the vertices of a 10-gon (a decagon). How many triangles do these points determine? Using the counting principle, we know that

536

there are $10 \cdot 9 \cdot 8$ ordered triples (P_i, P_j, P_k). But each triangle, for example, $\triangle P_1 P_2 P_3$, is determined by an unordered set, in this case, $\{P_1, P_2, P_3\}$; and these three vertices have $3 \cdot 2 \cdot 1$, or 6, orderings. Hence, the number of ordered triples is 6 times the number of triangles. Therefore, the number of triangles is one sixth the number of ordered triples. Thus, the number of triangles is $\dfrac{10 \cdot 9 \cdot 8}{6}$, or 120.

From the counting principle, one can derive the following two formulas.

a) The number of *ordered* sets, each of k different elements, that can be formed by selecting the k elements from a set of n different elements is

$$n(n-1)(n-2)\ldots[n-(k-1)] = \frac{n!}{(n-k)!}.*$$

b) The number of *unordered* sets, each of k different elements, that can be formed by selecting the k elements from a set of n different elements is

$$\frac{n(n-1)(n-2)\ldots[n-(k-1)]}{1 \cdot 2 \cdot 3 \cdot \ldots \cdot k} = \frac{n!}{k!(n-k)!}.$$

In the 10-gon example, the number of ordered sets of three vertices is, therefore, by formula a, $10 \cdot 9 \cdot 8 = \dfrac{10!}{7!} = 720$. The number of triangles is the number of unordered sets of three, and, by formula b, is $\dfrac{10 \cdot 9 \cdot 8}{1 \cdot 2 \cdot 3} = \dfrac{10!}{3!7!} = 120$.

---

* This formula is still correct for the case $n = k$ if one makes the definition that $0! = 1$.

537

The natural order of the integers in increasing size, . . . , -3, -2, -1, 0, 1, 2, 3, 4, . . . , suggests that all the integers greater than a particular integer are *successors* of that integer. For example, 20 is a successor of -8 because $20 > -8$. In particular, each integer n has a first, or least, successor, $n + 1$. The least successor of n is the integer immediately following n in the natural ordering. So we can speak of 6 as *the* successor of 5 and 32 as *the* successor of 31.

Now suppose that $\mathbb{S}$ is a set of integers about which two facts are known. First, it is known that a particular integer, say 3, belongs to $\mathbb{S}$. Second, it is known that, if any integer is in $\mathbb{S}$, then its successor is also in $\mathbb{S}$. From these two facts, it seems clear that $\mathbb{S}$ must contain 3 and *all* successors of 3. Certainly 4 is in $\mathbb{S}$ because 3 is in $\mathbb{S}$ and 4 is the successor of 3. Then 5 is in $\mathbb{S}$ as the successor of 4. This, in turn, implies that 6 is in $\mathbb{S}$ as the successor of 5. Proceeding step by step, it seems that every successor of 3 must be reached at some step and so must belong to $\mathbb{S}$. This very reasonable notion is called an *induction principle*.

A *proof by induction* arises very commonly if the nature of a property that we wish to establish depends upon the property holding for an integer n. Consider, for example, the theorem "A polygon with n vertices has $\dfrac{n(n-3)}{2}$ diagonals." If we label this statement T_n, then we have

$$T_3: \text{a polygon with three vertices has } \frac{3(3-3)}{2} \text{ diagonals,}$$

$$T_4: \text{a polygon with four vertices has } \frac{4(4-3)}{2} \text{ diagonals,}$$

and so on. Thus, we can regard the original theorem as an abbreviated way of stating infinitely many different theorems. To prove that they all are theorems is to prove that all the statements in the sequence T_3, T_4, T_5, . . . are valid. To use an induction principle in making such a proof, we define the statement T_4 to be the successor of T_3, and T_5 to be the successor of T_4, and, in general, T_{n+1} to be the successor of T_n, where $n \geq 3$. Next we define $\mathbb{S}$ to be the set of all statements in the sequence that are theorems. We then seek to establish the following two facts.

a) The first statement, T_3, is in S.
b) If a statement from the sequence $T_3, T_4, T_5, \ldots$ is in S, then its successor must also be in S.

If we can establish *both* a and b, then we assert, by an induction principle, that all the statements in the sequence belong to S.

To carry through the two parts of an induction proof for this example, first consider part a. To show that T_3 is in S, we must show that the number of diagonals of a triangle is $\dfrac{3(3 - 3)}{2}$, or 0.

This is correct because, in a triangle, the join of any two vertices is a side, so the triangle has no diagonals.

Next consider part b of an induction proof. We must show that, if a statement T_n is in S, then its successor $T_{n + 1}$ must also be in S. Let $\mathcal{P}_{n + 1} = P_1 P_2 \ldots P_n P_{n + 1}$ be a polygon with $n + 1$ vertices. Then $\mathcal{P}_n = P_1 P_2 \ldots P_n$ is a polygon with n vertices. If T_n is valid, then there are $\dfrac{n(n - 3)}{2}$ diagonals of polygon $\mathcal{P}_n$. To establish part b, we must now show that, if $\mathcal{P}_n$ has $\dfrac{n(n - 3)}{2}$ diagonals, then $\mathcal{P}_{n + 1}$ has $\dfrac{(n + 1)((n + 1) - 3)}{2}$ diagonals. As is apparent from D1, all the diagonals of $\mathcal{P}_n$ are also diagonals of $\mathcal{P}_{n + 1}$. And the diagonals of $\mathcal{P}_{n + 1}$ that are not already counted are the diagonals that have $P_{n + 1}$ as one endpoint and the segment $\overline{P_1 P_n}$, which is a side of $\mathcal{P}_n$ but a diagonal of $\mathcal{P}_{n + 1}$.

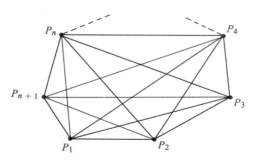

Diagram 1

In $\mathcal{P}_{n + 1}$, there are n segments joining $P_{n + 1}$ to the other vertices. Two of these segments are sides, so there are $n - 2$ diagonals from $P_{n + 1}$. These, along with $\overline{P_1 P_n}$, make $n - 2 + 1$, or $n - 1$, diagonals of $\mathcal{P}_{n + 1}$ that are not also diagonals of $\mathcal{P}_n$.

Therefore, if $\mathcal{P}_n$ has $\dfrac{n(n - 3)}{2}$ diagonals, then, the number of

539

diagonals of $\mathcal{P}_{n+1}$ is $\dfrac{n(n-3)}{2} + n - 1$. Now, by direct calcu-

lation, it follows that

$$\frac{n(n-3)}{2} + n - 1 = \frac{n^2 - n - 2}{2} = \frac{(n+1)(n-2)}{2}$$

$$= \frac{(n+1)((n+1) - 3)}{2}.$$

Thus, the number of diagonals of $\mathcal{P}_{n+1}$ is $\dfrac{(n+1)((n+1) - 3)}{2}$.

Since this conclusion is statement T_{n+1}, it follows that, *if T_n is valid*, so is T_{n+1}. Thus both parts a and b of the proof have been established. By induction, all the statements $T_3, T_4, T_5, \ldots$ are in $\mathcal{S}$, and so all are theorems.

In general, then, suppose that we have a set of statements that can be ordered, $T_a, T_{a+1}, T_{a+2}, \ldots$, where a is some particular integer, and that every statement in the set has a successor. (The set may or may not have a "last" statement, that is, it may or may not contain a statement T with a greatest subscript.) If we can show that the following statements are true, then, by induction, we can assert that all the statements in the set are theorems.

a) T_a is a theorem.
b) If any statement T_{a+k} in the set is a theorem, then its successor, T_{a+k+1}, is a theorem.

The only point about induction that is sometimes difficult to grasp is the fact that, in part b of an inductive proof, one is *not* proving that any of the statements are theorems. One is proving only that the nature of the sequence of statements is such that, if T_n *were* valid, then its successor T_{n+1} also *would be* valid.

A sequence of statements can have this second property even if all the statements of the sequence are actually false. For example, if T_n is the statement "$3 + 2n$ is an even integer," then T_n is false. But *if T_n were* valid, then T_{n+1} *would be* valid because $3 + 2(n + 1) = (3 + 2n) + 2$, and the addition of 2 to an even integer produces another even integer.

Once one sees the hypothetical character of part b of an inductive proof (if your father were a woman, he would be your mother), then it is not hard to see that parts a and b of such a proof are independent. One can have a sequence of statements $T_1, T_2, \ldots, T_n, \ldots$ such that none are theorems but also such that $T_n \Rightarrow T_{n+1}$ for every positive integer n. Then an inductive proof fails because part a cannot be established. On the other hand, $T_1, T_2, \ldots, T_{12}$, for example, might be theorems, but it might not be true that $T_{12} \Rightarrow T_{13}$. Then an inductive proof would fail because part b cannot be established.

The following are a few examples of problems that, in one way or another, have had a distinguished history. After each problem, we have indicated the stage of the text at which the student has sufficient background to formulate the solution we have in mind. In some instances, we have cited two chapters. The first chapter indicates the point at which the principal ideas of the solution can be understood, and the second represents the stage at which the solution can be done with greater precision or more naturalness.

Stewart's 1

theorem Let A, B, and C denote three points in a line t, and let a positive and negative direction be assigned in t. A *directed distance* from A to B is assigned by defining $\rho(A, B) = d(A, B)$ if $\overrightarrow{AB}$ is the positive direction and $\rho(A, B) = -d(A, B)$ if $\overrightarrow{AB}$ is the negative direction [so $\rho(A, B) = -\rho(B, A)$]. Finally, define $\rho(Q, Q) = 0$ for any Q. If P is any point in space, then $d(P, A)^2 \rho(B, C) + d(P, B)^2 \rho(C, A) + d(P, C)^2 \rho(A, B) + \rho(B, C) \rho(C, A) \rho(A, B) = 0.$*
[Chapter 2 for P in AB; Chapter 5 for the general case]

* Mathew Stewart (1717-1785) first stated the general theorem. It was proved independently by Thomas Simpson and Leonard Euler. The special case, where P is in the line, is in the "Collections" of Pappus.

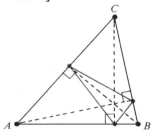
The nine- **3**

point circle Corresponding to a triangle, there exists a circle that passes through the midpoint of each side, the foot of each altitude, and the midpoint of each segment from the orthocenter to a vertex. (D2) [Chapter 4]

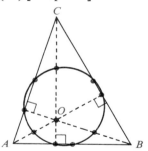

Diagram 2

Sylvester's **4**

problem If n points $P_1, P_2, P_3, \ldots, P_n$, with $n > 2$, are not collinear, then there exists a line that contains exactly two of the given n points.† [Chapters 4 and 5]

The Fermat **5**

point If △*ABC* exists and its angles all have measures less than 120, then there is a unique point P_0 for which the sum $d(P, A) + d(P, B) + d(P, C)$ has a minimum value. The point P_0 is interior

---

* Proposed and solved by G. F. Fagnano, an Italian, in 1775.
† James Sylvester, an English mathematician of the nineteenth century.

to the triangle and $\sphericalangle AP_0B$, $\sphericalangle BP_0C$, and $\sphericalangle CP_0A$ each has measure 120. (If $\sphericalangle ACB° \geq 120$ or if $<A, C, B>$, then $P_0 = C$.)* (D3) [Chapters 4 and 7]

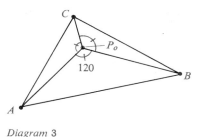

Diagram 3

The Euler line 6

Corresponding to $\triangle ABC$, the circumcenter, the centroid, the orthocenter, and the center of the nine-point circle (see problem 3) are collinear (in the Euler line).† (D4) [Chapter 5]

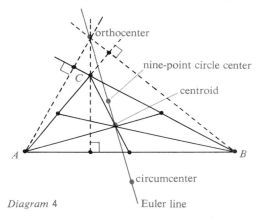

Diagram 4

The Gergonne 7

point If the incircle of $\triangle ABC$ is tangent to AB at C', to BC at A', and to CA at B', then AA', BB', and CC' are concurrent (at the Gergonne point).‡ [Chapter 5]

Morley's 8

theorem There are six rays that are the trisectors of the angles of a triangle. A pair of these rays that are adjacent to a side of the triangle and

---

* This problem was first proposed by Pierre de Fermat, a seventeenth-century French mathematician. It was solved by Evangelista Torricelli, and the solution was published in 1659.
† Leonard Euler, a Swiss mathematician of the eighteenth century.
‡ Joseph Diez Gergonne, a French geometer of the nineteenth century.

emanate from the endpoints of that side intersect in a point. The three such points corresponding to the three sides are the vertices of an equilateral triangle.* (D5) [Chapters 5 and 7]

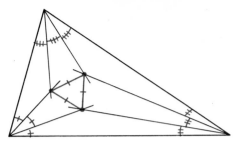

Diagram 5

A theorem 9
of Pappus Let P denote any point in the plane of $\triangle ABC$ such that PC intersects $\overline{AB}$ at Q between A and B, and let $ABDE$ denote a parallelogram on side $\overline{AB}$ such that $\overline{AE}$ is congruent and parallel to $\overline{PC}$. If $BCFG$ and $CAHI$ are parallelograms on sides $\overline{BC}$ and $\overline{CA}$ such that FG and HI intersect at P, then the area of $ABDE$ is the sum of the areas of $BCFG$ and $CAHI$. (D6) [Chapter 8]

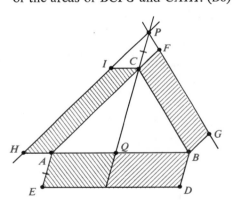

Diagram 6

The Erdos- 10
Mordell If P is interior to $\triangle ABC$, then the sum of its distances from A, B,
inequality and C is equal to or greater than twice the sum of its distances from lines BC, CA, and AB. The equality holds if and only if $\triangle ABC$ is equilateral and P is its incenter.† [Chapter 8, based on problem 9]

---

* The property was discovered by F. Morley around 1900. The first proof, by W. E. Phillips, was published in 1914.
† This relationship was conjectured by P. Erdos in 1935 and proved by L. J. Mordell in 1937. With proper interpretation, the theorem also holds if P is in $\triangle ABC$.

Ptolemy's 11
theorem If a quadrilateral $ABCD$ has a circumcircle, then the product of the lengths of the diagonals is the sum of the products of the lengths of pairs of opposite sides. That is,

$$d(A, C)\, d(B, D) = d(A, B)\, d(C, D) + d(B, C)\, d(D, A).*$$

[Chapter 9]

The Simson 12
line If point P is in the circumcircle of $\triangle ABC$ and is not a vertex, then the feet of P in lines AB, BC, and CA are collinear (in the Simson line corresponding to P).† (D7) [Chapter 9]

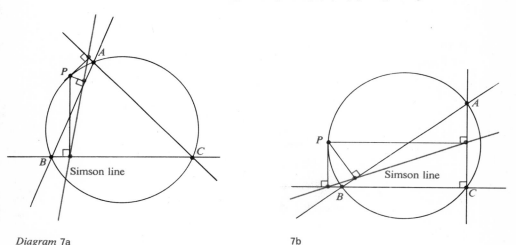

Diagram 7a   7b

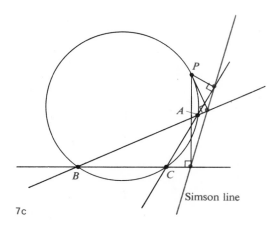

7c

* Claudius Ptolemy, Greek-Egyptian astronomer, geographer, and mathematician, second century A.D., was the author of a famous work, the "Almagest."
† Robert Simson (1687-1768).

A	alpha	α
B	beta	β
Γ	gamma	γ
Δ	delta	δ
E	epsilon	ϵ
Z	zeta	ζ
H	eta	η
Θ	theta	θ
I	iota	ι
K	kappa	κ
Λ	lambda	λ
M	mu	μ
N	nu	ν
Ξ	xi	ξ
O	omicron	o
Π	pi	π
P	rho	ρ
Σ	sigma	σ
T	tau	τ
Υ	upsilon	υ
Φ	phi	ϕ
X	chi	χ
Ψ	psi	ψ
Ω	omega	ω

Axioms, definitions, theorems, corollaries, and lemmas

This list contains the axioms, definitions, and theorems that are presented in the book. It also contains all the corollaries to the theorems and the lemmas that are needed to prove certain of the theorems.

Definition 1/2   *Space* [p. 28]

Axiom 1/2   A line is a nonempty set of points, and each two points belong to exactly one line. [p. 28]

Definition 2/2   *Linear set, collinear* [p. 28]

Axiom 2/2   A plane is a nonempty set of points, and each three noncollinear points belong to exactly one plane. [p. 31]

Definition 3/2   *Planar set, coplanar* [p. 31]

Axiom 3/2   If two points belong to a plane, then the line to which the points belong is contained in the plane. [p. 31]

Axiom 4/2   There are four points that are noncoplanar and noncollinear. [p. 32]

Theorem 1/2   If two lines intersect at a point, then they do not intersect at any other point. [p. 36]

Axiom 5/2   To each two points A and B, there corresponds one positive real number that is the distance between A and B. [p. 38]

Axiom 6/2
Ruler axiom   For each line, there exists a one-to-one correspondence between the points of the line and the set of all real numbers such that the distance between each two points of the line is the absolute value of the difference of the real numbers that correspond to the two points.

    In other words, there is a correspondence such that the following is true:
1) To each point A of the line, there corresponds exactly one real number a.
2) To each real number b, there corresponds exactly one point B of the line.
3) If point A and the number a correspond and if another point B and the number b correspond, then $d(A, B) = |a - b|$. [p. 39]

Definition 4/2   *Coordinate system for a line* [p. 39]

Axiom 7/2
Ruler placement axiom   If A and B are two points of a line, then there exists a coordinate system for the line that has the properties of Axiom 6/2 and is such that the coordinate of A is zero and the coordinate of B is a positive number. [p. 40]

Definition 5/2   *Equality of points* [p. 41]

Definition 6/2   *Betweenness for points* [p. 42]

Theorem 2/2   For three collinear points A, B, and C with coordinates a, b, and c respectively, if b is between a and c, then B is between A and C. That is, $\langle a, b, c \rangle \Rightarrow \langle A, B, C \rangle$. [p. 43]

Theorem 3/2   Exactly one of three collinear points is between the other two. [p. 43]

547

* *Theorem* 12/2   If each of points C and D in line AB is between A and B, then $d(C, D) < d(A, B)$. [p. 51]

* *Theorem* 13/2   If r is a positive number, then there is exactly one point P of $\overrightarrow{AB}$ such that B is between A and P and $d(B, P) = r$. [p. 51]

Theorem 14/2   If a point is not in a line, then there is exactly one plane that contains both the point and the line. [p. 52]

Corollary 14/2   If a point is not in the line of a ray, then there is exactly one plane that contains both the point and the ray. If a point is not in the line of a segment, there is exactly one plane that contains both the point and the segment. [p. 53]

* *Theorem* 15/2   If two lines intersect, then there is exactly one plane that contains both lines. [p. 53]

* *Corollary* 15/2   Each of the following pairs of sets determines exactly one plane that contains both sets: two noncollinear intersecting rays; two noncollinear intersecting segments; a ray and a segment that are noncollinear and that intersect. [p. 53]

Definition 14/2   *Convex set* [p. 57]

Axiom 8/2   Corresponding to each line t in a plane α, there are exactly two sets α' and α'' with the following properties. Sets α' and α'' are nonempty, convex sets. No two of the three sets α', α'', and t have a point in common. Plane α is the union of α', α'', and t. Every segment that joins a point of α' to a point of α'' intersects t. [p. 57]

Definition 15/2   *Open half-planes, closed half-planes* [p. 57]

Theorem 16/2   If two points A and B are in the same plane as a line t and if neither point is in t, then the points belong to the same side of t if and only if $\overline{AB}$ does not intersect t. [p. 58]

Theorem 17/2   If point B is not in line t, and point A is in t, then, in the plane of B and t, the open ray $\overrightarrow{AB}$ belongs to the B-side of t and the open ray opposite $\overrightarrow{AB}$ belongs to the opposite side of t. [p. 58]

Definition 16/2   *Angle* [p. 61]

Definition 17/2   *Interior of an angle, exterior of an angle* [p. 62]

Theorem 18/2   The intersection of any number of convex sets is a convex set. [p. 62]

* *Theorem* 19/2   Each of the following sets is a convex set: a segment, an open ray, a closed ray, a line, an open half-plane, a closed half-plane, a plane, and the interior of an angle. [p. 63]

Definition 18/2   *Betweenness for rays* [p. 64]

Theorem 20/2   Point P is in the interior of $\angle ABC$ if and only if $\overrightarrow{BP}$ is between $\overrightarrow{BA}$ and $\overrightarrow{BC}$. [p. 65]

* *Theorem* 21/2   All points of $\overline{AC}$ between A and C are in the interior of $\angle ABC$. [p. 66]

* *Theorem* 22/2   Each ray between $\overrightarrow{BA}$ and $\overrightarrow{BC}$ intersects $\overline{AC}$ at a point between A and C. If P is in the interior of $\angle ABC$, then $\overrightarrow{BP}$ intersects $\overline{AC}$ at a point between A and C. [p. 66]

* *Theorem* 23/2   If ray $\mathcal{S}$ is between rays $\mathcal{R}$ and $\mathcal{T}$, then, in the plane of the rays, each two of the closed rays of $\mathcal{R}$, $\mathcal{S}$, and $\mathcal{T}$ form an angle; the open rays of $\mathcal{R}$ and $\mathcal{T}$

are in the opposite sides of the line of S; $\mathcal{T}$ is not between $\mathcal{R}$ and S, and $\mathcal{R}$ is not between $\mathcal{T}$ and S. [p. 66]

Theorem 24/2   If $\overrightarrow{AC}$ and $\overrightarrow{AD}$ are two open rays that are in an open half-plane of line AB, then one of the open rays $\overrightarrow{AC}$ and $\overrightarrow{AD}$ is between the other ray and $\overrightarrow{AB}$. [p. 66]

Definition 19/2   *Opposite angles* [p. 67]

Theorem 25/2   Two opposite angles belong to the same plane. The interiors of the angles are in opposite sides of the line of each arm of the angles. If a ray is between the arms of one angle, then an opposite ray is between the arms of the opposite angle. [p. 67]

Axiom 9/2   To each angle there corresponds a real number between 0 and 180 that is the measure of the angle. [p. 72]

Definition 20/2   *Acute angle, right angle, obtuse angle* [p. 72]

Axiom 10/2
Protractor axiom   If $\overrightarrow{AB}$ is a closed ray in the edge of an open half-plane α', there exists a one-to-one correspondence between a set of open rays in α' and the set of real numbers between 0 and 180 with the following properties. For each open ray $\overrightarrow{AR}$ in α', there is just one number r between 0 and 180 that is the measure of $\sphericalangle BAR$. For each number r between 0 and 180, there is exactly one open ray $\overrightarrow{AR}$ in α' such that $\sphericalangle BAR$ has measure r. [p. 73]

Axiom 11/2
Angle addition axiom   If P is in the interior of $\sphericalangle BAQ$, then the measure of $\sphericalangle BAQ$ is the sum of the measures of $\sphericalangle BAP$ and $\sphericalangle PAQ$. That is, if P is in the interior of $\sphericalangle BAQ$, then $\sphericalangle BAQ° = \sphericalangle BAP° + \sphericalangle PAQ°$. [p. 73]

Theorem 26/2   If $\overrightarrow{AX}$ and $\overrightarrow{AY}$ are two open rays in an open half-plane α' and have ray coordinates x and y respectively, then $\sphericalangle XAY° = |x - y|$; $\sphericalangle XAY° = x - y$ if and only if $\overrightarrow{AY}$ is between $\overrightarrow{AX}$ and the initial ray of the coordinate system. [p. 73]

Theorem 27/2   If point Q is in the plane of $\sphericalangle PAB$ and in the same side of AB as P, then Q is interior to, is in, or is exterior to $\sphericalangle PAB$ according as the measure of $\sphericalangle QAB$ is less than, equal to, or greater than the measure of $\sphericalangle PAB$. [p. 74]

Corollary 27/2   If $\overrightarrow{AQ}$ is between $\overrightarrow{AB}$ and $\overrightarrow{AP}$, then the sum of the measures of $\sphericalangle QAB$ and $\sphericalangle QAP$ is equal to the measure of $\sphericalangle PAB$. In particular, each of the measures of $\sphericalangle QAB$ and $\sphericalangle QAP$ is less than the measure of $\sphericalangle PAB$. [p. 74]

Definition 21/2   *Supplementary angles* [p. 74]

**Theorem 28/2*
Angle supplement theorem   If $\overrightarrow{AB}$ and $\overrightarrow{AC}$ are opposite closed rays and $\overrightarrow{AP}$ is a third closed ray, then $\sphericalangle PAB$ and $\sphericalangle PAC$ are supplementary angles. That is, $\sphericalangle PAB° + \sphericalangle PAC° = 180$. [p. 74]

Theorem 29/2   A supplement of an acute angle is an obtuse angle. A supplement of a right angle is a right angle. A supplement of an obtuse angle is an acute angle. [p. 75]

Definition 22/2   *Adjacent angles* [p. 75]

Theorem 30/2   If $\sphericalangle PAB$ and $\sphericalangle PAC$ are adjacent and supplementary, then $\overrightarrow{AB}$ and $\overrightarrow{AC}$ are opposite closed rays. [p. 75]

Theorem 31/2   If point P is in the interior of $\sphericalangle QAB$ and $\overrightarrow{AC}$ is the closed ray opposite $\overrightarrow{AB}$, then Q is in the interior of $\sphericalangle PAC$, and $\sphericalangle BAP° + \sphericalangle PAQ° + \sphericalangle QAC° = 180$. [p. 75]

555

Theorem 152/5	If a transversal t intersects parallel lines a, b, c, and d (some of which may be identical) at points A, B, C, and D respectively and if segments $\overline{AB}$ and $\overline{CD}$ exist, then $\overline{AB}$ and $\overline{CD}$ are congruent if and only if the distance between a and b equals the distance between c and d. [p. 255]
Corollary 152/5	If lines s and t are transversals of a set of parallel lines, two segments in s are congruent if and only if the corresponding segments in t are congruent. [p. 258]
Definition 86/5	*Successive points and segments in a line* [p. 259]
★ *Theorem* 153/5	If the n collinear points P_1, P_2, P_3, $\ldots$, P_n are successive in a line in the order $(P_1, P_2, P_3, \ldots, P_n)$, then the length of $\overline{P_1 P_n}$ is the sum of the lengths of the successive segments $\overline{P_1 P_2}$, $\overline{P_2 P_3}$, $\overline{P_3 P_4}$, $\ldots$, $\overline{P_{n-1} P_n}$. [p. 259]
★ *Theorem* 154/5	If s and t are transversals of a set of parallel lines and the points P_1, P_2, P_3, $\ldots$, P_n are successive in s in the order $(P_1, P_2, P_3, \ldots, P_n)$, then the corresponding points Q_1, Q_2, Q_3, $\ldots$, Q_n are successive in t in the order $(Q_1, Q_2, Q_3, \ldots, Q_n)$. [p. 260]
Theorem 155/5	If m is any positive integer and if s and t are transversals of a set of parallel lines such that a segment in s of length x corresponds to a segment in t of length y, then a segment in s of length mx corresponds to a segment in t of length my. [p. 261]
Theorem 156/5	If s and t are transversals of a set of parallel lines with segments $\overline{AB}$ and $\overline{CD}$ in s corresponding respectively to $\overline{EF}$ and $\overline{GH}$ in t, and if the ratio of the length of $\overline{AB}$ to that of $\overline{CD}$ is $\dfrac{m}{n}$, where m and n are positive integers, then the ratio of the length of $\overline{EF}$ to that of $\overline{GH}$ is also $\dfrac{m}{n}$. [p. 264]
Theorem 157/5 *Parallel-proportion theorem*	If s and t are transversals of a set of parallel lines, with points A, B, C, and D in s corresponding to points E, F, G, and H in t so that segments $\overline{AB}$ and $\overline{CD}$ exist, then $\dfrac{d(A, B)}{d(C, D)} = \dfrac{d(E, F)}{d(G, H)}$. [p. 269]
Theorem 158/5	Let s and t denote transversals of a set of parallel lines, and let A, B, C, and D denote points in s for which $\overline{AB}$ and $\overline{CD}$ exist. If points E, F, and G in t correspond to A, B, and C respectively and if point H in t is in the D-side of the parallel through C, then $\dfrac{d(A, B)}{d(C, D)} = \dfrac{d(E, F)}{d(G, H)}$ implies that H is the point in t corresponding to D. If $H \neq D$, then line HD is parallel to the lines of the parallel set. [pp. 271-272]
Corollary 158/5	If a line w intersects $\measuredangle BAD$ at P in the open ray $\overrightarrow{AB}$ and at Q in the open ray $\overrightarrow{AD}$, then the lines BD and PQ are identical or parallel if and only if $\dfrac{d(A, P)}{d(A, B)} = \dfrac{d(A, Q)}{d(A, D)}$. [p. 272]
Definition 87/5	*Similarity of triangles* [p. 275]
Theorem 159/5	The existence of a similarity between triangles is a transitive relation, that is, $\triangle ABC \sim \triangle DEF$ and $\triangle DEF \sim \triangle GHI$ imply $\triangle ABC \sim \triangle GHI$. [p. 275]
Lemma 160/5	If Y' belongs to the open ray $\overrightarrow{XY}$ and if $\measuredangle XYZ$ and $\measuredangle XY'Z'$ are congruent coplanar angles with $\overrightarrow{YZ}$ and $\overrightarrow{Y'Z'}$ in the same side of line XY, then the lines YZ and $Y'Z'$ are either identical or parallel. [p. 276]

561

562

563

565

566

567

Theorem 230/9 The measure of an angle that is in the plane of a circle and whose vertex is interior to the circle is equal to one half the sum of the measures of the arcs intercepted by the angle and its opposite angle. [p. 507]

Theorem 231/9 If $\overline{AB}$ and $\overline{CD}$ are two chords of a circle that intersect at an interior point P, then $\triangle PAC \sim \triangle PDB$. (Also, $\triangle PAD \sim \triangle PCB$.) [p. 508]

Corollary 231/9 The chords of a circle that are concurrent at an interior point P are each separated by P into two segments such that the product of the lengths of the two segments is the same for each chord. [p. 508]

Definition 164/9 *Power of a point interior to a circle* [p. 508]

Theorem 232/9 If P is exterior to a circle and $\overrightarrow{PX}$ intersects the circle at A and C and $\overrightarrow{PY}$ intersects the circle at B and D so that $\measuredangle XPY$ intercepts arcs $\overarc{AB}$ and $\overarc{CD}$, then $d(P, A)d(P, C) = d(P, B)d(P, D)$, and the measure of $\measuredangle XPY$ is one half the positive difference of the measures of the arcs intercepted by the angle. [p. 509]

Definition 165/9 *Power of a point exterior to a circle* [p. 510]

Theorem 233/9 If PX is tangent to circle $C(O, r)$ at P and if B is any other point of the circle, then the measure of $\measuredangle XPB$ is one half the measure of the arc $\overarc{PQB}$ where Q is interior to the angle. [p. 510]

Theorem 234/9 The measure of an angle formed at a point external to a circle by a ray tangent to the circle and a ray that intersects the circle in two points is one half the positive difference of the measures of the arcs intercepted by the angle. [p. 510]

Corollary 234/9 If point P is external to a circle and if a tangent line through P intersects the circle at A, then the power of P with respect to the circle is $d(P, A)^2$. [p. 511]

Theorem 235/9 If point P is external to circle $C(O, r)$ and if PA and PB are two lines tangent to the circle at A and B respectively, then the segments $\overline{PA}$ and $\overline{PB}$ are congruent and the measure of $\measuredangle APB$ is one half the positive difference of the measures of the opposite arcs $\overarc{AB'}$ and $\overarc{AB''}$. [p. 511]

Definition 166/9 *Tangent circles* [p. 515]

Theorem 236/9 If two circles are tangent, their centers are collinear with the point of tangency. [p. 515]

Corollary 236a/9 Two tangent circles intersect only at their point of tangency. [p. 516]

Corollary 236b/9 If two circles are internally tangent, then, except for the point of tangency, one circle is contained in the interior of the other. [p. 516]

Theorem 237/9 If point P is external to a circle and in the plane of the circle, then there are exactly two lines through P that are tangent to the circle. [p. 518]

Theorem 238/9 If neither of two coplanar circles $C(A, x)$ and $C(B, y)$ is internal or internally tangent to the other, then there are two lines that are tangent to both circles and are such that the two centers are in the same side of each tangent. Either these two tangents t and t' intersect in the line of centers or else they are parallel. [p. 519]

Theorem 239/9 If two coplanar circles $C(A, x)$ and $C(B, y)$ are nonintersecting and are exterior to each other, then there exist two lines t and t' that are tangent to both circles and are such that the centers of the circles are in opposite sides of each of the tangents. [p. 522]

Certain of the exercises in the various sections of each chapter are labeled with the word *Answer*. Some of the exercises so labeled were chosen because they are representative of a whole group of exercises; some were chosen because their answers involve important generalizations; and some were chosen because they are considered particularly difficult. The answers to these exercises are given in this section. The numerals in the margin indicate the pages on which the exercises are located.

11   **2** $n^3 = 8 + 12(n - 2) + 6[(n - 2)^2] + (n - 2)^3$. For a painted cube n inches on each edge, $n \geq 2$, the number of one-inch cubes with paint on three, on two, on one, and on none of its faces is given respectively by 8, $12(n - 2)$, $6[(n - 2)^2]$, and $(n - 2)^3$.

33   **1** $t = m$ by Axiom 1/2.

4 A and B belong to $\alpha(A, B, C)$ by convention and AB is contained in $\alpha(A, B, C)$ by Axiom 3/2. Since P belongs to AB, P must also belong to a plane that contains AB.

34   **6g** If two planes intersect, then their intersection is a line. The two "planes" intersect in a "point."

36   **1d** My dog has eight legs.

2a Meaningless

37   **3b** Might be correct

4c Hypothesis: Two lines in the same plane are both perpendicular to a third line. Conclusion: The two lines are parallel to each other.

7a P

7e T

41   **1b** 11

1j $3\frac{1}{4}$

2b $|x| = -x$.

3f $\sqrt{5} - \sqrt{3}$

4c $d(P, Q) = p - q$.

5b $|b - a + c| = |-(b - a + c)|$
$= |-b + a - c|$
$= |a - c - b|$.

7a $b = 9$ or $b = -15$.

42   **8a** 14

48 **1a** $\langle a, b, c\rangle$ and Theorem 3/2

2b $b < 0$.

2e No conclusion possible

3d B

5c $\overline{PR}$

49 **7** Statements a, c, d, f, g, and h are correct.

50 **12d** The union of two nonintersecting collinear open rays

12f A point

54 **1b** $m = -1$; since $q < m < p$, it follows that $\langle p, m, q\rangle$.

2c $m = -2$; $d(M, P) = 6$; $d(M, Q) = 6$.

3b -3, 13

4d -1

5a Since $d(A, B) = d(C, B) + d(A, C)$, $\langle A, C, B\rangle$.

56 **1a** Yes, by Axiom 3/2

2c $\overline{AB}$ and $\overline{BP}$ may be collinear segments where $\overline{AB} \cap \overline{BP} = B$. Then infinitely many planes would contain both segments.

3a The lines of two nonintersecting segments intersect in exactly one point.

59 **2d** All but c are convex.

3b No

60 **4a** Let B with coordinate b and C with coordinate c be on the positive side and the negative side of A respectively. Then $b > 0$ and $c < 0$, and $c < 0 < b$. A is between B and C by Theorem 2/2, and A is in $\overline{BC}$ by Definition 7/2.

5a If a set is convex, then the set is a segment. False. If a set is a segment, then the set is convex. True

6 Statements b, d, e, and f are correct.

63 **1c** $\{B, E, F\}$

2a The two rays may not have the same origin.

5 By Definition 16/2, $\sphericalangle ABC = \overrightarrow{BA} \cup \overrightarrow{BC}$ and $\sphericalangle DBE = \overrightarrow{BD} \cup \overrightarrow{BE}$. $\overrightarrow{BA} = \overrightarrow{BD}$ and $\overrightarrow{BC} = \overrightarrow{BE}$ by Corollary 5c/2. Therefore, $\overrightarrow{BA} \cup \overrightarrow{BC} = \overrightarrow{BD} \cup \overrightarrow{BE}$ and $\sphericalangle ABC = \sphericalangle DBE$.

7 By exercise 6, the interior of an angle is convex. Since P and Q are in the interior of $\sphericalangle ABC$, $\overline{PQ}$ is in the interior of $\sphericalangle ABC$. $\langle P, R, Q\rangle$ implies R is in $\overline{PQ}$. Hence, R is in the interior of $\sphericalangle ABC$.

67 **1b** The statement contradicts Theorem 20/2.

1c Q may not be in the plane of $\sphericalangle BAC$.

2a Interior of $\sphericalangle BAC$

68 **3c** Yes

6 $\sphericalangle DAC$

7b $\alpha'' \cap \beta''$

75   **1c** 115

76   **1h** 25

6a $\sphericalangle DEF° = \sphericalangle DEA° + \sphericalangle AEF°.$

7b 112

77   **9a** Q

9f P

80   **1b**

2a $\overrightarrow{AP} = \overrightarrow{AQ}.$

3d $\dfrac{\sqrt{3} + 1}{2}$

81   **6a** Yes; yes; no

8a 45

10f Right angle

85   **1b** $\overline{QR}$

86   **2** If a point P is a member of $\mathcal{A} \cap \mathcal{B} \cap \mathcal{C}$, P is a member of $\mathcal{A}$, $\mathcal{B}$, and $\mathcal{C}$. Then P must also be a member of $\mathcal{A} \cap \mathcal{B}$, since P is a member of $\mathcal{A}$ and $\mathcal{B}$.

5b A set of one point, two points, or a segment

87   **9a** $p = 28.$

9e $0 < p < 18.$

93   **1a** $(A, B, C), (B, A, C), (C, A, B), (C, B, A), (B, C, A)$

3a 5

5 If D is collinear with A, B, and C, no simple circuit can be made. If D is not collinear with A, B, and C, and $<A, B, C>$, all the orderings except (A, B, C, D) and its equivalents are such that the corresponding circuit is not simple. Thus, (A, C, B, D) is not simple because vertex B belongs to $\overline{AC}$, $\overline{CB}$, and $\overline{BD}$.

8b None

94   **9b** 53

11e Diagonal

96   **1a** A and C

2b No; Q may not belong to α.

97   **3c** P is in the interior of $C(O, 6)$ and 2 units from A on $\overline{AB}$.

4a If P is a point of $C(O, r)$, then $\overline{PO}$ is a radial segment.

105   **1a** False. If $\overline{AB} \cong \overline{CD}$, then $d(A, B) = d(C, D)$.

106   **2b** True

     2c False. If $\measuredangle ABC \cong \measuredangle DEF$, then $\measuredangle ABC° = \measuredangle DEF°$.

     3c $\overline{JK}$

     4 KHJ, HKJ, TSR

     5f $\measuredangle ACB$

     7c $\overline{FE}$

     7n $\triangle CAB$

107   **8c** Yes; yes

     8g Yes

108   **2a** $\measuredangle C \cong \measuredangle F$, $\triangle ABC \cong \triangle DEF$.

     3 a, b, d, e, and f

109   **6** $AEC \leftrightarrow BED$

     9 $\overline{DB}$ is a segment in $\triangle ABD$ and in $\triangle DBC$. From the hypothesis and definition of perpendicular lines, $\measuredangle ABD° = \measuredangle DBC°$, and $\overline{AB} \cong \overline{BC}$. We can apply the s.a.s. axiom to conclude that $\triangle ABD \cong \triangle CBD$ and, by corresponding parts, $\overline{AD} \cong \overline{DC}$.

110   **13** $ABC \leftrightarrow BAD$

     16 Let $ABCD$ be a square with diagonals $\overline{AC}$ and $\overline{BD}$. Since the sides of a square are congruent and the angles of a square are congruent, the correspondence $DAB \leftrightarrow ABC$ is a congruence by the s.a.s. axiom. Hence, by corresponding parts, $\overline{AC} \cong \overline{BD}$.

113   **1d** $\langle M, N, G \rangle$.

     2b $\measuredangle PAB° < \measuredangle QAB°$.

114   **4c** $\measuredangle E \cong \measuredangle Y$, $\measuredangle F \cong \measuredangle Z$.

     6 Since $\measuredangle 1 \cong \measuredangle 3$, $\overline{AB} \cong \overline{AB}$, and $\measuredangle 4 \cong \measuredangle 2$, $\triangle ACB \cong \triangle ADB$ by the a.s.a. theorem.

115   **15a** $\triangle BCD \cong \triangle P_{16}P_{17}P_{18}$.

     15b $\measuredangle P_{10}P_8P_9 \cong \measuredangle ADE$, $\measuredangle P_8P_{10}P_9 \cong \measuredangle DAE$.

     17 No

117   **28a** 1 and 5

     28b 1 and 2

     28c 1, 3, 4, and 5

     28d 1

122   **1b** Point K

123   **2b** $\measuredangle A$; $\measuredangle B$; none

     3 Statements a and d are necessarily valid.

     4a $\measuredangle C° < 90$.   **4g** $\measuredangle C° < 97$.

124   **7e** $a < c$.

       10a $\measuredangle 1$ and $\measuredangle 3$ are acute; $\measuredangle 2$ and $\measuredangle 4$ are right; $\triangle ABC$ is a right triangle.

125   **12b** $d(P, A) = d(P, B)$.

130   **1c** $\overline{RS}$ and $\overline{ST}$

       2 $\triangle BFR$ is isosceles and $\measuredangle RBF \cong \measuredangle RFB$. $\measuredangle RBA$ and $\measuredangle RFH$ are congruent because they are supplements of congruent angles. By the s.a.s. axiom, $\triangle ABR \cong \triangle HFR$.

       3 Since supplements of congruent angles are congruent, $\measuredangle RBF \cong \measuredangle RFB$, and therefore $\overline{RB} \cong \overline{RF}$. By the s.a.s. axiom, $\triangle ARB \cong \triangle HRF$ and the corresponding angles, $\measuredangle ARB$ and $\measuredangle FRH$, are congruent.

131   **7a** $\measuredangle P$; $\measuredangle M$

       7b $\measuredangle B$; $\measuredangle A$

135   **1** b, c, e, and h

       2a Collinear; $<B, C, A>$.

       4a $1 < x < 7$.

       5a $a - b < x < a + b$.

136   **8** Since $\overline{CD}$ bisects $\measuredangle C$, $\measuredangle FCD \cong \measuredangle ECD$. By the hypotenuse, angle theorem, $\triangle FDC \cong \triangle EDC$, and the corresponding sides, $\overline{FC}$ and $\overline{EC}$, are congruent.

       9a $\overline{AB}$ is the hypotenuse of right triangle $\triangle ABD$ and right triangle $\triangle BAE$. $\overline{AE} \cong \overline{BD}$ by hypothesis, so $\triangle ABD \cong \triangle BAE$ by the hypotenuse, side theorem.

139   **2b** From part a, $\measuredangle EDA \cong \measuredangle EBC$. $\triangle ACD \cong \triangle CAB$ by the s.s.s. theorem, so that $\measuredangle EAD \cong \measuredangle ECB$. Thus, by the a.s.a. theorem, $\triangle BCE \cong \triangle DAE$.

       4 $\overline{AR} \cong \overline{CS}$, $<A, R, S>$, and $<R, S, C>$ imply $\overline{AS} \cong \overline{RC}$. Also, $\overline{AB} \cong \overline{CD}$ and $\overline{BS} \cong \overline{DR}$. Hence, $\triangle ASB \cong \triangle CRD$ by the s.s.s. theorem, and the corresponding angles, $\measuredangle BSA$ and $\measuredangle DRC$, are congruent.

       10 Let A and B be points in line t and let G be in $\overrightarrow{AP}$ such that $<A, P, G>$. There is a coordinate system with initial ray $\overrightarrow{PQ}$ such that Q is in the B-side of $\overrightarrow{AP}$ and $\measuredangle GPQ \cong \measuredangle PAB$. Assume that PQ intersects t at X, where X is in the B-side of $\overrightarrow{AP}$. Then $\measuredangle GPQ$ is an exterior angle of $\triangle PAX$ and, by Theorem 52/3, $\measuredangle GPQ > \measuredangle PAX$. Since A, B, and X are collinear and B and X are in the same side of $\overrightarrow{AP}$, $\measuredangle PAX \cong \measuredangle PAB$. Thus, $\measuredangle GPQ > \measuredangle PAB$. This contradicts $\measuredangle GPQ \cong \measuredangle PAB$. If X is in the ray opposite $\overrightarrow{AB}$, then $\measuredangle PAB$ is an exterior angle of $\triangle PAX$ and is greater than $\measuredangle ABX$. Since $\measuredangle APX \cong \measuredangle GPQ$, this also contradicts $\measuredangle GPQ \cong \measuredangle PAB$. Therefore, the assumption that PQ intersects t is false, and there is a line in the plane of P and t that contains P and does not intersect t.

143   **1** Statements a, b, d, and e

       2b AB

144   **2i** Empty set

       4 Statements a, b, and d

147   **1b** B

148   **1g** B

2c 3

2e Yes, by Corollary 70/3 and by Theorem 32/3, and Corollary 53b/3. $\angle A$ and $\angle C$ are acute angles. If the foot of B in AC is not between A and C, either $\angle A$ or $\angle C$ would be a right angle or greater than a right angle, which is impossible.

3a $E, F, G,$ and H

3f F

155   **1** Statements c, d, f, and g

156   **5** Statements c and e

7 Since Q is not F, the foot of Q in t is F, the intersection of t with the line through Q that is perpendicular to t.

157   **10b** Yes

11a No; no

12d No

161   **1** Since Q is not in α, the foot of Q is F, the intersection of α with the line through Q that is perpendicular to α.

162   **9a** False

163   **10c** No; yes

11 By Corollary 79/3, the plane β through P and perpendicular to t contains the foot in α of P, or point F. Since G is the foot in t of P and β is perpendicular to t, β contains G. Hence β contains $\overline{GF}$. Since β is perpendicular to t, $\overline{GF}$ is perpendicular to t, and G is the foot in t of F.

15 A plane perpendicular to PQ at Q, excluding point Q

16 By Theorem 78/3, there exist planes $\alpha(AB, CD)$, $\beta(AB, EF)$, and $\delta(EF, CD)$. Let t be the line of γ containing F so that $t \perp BD$. Then $t \perp EF$, since $EF \perp \gamma$. Thus $t \perp \beta$ at F. Also, $t \perp \delta$ at F. By Theorem 72/3, $\beta = \delta$. Since β contains $A, B, C, D, E,$ and F, $\beta = \alpha$, and EF is in α.

174   **2d** False

2g False

6 Statement e

7b No, s may not be in β.

175   **8d** No; yes

177   **1e** No

2 Statements a, d, and e

3a $\overrightarrow{AB}$ and $\overrightarrow{CD}$ must be like directed.

4c Two rays, $\overrightarrow{PD}$ and $\overrightarrow{PD}$

181 **2a** $\angle BAD$

4a $\angle 5$

4c Yes; no

182 **7c** False

8 Since $AB \parallel CD$, $\angle BAM \cong \angle MDC$. Since M is the midpoint of $\overline{AD}$, $\overline{AM} \cong \overline{MD}$. $\angle AMB \cong \angle CMD$ because they are opposite angles. Hence $\triangle AMB \cong \triangle DMC$ by the a.s.a. theorem, and the corresponding sides, $\overline{BM}$ and $\overline{MC}$, are congruent. Hence M is the midpoint of $\overline{BC}$.

12a Yes, by Theorem 89/4.

12e A; $d(A, C)$; $\overline{BC}$

185 **1e** Yes

2d $180 - (y + z)$

3d 63

6 70

186 **8a** $\angle A° = 64$ and $\angle B° = 26$.

8c $\angle A° = 30$, $\angle B° = 60$, and $\angle C° = 90$.

13b Assume that $d(A, Q) > \frac{1}{2}d(B, C)$. Then, because $d(C, Q) = d(Q, B)$, $d(A, Q) > d(Q, B)$ and $d(A, Q) > d(Q, C)$. Hence, $\angle QBA° > \angle QAB°$ and $\angle QCA° > \angle QAC°$. Hence, $\angle QBA° + \angle QCA° > \angle CAB°$. But since $\triangle ABC$ is a right triangle, $\angle QBA° + \angle QCA° = \angle CAB°$. Similarly, $d(A, Q) < \frac{1}{2}d(B, C)$ implies $\angle QBA° + \angle QCA° < \angle CAB°$. Hence, the only possible conclusion is $d(A, Q) = \frac{1}{2}d(B, C)$.

187 **17** Each of the ratios $\dfrac{d(A, G)}{d(A, F)}$, $\dfrac{d(A, F)}{d(A, E)}$, $\dfrac{d(A, E)}{d(A, D)}$, $\dfrac{d(A, D)}{d(A, C)}$, and $\dfrac{d(A, C)}{d(A, B)}$ is equal to $\frac{1}{2}$. Therefore the product of these ratios, $\dfrac{d(A, G)}{d(A, B)}$, is equal to $(\frac{1}{2})^5$, or $\frac{1}{32}$.

192 **1f** No

193 **3** $\overrightarrow{CX}$ must intersect AB at a point P; otherwise, two lines through C, CX and CD, would be parallel to AD, contradicting Axiom 14/4. Since P is in AB, P and X are in the same side of CD. Hence, $<C, X, P>$, and $\overrightarrow{CX}$ intersects AB at P.

6 When $CD \perp r$; yes; no

8a No

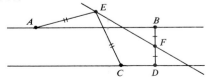

194   **9** Statements a, d, i, and j

13 Let DC be the line through C that is parallel to AB. Then by Corollary 99a/4, the line t parallel to $\overline{AB}$ through M is the midparallel of CD and AB, and N is in t. Since MN and t have two points in common, $MN = t$. Hence, $\overline{MN} \parallel \overline{AB}$. Let AF be the line through A that is parallel to CB and let MG be the line through M that is parallel to CB and AF. By Theorem 95/4, MG intersects $\overline{AB}$ at a point H, and, by Corollary 99b/4, MH bisects $\overline{AB}$. Hence, $d(A, H) = \frac{1}{2}d(A, B)$. In $\triangle MCN$ and $\triangle AMH$, $\angle CMN \cong \angle MAH$ since $MN \parallel AH$, $\overline{AM} \cong \overline{MC}$, and $\angle NCM \cong \angle HMA$ since $CN \parallel MH$. Hence, $\triangle MCN \cong \triangle AMH$ by the a.s.a. theorem and, by corresponding parts, $\overline{MN} \cong \overline{AH}$. Hence, $d(M, N) = d(A, H) = \frac{1}{2}d(A, B)$.

17 $\dfrac{2^8}{1}; \dfrac{2^n}{1}$

198   **1** Statements a, b, c, and d

2 The sides of pentagon $ABCDE$ and diagonals $\overline{AC}$ and $\overline{EC}$ form three triangles so that the sum of the measures of the angles of the pentagon is $3 \cdot 180; 4 \cdot 180; (n - 2)180$.

4a Because $\overline{DC} \parallel \overline{AB}$, $\angle DCA \cong \angle CAB$. $\overline{AC} \cong \overline{AC}$. Because $\overline{AD} \parallel \overline{CB}$, $\angle DAC \cong \angle ACB$. By the a.s.a. theorem, $\triangle ADC \cong \triangle CBA$, and, by corresponding parts, $\overline{AD} \cong \overline{CB}$ and $\overline{DC} \cong \overline{BA}$.

199   **7b** 72

8a Since each angle of rectangle $ABCD$ is a right angle, $\overline{AB} \perp \overline{BC}$ and $\overline{AB} \perp \overline{AD}$. Hence $\overline{BC} \parallel \overline{AD}$. Similarly, $\overline{AB} \parallel \overline{CD}$, so the rectangle is a parallelogram.

11a Yes

12b 140 and 40

14c 60

16a Let $ABCD$ be a trapezoid with shorter base $\overline{CD}$, and let P be the point of intersection of AD and BC. If P is in the same side of DC as AB, then the sum of the measures of the angles of $\triangle PDC$ is greater than 180. If P is in DC, then $P = D = C$. But D and C are distinct points. Hence, P must be in the side of DC that does not contain AB.

200   **20g** 2

205   **2a** From point P construct $\overline{PA} \perp t$ with A in t. Construct a circle with center A whose radius is the same length as $d(P, A)$. This circle intersects t in two points B and B' in opposite sides of A. Either $\triangle PAB$ or $\triangle PAB'$ is the desired triangle because $\angle A$ is a right angle and $\overline{PA} \cong \overline{AB} \cong \overline{AB'}$.

5d On $\overrightarrow{RS}$ an angle $\angle TRS$ can be constructed so that $\angle TRS° = 60$. Also, on $\overrightarrow{RT}$ an angle $\angle URT$ can be constructed so that $\overrightarrow{RT}$ is between $\overrightarrow{RS}$ and $\overrightarrow{RU}$. $\angle URT° = 15$. Hence, $\angle SRU° = 75$.

209   **1b** $\alpha(A, B, C)$, $\beta(P, A, C)$, $\gamma(P, A, B)$

2c Yes

4a By Corollary 75b/3, the perpendicular bisector of a chord is the locus of points equidistant from the endpoints of the chord. Since the center of the circle is equidistant from the endpoints of a chord, the perpendicular bisector contains the center of the circle.

210   **8d** 4

11 Since $ABCDEF$ is regular, $\overline{AB} \cong \overline{BC} \cong \overline{CD} \cong \overline{DE} \cong \overline{EF} \cong \overline{FA}$ and $\measuredangle B \cong \measuredangle D \cong \measuredangle F$. $\triangle ABC \cong \triangle CDE \cong \triangle EFA$ by the s.a.s. axiom, and the corresponding parts, $\overline{AC}$, $\overline{CE}$, and $\overline{EA}$, are congruent. Thus, $\triangle ACE$ is equilateral.

14a Since $\overline{MN} \perp \overline{CD}$, $\measuredangle MNC \cong \measuredangle MND$. Also $\overline{MN} \cong \overline{MN}$ and $\overline{CN} \cong \overline{ND}$. Hence, $\triangle MCN \cong \triangle MDN$ by the s.a.s. axiom. By corresponding parts, $\overline{CM} \cong \overline{MD}$ and $\measuredangle CMN \cong \measuredangle DMN$. Since $\measuredangle AMN \cong \measuredangle BMN$, $\measuredangle AMC \cong \measuredangle BMD$. Also $\overline{AM} \cong \overline{MB}$. Hence, $\triangle AMC \cong \triangle DMB$ by the s.a.s. axiom, and by corresponding parts, $\overline{AC} \cong \overline{BD}$. Hence, trapezoid $ABCD$ is isosceles.

212   **1b** False. $\measuredangle ABC° = 90$ and $\measuredangle ACB° < 90$.

213   **2a** If $\triangle ABC$ is obtuse with $\measuredangle B$ as the obtuse angle, then the altitude from C of $\triangle ABC$ does not intersect $\overline{AB}$ and is not perpendicular to either $\overline{AC}$ or $\overline{CB}$.

4a Let ABC be a right triangle with the right angle at B. Then $\overline{AB}$ and $\overline{BC}$ are altitudes of the triangle, and they intersect at the orthocenter B, which is a vertex of the triangle.

5 Let $\overline{AX}$, $\overline{BY}$, and $\overline{CZ}$ be the three altitudes of obtuse or acute triangle $\triangle ABC$ where X, Y, and Z are in BC; AC; and AB respectively. Let $d(A, B) \geqq d(A, C) \geqq d(C, B)$. In right triangles $\triangle ACZ$ and $\triangle CZB$, $d(A, C) > d(C, Z)$ and $d(B, C) > d(C, Z)$. Since $d(B, C) \leqq d(A, B)$, $d(A, B) > d(C, Z)$. Thus $\overline{CZ}$ is shorter than each side of $\triangle ABC$. In right triangles $\triangle AYB$ and $\triangle CYB$, $d(A, B) > d(Y, B)$ and $d(C, B) > d(Y, B)$. Therefore $d(A, C) > d(Y, B)$ and $\overline{YB}$ is shorter than each side of $\triangle ABC$.

214   **10c** $\overline{AF}, \overline{FC}$

15 The locus is the lines of the sides of the midpoint triangle of $\triangle ABC$.

216   **1a** False; X also must be in the plane of $C(O, r)$.

217   **2a** Construct the perpendicular bisectors of two nonparallel chords of the given circle. Since the perpendicular bisectors of the chords pass through the center of the circle, their point of intersection must be the center of the given circle.

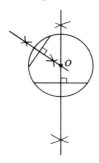

7c X belongs to $\overset{\rightarrow}{CD}$.

1c No

3a $y > 3$.

4b Because $\overline{PB}$ is the hypotenuse and $\overline{PF}$ is a leg of right triangle $\triangle PBF$

5 t and s form two pairs of congruent angles. Let the measure of each angle in one pair be x and the measure of each angle in the other pair be y. The measure of each angle formed by the two bisectors is $\frac{1}{2}x + \frac{1}{2}y$ or $\frac{1}{2}(x + y)$. Since $x + y = 180$, the measure of each angle formed by the two bisectors is $\frac{1}{2}(180)$ or 90. Hence, the two bisectors are perpendicular to each other.

9 Let $\overset{\rightarrow}{BD}$ be the ray bisecting $\measuredangle ABC$. The locus is the union of the open ray $\overset{\rightarrow}{BD'}$ opposite $\overset{\rightarrow}{BD}$ and the two opposite open rays with origin B whose line is perpendicular to BD.

12b No

1e Yes; yes

3 If a triangle is isosceles, then the median from the vertex angle is also an altitude. Yes

7a 8

7d $d(B, P) < 8$.

10a Construct the perpendicular bisector t of $\overline{AB}$, intersecting $\overline{AB}$ at M. Find a point N in t such that $d(M, N) = r$. Construct $C(N, r)$, the incircle of the desired triangle. Find the points other than M where $C\big(A, d(A, M)\big)$ and $C\big(B, d(B, M)\big)$ intersect $C(N, r)$. Let these points be P and Q respectively. Construct AP and QB, which intersect at point C. $\triangle ABC$ is the desired triangle.

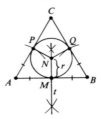

Discussion: For this construction, $r < \frac{1}{2}d(A, B)$; otherwise $AP \parallel QB$ or AP and QB would intersect in the side of AB that does not contain N. Since $\triangle APN \cong \triangle AMN \cong \triangle BMN = \triangle BQN$, the angles at P and Q as well as the angles at M are right angles. Since $d(P, N) = d(N, M) = d(N, Q) = r$, N is the incenter of $\triangle ABC$. Since $\measuredangle PAN \cong \measuredangle NAM \cong \measuredangle NBM \cong \measuredangle QBN$, $\measuredangle PAM \cong \measuredangle QBM$ and $\triangle ABC$ is isosceles.

2a Necessarily true

5 Since $\overline{AB} \parallel \overline{BD}$, they determine a plane γ that intersects α and β at AC and BD respectively. By Theorem 133/4, $AC \parallel BD$. Hence, $ABDC$ is a parallelogram and $\overline{AB} \cong \overline{CD}$.

8 Let β be a plane that contains t. If $\beta \not\parallel \alpha$, then β intersects α in a line r. Since r is in α and $\alpha \parallel t, r \parallel t$.

237 **2d** $\overrightarrow{PB}$; P; $\overrightarrow{PA}$

    5a $\measuredangle ABC$, $\measuredangle EFG$

    5b $\measuredangle ADH$, $\measuredangle BCG$

    5c $\measuredangle CGD$, $\measuredangle BFA$

    5d $\measuredangle ABE$, $\measuredangle DCH$

238 **7a** Since $PF \perp \alpha$, $PF \perp AF$. It is given that $AF \perp FX$. Since AF is perpendicular to two lines at their point of intersection, $AF \perp \beta(P, F, X)$.

    8a The locus is two right circular cones in opposite half-spaces of α with vertices at A, excluding point A.

240 **2** A is in the intersection, so the intersection is nonempty. By Axiom 13/3, the intersection is a line. Theorem 37/2; Definition 24/2; theorem of exercise 1, page 239

245 **1b** $\measuredangle \beta'' t \alpha'$

    2b γ_{90}

    3b γ_{14}

246 **6e** By Theorem 136/4, $AE \perp \alpha$ and $BF \perp \alpha$. Hence, A and B must be the feet of E and F respectively in α.

    9d True

247 **10c** Seven; each three points determine a plane α with the fourth point not in the plane. The plane parallel to α and bisecting the segment whose endpoints are P and the foot of P in α is equidistant from the four given points. Four such planes are determined. The other three are determined as follows. The lines determined by any two pairs of the four points must be skew lines. By exercise 9 on page 241, there is a unique line that is perpendicular to each of two skew lines. The plane that is the perpendicular bisector of the segment perpendicular to the two skew lines is equidistant from the four given points.

257 **1a** Line c

    1e $\overline{GE}$; $\overline{DB}$

258 **1c** Yes

    2a No

    2d Yes

    2g 8

260 **1a** By the definition of A, B, C, and D as successive in that order

261 **2a** $a = 0$ and $b > 0$ imply $a < b$. $<A, B, C>$ and $a < b$ imply $a < b < c$. $<B, C, D>$ and $b < c$ imply $b < c < d$. Thus $a < b < c < d$.

262 **1b** -6, -9, and -13

    2a 28

263 **3a** Yes. Because equality is symmetric, if $\frac{a}{b} = \frac{c}{d}$, then $\frac{c}{d} = \frac{a}{b}$.

4a $\frac{21}{5}$

7b $x = \frac{14}{3}$ and $y = \frac{3}{2}$.

267 **1a** $m = 3$, $n = 5$, and $x = 1$.

1c $m = 16$, $n = 3$, and $x = \frac{\sqrt{7}}{24}$.

268 **2a** $d(A, B) = \frac{28}{3}$ and $\overline{AB}$ can be divided into 392 consecutive segments of length $x = \frac{1}{42}$. $d(C, D) = \frac{19}{14}$ and $\overline{CD}$ can be divided into 57 consecutive segments of length $x = \frac{1}{42}$.

5a By the first property, $\frac{a}{b} > \frac{c}{b}$ and $b > 0 \Rightarrow (\frac{a}{b})b > (\frac{c}{b})b$, or $a > c$.

273 **1a** $\frac{15}{2}$ **1f** $\frac{2}{3}$

3d 8 ; $\frac{3\sqrt{2}}{7}$

274 **4c** $4\frac{1}{2}$ or $13\frac{1}{2}$

7b $\frac{1}{2}$

11a Let X be a point that is not in AB. $\overrightarrow{AX}$ can be coordinatized so that the coordinate of A is 0 and the coordinates of the other points in $\overrightarrow{AX}$ are greater than 0. Let R be the point in $\overrightarrow{AX}$ with coordinate r, where $r > 0$, and let S be the point in $\overrightarrow{AX}$ with coordinate $r + 1$. Let t be the line through R that is parallel to $\overline{SB}$ and intersects AB at P. Then $\frac{r}{1} = \frac{d(A, R)}{d(R, S)} = \frac{d(A, P)}{d(P, B)}$. Let Q be any point in $\overline{AB}$ such that $\frac{d(A, Q)}{d(Q, B)} = \frac{r}{1}$. This implies $QR \parallel BS$. Since $PR \parallel BS$, $Q = P$.

279 **1d** Yes; no

3 $\frac{45}{4}$, $\frac{50}{4}$; $\frac{4}{5}$

5 Let $\triangle ABC \sim \triangle XYZ$ and let $\overline{BB'}$ and $\overline{YY'}$ be corresponding altitudes. In $\triangle ABB'$ and $\triangle XYY'$, $\angle BB'A \cong \angle YY'X$ and $\angle A \cong \angle X$. Hence, by Theorem 160/5, $ABB' \leftrightarrow XYY'$ is a similarity and the ratio of $\overline{BB'}$ to $\overline{YY'}$ is the same as the ratio of $\overline{AB}$ to $\overline{XY}$.

280 **9b** Let the measure of each vertex angle be x. Then the measure of each base angle is $\frac{1}{2}(180 - x)$. Hence, any two isosceles triangles with congruent vertex angles will also have congruent base angles, and therefore the two triangles will be similar.

10c 2, since $\triangle BAC \sim \triangle ACD$ and $\frac{d(A, C)}{d(C, D)} = \frac{d(A, B)}{d(A, C)}$

285 **2b** No

3 $d(D, X) = \frac{ab}{c}$ or $d(D, X) = \frac{bc}{a}$.

286 **7a** 6   **7b** 12   **7c** $\frac{ac}{b}$ **7d** $\frac{55}{13}$

287 **9c** $\triangle ACD \sim \triangle CBA$.

10d Since $\frac{1}{a} = \frac{c}{x(c + d)}$ and $\frac{1}{b} = \frac{d}{x(c + d)}$, $\frac{1}{a} + \frac{1}{b} = \frac{c}{x(c + d)} + \frac{d}{x(c + d)} = \frac{c + d}{x(c + d)} = \frac{1}{x}$.

288 **14a** 6, $2\sqrt{5}$, $3\sqrt{5}$, 4, 5

18 The sides opposite A', B', and C' have lengths $\frac{20}{3}$, $\frac{10}{3}$, and 5 respectively. No; as small as possible; 28

291　　**1e** $\frac{1}{6}\sqrt{5}$

　　2c No

292　　**4a** $16\sqrt{3}$

　　6 13

　　10b $\frac{q(p+q)}{\sqrt{q^2+p^2}}$ and $\frac{p(p+q)}{\sqrt{q^2+p^2}}$

293　　**12c** 2

294　　**20** In right triangle $\triangle YDA$, $d(Y, A) = 1$ and $d(D, A) = 2$. Hence, $d(Y, D) = \sqrt{3}$. In right triangle $\triangle XYD$, $d(X, D) = 1$. Hence, $d(X, Y) = \sqrt{2}$.

296　　**2a** Two

　　3 Let X be the foot of O in $\overline{MN}$. In $\triangle XON$, $\overline{ON}$ is the hypotenuse and $\overline{OX}$ is a leg. Since $d(O, N) = r$ and $d(O, X) = x$, $x < r$.

　　5d Yes; yes

　　6b $\frac{3\sqrt{145}}{5}$

299　　**5a** $\sqrt{391} \pm 4$

　　6a $4 < r < 9$.

302　　**1d** No; yes

　　2a $\measuredangle Q$; $\measuredangle U$; $\measuredangle TSR$

　　2f $d(D, E), d(T, S)$

　　3b True

304　　**7b** $d(F, G) = \frac{\pi\sqrt{2}}{3}$ and $d(K, J) = \frac{\pi\sqrt{2}}{2}$.

　　8a $ABCD \leftrightarrow DCBA$, $ABCD \leftrightarrow BADC$, $ABCD \leftrightarrow CDAB$

307　　**1b** $\frac{1}{1}$; $\frac{4}{3}$

308　　**2b** No; no

　　3a P_6; D

　　7 The lengths of the sides of R_1 are 6 and 3. The lengths of the sides of R_2 are 5 and 10.

　　8 $\frac{2}{3}\sqrt{41}$

309　　**11** 12; 5; 182

　　13b 18

321　　**1** The circles described in parts a, d, e, and f

　　5b $\overline{AB}$

　　5d $\overline{AB}$

322　　**6a** The set does not qualify because it is not convex.

　　7 $d(A, C) \leqq d(A, B) + d(B, C)$. Since $d(A, B)$ and $d(B, C)$ are each less than r, $d(A, C) < 2r$.

327　　**2** Sets described in parts g, h, and j; sets described in parts a, b, c, d, and e

583

4a Yes; no

5 Assume that A and B are two different boundary points in $\overrightarrow{PQ}$, $A \neq P$, and $B \neq P$. Then either $\langle P, A, B \rangle$ or $\langle P, B, A \rangle$. If $\langle P, A, B \rangle$, then A must be an inner point; and if $\langle P, B, A \rangle$, B must be an inner point. Since the assumption that A and B are two boundary points leads to a contradiction, there cannot be two boundary points in $\overrightarrow{PQ}$.

328

11 Let M be the circumcenter of $\triangle ABC$. Let $d(M; C) = r$. Then $C(M, r)$ is the circumcircle of $\triangle ABC$. This circle and its interior are a convex set, $\mathbb{S}$, and the sides of $\triangle ABC$ are in $\mathbb{S}$. Let $d = r + c$ where $c > 0$. Then $C(M, d)$ contains all points in $\mathbb{S}$. Hence, $\triangle ABC$ is bounded.

1 The sets described in parts a, b, and d

3a False

3b True

3c True

3d False

3e False

4e True

5a 3; 4; 5

5d $\frac{17\sqrt{13}}{13}$

7 If $\angle A$ and $\angle B$ are acute or if either angle is a right angle, then the width is $d(A, B)$. If $\angle A$ is obtuse, then the width is $d(F, B)$, where F is the foot of C in AB. If $\angle B$ is obtuse, then the width is $d(F, A)$. The width in the direction perpendicular to $\overrightarrow{AB}$ is the length of the altitude from C to AB.

337

2c

3 $\mathbb{S}$ and $\mathbb{R}$ are not coplanar. To illustrate, use two rings looped inside each other.

6d They intersect in two points.

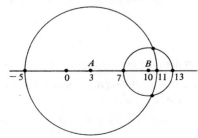

338   **7** Let P be the point in $\overrightarrow{AB}$ such that $d(A, P) = x$. Then since $d(A, B) = x + y$, $<A, P, B>$ and $d(P, B) = y$. Hence, P belongs to both circles. Since $d(A, B) = x + y$, P is the only point of intersection, by Theorem 177/6.

9 If the circles intersect, then $x + y \geq d(A, B)$, which contradicts the condition that $d(A, B) > x + y$. Hence, the two circles do not intersect.

11a If $x \geq y$, then $2x$ is the least width. If $x < y$, then $2y$ is the least width. The set of widths has no upper bound; hence, there is no greatest width.

340   **1c** In the interior

341   **3d** Yes

5 Since $\mathcal{S}$ is interior to some circle $C(A, r)$, it must be interior to the sphere $S(A, r)$.

342   **7b** Yes. The empty set is such a set.

10 Let $\mathcal{S}$ be a set that is bounded and let $S(A, r)$ be a sphere whose interior contains $\mathcal{S}$. Let $b = 2r$. Then any two points X and Y in $\mathcal{S}$ determine a segment whose length is less than $2r$, since $d(X, Y) \leq d(X, A) + d(A, Y)$, and $d(X, A) + d(A, Y) < r + r$, or $2r$. Assume that a positive number b exists such that no two points of $\mathcal{S}$ are further apart than b. Choose a point P of $\mathcal{S}$. Then $S(P, b + 1)$ is a sphere whose interior contains $\mathcal{S}$ since any point Z of $\mathcal{S}$ has the property that $d(Z, P) \leq b$. Hence, Z is in the interior of $S(P, b + 1)$.

13c No

343   **1d** The set is not bounded nor does it contain its own boundary.

344   **2b** Yes

3 Yes

348   **2a** The set is an open half-plane that bisects the dihedral angle.

3b Since Y is equidistant from A, B, and C, Y must be in β, the perpendicular bisector of $\overline{AB}$, and Y must be in γ, the perpendicular bisector of $\overline{BC}$. Since β and γ are not parallel, they intersect in a line s which is the set of points equidistant from A, B, and C. By exercise 3a, any two points in t are equidistant from A, B, and C, so the points in t must be in s, and $s = t$. Since Y is in s, Y is in t.

349   **9** The sets described in parts a, c, d, and g

353   **1c** All except a convex set

3b By part a, both P and Q belong to $\mathcal{S}$. Since every point between two inner points is an inner point, $\overline{PQ}$ is contained in $\mathcal{S}$.

354   **6a** No

6d The set $\mathcal{S}$ itself

7a If $X = A$ or $X = B$, then $d(P, X) \leq a$ by definition of a. If $<A, X, B>$, then $\angle PXA$ and $\angle PXB$ are supplementary, and one of these angles has a measure greater than or equal to 90. Assume $\angle PXA° \geq 90$. Then $\angle PXA° > \angle PAX°$ and $d(P, X) < d(P, A)$. Since $d(P, A) \leq a$, $d(P, X) < a$.

355   **11a** $\overline{AB}$

357   **3a** There is exactly one plane perpendicular to $\overline{PA}$ at A and therefore, by the theorem of exercise 2, exactly one plane is tangent to $S(P, r)$ at A.

4a A closed convex curve

5b The maximum width is the length of the longest edge. The minimum width is the length of the shortest altitude.

362   **3c** $3 ; 4$

363   **5a** 8

6 a, b, c, d, e, f, and h

364   **9a** $2\sqrt{29}$ and 4

374   **4** $\{(A, D), (B, E), (C, F)\}, \{(A, E), (B, F), (C, D)\}, \{(A, F), (B, D), (C, E)\}, \{(A, D), (B, F), (C, E)\}, \{(A, E), (B, D), (C, F)\}, \{(A, F), (B, E), (C, D)\}$

6d $\{(1, 1), (4, 2), (9, 3), (16, 4), (25, 5)\}$

375   **9b** Yes. If $a + b$ is an even integer, where a and b are in I, then either a and b are even integers or a and b are odd integers. Correspondingly, a^2 and b^2 are even or a^2 and b^2 are odd, and, in both cases, $a^2 + b^2$ is even.

11 Many different triangles can have the same circumcircle. Since we are considering only one-to-one mappings and the correspondence in question is not one-to-one, it is not a mapping in our usage of the term.

376   **1** Statements a, c, e, g, and h

377   **3b** $\{a, b, c\}, \{A, B\}$

4b $x = -21$.

5b The coordinate of a fixed element must satisfy $x = 3x - 4$ or $x = 2$. Hence, the only fixed element is the point with coordinate 2.

10 Two, $\{(A, B), (B, C), (C, A)\}$ and $\{(A, C), (B, A), (C, B)\}$

379   **1c** No ; yes, R

3 $5 \cdot 3 \cdot 3 \cdot 1 \cdot 1$, or 45, is the total number of mappings having exactly one fixed element. No mapping of five different elements can have exactly four fixed points.

5 $2n$ correspondences

380   **6a** A-D-E-G-A, B-C-F-B

381   **1a** $\{(1, 3), (2, 4), (3, 1), (4, 2)\}$

2 $\Gamma\Phi$ does not exist. $\Phi\Gamma : \{(1, -1), (3, 6), (-2, 8)\}$.

4a $4\Gamma\Psi = 1$.

4e 2

382   **5e** 2

384   **1b** $4\sqrt{2}$

2a $19 ; 7$

2 $a \rightarrow 3a - 4$ and $b \rightarrow 3b - 4$. $|3a - 4 - (3b - 4)| = |3a - 3b| = 3|a - b|$. Therefore $|a - b| \neq |3a - 4 - (3b - 4)|$, and Γ is not a distance-preserving mapping.

3 Let a and b be the coordinates of two points in the line. $a \rightarrow -a - 6$ and $b \rightarrow -b - 6$. $|-a - 6 - (-b - 6)| = |-a + b| = |a - b|$. If $x = -x - 6$, $x = -3$. Hence, Γ is a distance-preserving mapping with one fixed point, that is, the point with coordinate -3. Since $|x - \bar{x}| = |x + 3|$ and $|x\Gamma - \bar{x}| = |-x - 6 + 3| = |-x - 3| = |x + 3|$, $\bar{x}$ is the midpoint of every pair x and $x\Gamma$.

1 Statements a, b, e, f, g, h, j, k, l, and m

2a $(0, a)$; $(\frac{a}{2}, \frac{a}{2})$

6 Since C is in $\overrightarrow{AB}$, C' must be in $\overrightarrow{A'B'}$. Since Γ is distance preserving, $d(A, C) = d(A', C')$. But $d(A', D) = d(A, C)$ and D in $\overrightarrow{A'B'}$ imply $D = C'$.

8 The plane of $C(P, r)$ maps onto a plane so the image of $C(P, r)$ is planar. Let P' be the image of P. Let X be any point in $C(P, r)$. Since the mapping is distance preserving, $d(P, X) = d(P', X') = r$. Hence, X' is in $C(P', r)$. If $\bar{Y}$ is any point of $C(P', r)$, then by the same argument, the inverse mapping maps $\bar{Y}$ onto Y in $C(P, r)$. Hence $\bar{Y} = Y'$, and every point in $C(P', r)$ is the image of a point in $C(P, r)$. Hence, $C(P, r) \rightarrow C(P', r)$.

1a All t in α and all $t \perp \alpha$

1a Line t and all lines perpendicular to t

2 Infinitely many; one, the plane that is the perpendicular bisector of $\overline{AB}$.

5 Let $C(A, r)$ denote a circle in plane α. Then any line containing a diameter and the line through A perpendicular to α is a line of symmetry of the circle. Plane α and all planes through A that are perpendicular to α; point A

8 Let t be the axis containing centers O and O' of the bases. The center of symmetry is the midpoint M of $\overline{OO'}$. The lines of symmetry are t itself and all the lines through $M \perp t$. The planes of symmetry are all planes containing t and the plane perpendicular to t at M.

1a $X\Gamma = X$ if and only if $2a - x = x$, or $x = a$.

2 $x \rightarrow x + k$ is a translation of t onto itself by the number k and in the positive direction. $x \rightarrow x - k$ is a translation of t onto itself by the number k in the negative direction. The reflection of the point $x + k$ through point x is the point $x - k$.

1 Statements a, b, d, e, f, and g

2d Any point of the sphere $S(A, r)$, where $r = d(A, B)$

6 Let $\triangle A'B'C'$ be the reflection of $\triangle ABC$ through M. M is the midpoint of the segment determined by each point in $\triangle A'B'C' \cap t$ and the image of that point in $\triangle ABC$. Since $\triangle A'B'C' \cap t$ may be the empty set, a set of one point, two points, or a segment, M may be the midpoint of no segments, one segment, two segments, or infinitely many segments.

405   **1c** The plane of s and t, since $\Phi_s\Phi_t = \Phi_t\Phi_s = \Psi$. Thus $\Psi\Phi_s\Phi_t$ is the identity mapping of α onto itself.

       2c All lines perpendicular to t and line m parallel to t that satisfy the following conditions: $d(m, t) = \frac{1}{2}d(A, B)$, m intersects AB at S, and $\overrightarrow{SF}$ has the same direction as $\overrightarrow{AB}$

406   **5a** If $A\Gamma$ is known for any one point A, then Γ is known. The point of reflection is A if $A = A\Gamma$, or it is the midpoint of $\overline{A(A\Gamma)}$.

409   **3a** The circle $C(F, r)$ in the plane perpendicular to AB, where F is the foot of C in AB and $r = d(F, C)$

410   **5b** BC is the bisector of $\sphericalangle ABE$.

       7a If $O = A$, then $D\Gamma$ would have the property that $<D\Gamma, A, D>$ where $D\Gamma = B$ or $D\Gamma = C$. But no three vertices of a tetrahedron are collinear.

411   **7h** If no vertices were fixed, they would interchange in pairs, say A with B and C with D. Then α would have to contain the midpoints of $\overline{AB}$ and $\overline{CD}$ and be perpendicular to $\overline{AB}$ and $\overline{CD}$. Hence, AB and CD would have to be parallel, which is not the case, since AB and CD are skew lines. There cannot be 1 or 3 fixed vertices because the number of unfixed vertices must be even. There cannot be 4 fixed vertices because the vertices are not coplanar.

       8b 6

415   **1a** 3; $\frac{3}{10}$; 24π

416   **7a** Since $a \to 3a - 5$ and $b \to 3b - 5$, $d(A', B') = |3a - 5 - (3b - 5)| = |3a - 3b| = 3|a - b| = 3\,d(A, B)$. For any pair of points A and B, $d(A, B) = 3\,d(A', B')$. Hence, $x \to 3x - 5$ is a similarity mapping of ratio 3.

       8 Under Γ, $3x + 2 \to 5(3x + 2) - 1$ or $15x + 9$; therefore, $\Gamma_1\Gamma_2 : x \to 15x + 9$. The fixed points of Γ_1, Γ_2, and $\Gamma_1\Gamma_2$ correspond to -1, $\frac{1}{4}$, and $\frac{9}{14}$ respectively.

421   **5b** If $k \neq 1$ and $x = kx + (1 - k)a$, then $(1 - k)x = (1 - k)a$ and $x = a$. Hence, A is the only fixed point.

       6b The fixed point F' has coordinate 4. For any point P, $d(F, P) = |p - 4|$ and $d(F, P') = |4p - 12 - 4|$. Therefore $d(F, P) = 4\,d(F, P')$. Thus Ψ is an expansion of t at F in the ratio 4.

422   **8c** The expansion Γ is $x \to x' = 2x - 3$. The reflection Ψ is $x' \to x'' = 6 - x'$. Thus $\Gamma\Psi: x \to -2x + 9$.

       9a Since Γ is a similarity mapping of ratio k, $d(P\Gamma, F\Gamma) = k\,d(P, F)$. Any other point S in $\mathfrak{S}$ has the property that $d(P, F) \leq d(P, S)$. Hence, $k\,d(P, F) \leq k\,d(P, S)$ or $d(P\Gamma, F\Gamma) \leq d(P\Gamma, S\Gamma)$ which implies that $F\Gamma$ is the foot of $P\Gamma$ in $\mathfrak{S}\Gamma$.

438   **1d** $3\sqrt{14}$

439   **2c** 405

       5b $\frac{1}{4}$

6b $\frac{1}{12}$

9b 14

440 **10b** $9, \frac{\pi^2}{4}$

441 **15c** $\frac{4\sqrt{3}}{3}$

18 a or $a\sqrt{3}$

442 **1d** 5

4 $\frac{40}{7}$

443 **7b** $145\sqrt{3}$

8b $\frac{5}{48}$

9a $21\sqrt{3}$

11 180

446 **1d** $36 + 36\sqrt{3}$

3a $\frac{1}{2}; \frac{1}{2}(1 + \sqrt{2}); \frac{1}{2}(1 + \sqrt{2} + \sqrt{3}); \frac{1}{2}(1 + \sqrt{2} + \sqrt{3} + \sqrt{4})$

4 $y^2 - 2xy$

6 The total area is 140, and the area of the shaded regions is 16. Thus the actual area is 124.

448 **15** $Ar(\triangle DEG) = \frac{1}{2} \cdot x\sqrt{2} \cdot \frac{x\sqrt{6}}{2} = \frac{x^2\sqrt{3}}{2}.$

452 **1a** $10; 80; 400$

2 $\frac{a}{10m}; \frac{1}{10m}(\sqrt{25m^4 + a^2})$

5 $Ar(ABCD) = Ar(\triangle AOB) + Ar(\triangle BOC) + Ar(\triangle COD) + Ar(\triangle DOA)$
$= \frac{1}{2} \cdot 6 \cdot [d(A, B) + d(B, C) + d(C, D) + d(D, A)]$
$= \frac{1}{2} \cdot 6 \cdot 48$
$= 144.$

453 **12b** $314; 62.8$

454 **13b** $2\pi + 2\sqrt{2}$

15c $\frac{9}{\pi}$

16a $25\pi - 9\pi$, or 16π

19 240

457 **1d** $\frac{5}{64}$

458 **6** Since DE passes through the centroid and $DE \parallel AB$, $\overline{CA}$ is divided into the ratio $2:1$. Hence, $\frac{d(C, D)}{d(C, A)} = \frac{2}{3}$. By Corollary 211b/8, $\frac{Ar(\triangle DEC)}{Ar(\triangle ABC)} = \frac{4}{9}$. If $Ar(\triangle ABC) = x$, then $Ar(\triangle DEC) = x - 10$, $9(x - 10) = 4x$, and $x = 18$.

9 The ratio of the area of the equilateral triangle to the area of the square is $\frac{4\sqrt{3}}{9}$.

11a $\frac{1}{81}; \frac{1}{9}$

459 **12a** Construct a semicircle with $x + y$ the length of the diameter $\overline{AB}$ and C in $\overline{AB}$ so that $d(A, C) = x$ and $d(C, B) = y$. Construct $CD \perp AB$ with D in the semicircle. $\triangle ABD$ is a right triangle with hypotenuse $\overline{AB}$ and altitude $\overline{DC}$ (Theorem 119/4). Let $d(D, C) = a$. Then $\frac{x}{a} = \frac{a}{y}$ and $a^2 = xy$.

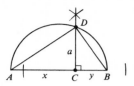

464 **1c** $b' = \frac{1}{2}$.

465 **3b** $2\sqrt{109}$

4b $20\sqrt{15}$

6b 6

466 **10b** $V = K\sqrt{K}$.

14 $234\sqrt{3}$

16c 720

18 $e = 4$; no, for any right square prism with a 4 by 4 base, volume equals lateral area.

473 **2d** $2\sqrt{15}$

474 **4** 180

8 $24\sqrt{3}$

11a Two planes parallel to the plane of the base and at a distance of 18 units from the plane of the base

475 **14a** 154

17 $20\pi\sqrt{2}$

476 **21** 260

479 **1c** $\frac{49}{484}$

2 18

480 **5c** 2640

6 400π

12 $\frac{6}{\pi}$

481 **16b** $V = \pi(2z + x)xy = \pi(2xyz + x^2y)$, and $\pi(x + z)^2y - \pi z^2y = \pi y(x^2 + 2xz + z^2 - z^2) = \pi(2xyz + x^2y)$.

488 **1** Statements a, b, c, e, f, and h

493 **1d** No, O may be between R and S, or R and S may not be in the plane of $C(O, r)$.

2b 270; 359; 181; $360 - \pi$

2c $\widehat{APB}^\circ = 70$; $\widehat{AQB}^\circ = 290$.

494 **4e** $\widehat{ACD}$

5b 60

496 **1a** $\overline{AB} = \overline{CD}$.

5 Yes

8a 60; 300

500 **1** 40; 20; 60

4a Let t be the line through O that is perpendicular to $\overline{AB}$ and $\overline{CD}$. Then t bisects $\overline{AB}$ and $\overline{CD}$, and M must be in t. Reflect $C(O, r)$ in t. $A \rightarrow B$, $C \rightarrow D$, and $M \rightarrow M$. Hence, $\triangle ACM \cong \triangle BDM$.

6 $\triangle AMN$ and $\triangle BMN$ are right triangles by Theorem 119/4. $\triangle AMN \cong \triangle BMN$ by the hypotenuse, side congruence theorem. Hence, $\overline{NA} \cong \overline{NB}$.

501 **13** Let t be the perpendicular bisector of $\overline{AB}$ and $\overline{CD}$. Reflect $C(O, r)$ in t. $A \rightarrow B$ and $D \rightarrow C$. Hence, $\measuredangle DAB \cong \measuredangle CBA$.

14e $\frac{1}{2}(180 - x)$

505 **1** Statements a, c, and d

506 **3c** $\widehat{AB}° = 176$, $\widehat{BC}° = 8$, and $\widehat{CA}° = 176$.

4e 160

5 $d(N, P) = r$ and $d(M, P) = r\sqrt{3}$.

12a Since $\overline{MN}$ is a diameter, $\triangle MXN$ with altitude $\overline{XF}$ is a right triangle. Hence, $d(X, F)^2 = d(M, F)\, d(F, N) = [\frac{1}{2} d(X, Y)]^2 = \frac{1}{4} d(X, Y)^2$, and $d(X, Y)^2 = 4\, d(M, F)\, d(F, N)$.

12b 60

511 **1a** $\widehat{AGF}$; $\widehat{FED}$; $\widehat{BDE}$

512 **2e** 75

3b 10

513 **5c** $8x$

6c 80

8a 20; 6

9b 55

514 **18** Let $\widehat{RN}° = x$ and $\widehat{NS}° = y$. Then $\widehat{RM}° = 180 - x$ and $\widehat{MS}° = 180 - y$. $\measuredangle P° = \frac{1}{2}(180 - y - x)$ and $\measuredangle Q° = \frac{1}{2}(180 - x - y)$. Hence, $\measuredangle P \cong \measuredangle Q$.

516 **1** Statements b and e

517 **4** Let $C(A, r)$ and $C(B, s)$ be internally tangent at P in line t and $s < r$. Let X be any point in $C(B, s)$ other than P. P, B, and A are collinear and since $s < r$, $<P, B, A>$. If X is in PA, $<P, B, X>$ and $d(P, X) = 2s < 2r$. Hence, X is in the interior of $C(A, r)$. If X is not in PA, then, in $\triangle PBX$, $\measuredangle P \cong \measuredangle X$. Since $<P, B, A>$, B is in the interior of $\measuredangle PXA$ and $\measuredangle PXA° > \measuredangle PXB° = \measuredangle XPA°$. Hence, in $\triangle PXA$, $d(A, P) > d(A, X)$. Hence, X is in the interior of $C(A, r)$.

10 If A' is the foot of A in BY, then $<B, A', Y>$, $d(A, A') = d(X, Y)$, and $d(B, A') = 1$. $d(A, A') = 2\sqrt{6}$ by the Pythagorean theorem. Hence $d(X, Y) = 2\sqrt{6}$.

12a 105

1c Yes; no

5 20, $20\sqrt{3}$

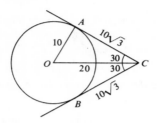

9 Let $\overrightarrow{BP}$ intersect $C(O, r)$ at D. Since P is in the interior of the circle, $<D, P, B>$. $\angle ADB$ is a right angle and $\angle APB$ is an exterior angle of $\triangle ADP$. Hence, $\angle APB° > \angle ADP° = 90$.

16 $40\sqrt{3} + \frac{104\pi}{3}$

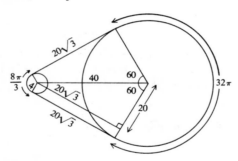

Index

Fundamental Mathematical Structures *Fundamental Mathematical Structures* *Fundamental Mathematical Struc*